ELEMENTS

OF NUMERICAL

ANALYSIS

OTHER BOOKS BY PETER HENRICI

Discrete Variable Methods in Ordinary Differential Equations, Wiley, 1962

Error Propagation for Difference Methods, Wiley, 1963

ELEMENTS

OF NUMERICAL

ANALYSIS

PETER HENRICI

Professor of Mathematics
Eidgenössische Technische Hochschule
Zürich, Switzerland

John Wiley & Sons, Inc. New York · London · Sydney

to George Elmer Forsythe

PREFACE

The present book originated in lecture notes for a course entitled "Numerical Mathematical Analysis" which I have taught repeatedly at the University of California, Los Angeles, both in regular session and in a Summer Institute for Numerical Analysis, sponsored regularly by the National Science Foundation, whose participants are selected college teachers expecting to teach similar courses at their own institutions. The prerequisites for the course are 12 units of analytic geometry and calculus plus 3 units of differential equations.

The teaching of numerical analysis in a mathematics department poses a peculiar problem. At a time when the prime objectives in the instruction of most mathematical disciplines are rigor and logical coherence, many otherwise excellent textbooks in numerical analysis still convey the impression that computation is an art rather than a science, and that every numerical problem requires its own trick for its successful solution. It is thus understandable that many analysts are reluctant to take much interest in the teaching of numerical mathematics. As a consequence these courses are frequently taught by instructors who are not primarily concerned with the mathematical aspects of the subject. Thus little is done to whet the computational appetite of those students who feel attracted to mathematics for the sake of its rich logical structure and clarity, and our schools fail to turn out computer-trained mathematicians in the large numbers demanded by modern science and technology.

Contrary to the view of computation as an art, I have always taken the attitude that numerical analysis is primarily a *mathematical* discipline. Thus I have tried to stress unifying principles rather than tricks, and to establish connections with other branches of mathematical analysis. Indeed, if looked at in this manner, numerical analysis provides the instructor with a wonderful opportunity to strengthen the student's grasp of some of the basic notions of analysis, such as the idea of a sequence, of a limit, of a recurrence relation, or of the concept of a definite integral. To achieve a balance between practical and theoretical content, I have made — for the first time in a numerical analysis text — a clearcut distinction between algorithms and theorems. An algorithm is a computational procedure; a theorem is a statement about what an algorithm does.

In addition to standard material the book features a number of modern algorithms (and corresponding theorems) that are not yet found in most textbooks of numerical analysis, such as: the quotient-difference algorithm, Muller's method, Romberg integration, extrapolation to the limit, sign wave analysis, computation of logarithms by differentiation, and Steffensen iteration for systems of equations. In the last chapter I have given an elementary theory of error propagation that is sufficiently general to cover many algorithms of practical interest.

Another novelty for a textbook in numerical analysis is my attempt to treat the theory of *difference* equations with the same amount of rigor and generality that is usually given to the theory of *differential* equations. Thus this important research tool becomes available for systematic use in a number of contexts. In fact, difference equations form one of the unifying themes of the book.

On the basis of my teaching experience I have found it necessary to include a rather extensive chapter on complex numbers and polynomials. The modern trend of replacing the course in classical theory of equations by a course in linear algebra has had the rather curious consequence that, at the level for which this book is intended, students now are less familiar with the basic properties of the complex field than they used to be.

The book contains about 300 problems of varying computational and analytical difficulty. (Some of the more demanding problems are marked by an asterisk.) In addition, a small number of *research problems* have been stated at the end of some of the chapters. Some of these problems are in the form of non-trivial theoretical assignments requiring library work. The others pose practical questions of some general interest and are intended to stimulate undergraduate research participation. Their solution usually presents a non-trivial challenge in experimental computation.

I have omitted all references to numerical methods in *algebra* and matrix theory, because I feel that this topic is best dealt with in a separate course. As its theoretical foundations are quite different, to treat it with the same attitude that I have tried to adopt towards numerical *analysis* would roughly have doubled the size of the book.

For a similar reason I have omitted material on programming and programming languages. It goes without saying, however, that no curriculum in numerical mathematics can be complete without permitting the student to acquire some experience in actual computation. At the Institute for Numerical Analysis, this experience is acquired in a simultaneous three unit programming course (one unit lectures, two units laboratory). The subject matter in this book is deliberately arranged so that the easy-to-program algorithms occur early, and a course based on it can easily be synchronized with a programming course.

A preliminary version of the book has been used on a trial basis at a number of schools, and I have been fortunate to receive a number of comments and constructive criticisms. In particular I wish to express my gratitude to Christian Andersen, P. J. Eberlein, Gene H. Golub, M. Melkanoff, Duane Pyle, T. N. Robertson, Sydney Spital, J. F. Traub, and Carroll Webber for suggestions which I have been able to incorporate in the final text. I also wish to thank Thomas Bray and Gordon Thomas of the Boeing Scientific Research Laboratories for assistance in planning some of the machine-computed examples. Finally I record my debt to my wife, Eleonore Henrici, for her unflinching help, far beyond the call of conjugal duty, in preparing both the preliminary and the final version of the manuscript.

I dedicate this book to my mentor and former collegue, George E. Forsythe, who had a decisive influence on my view of the whole area of mathematical computation.

Zurich, Switzerland   P. HENRICI
June 1964

CONTENTS

PART ONE   SOLUTION OF EQUATIONS

---

* Sections that may be omitted at first reading without essential loss of continuity.

INTRODUCTION

chapter 1 what is numerical analysis?

1.1 Attempt of a Definition

Unlike other terms denoting mathematical disciplines, such as calculus or linear algebra, the exact extent of the discipline called numerical analysis is not yet clearly delineated. Indeed, as recently as twenty years ago this term was still practically unknown. It did not become generally used until the Institute of Numerical Analysis was founded at the University of California in Los Angeles in 1947. But even today there are widely diverging views of the subject. On the one hand, numerical analysis is associated with all those activities which are more commonly known as *data processing*. These activities comprise—to quote only some of the more spectacular examples—such things as the automatic reservation of airline seats, the automatic printing of paychecks and telephone bills, the instantaneous computation of stock market averages, and the evaluation and interpretation of certain medical records such as electroencephalograms. On the other hand, the words "numerical analysis" have connotations of endless arithmetical drudgery performed by mathematical clerks armed with a pencil, a tremendous sheet of paper, and the indispensable eraser.

Between these extreme views we wish to steer a middle course. As far as this volume is concerned, we shall mean by numerical analysis the *theory of constructive methods in mathematical analysis*. The emphasis is on the word "constructive." By a constructive method we mean a procedure that permits us to obtain the solution of a mathematical problem with an arbitrary precision in a finite number of steps that can be performed rationally. (The number of steps may depend on the desired accuracy.) Thus, the mere proof that nonexistence of the solution would lead to a logical contradiction does not represent a constructive method.

A constructive method usually consists of a set of directions for the performance of certain arithmetical or logical operations in predetermined order, much as a recipe directs the housewife to perform certain chemical operations. As with a good cookbook, this set of directions must be complete and unambiguous. A set of directions to perform mathematical operations designed to lead to the solution of a given problem is called an *algorithm*. The word algorithm was originally used primarily to denote procedures that terminate after a finite number of steps. Finite algorithms are suitable mainly for the solution of problems in algebra. The student is likely to be familiar with the following two examples:

1. The Euclidean algorithm for finding the greatest common divisor of two positive integers.
2. The Gaussian algorithm for solving a system of n linear equations with n unknowns.

The problems occurring in analysis, however, usually cannot be solved in a finite number of steps. Unlike the recipes of a cookbook, the algorithms designed for the solution of problems in mathematical analysis thus necessarily consist of an *infinite* (although denumerable) sequence of operations. Only a finite number of these can be performed, of course, in any practical application. The idea is, however, that the accuracy of the answer increases with the number of steps performed. If a sufficient number of steps are performed, the accuracy becomes arbitrarily high.

Problems

1. Formulate a (finite) algorithm for deciding whether a given positive integer is a prime.
2. Formulate an algorithm for computing $\sqrt{2}$ to an arbitrary number of decimal places. (The algorithm is necessarily infinite. Why?)

1.2   A Glance at Mathematical History

Confronted with the definition of a constructive method given above, an unspoiled student is likely to ask: Is not all mathematics constructive in the indicated sense?

There indeed was a time when most of the work done in mathematics was not only inspired by concrete questions and problems but also aimed directly at solving these problems in a constructive manner. This was the period of those classical triumphs of mathematics that fill the layman with awe to the present day: The prediction of celestial phenomena such as eclipses of the sun or the moon, or the accurate prophecy of the appearance of a comet. Those predictions were possible, because the solutions of the underlying mathematical problem were not merely shown to *exist*, but were actually *found* by constructive methods.

The high point of this classical algorithmic age was perhaps reached in the work of Leonhard Euler (born 1707 in Basel, died 1781 in St. Petersburg). Euler was possessed of a faith in the all-embracing power of mathematics which today appears almost naive. At the age of twenty, before he had ever seen the ocean, he won a competition of the Paris Academy of Sciences with an essay on the best way to distribute masts on sailing vessels. Innumerable numerical examples are dispersed in the (so far) seventy volumes of his collected works, showing that Euler always kept foremost in his mind the immediate numerical use of his formulas and algorithms. His infinite algorithms frequently appear in the form of series expansions.

After Euler's time, however, the faith in the numerical usefulness of an algorithm appears to have decreased slowly but steadily. While the problems subjected to mathematical investigation increased in scope and generality, mathematicians became interested in questions of the existence of their solutions rather than in their construction. It is true that up to 1900 most existence theorems were proved by methods which we would call constructive; however, the computational demands made by these methods were such as to render absurd the idea of actually carrying through the construction. It is hardly conceivable, for instance, that Emile Picard (1856–1941) ever thought of going through the motions required by his iteration method for solving, say, a nonlinear partial differential equation.

In view of the feeling of algorithmic impotence which must have pervaded the mathematical climate at that time, it is easily understandable that mathematicians were increasingly inclined to use purely logical rather than constructive methods in their proofs. An early significant instance of this is the Bolzano-Weierstrass theorem (see Buck [1959], p. 10) where we are required infinitely many times to decide whether a given set is finite or not. To make this decision even once is, in general, not possible by any constructive method. During the second half of the 19th century the nonconstructive, purely logical trend in mathematics was rapidly picking up momentum. Some main stations of this development are marked by the names of Dedekind (1831–1916), Cantor (1845–1918), Zermelo (1871–1953). In spite of some countertrends inspired by outstanding mathematicians such as Hermann Weyl (1885–1955), the logical point of view appeared to be steering towards an almost absolute victory near the end of the first half of the 20th century. Mathematics finally seemed at the threshold of making true the proud statement of Jacobi (1804–1851) that: "Mathematics serves but the honor of the human spirit."

By a strange coincidence, algorithmic mathematics has been liberated from the vincula of numerical drudgery at the very moment when pure mathematics finally seems to have liberated itself from the last ties of algorithmic thought. From the beginnings of the art of computation to the early 1940's the speed of computation had been increased by a factor of about ten, due to the invention of various computing devices which today seem primitive. Since the early 1940's the speed of computation has increased a millionfold due to the invention of the electronic digital computer. To put into effect even the most complicated algorithms presents no difficulty today. As a consequence, the demand for algorithms of all kinds has increased enormously.

Problem

3. Look up Dedekind's axiom concerning the so-called Dedekind sections (see Taylor [1959], p. 447) and give three examples of its application in elementary calculus.

1.3 Polynomial Equations: An Illustration

To illustrate the types of problems and concepts we wish to deal with, we will consider the problem of solving *polynomial equations*. We are all familiar with the quadratic equation

$$(1\text{-}1) \qquad x^2 + a_1 x + a_2 = 0,$$

where a_1 and a_2 denote arbitrary real numbers. It is well known that the solutions of this equation are given by the formula

$$(1\text{-}2) \qquad x = -\tfrac{1}{2}a_1 \pm [(\tfrac{1}{2}a_1)^2 - a_2]^{1/2};$$

in certain cases the computation of the square root leads to complex numbers (see chapter 2). Formula (1-2) states more than the mere existence of a solution of equation (1-1); in fact it indicates an algorithm which permits us to calculate the solution. More precisely, the problem of computing the solution is reduced to the simpler problem of computing a square root. If an instrument for computing roots is available (this could be a table of logarithms, a computing machine especially programmed for the purpose, or the reader of this book armed with the algorithm he developed when solving problem 2), then any quadratic equation can be solved. Is the same also true for equations of higher degree?

Let there be given an arbitrary polynomial of degree n,

$$(1\text{-}3) \qquad p(x) = x^n + a_1 x^{n-1} + a_2 x^{n-2} + \cdots + a_n;$$

the problem is to find the solutions of the equation $p(x) = 0$. In the golden age of algorithmic mathematics Scipione dal Ferro (1496–1525) and Rafaello Bombelli (*L'Algebra*, 1579) discovered that in the cases $n = 3$ and $n = 4$ there exist algorithms for finding all solutions of equation (1-3) that merely require an instrument for computing roots.   Through several centuries attempts were made to solve equations of higher than the fourth degree in a similar manner, but all these efforts remained fruitless. Finally Galois (1811–1832) proved, in a paper written on the eve of his premature death in a duel, that it is not possible in the case $n > 4$ to compute the solutions of equation (1-3) with an instrument that merely calculates roots.   This, then, is a typical instance of nonexistence of a certain type of algorithm.   Modern numerical analysis, too, knows of such instances of nonexistence of algorithms.

If a problem cannot be solved with an algorithm of a certain type, this does not mean that the problem cannot be solved at all.   The problem is merely that of discovering a new algorithm.   Today there are no practical limits to mathematical inventiveness in the discovery of new algorithms. It must be admitted, though, that the talent for discovering algorithms is in no way confined to mathematicians.   Some of the most effective algorithms of numerical analysis have been discovered by aerodynamicists such as L. Bairstow (1880–   ); by astronomers such as P. L. Seidel (1821–1896); by the meteorologist L. F. Richardson (1881–1953); and by the statistician A. C. Aitken (1895–   ).

The problem of finding the solutions of a polynomial equation of arbitrary degree has attracted mathematicians of many generations such as Newton (1643–1727), Bernoulli (1700–1782), Fourier (1768–1830), Laguerre (1834–1886), and even today significant contributions to the problem are made almost every year.   One of the simplest algorithms for solving equation (1-3) is due to Daniel Bernoulli.   If a sequence of numbers $z_1, z_2, z_3, \ldots$ is determined by setting $z_k = 0$ for $k < 0$, $z_0 = 1$, and calculating z_k for $k > 0$ by means of the recurrence relation

$$(1\text{-}4) \quad z_k = -a_1 z_{k-1} - a_2 z_{k-2} - \cdots - a_n z_{k-n} \quad (k = 1, 2, \ldots),$$

then the sequence of quotients

$$(1\text{-}5) \qquad\qquad q_k = \frac{z_{k+1}}{z_k}$$

—if certain hypotheses are fulfilled—tends to a solution of equation (1-3) (see chapter 7).   Here we have a typical example of an infinite algorithm, for the sequence $\{z_k\}$ never terminates.   The recursive nature of Bernoulli's process—the same formula (1-4) is evaluated over and over again—also is typical of many processes of modern numerical analysis.

1.4   How to Describe an Algorithm

An algorithm is not well defined unless there can be no ambiguity whatsoever about the operation to be performed next.   Obvious causes for the breakdown of an algorithm are divisions by zero, or (in the real domain) square roots of negative numbers.   More generally, an algorithm will always break down if a function is to be evaluated at a point where it is undefined.   All such occurrences must be foreseen and avoided in the statement of the algorithm.

EXAMPLES

3.   Let an algorithm be defined as follows: Choose z_0 arbitrarily in the interval $(0, 2)$, and compute $z_1, z_2, \ldots$ by the recurrence relation

$$z_{k+1} = \frac{1}{2 - z_k}.$$

This algorithm is not well defined, since the formula does not make sense when $z_k = 2$, which happens to be the case for instance, if $z_0 = \frac{5}{4}$ and $k = 3$.   The algorithm can be turned into a well-defined one by a statement such as the following: "Whenever $z_k = 2$, set $z_{k+1} = 13$."

4.   Bernoulli's algorithm described in §1.3 is well defined to the extent that the right-hand side of equation (1-4) always has a meaning and the sequence $\{z_k\}$ thus always exists.   However, it still could be the case that infinitely many z_k's are zero.   The corresponding elements q_k would then be undefined.   (Consider, for example, the polynomial $p(z) = z^2 - 1$.) Under suitable hypotheses on the polynomial (1-3) it can be shown, however, that the quotients q_k are always defined for k sufficiently large (see chapter 7).

Many simple algorithms can be perfectly well described by means of the conventional symbolism of algebra, supplemented, if necessary, by English sentences.   In this manner we shall for instance describe most of the algorithms given in this book.   Ordinary algebraic language is not the only language, however, in which an algorithm can be expressed.   As a matter of fact, recent experience has shown that for very involved algorithms, especially those occurring in numerical linear algebra, the traditional mathematical language is sometimes grossly inadequate.

Ordinary mathematical language has one further disadvantage: It cannot be understood directly by computing machines without first being "coded."   In the interest of breaking down the communication barrier between man and machine as well as between man and man, it becomes very desirable to describe algorithms in a language that can be understood by both.

An algorithmic language with this property, called FORTRAN (= *for*mula *tran*slator), was created around 1957 by the International Business Machines Corporation (IBM).   It is very widely used not only on IBM machines, but on other machines as well.   FORTRAN is a completely adequate tool (especially in view of some recent refinements) for describing and communicating to the machine the vast majority of algorithms currently used in computational practice.   It is strongly suggested that the student of this book familiarize himself with FORTRAN and use it to solve the computational problems posed in subsequent chapters.   Excellent introductions to FORTRAN are available (McCracken [1961]).

FORTRAN was designed primarily as a practical research tool.   Its great advantages are its simplicity and its wide circulation.   From a theoretical point of view, though, the FORTRAN language has some serious shortcomings, and some of its rules appear highly artificial.   Realizing this, an international team of computer scientists gathered in 1957 with the aim of creating a universal algorithmic language that would be satisfactory from a theoretical point of view and that would not suffer from any artificial limitations.   The result of their efforts was the language known as ALGOL (= *algo*rithmic *l*anguage).   A revised version called ALGOL 60 has found wide acceptance, especially in Europe.   At the time this is being written, there are not yet many machines in the United States equipped to read ALGOL, although there are reasons to believe that this will change in the future.   ALGOL is described in an official document of the Algol committee (Naur [1960]); there are also some less formal, but more readable, introductions to the language (McCracken [1962], Schwarz [1962]).

1.5 Convergence and Stability

Once an algorithm is properly formulated, we wish to know the exact conditions under which the algorithm yields the solution of the problem under consideration.   If, as is most commonly the case, the algorithm results in the construction of a sequence of numbers, we wish to know the conditions for *convergence* of this sequence.   The practitioner of the art of computation is frequently inclined to judge the performance of an algorithm in a purely pragmatic way: The algorithm has been tried out in a certain number of examples, and it has worked satisfactorily in 95 per cent of all cases.

Mathematicians tend to take a dim view of this type of scientific investigation (although it is basically the standard method of research in such vital disciplines as medicine and biology).   It is indeed always desirable to base a statement about the performance of a given algorithm on logic rather than empirical evidence. Such logically provable statements are called *theorems* in mathematics. As we shall see, theorems about the convergence of algorithms can be stated in a good many cases.

EXAMPLE

5. The following is a necessary and sufficient condition for the convergence of Bernoulli's method mentioned in §1.3: Among all zeros of maximum modulus of the polynomial (1-3) there exists exactly one zero of maximum multiplicity (see chapter 2 for an explanation of these concepts). If this condition is fulfilled, the sequence $\{q_n\}$ converges to that zero of maximum modulus and multiplicity.

Once the question of convergence is settled, numerous other questions can be asked about the performance of an algorithm. One might want to know, for instance, *how fast* the algorithm converges. Or one may wish to know something about the size of the error, if the algorithm is artificially terminated after a finite number of steps. The latter question can be interpreted in two ways: Either one wishes to know how big the error is *at most*, or how big the error is *approximately*. The answer to the first question is given by an *error bound*; the answer to the second by an *asymptotic formula*. Mathematicians, who like to think in categories, usually give preference to error bounds. However, an error bound which exceeds the true error by a factor 10^6 is practically useless, whereas an approximate formula, while not representing a guaranteed bound, still can be very useful from a practical point of view. (Our scientists, if they depended on guaranteed error bounds, would never have dared to put a manned satellite in orbit.) Last but not least, the study of the asymptotic behavior frequently reveals information which enables one to *speed up* the convergence of the algorithm. Examples of this will occur in almost every chapter of this volume.

Even the theoretical convergence of an algorithm does not always guarantee that it is practically useful. One more requirement must be met: The algorithm must be *numerically stable*. In high school we learned how to express the result of multiplying two six-digit decimal fractions (which in general has twelve digits) approximately in terms of a six-digit fraction by a process known as *rounding*. Although the resulting fraction is not the exact value of the product, we readily accept the minor inaccuracy in view of the greater manageability of the result. If several multiplications are to be performed in a row, rounding becomes a practical necessity, as it is impossible to handle an ever-increasing number of decimal places. In view of the fact that the individual errors due to rounding are small, we usually assume that the accuracy of the final result is not seriously affected by the individual rounding errors.

Modern electronic digital computers, too, work with a limited number of decimal places. The number of arithmetic operations that can be performed per unit time, however, is about a million times as large as that performed in manual computation. Although the individual rounding errors are still small, their cumulative effect can, in view of the large number of arithmetic operations performed, grow very rapidly like a cancer, and completely invalidate the final result. In order to be sound, an algorithm must remain immune to the accumulation of rounding errors. This immunity is called *numerical stability*.

The concept of numerical stability can be very well illustrated by means of Bernoulli's algorithm discussed in §1.3. As mentioned above, this algorithm will, under certain conditions, yield the zero of maximum modulus of the polynomial (1-3). This algorithm is stable in the sense that it furnishes the zero to the same number of significant digits as are carried in the computation of elements of the sequence $\{z_k\}$. We shall have the opportunity to discuss the following extension of the Bernoulli method: If we form the quantities

$$q'_k = \frac{q_{k+1} - q_k}{q_k - q_{k-1}}$$

then under certain hypotheses (which can be specified) the sequence $\{q'_k\}$ tends to the zero of next smaller modulus of the polynomial p (see chapter 8). We have thus again an instance of a convergent algorithm or, to put it differently, of a logically impeccable mathematical theorem. In spite of all this the algorithm just formulated is practically useless. The quantities q'_k are affected by rounding errors to an extent which completely spoils convergence.

In spite of the above example, the reader should not form the impression that stability is an invariant property which an algorithm either has or does not have. In the last analysis, the stability of an algorithm depends on the computing machine with which it is performed. The modification of Bernoulli's algorithm described above is unstable if performed on an ordinary computing machine but it could be rendered stable on a machine equipped to compute with a variable number of decimal places. In a similar way it is possible to increase the stability of certain algorithms in numerical linear algebra by performing certain crucial operations with increased precision.

Rather than trying to set up absolute standards of stability, it should be the aim of a theory of numerical stability to predict in a quantitative manner the extent of the influence of the accumulation of rounding errors if certain hypotheses are made on the individual rounding errors.   Such a theory will be descriptive rather than categorical.   Ideally, it will predict the outcome of a numerical experiment, much as physical theories predict the outcome of physical experiments.   A particularly useful model of error propagation is obtained if the individual errors are treated as if they were statistically independent random variables.   In chapter 16 we will show how this model can be applied to a large variety of algorithms discussed elsewhere in this volume.

chapter 2 complex numbers and polynomials

One of the recurring topics in the following chapters will be the solution of polynomial equations. Complex numbers are an indispensable tool for any serious work on this problem.

2.1 Algebraic Definition

The reader is undoubtedly aware of the fact that within the realm of real numbers the operations of addition, subtraction, multiplication, and division (except division by zero) can be carried out without restriction. However, the same is not true for the extraction of square roots. The equation

$$(2\text{-}1) \qquad\qquad x^2 = a$$

is not always soluble. If $a < 0$, there is no real number x which satisfies equation (2-1), because the square of any real number is always nonnegative.

Historically, complex numbers originated out of the desire to make equation (2-1) always solvable. This was achieved by simply *postulating* the existence of a solution also for negative values of a. Actually, only the solution of one special equation, namely the equation

$$(2\text{-}2) \qquad\qquad x^2 = -1$$

has to be postulated. Following Euler, we denote a solution of this equation by i. The symbol i is called imaginary unit; it is a "number" satisfying

$$i^2 = -1.$$

Postulating further that i can be treated as an ordinary number, we can now solve any equation (2-1) with $a < 0$.

13

EXAMPLE

1. A solution of $x^2 = -25$ is given by $x = i5$, for

$$(i5)^2 = i^2 5^2 = (-1)25 = -25.$$

Another solution is $x = -i5$, for

$$(-i5)^2 = (-1)^2 i^2 5^2 = 1(-1)25 = -25.$$

Not only special equations of the form (2-1), but any quadratic equation of the form (2-3)

(2-3) $x^2 + 2bx + c = 0$

with real coefficients b and c can now be solved.   As is well known, the method consists in writing the term on the left in the form of a complete square plus correction term:

$$x^2 + 2bx + c = (x + b)^2 + c - b^2.$$

Equation (2-3) demands that

$$(x + b)^2 = b^2 - c.$$

For $b^2 - c \geq 0$ we obtain the solutions familiar from elementary algebra. If $b^2 - c < 0$, then $c - b^2 > 0$, and our equation is equivalent to

$$(x + b)^2 = -(c - b^2).$$

According to the above, it has the "solutions"

$$x + b = \pm i\sqrt{c - b^2}$$

or

$$x = -b \pm i\sqrt{c - b^2}.$$

EXAMPLE

2. The equation $x^2 + 6x + 25 = 0$ is equivalent to

$$(x + 3)^2 + 25 - 9 = 0$$

or

$$(x + 3)^2 = -16.$$

It therefore has the solutions

$$x = -3 \pm i4.$$

Any expression of the form $a + ib$, where a and b are real, is called a *complex number* and may henceforth be denoted by a single symbol such as z. If $z = a + ib$, we call a the *real part* of z and b the *imaginary part* of z. In symbols this relationship is expressed as follows:

$$a = \operatorname{Re} z, \qquad b = \operatorname{Im} z.$$

Two complex numbers are considered equal if and only if both their real and their imaginary parts are equal.

What has been gained by the introduction of complex numbers besides the ability of solving all quadratic equations in what at the moment may appear as a rather formalistic manner? Certainly nothing has been lost, because all real numbers are contained in the set of complex numbers. They are simply the complex numbers with imaginary part zero. Also, nothing has been spoiled, because we shall see that the ordinary rules of arithmetic still hold for complex numbers.

To justify this statement, let

$$z_1 = a + ib$$
$$z_2 = c + id$$

be any two complex numbers. We *define*

(2-4)
$$\begin{cases} z_1 + z_2 = a + ib + c + id = a + c + i(b + d) \\ z_1 - z_2 = a + ib - (c + id) = a - c + i(b - d). \end{cases}$$

Two complex numbers are added (subtracted) by adding (subtracting) their real and imaginary parts. The role of the "neutral element," i.e., of the number ω satisfying $z + \omega = z$ for all z, is played by the complex number†

$$0 = 0 + i0.$$

Multiplying two complex numbers formally, we obtain

$$z_1 z_2 = (a + ib)(c + id) = ac + i(ad + bc) + i^2 bd.$$

But $i^2 = -1$. We thus define:

(2-5)
$$z_1 z_2 = ac - bd + i(ad + bc).$$

For the special case of real numbers ($b = d = 0$) the above definitions reduce to the ordinary sum and product of real numbers. Moreover, the following rules, familiar from ordinary arithmetic, still hold for any complex numbers z_1, z_2, z_3:

---

† Two different kinds of zeros are used in this equation. On the right, we have twice the real number zero. On the left, we have the complex number zero, whose real and imaginary parts are the real number zero. As no misunderstandings can arise, one does not try to make a graphical distinction between the two zeros.

The commutative laws

$$z_1 + z_2 = z_2 + z_1, \qquad z_1 z_2 = z_2 z_1,$$

the associative laws

$$(z_1 + z_2) + z_3 = z_1 + (z_2 + z_3), \qquad z_1(z_2 z_3) = (z_1 z_2)z_3,$$

and the distributive law

$$z_1(z_2 + z_3) = z_1 z_2 + z_1 z_3.$$

The proof of these relations is an immediate consequence of our definitions and of the corresponding rules for real numbers.

We have yet to define the *quotient* z_2/z_1 of two complex numbers. The real case shows that some restriction has to be imposed here: The case $z_1 = 0$ will have to be excluded. Is it possible, however, to define z_2/z_1 for all $z_1 \neq 0$? To answer this question, we recall the meaning of the quotient. In the real case we mean by $x = b/a$ the (unique) solution of the equation $ax = b$. Analogously, we understand by $z = z_2/z_1$ the solution of

$$z_1 z = z_2.$$

If $z = x + iy$, this amounts to

$$(a + ib)(x + iy) = c + id,$$

or, after separating real and imaginary parts,

(2-6)
$$\begin{cases} ax - by = c \\ bx + ay = d \end{cases}$$

The two relations (2-6) can be regarded as a system of two linear equations for the two unknowns x and y. This system has a unique solution for arbitrary values of c and d if and only if its determinant is different from zero. The determinant is

$$\begin{vmatrix} a & -b \\ b & a \end{vmatrix} = a^2 + b^2;$$

it will be different from zero if and only if at least one of the numbers a and b is different from zero, that is, if $z_1 \neq 0$. If $z_1 \neq 0$, the solution of equation (2-6) is easily found to be

$$x = \frac{ac + bd}{a^2 + b^2}, \qquad y = \frac{ad - bc}{a^2 + b^2}.$$

We thus define

(2-7)
$$\frac{z_2}{z_1} = \frac{ac + bd}{a^2 + b^2} + i\,\frac{ad - bc}{a^2 + b^2}.$$

The same result could have been obtained by formal manipulation, as follows: Let

$$z = \frac{z_2}{z_1} = \frac{c + id}{a + ib}.$$

In the fraction on the right we multiply both numerator and denominator by $a - ib$. In the denominator we obtain

$$(a + ib)(a - ib) = a^2 + b^2 + i(ba - ab) = a^2 + b^2,$$

and carrying out the multiplication in the numerator we again find equation (2-7). This procedure cannot replace the proof that $z_1 z = z_2$ has the solution (2-7), because it assumes the existence of the solution; once existence has been established, however, it is very useful for the computation of the numerical value of z_2/z_1.

EXAMPLES

3. $$\frac{1 + i2}{3 + i4} = \frac{(1 + i2)(3 - i4)}{(3 + i4)(3 - i4)} = \frac{11 + i2}{9 + 16} = \frac{11}{25} + i\frac{2}{25}.$$

4.   The reciprocal $z = 1/(a + ib)$ of a complex number $a + ib \neq 0$ is calculated as follows:

$$z = \frac{1}{a + ib} = \frac{a - ib}{(a + ib)(a - ib)} = \frac{a - ib}{a^2 + b^2} = \frac{a}{a^2 + b^2} - i\frac{b}{a^2 + b^2}.$$

5.   To express

$$z = \cfrac{1}{i + \cfrac{1}{i + \cfrac{1}{i + 1}}}$$

in the form $a + ib$. Successive applications of the above method of reduction yield

$$\cfrac{1}{i + \cfrac{1}{i + \cfrac{1}{i + 1}}} = \cfrac{1}{i + \cfrac{1}{i + \cfrac{1 - i}{2}}} = \cfrac{1}{i + \cfrac{2}{i + 1}} = \cfrac{1}{i + \cfrac{2(1 - i)}{2}}$$

$$= \frac{1}{i + 1 - i} = 1.$$

Problems

1. Express in the form $a + ib$

(a) $\left(\dfrac{1 + i\sqrt{3}}{2}\right)^2$;

(b) $(1 - i)^4$;

(c) $(\cos \varphi + i \sin \varphi)^2$;

(d) $\dfrac{1}{\cos \varphi - i \sin \varphi}$;

(e) $\dfrac{1}{1 + (7 + 8i)} + \dfrac{1}{1 + \dfrac{1}{7 + 8i}}$.

2. What are the values of z for which the complex number

$$\frac{1}{1 + z} + \frac{1}{1 + 1/z}$$

is undefined?

3. Let $s = 1 + z + z^2 + \cdots + z^n$, where z is a complex number, $z \neq 1$. Find a closed formula for s by forming the expression $s - zs$.

2.2 Geometrical Interpretation

The discussion of §2.1 will have satisfied the student that complex numbers can be manipulated exactly like real numbers. At the moment this result may seem a mere formal curiosity. However, the significance of complex numbers in analysis is based on the fact that the algebraic operations discussed in §2.1 admit simple and beautiful geometric interpretations.

A complex number $z = a + ib$ can be represented geometrically in either of two ways:

(*i*) We can associate with z the point with coordinates (a, b) in the (x, y)-plane. If the points of an (x, y)-plane are thought of as complex numbers, that plane is called *complex plane*. Its x-axis is the locus of complex numbers that are real; it is therefore called the *real axis*. Its y-axis carries the points with real part zero; it is called the *imaginary axis* of the complex plane.

(*ii*) We can associate with a complex number z the two-dimensional vector with components a and b. We think of this vector as a *free* vector, i.e., a vector that may be shifted around arbitrarily as long as its direction remains unchanged.

Both interpretations can be combined into one by attaching the *vector z* to the origin of the plane. It then becomes the radius vector pointing from the origin to the *point z*.

EXAMPLE

6. To the four complex numbers $z = 1$, $z = i$, $z = -1$, $z = -i$ there correspond points (Fig. 2.2c) or radius vectors (Fig. 2.2d).

If complex numbers are interpreted as vectors, addition of two complex numbers amounts to ordinary addition of the corresponding vectors. For indeed, the sum of two vectors is obtained by forming the sum of corresponding components, just as in the case of complex numbers (see Fig. 2.2e).

The difference $z_1 - z_2$ of two complex numbers can be interpreted as the difference of the corresponding vectors. As is well known, the difference of two vectors z_1 and z_2 can be defined by adding to z_1 the vector $-z_2$, i.e., the vector which has the same length as z_2, but direction opposite to z_2. If we attach both vectors z_1 and z_2 to the same point, then the difference $z_1 - z_2$ corresponds to the vector pointing from the head of z_2 to the head of z_1 (see Fig. 2.2f).

Multiplication of a complex number by a real number can be similarly interpreted. Let c be a real number, and let $z = a + ib$. Writing $c = c + i0$, we obtain from the multiplication rule

$$cz = (c + i0)(a + ib) = ca + icb.$$

The vector cz thus has the same direction as z, if $c > 0$, and it has the opposite direction, if $c < 0$. If $c = 0$, cz is the zero vector. The length of cz is always $|c|$ times the length of z.

(a)   (b)

Figure 2.2

(c)   (d)

(e)   (f)

(g)

Figure 2.2

The question of how to interpret the product of two *arbitrary* complex numbers now arises.   In order to arrive at a suitable interpretation, we require the notions of the *absolute value* and of the *argument* of a complex number.

The *absolute value* or *modulus* of a complex number $z = a + ib$ is denoted by $|z|$ and is defined as the length of the vector representing z, or equivalently, as the distance from the origin of the point in the complex plane representing z.   It follows from Pythagoras' theorem that

$$(2\text{-}8) \qquad\qquad |z| = \sqrt{a^2 + b^2}.$$

The absolute value of a complex number z is zero if and only if $z = 0$. Otherwise the absolute value is positive.

The argument of a complex number is defined only when $z \neq 0$.   It is denoted by arg z and denotes any angle subtended by the vector z and the positive real axis.   The angle is counted positively if a counterclockwise rotation of the positive real axis would be required to make its direction coincide with the direction of the vector z (see Fig. 2.2g).

The argument of a complex number is not uniquely determined.   If φ is a value of arg z, then every angle $\varphi + 2\pi k$ (k an arbitrary integer) is also a possible value of arg z.   Thus, the argument of a complex number is determined only† up to multiples of 2π.

To compute an argument φ of $z = a + ib \neq 0$ we proceed as follows. Letting $|z| = r$, we have from figure 2.2g

$$(2\text{-}9) \qquad\qquad a = r \cos \varphi, \qquad b = r \sin \varphi.$$

We can use the first of these equations to determine the absolute value of φ by means of the relations

$$\cos \varphi = \frac{a}{r}, \qquad |\varphi| \leq \pi.$$

If $b \neq 0$, the sign of φ is the same as the sign of b, as follows from the relations

$$\text{sign } \varphi = \text{sign (sin } \varphi) = \text{sign } \frac{b}{r} = \text{sign } b,$$

since $r > 0$.   If $b = 0$, then $a = r$ or $a = -r$.   In the former case, $\varphi = 0$.   In the latter case, $\varphi = \pm \pi$.   Since π and $-\pi$ differ by 2π, both values are equally admissible values of arg z.

---

† The more advanced development of the theory of complex numbers shows that it would be unwise to restrict the argument artificially to an interval of length 2π by stipulating a condition such as $-\pi < \varphi \leq \pi$ or $0 \leq \varphi < 2\pi$.

EXAMPLES

7. Let $z = 4 + i3$. From (2-8)

$$|z| = \sqrt{4^2 + 3^2} = \sqrt{25} = 5.$$

To compute $\varphi = \arg z$, we first use the relation

$$\cos \varphi = \tfrac{4}{5} \text{ to find } |\varphi| = 36° \; 52'.$$

Since Im $z = 3 > 0$, it follows that $\varphi = 36° \; 52'$.

8. For $z = -4 - i3$ we likewise find $|z| = 5$, but in view of $\cos \varphi = -\tfrac{4}{5}$ we now have $|\varphi| = 143° \; 8'$ and, since Im $z = -3 < 0$, $\varphi = -143° \; 8'$.

9. The absolute value of a complex number with imaginary part zero coincides with the absolute value (as defined for real numbers) of its real part. Its argument is 0 (or $2\pi k$), if the real part is positive, and π (or $\pi + 2\pi k$), if the real part is negative.

Relation (2-9) shows that every complex number $z \neq 0$ can be represented in a unique manner as the product of a real, positive number and of a complex number with absolute value 1. This representation is given by

$$(2\text{-}10) \qquad\qquad z = r(\cos \varphi + i \sin \varphi),$$

where $r = |z|$, and where φ denotes any value of $\arg z$. The representation (2-10) is called the *polar representation* or *polar form* of the complex number z.

The polar representation enables us to give a geometric interpretation of the product and the quotient of two complex numbers. Let

$$z_1 = r_1(\cos \varphi_1 + i \sin \varphi_1)$$
$$z_2 = r_2(\cos \varphi_2 + i \sin \varphi_2)$$

be any two nonzero complex numbers. Multiplying by the algebraic rules of §2.1 we find

$$z_1 z_2 = r_1 r_2 [\cos \varphi_1 \cos \varphi_2 - \sin \varphi_1 \sin \varphi_2 \\ + i(\cos \varphi_1 \sin \varphi_2 + \sin \varphi_1 \cos \varphi_2)]$$

or, by virtue of the addition theorems of the trigonometric functions,

$$z_1 z_2 = r_1 r_2 [\cos (\varphi_1 + \varphi_2) + i \sin (\varphi_1 + \varphi_2)].$$

This, however, is the polar representation of the complex number with absolute value $r_1 r_2$ and argument $\varphi_1 + \varphi_2$. We thus have proved the relations

$$(2\text{-}11) \qquad |z_1 z_2| = |z_1| \, |z_2|, \qquad \arg (z_1 z_2) = \arg z_1 + \arg z_2.$$

The second of these is to be interpreted in the following sense: The sum of any two admissible values of $\arg z_1$ and $\arg z_2$ yields an admissible value of $\arg (z_1 z_2)$.

EXAMPLES

10. Let z_2 be a positive real number. We then have $|z_2| = z_2$, $\varphi_2 = 0$. Multiplication of z_1 by z_2 amounts to a dilatation or contraction of the vector z_1, according to whether $z_2 > 1$ or $0 < z_2 < 1$.

11. If z_2 is a complex number of absolute value 1, multiplication by z_2 amounts to a counterclockwise rotation by $\arg z_2$. Special case: Multiplication by i amounts to a rotation by $\pi/2$.

It has already been noted that for real numbers complex multiplication reduces to ordinary real multiplication. Inasmuch the argument of a negative real number may be taken as $\pm \pi$, the rules (2-11) can be thought of as a generalization of the rule "minus × minus = plus" of high school algebra.

We now compute the quotient of two complex numbers given in polar form. Using (2-7) we find

$$\frac{z_2}{z_1} = \frac{r_1 r_2 (\cos \varphi_1 \cos \varphi_2 + \sin \varphi_1 \sin \varphi_2)}{r_1^2}$$

$$+ i \frac{r_1 r_2 (\cos \varphi_1 \sin \varphi_2 - \cos \varphi_2 \sin \varphi_1)}{r_1^2}$$

$$= \frac{r_2}{r_1} [\cos (\varphi_2 - \varphi_1) + i \sin (\varphi_2 - \varphi_1)].$$

The expression on the right is the polar form of the complex number with absolute value r_2/r_1 and argument $\varphi_2 - \varphi_1$. We thus have the formulae

$$(2\text{-}12) \qquad \left|\frac{z_2}{z_1}\right| = \frac{|z_2|}{|z_1|}, \qquad \arg\left(\frac{z_2}{z_1}\right) = \arg z_2 - \arg z_1.$$

An important special case arises when $z_2 = 1$. Since $|1| = 1, \arg 1 = 0$ we then have

$$(2\text{-}13) \qquad \left|\frac{1}{z}\right| = \frac{1}{|z|}, \qquad \arg\left(\frac{1}{z}\right) = -\arg z.$$

The construction of the reciprocal $1/z$ for a given z thus involves two interchangeable steps: (i) Multiply z by $1/|z|^2$; (ii) Reverse the sign of the argument of the number thus obtained. The second of these steps—reversal of the sign of the argument—geometrically amounts to a reflection of the number on the real axis. As this operation of reflection occurs frequently in other contexts, too, a special notation has been devised for it.

If $z = a + ib$ is any complex number, reflection on the real axis yields the number $a - ib$. This number is called the complex conjugate of z and is usually denoted by $\bar{z}$. Evidently,

$$(2\text{-}14) \qquad\qquad |\bar{z}| = |z|, \qquad \arg \bar{z} = -\arg z.$$

The real and imaginary parts of a complex number can be expressed in terms of a complex number and its conjugate. By adding and subtracting the relations $z = a + ib$, $\bar{z} = a - ib$ we obtain

$$z + \bar{z} = 2a, \qquad z - \bar{z} = 2ib,$$

hence

$$(2\text{-}15) \qquad\qquad a = \operatorname{Re} z = \frac{z + \bar{z}}{2}, \qquad b = \operatorname{Im} z = \frac{z - \bar{z}}{2i}.$$

From

$$z\bar{z} = (a + ib)(a - ib) = a^2 + b^2 = |z|^2$$

there follows the relation

$$(2\text{-}16) \qquad\qquad |z| = \sqrt{z\bar{z}}.$$

The following rules of computation are easily verified:

$$(2\text{-}17) \qquad\qquad \begin{aligned} \overline{z_1 + z_2} &= \bar{z}_1 + \bar{z}_2 \\ \overline{z_1 z_2} &= \bar{z}_1 \bar{z}_2. \end{aligned}$$

These rules say, in effect, that in forming the complex conjugate of a sum or a product it is immaterial whether we take the complex conjugate of the result of the algebraic operation, or whether we perform the algebraic operation on the complex conjugate quantities. In the case of the reciprocal we have

$$\frac{1}{\bar{z}} = \overline{\left(\frac{1}{z}\right)}.$$

We shall use the rules just established to give a purely analytical proof of the so-called *triangle inequalities*. These inequalities say that in an arbitrary triangle the length of one edge is at most equal to the sum, and at least equal to the difference, of the lengths of the two other sides. If we represent the sides of the triangle by the vectors z_1, z_2, and $z_1 + z_2$ (see Fig. 2.2e), the triangle inequalities are given by

$$(2\text{-}18) \qquad\qquad \big||z_1| - |z_2|\big| \leq |z_1 + z_2| \leq |z_1| + |z_2|.$$

To prove this analytically, we note that by (2-16) and (2-17)

(2-19)

$$|z_1 + z_2|^2 = (z_1 + z_2)\overline{(z_1 + z_2)}$$
$$= (z_1 + z_2)(\bar{z}_1 + \bar{z}_2)$$
$$= z_1\bar{z}_1 + z_1\bar{z}_2 + z_2\bar{z}_1 + z_2\bar{z}_2$$
$$= |z_1|^2 + z_1\bar{z}_2 + z_2\bar{z}_1 + |z_2|^2.$$

In view of $\bar{z}_1 z_2 = \bar{z}_1 \bar{\bar{z}}_2 = \overline{z_1 \bar{z}_2}$ we have by (2-15)

$$z_1\bar{z}_2 + \bar{z}_1 z_2 = z_1\bar{z}_2 + \overline{z_1\bar{z}_2} = 2 \operatorname{Re} z_1\bar{z}_2.$$

Now for an arbitrary complex number z,

$$|\operatorname{Re} z| \leq |z|.$$

Setting $z = z_1\bar{z}_2$, we thus have by (2-11) and (2-14)

$$|\operatorname{Re} z_1\bar{z}_2| \leq |z_1\bar{z}_2| = |z_1||\bar{z}_2| = |z_1||z_2|.$$

Thus there follows from (2-19)

$$|z_1 + z_2|^2 \leq |z_1|^2 + |z_2|^2 + 2|z_1||z_2|$$
$$= (|z_1| + |z_2|)^2$$

and hence by taking square roots,

$$|z_1 + z_2| \leq |z_1| + |z_2|.$$

On the other hand, since $\operatorname{Re} z \geq -|z|$, we also have

$$|z_1 + z_2|^2 \geq |z_1|^2 + |z_2|^2 - 2|z_1||z_2|$$
$$= (|z_1| - |z_2|)^2$$

and hence, by taking square roots,

$$|z_1 + z_2| \geq ||z_1| - |z_2||.$$

This completes the proof of (2-18).

Problems

4. Compute the absolute value and all arguments of the complex numbers

$$\text{(a)} \ -i2, \quad \text{(b)} \ -6 + i8, \quad \text{(c)} \ \frac{1 + i}{2}.$$

5. Let $\omega = -\frac{1}{2} + i(\sqrt{3}/2)$. Show algebraically that $\omega^3 = 1$. What do you conclude about $\arg \omega$? What about $|\omega|$? Verify your conclusions by calculating $|\omega|$ and $\arg \omega$.

6. Show that the arguments φ of the complex number $z = a + ib$ ($a \neq 0$) are given by

$$\varphi = \arctan \frac{b}{a} + 2\pi k, \quad \text{if } a > 0,$$

$$\varphi = \arctan \frac{b}{a} + (2k + 1)\pi, \quad \text{if } a < 0,$$

where k denotes an arbitrary integer, and where arctan x denotes the principal value (lying between $-\pi/2$ and $\pi/2$) of the arcus tangens function. What is arg z if $a = 0$?

7. Using induction, prove that for arbitrary complex numbers $z_1, z_2, \ldots, z_n$

$$|z_1 + z_2 + \cdots + z_n| \leq |z_1| + |z_2| + \cdots + |z_n|.$$

8. Determine the equation of the locus of those points $z = x + iy$ of the complex plane with the following property: The ratio of the distances of z from the points $+1$ and -1 has the constant value k. (Hint: The distances can be expressed in the form $|z - 1|$ and $|z + 1|$.)

9. What is i^n for arbitrary integral n?

2.3 Powers and Roots

Applying the multiplication formula (2-11) to a product of n equal factors $z = r(\cos \varphi + i \sin \varphi)$, we obtain

$$(2\text{-}20) \qquad [r(\cos \varphi + i \sin \varphi)]^n = r^n(\cos n\varphi + \sin n\varphi).$$

Setting $r = 1$, there results Moivre's formula

$$(2\text{-}21) \qquad (\cos \varphi + i \sin \varphi)^n = \cos n\varphi + \sin n\varphi.$$

We expand the expression on the left by the binomial theorem and observe that $i^2 = -1, i^3 = -i, i^4 = 1, \ldots$. Equating real and imaginary parts on both sides of (2-21), we obtain

$$\cos^n \varphi - \binom{n}{2} \cos^{n-2} \varphi \sin^2 \varphi + \binom{n}{4} \cos^{n-4} \varphi \sin^4 \varphi - \cdots = \cos n\varphi,$$

$$\binom{n}{1} \cos^{n-1} \varphi \sin \varphi - \binom{n}{3} \cos^{n-3} \varphi \sin^3 \varphi + \cdots = \sin n\varphi.$$

Here the symbol $\binom{n}{k}$ denotes the *binomial coefficient* defined by

$$\binom{n}{k} = \frac{n!}{k!(n-k)!}, \qquad k = 0, 1, \ldots, n.$$

EXAMPLE

12. For $n = 3$ we obtain

$$\cos 3\varphi = \cos^3 \varphi - \binom{3}{2} \cos \varphi \sin^2 \varphi = \cos^3 \varphi - 3 \cos \varphi \sin^2 \varphi,$$

$$\sin 3\varphi = \binom{3}{1} \cos^2 \varphi \sin \varphi - \binom{3}{3} \sin^3 \varphi = 3 \cos^2 \varphi \sin \varphi - \sin^3 \varphi.$$

We are now ready to tackle the problem of computing the nth roots of a complex number. In the real domain we call nth root of a real number a any number x satisfying the equation

$$x^n = a.$$

Analogously we shall call nth root of the complex number w any number $z = x + iy$ satisfying the equation

(2-22) $$z^n = w.$$

If $w = 0$ this clearly has the only solution $z = 0$. In order to determine all possible solutions z for $w \neq 0$, we write

$$w = \rho(\cos \alpha + i \sin \alpha)$$

and seek to determine the polar form $z = r(\cos \varphi + i \sin \varphi)$. By (2-20),

$$z^n = r^n(\cos n\varphi + i \sin n\varphi),$$

and condition (2-22) assumes the form

(2-23) $$r^n(\cos n\varphi + i \sin n\varphi) = \rho(\cos \alpha + i \sin \alpha).$$

This condition evidently will be satisfied if

$$r^n = \rho, \quad \text{i.e., } r = \sqrt[n]{\rho}$$

and

$$n\varphi = \alpha, \quad \text{i.e., } \varphi = \frac{\alpha}{n}.$$

Thus the number

$$z = \sqrt[n]{\rho} \left(\cos \frac{\alpha}{n} + i \sin \frac{\alpha}{n} \right)$$

certainly is an nth root of the complex number $\rho(\cos \alpha + i \sin \alpha)$. Is it the only one? The absolute value of a nonzero complex number being positive, $\sqrt[n]{\rho}$ evidently is the only possible absolute value of z. However, other values of the argument are possible. We recall that the argument of a complex number is determined only up to multiples of 2π. Thus condition (2-23) is also satisfied if

$$n\varphi = \alpha + k2\pi,$$

where k is an arbitrary integer. We thus obtain an infinity of possible values of φ:

$$\varphi = \frac{\alpha}{n} + \frac{k2\pi}{n}, \qquad k = 0, \pm 1, \pm 2, \ldots.$$

Not all these values yield different solutions of (2-23), however. The same solution z is defined by two values of φ that differ merely by an integral multiple of 2π. This will occur as soon as the corresponding values of k differ by an integral multiple of n. Different solutions of (2-23) thus are obtained only by selecting the values $k = 0, 1, \ldots, n - 1$. We summarize this result as follows:

Theorem 2.3 The equation $z^n = w$, where $w \neq 0$ and n is a positive integer, has exactly n solutions. They are given by

$$z = r(\cos \varphi + i \sin \varphi),$$

where

$$r = \sqrt[n]{|w|} \quad \text{and} \quad \varphi = \frac{\arg w}{n} + k\frac{2\pi}{n}, \qquad k = 0, 1, 2, \ldots, n - 1.$$

Geometrically, these solutions all lie on a circle of radius r. The argument of one solution is $1/n$ times the argument (*any* argument) of w; the remaining solutions divide the circumference of the circle in n equal parts.

EXAMPLES

13. To compute all solutions of $z^4 = i$. Since $|i| = 1$, all solutions have absolute value one. In view of $\arg i = \pi/2$, one solution has the argument $\pi/8$; the remaining solutions divide the unit circle into four equal parts (see Fig. 2.3).

14. In the real domain the number 1 has either one or two nth roots, according to whether n is odd or even. In the complex domain the number $1 = 1 + i0$ must have n nth roots. Since $\sqrt[n]{1} = 1$, all roots have absolute value 1. Since $\arg 1 = 0$, the arguments of these n nth roots of unity are given by $2\pi k/n$, $k = 0, 1, \ldots, n - 1$. Special example: For $n = 3$ we obtain the following three third roots of unity:

$$\cos \frac{2\pi 0}{3} + i \sin \frac{2\pi 0}{3} = 1$$

$$\cos \frac{2\pi}{3} + i \sin \frac{2\pi}{3} = -\frac{1}{2} + i\frac{\sqrt{3}}{2}$$

$$\cos \frac{4\pi}{3} + i \sin \frac{4\pi}{3} = -\frac{1}{2} - i\frac{\sqrt{3}}{2}.$$

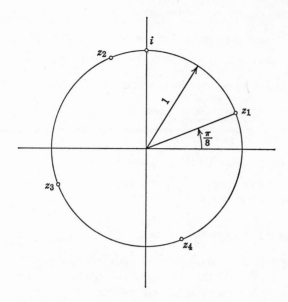

Figure 2.3

For n even one root of unity (namely the one obtained for $k = n/2$) has the argument

$$\frac{2\pi}{n} \frac{n}{2} = \pi,$$

and thus is real and negative, i.e., we obtain two real nth roots of unity. For n odd the equation

$$\frac{2\pi}{n} k = \pi$$

is not satisfied for any integer k, thus there is no negative root of unity. The example shows how by introducing complex numbers cumbersome distinctions of special cases can be avoided or dealt with from a unified point of view.

Problems

10. Determine all solutions of the equation

$$1 + z + z^2 + \cdots + z^n = 0.$$

(Use problem 3.)

11. Find closed expressions for the sums

$$A_n = 1 + r \cos \varphi + r^2 \cos 2\varphi + \cdots + r^n \cos n\varphi,$$

$$B_n = r \sin \varphi + r^2 \sin 2\varphi + \cdots + r^n \sin n\varphi.$$

(Hint: Let $z = r(\cos \varphi + i \sin \varphi)$ and consider $A_n + iB_n$.)

12. Determine all solutions of the equations

(a) $z^4 = -4$,   (b) $z^6 = i$,   (c) $z^3 = 3\sqrt{3}$.

13. Express the function $\cos 4\varphi$ as a polynomial in $\cos \varphi$.
14. Express the two values of $\sqrt{x + iy}$ in the form $a + ib$.   (Hint: Square and compare real and imaginary parts.)

2.4   The Complex Exponential Function

Beginning with this section we shall study certain important *functions* of a complex variable.   In the real domain, a function is defined if to every real number of a certain set of real numbers (called the *domain* of the function) there is made to correspond (for instance, by an algebraic formula) a number of another set (called the *range* of the function).   A complex function is defined in the same manner, with the difference that now both domain and range of the function are, in general, sets of complex numbers.

We begin by defining the exponential function for complex values of the variable.   In the real domain the exponential function can be defined by the exponential series,

$$e^x = 1 + \frac{x}{1!} + \frac{x^2}{2!} + \frac{x^3}{3!} + \cdots .$$

Replacing x by iy, where y is real, we obtain formally

$$e^{iy} = 1 + \frac{iy}{1!} + \frac{(iy)^2}{2!} + \frac{(iy)^3}{3!} + \cdots .$$

Using the fact that $i^2 = -1$, $i^3 = -i$, $i^4 = 1, \ldots$, this may be written

$$e^{iy} = 1 + \frac{iy}{1!} - \frac{y^2}{2!} - \frac{iy^3}{3!} + \cdots ,$$

or, collecting real and imaginary terms,

$$e^{iy} = 1 - \frac{y^2}{2!} + \frac{y^4}{4!} - \cdots + i \left(\frac{y}{1!} - \frac{y^3}{3!} + \frac{y^5}{3!} - \cdots \right).$$

The two series on the right are recognized as the Maclaurin expansions of $\cos y$ and $\sin y$. Thus we obtain

(2-24) $$e^{iy} = \cos y + i \sin y.$$

The above computations are purely formal in the sense that they lack analytic justification. (It has not been defined, for instance, what is meant by the sum of an infinite series with complex terms, nor do we know whether it is permissible to rearrange the terms in such a series.) However, nothing keeps us from adopting equation (2-24) as the *definition* of the exponential function e^z for purely imaginary values of z. It will soon be obvious that this definition is reasonable for a number of reasons.

We notice, first of all, that the polar form of a complex number $z \neq 0$, where $r = |z|$ and $\varphi = \arg z$, can be written thus:

$$z = re^{i\varphi}.$$

We also note the following properties of the function e^{iy}, which are analogous to properties of the real exponential function:

(a) $$e^{i0} = \cos 0 + i \sin 0 = 1 + i0 = 1.$$

For the one number which is real as well as purely imaginary, the new definition (2-24) is compatible with the real definition.

(b) The real exponential function satisfies the so-called addition theorem

$$e^{x_1}e^{x_2} = e^{x_1 + x_2}$$

for arbitrary real numbers x_1 and x_2. In analogy, the following identity holds for arbitrary real y_1 and y_2:

(2-25) $$e^{iy_1}e^{iy_2} = e^{i(y_1 + y_2)}.$$

The proof follows from the multiplication rule (2-11) in view of the fact that e^{iy} is a complex number with absolute value 1 and argument y.

The following two properties of the complex exponential function have no direct analog in the realm of real numbers.

(c) We have $e^{2\pi i} = \cos 2\pi + i \sin 2\pi$ and hence

$$e^{2\pi i} = 1.$$

(This formula connects several important numbers of analysis.)

(d) It follows from (2-25) and (c) that

$$e^{i(y + 2\pi)} = e^{iy}e^{2\pi i} = e^{iy}$$

for arbitrary y. This relation expresses the fact that the exponential function is *periodic* with period $2\pi i$.

Above, we have defined e^{iy} in terms of $\cos y$ and $\sin y$. We now shall show how to express the trigonometric functions in terms of the exponential function. Replacing in (2-24) y by $-y$, we get

(2-26) $e^{-iy} = \cos(-y) + i \sin(-y) = \cos y - i \sin y.$

Adding and subtracting (2-24) and (2-26) and solving for $\cos y$ and $\sin y$, we obtain Euler's formulas

(2-27) $\cos y = \dfrac{e^{iy} + e^{-iy}}{2}, \qquad \sin y = \dfrac{e^{iy} - e^{-iy}}{2i}.$

EXAMPLE

15. Moivre's formulas enable us to express $\cos n\varphi$ and $\sin n\varphi$ in terms of powers of $\cos \varphi$ and $\sin \varphi$. Here we are concerned with the converse problem: To express a power of $\cos \varphi$ or $\sin \varphi$ as a linear combination of the functions $\cos \varphi$, $\cos 2\varphi$, ..., $\sin \varphi$, $\sin 2\varphi$, ... We explain the method by considering the function $\cos^4 \varphi$. By Euler's formula,

$$(\cos \varphi)^4 = \left(\frac{e^{i\varphi} + e^{-i\varphi}}{2}\right)^4$$

or, using the binomial theorem, since $(e^{i\varphi})^k = e^{ik\varphi}$,

$$(\cos \varphi)^4 = \tfrac{1}{16}(e^{4i\varphi} + 4e^{2i\varphi} + 6 + 4e^{-2i\varphi} + e^{-4i\varphi}).$$

Collecting the terms with the same absolute value of the exponents and applying Euler's formula again, we find

$$(\cos \varphi)^4 = \tfrac{1}{16}(e^{4i\varphi} + e^{-4i\varphi}) + \tfrac{1}{4}(e^{2i\varphi} + e^{-2i\varphi}) + \tfrac{3}{8}$$
$$= \tfrac{1}{8}\cos 4\varphi + \tfrac{1}{2}\cos 2\varphi + \tfrac{3}{8}.$$

There remains the problem of defining e^z for an arbitrary complex number $z = x + iy$. We adopt the following definition:

(2-28) $e^{x+iy} = e^x e^{iy} = e^x(\cos y + i \sin y).$

With this definition, the addition theorem

(2-29) $e^{z_1} e^{z_2} = e^{z_1 + z_2}$

holds for arbitrary complex numbers $z_1 = x_1 + iy_1$ and $z_2 = x_2 + iy_2$. Proof:

$$\begin{aligned}
e^{z_1} e^{z_2} &= e^{x_1} e^{x_2} e^{iy_1} e^{iy_2} && \text{(by (2-28))} \\
&= e^{x_1 + x_2} e^{i(y_1 + y_2)} && \text{(by (2-25))} \\
&= e^{x_1 + x_2 + i(y_1 + y_2)} && \text{(by (2-28))} \\
&= e^{z_1 + z_2}.
\end{aligned}$$

As a consequence of the addition theorem we find that for any positive integer n

$$(e^z)^n = e^{nz};$$

furthermore, setting $z_1 = z$ and $z_2 = -z$ and observing property (a) we obtain

$$e^z e^{-z} = e^{z-z} = e^0 = 1.$$

Consequently the relation

$$e^{-z} = \frac{1}{e^z},$$

familiar for real values of z, holds true also for arbitrary complex values. It shows, among other things, that the complex exponential function never assumes the value zero.

Problems

15. Express $\sin^4 \varphi \cos^3 \varphi$ in terms of the functions $\cos \varphi$, $\cos 2\varphi$, ...

16. Prove that

$$\int_0^{2\pi} (\cos \varphi)^{2n} \, d\varphi = 2\pi \frac{\binom{2n}{n}}{2^{2n}}.$$

17. The logarithm $y = \log x$ of a real, positive number x is defined as the unique solution of the equation $e^y = x$. How would you define the logarithm of a complex number w? Does your definition lead to a unique value of $\log w$? What are the possible value(s) of $\log(-1)$?

18. If t is regarded as the time, the point $z = z(t) = Re^{it}$ travels on a circle of radius R. What is the locus of the points

(a) $\qquad z = ae^{it} + be^{-it} \qquad (a, b \text{ real});$

(b) $\qquad z = \cos 2t + i \cos t \qquad (0 \leqq t \leqq \pi)?$

19. Prove that $e^{\bar{z}} = \overline{e^z}$ for all complex z.

2.5 Polynomials

Let $a_0, a_1, a_2, \ldots, a_n$ be $n + 1$ arbitrary complex numbers, $a_0 \neq 0$. The complex-valued function p defined by

(2-30) $\qquad p(z) = a_0 z^n + a_1 z^{n-1} + a_2 z^{n-2} + \cdots + a_n$

is called a *polynomial* of degree n. The constants $a_0, \ldots, a_n$ are called the *coefficients* of the polynomial. The number a_0 is called the *leading* coefficient. A polynomial is called *real* if all its coefficients are real.

Any real or complex number z for which

$$p(z) = 0$$

is called a *zero* of the polynomial p. We know that a real polynomial does not necessarily have real zeros; it suffices to recall the case of polynomials of degree 2. In the complex case, however, the situation is different.

Theorem 2.5a   Every polynomial of degree $n \geqq 1$ has at least one zero.

This is the so-called fundamental theorem of algebra, which was first stated and proved (in five different ways) by C. F. Gauss (1777–1855). The proofs of Gauss were either algebraically involved, or they used advanced methods. Today the modern tools of analysis make it possible to give a relatively simple proof that is accessible to any student of advanced calculus (see e.g., Landau [1951], p. 233). However, a presentation of this proof would lead us too far astray from the main themes of this book and it is therefore omitted.

Taking the fundamental theorem for granted, we now discuss several of its applications.

Theorem 2.5b   Let p be a polynomial of degree $n \geqq 1$, and let $p(z_1) = 0$. Then there exists a polynomial p_1 of degree $n - 1$ such that

$$p(z) = (z - z_1)p_1(z)$$

identically in z.

Proof.   Let the polynomial p be given by (2-30). In view of $p(z_1) = 0$ we have

$$
\begin{aligned}
p(z) &= p(z) - p(z_1) \\
&= a_0(z^n - z_1^n) + a_1(z^{n-1} - z_1^{n-1}) + \cdots + a_{n-1}(z - z_1).
\end{aligned}
$$

We now make use of the identities

$$z^k - z_1^k = (z - z_1)(z^{k-1} + z^{k-2}z_1 + z^{k-3}z_1^2 + \cdots + z_1^{k-1})$$

$(k = 1, 2, \ldots, n)$.   Factoring out $z - z_1$, we obtain

$$
\begin{aligned}
p(z) = (z - z_1)[&a_0(z^{n-1} + z^{n-2}z_1 + \cdots + zz_1^{n-2} + z_1^{n-1}) \\
&+ a_1(z^{n-2} + z^{n-3}z_1 + \cdots + z_1^{n-2}) \\
&+ \cdots \\
&+ a_{n-2}(z + z_1) + a_{n-1}].
\end{aligned}
$$

Calling the expression in brackets $p_1(z)$, we find upon rearranging that

$$p_1(z) = a_0 z^{n-1} + (a_0 z_1 + a_1) z^{n-2} + \cdots$$
$$+ (a_0 z_1^{n-1} + a_1 z_1^{n-2} + \cdots + a_{n-1});$$

p_1 thus is again a polynomial; since $a_0 \neq 0$, the degree of p_1 is $n - 1$. This completes the proof of theorem 2.5b.

Let now p be a polynomial of degree $n > 1$. By the fundamental theorem, it has at least one zero, z_1 say. By theorem 2.5b, p can thus be represented in the form $(z - z_1)p_1(z)$, where p_1 is of degree $n - 1 \geqq 1$. Again by the fundamental theorem, p_1 has at least one zero, say z_2, and thus is representable in the form $(z - z_2)p_2(z)$, where p_2 is a polynomial of degree $n - 2$. The process evidently can be continued until we arrive at a polynomial p_n of degree zero. Since the leading coefficient of every p_k is a_0, it follows that $p_n(z) = a_0 \neq 0$. We thus find the following representation for the polynomial p:

(2-31) $$p(z) = (z - z_1)(z - z_2)\ldots(z - z_n)a_0.$$

We thus have represented $p(z)$ as a product of polynomials of degree 1, or *linear* polynomials, of the form $z - z_k$. The numbers z_k ($k = 1, 2, \ldots, n$) evidently all are zeros of p. Any number different from all the z_k's cannot be a zero, since a product of nonzero complex numbers never vanishes. It is not asserted that the numbers z_k are all different. However, we have proved the following: *A polynomial of degree $n \geqq 1$ has, at most, n distinct zeros.*

An important consequence of this statement is as follows: *If two polynomials p and q, both known to have degrees $\leqq n$, assume the same values at $n + 1$ points, then they are identical.* For the proof, consider the polynomial $p - q$. Its degree is at most n, and yet its value is zero at the $n + 1$ points where p and q agree. This can only be if $p - q$ vanishes identically.

Above, we have in the relation (2-31) represented a polynomial of degree n as a product of linear factors. It is conceivable that this representation depends on the order in which the zeros $z_1, z_2, \ldots, z_n$ have been split off. However, we now shall show that *for a given polynomial p the representation* (2-31) *is unique* (apart, obviously, from the order in which the factors appear).

Our assertion is trivial if p has n *distinct* zeros, for in this case each zero must appear in the representation (2-31), and since each must occur, each can occur only once. It is quite possible, however, that a polynomial of degree $n > 1$ has less than n distinct zeros, and that as a consequence the numbers $z_1, z_2, \ldots, z_n$ are not all different from each other.

EXAMPLE

16. The polynomial $p(z) = z^4 - 4z^3 + 6z^2 - 4z + 1$ has the representation

$$p(z) = (z - 1)^4 = (z - 1)(z - 1)(z - 1)(z - 1).$$

There is only one zero, $z = 1$; in the representation (2-31) we have $z_1 = z_2 = z_3 = z_4 = 1$.

In order to prove the uniqueness of the representation (2-31) even in the case of repeated zeros, assume p has another representation of the same form, say

(2-32) $p(z) = (z - z_1')(z - z_2')\ldots(z - z_n')b_0.$

From equations (2-31) and (2-32) we obtain the identity

$$(z - z_1)(z - z_2)\ldots(z - z_n)a_0 = (z - z_1')(z - z_2')\ldots(z - z_n')b_0.$$

The expression on the left is zero for $z = z_1$. Hence the expression on the right, too, must vanish when $z = z_1$. This is possible only if one of the numbers z_k', say z_1', equals z_1. Cancelling the factor $z - z_1$, we obtain

$$(z - z_2)\ldots(z - z_n)a_0 = (z - z_2')\ldots(z - z_n')b_0.$$

Because we have divided by $z - z_1$, this identity is at the moment proved for $z \neq z_1$ only; however, since both sides are polynomials (of degree $n - 1$), and since the set of all points $\neq z_1$ comprises more than $n - 1$ points, the identity must in fact hold for all z. Now we can continue as above: One of the numbers $z_2', \ldots, z_n'$, say z_2', must be equal to z_2 (even though z_2 could be the same as z_1). Splitting off the factor $z - z_2'$ and continuing in the same vein, we find that for a suitable numbering of the z_k'

$$z_k = z_k', \qquad k = 1, 2, \ldots, n.$$

We thus have proved:

Theorem 2.5c   A polynomial $p(z) = a_0 z^n + a_1 z^{n-1} + \cdots + a_n$ of degree n can be represented in a unique manner (up to the order of the factors) in the form

$$p(z) = (z - z_1)(z - z_2)\ldots(z - z_n)a_0.$$

Each zero of p occurs at least once among the numbers $z_1, z_2, \ldots, z_n$.

If a zero z of p occurs precisely k times among the numbers $z_1, z_2, \ldots, z_n$, the zero is said to have *multiplicity* k. A zero of multiplicity one is also called a *simple* zero. The zeros alone do not completely determine a polynomial, not even up to a constant factor, but the zeros together with their multiplicities do.

EXAMPLE

17. The two third degree polynomials

$$p(z) = (z - 1)(z + 1)^2 = z^3 + z^2 - z - 1$$

$$q(z) = (z - 1)^2(z + 1) = z^3 - z^2 - z + 1$$

both have the zeros $z = 1$ and $z = -1$, and no other zeros.   In the case of p, $z = 1$ has multiplicity 1 and $z = -1$ has multiplicity 2.   In the case of q the multiplicities are reversed.

Multiplying out the factors in (2-31) and comparing the coefficients with those of (2-30) we obtain relations between the numbers z_k and the coefficients of the polynomial.   These relations are known as Vieta's formulas.   The simplest of these formulas are those obtained by comparing the coefficients of z^{n-1} and by comparing the constant terms:

(2-33) $$z_1 z_2 \ldots z_n = (-1)^n \frac{a_n}{a_0}$$

(2-34) $$z_1 + z_2 + \cdots + z_n = -\frac{a_1}{a_0}.$$

The fundamental theorem of algebra guarantees the *existence* of at least one zero of any polynomial of positive degree, and thus indirectly of the representation (2-31) in terms of linear factors.   A completely different problem is the actual *computation* of these zeros.   As pointed out already in §1.3, explicit formulas (involving root operations) can be given only if the degree does not exceed four, and are frequently impractical already when the degree is three.   For polynomials of degree > 4 the zeros can be found, in general, only by algorithmic techniques.   However, for some special polynomials of arbitrary degree the zeros can be found explicitly.

EXAMPLES

18. Let $p(z) = z^n - 1$.   According to §2.3 the zeros of this polynomial are the nth roots of unity.   Since $a_0 = 1$, the representation in terms of linear factors is thus given by

$$z^n - 1 = (z - 1)(z - e^{i\varphi})(z - e^{2i\varphi}) \ldots (z - e^{(n-1)i\varphi}),$$

where $\varphi = 2\pi/n$.

19. To determine the representation of the polynomial

$$p(z) = z^n + z^{n-1} + z^{n-2} + \cdots + 1$$

in terms of linear factors. We find

$$zp(z) = z^{n+1} + z^n + z^{n-1} + \cdots + z,$$

and upon subtracting $p(z)$ and dividing by $z - 1$,

$$p(z) = \frac{z^{n+1} - 1}{z - 1} \qquad (z \neq 1).$$

The zeros of p thus are the $(n + 1)$st roots of unity, with the exception of $z = 1$. For instance for $n = 3$,

$$1 + z + z^2 + z^3 = (z - i)(z + 1)(z + i).$$

The above theory refers to arbitrary polynomials with complex coefficients. Real polynomials are contained in this class as a special case. We now shall state two theorems that are true only for real polynomials.

Theorem 2.5d If z is a zero of the real polynomial p, then $\bar{z}$ is a zero also.

Proof. Let

$$p(z) = a_0 z^n + a_1 z^{n-1} + \cdots + a_n$$

be the given real polynomial. If

$$0 = a_0 z^n + a_1 z^{n-1} + \cdots + a_n,$$

then by repeated applications of the relations (2-17)

$$\begin{aligned} 0 = \bar{0} &= \overline{a_0 z^n + a_1 z^{n-1} + \cdots + a_n} \\ &= \overline{a_0 z^n} + \overline{a_1 z^{n-1}} + \cdots + \overline{a_n} \\ &= \overline{a_0}\,\overline{z^n} + \overline{a_1}\,\overline{z^{n-1}} + \cdots + \overline{a_n}. \end{aligned}$$

However, since the a_k are real, $\overline{a_k} = a_k$ $(k = 0, 1, \ldots, n)$; furthermore, $\overline{z^k} = (\bar{z})^k$. We thus have

$$0 = a_0 \bar{z}^n + a_1 \bar{z}^{n-1} + \cdots + a_n,$$

i.e., the number $\bar{z}$ is a zero of p.

In addition to the statement of theorem 2.5d, it is also true that the multiplicities of z and $\bar{z}$ are the same. For a proof see problem 26 in §2.6. As a consequence, we find that in the factored representation of a real polynomial each factor $z - z_k$ involving a nonreal z_k can be grouped with a factor $z - z_{k+1}$ where $z_{k+1} = \overline{z_k}$. Multiplying out such a pair of complex conjugate factors we obtain

$$(z - z_k)(z - \overline{z_k}) = z^2 - (z_k + \overline{z_k})z + z_k\overline{z_k},$$

a quadratic polynomial with the real coefficients $-(z_k + \overline{z_k}) = -2\operatorname{Re} z_k$ and $z_k\overline{z_k} = |z_k|^2$. We thus have obtained:

Theorem 2.5e Any real polynomial of degree $n \geqq 1$ can be represented in a unique manner as a product of real linear factors and of real quadratic factors with complex conjugate zeros.

EXAMPLES

20.
$$z^3 + z^2 + z + 1 = (z - i)(z + 1)(z + i)$$
$$= (z^2 + 1)(z + 1).$$

21. Let

$$p(z) = z^6 - 1 = (z - 1)\left(z - \frac{1 + i\sqrt{3}}{2}\right)\left(z - \frac{-1 + i\sqrt{3}}{2}\right)$$

$$\times (z + 1)\left(z - \frac{-1 - i\sqrt{3}}{2}\right)\left(z - \frac{1 - i\sqrt{3}}{2}\right).$$

The representation by real factors is

$$p(z) = (z - 1)(z^2 - z + 1)(z^2 + z + 1)(z + 1).$$

Problems

20. Prove: A real polynomial of odd degree has at least one real zero.
21. Applying Vieta's formulas to $z^n - 1$, prove that

$$1 + \cos\frac{2\pi}{n} + \cos\left(2\frac{2\pi}{n}\right) + \cdots + \cos\left((n - 1)\frac{2\pi}{n}\right) = 0,$$

$$\sin\frac{2\pi}{n} + \sin\left(2\frac{2\pi}{n}\right) + \cdots + \sin\left((n - 1)\frac{2\pi}{n}\right) = 0.$$

22. Find all zeros of the following polynomials: (a) $z^4 + 6z^2 + 25$, (b) $z^4 - 6z^2 + 25$, (c) $z^8 + 14z^4 + 625$. (Use problem 14.)
23. The real polynomial $p(z) = z^4 + a_1z^3 + a_2z^2 + a_3z + a_4$ is known to have the zeros $1 + i$ and $-1 - i$. Determine the coefficients $a_1, \ldots, a_4$.

2.6 Multiplicity and Derivative

In this section we wish to point out the following connection between the multiplicity of a zero of a polynomial p and the values of the derivatives of p at the zero: If the multiplicity of a zero z of a polynomial p is k, then

(2-35)
$$\begin{cases} p(z) = p'(z) = \cdots = p^{(k-1)}(z) = 0, \\ p^{(k)}(z) \neq 0. \end{cases}$$

The multiplicity of a zero of a polynomial thus can be determined without completely factoring the polynomial simply by evaluating the derivatives of the polynomial at the zero.

For real zeros of real polynomials the relations (2-35) are a straight-forward consequence of elementary differentiation rules of calculus. If x_1 is a real zero of multiplicity k, we need only to observe that by theorem 2.5c we can write

(2-36)
$$p(x) = (x - x_1)^k q(x),$$

where q is a polynomial such that $q(x_1) \neq 0$. Differentiating (2-36) by means of the Leibnitz formula for differentiation of a product (see Kaplan [1953], p. 19), we get precisely the relations (2-35).

For complex zeros and complex polynomials, however, there arises first of all the question of what is meant by the derivatives $p', p'', \ldots$ (After all, the variables considered in the definition of the derivative in calculus are always real.) It is possible to extend the limit definition of the derivative to the complex domain in such a manner that the calculus proof of (2-35) retains its validity. However, some of the issues involved in the theory of complex differentiation are fairly sophisticated, and their discussion is best left to a course in complex analysis. Fortunately, as far as polynomials are concerned, it is possible to discuss derivatives in a purely algebraic manner, without considering limits.

If p is a polynomial of degree n with real or complex coefficients,

(2-37)
$$p(z) = a_0 z^n + a_1 z^{n-1} + \cdots + a_n,$$

we *define* the derivative of first order of p to be the polynomial of degree $n - 1$,

(2-38)
$$p'(z) = na_0 z^{n-1} + (n-1)a_1 z^{n-2} + \cdots + a_{n-1}.$$

Derivatives of higher orders are defined recursively, for instance

$$p''(z) = (p')'(z) = n(n-1)a_0 z^{n-2} + (n-1)(n-2)a_1 z^{n-3} + \cdots + 2a_{n-2}.$$

EXAMPLES†

22. Using binomial coefficients, the kth derivative of the polynomial (2-37) can be expressed as follows:

$$p^{(k)}(z) = k! \left[\binom{n}{k} a_0 z^{n-k} + \binom{n-1}{k} a_1 z^{n-k-1} + \cdots + \binom{k}{k} a_{n-k} \right].$$

---

† Readers unfamiliar with binomial coefficients should at this point consult §3.5 for the definition and basic properties of these coefficients.

23. If p denotes the polynomial (2-37), then clearly

$$p^{(n)}(z) = n!a_0.$$

24. We wish to calculate the kth derivative of the special polynomial

$$p(z) = (z - a)^n$$

$$= z^n - \binom{n}{1}az^{n-1} + \binom{n}{2}a^2z^{n-2} - \cdots + (-1)^n\binom{n}{n}a^n.$$

By example 22, we have

$$p^{(k)}(z) = k!\left[\binom{n}{k}z^{n-k} - \binom{n-1}{k}\binom{n}{1}az^{n-k-1}\right.$$

$$\left. + \binom{n-2}{k}\binom{n}{2}a^2z^{n-k-2} - \cdots + (-1)^{n-k}\binom{k}{k}\binom{n}{n-k}a^{n-k}\right].$$

The products of binomial coefficients occurring here can be recombined as follows:

$$\binom{n-m}{k}\binom{n}{m} = \frac{(n-m)!}{k!(n-m-k)!}\frac{n!}{m!(n-m)!}$$

$$= \frac{n!}{k!(n-k)!}\frac{(n-k)!}{m!(n-k-m)!}$$

$$= \binom{n}{k}\binom{n-k}{m}.$$

Thus we have

$$p^{(k)}(z) = k!\binom{n}{k}\left[\binom{n-k}{0}z^{n-k} - \binom{n-k}{1}az^{n-k-1}\right.$$

$$\left. + \binom{n-k}{2}a^2z^{n-k-2} - \cdots + (-1)^{n-k}\binom{n-k}{n-k}a^{n-k}\right].$$

By the binomial theorem, the expression in brackets reduces to $(z - a)^{n-k}$. We thus find

$$p^{(k)}(z) = k!\binom{n}{k}(z - a)^{n-k}.$$

This result is familiar, of course, when z and a are real.

It is clear that the derivative defined by equation (2-38) satisfies some of the laws that we expect from real calculus. Thus, if c is an arbitrary constant, we have

$$(cp)' = cp';$$

furthermore, if p and q are any two polynomials, then

$$(p + q)' = p' + q'.$$

It is somewhat less obvious that the familiar rule for the differentiation of a product also holds in the complex case:

(2-39) $$(pq)' = p'q + pq'.$$

In order to prove (2-39), let p be given by (2-37) and q by

$$q(z) = b_0 z^m + b_1 z^{m-1} + \cdots + b_m.$$

We agree to set $a_k = 0$ for $k > n$ and $b_k = 0$ for $k > m$. The product of the two polynomials then can be written

$$p(z)q(z) = c_0 z^{n+m} + c_1 z^{n+m-1} + \cdots + c_{m+n},$$

where

$$c_k = a_0 b_k + a_1 b_{k-1} + \cdots + a_{k-1} b_1 + a_k b_0,$$

$k = 0, 1, 2, \ldots, m + n$. The coefficient of $z^{m+n-1-k}$ in the derivative of pq then is $(m + n - k)c_k$. If, on the other hand, we form the expression $p'q + pq'$ directly, we find

$$p'(z)q(z) + p(z)q'(z)$$

$$= (na_0 z^{n-1} + (n-1)a_1 z^{n-2} + \cdots + a_{n-1})(b_0 z^m + b_1 z^{m-1} + \cdots + b_m)$$

$$+ (a_0 z^n + a_1 z^{n-1} + \cdots + a_n)(mb_0 z^{m-1} + (m-1)b_1 z^{m-2} + \cdots + b_{m-1}).$$

Collecting the coefficients of all terms combining to $z^{m+n-1-k}$, we find

$$na_0 b_k + (n-1)a_1 b_{k-1} + \cdots + (n-k)a_k b_0$$
$$+ a_0(m-k)b_k + a_1(m-k+1)b_{k-1} + \cdots + a_k m b_0$$
$$= (n+m-k)(a_0 b_k + a_1 b_{k-1} + \cdots + a_k b_0).$$

Since this agrees with $(m + n - k)c_k$, our assertion is proved.

As in real calculus, we now obtain by induction from (2-39) the Leibnitz formula for the kth derivative of a product of two polynomials:

(2-40) $$(pq)^{(k)} = \binom{k}{0} p^{(k)} q + \binom{k}{1} p^{(k-1)} q' + \cdots + \binom{k}{k} p q^{(k)}.$$

We now are ready to prove:

Theorem 2.6 Let p be a polynomial of positive degree, and let $z = z_1$ be a zero of multiplicity m of p. Then

$$p(z_1) = p'(z_1) = \cdots = p^{(m-1)}(z_1) = 0, \qquad p^{(m)}(z_1) \neq 0.$$

Proof. By theorem 2.5c, the polynomial p can be written in the form

(2-41) $$p(z) = (z - z_1)^m q(z),$$

where q is a polynomial such that $q(z_1) \neq 0$. We now form the kth derivative of (2-41) by the Leibnitz formula (2-40). By example 24 we find

$$p^{(k)}(z) = \binom{k}{0} k! \binom{m}{k} (z - z_1)^{m-k} q(z)$$
$$+ \binom{k}{1} (k - 1)! \binom{m}{k-1} (z - z_1)^{m-k+1} q'(z)$$
$$+ \cdots$$
$$+ \binom{k}{k} (z - z_1)^m q^{(k)}(z).$$

Here we set $z = z_1$ and distinguish two cases. If $k < m$, each term contains a positive power of $z - z_1$ and thus vanishes for $z = z_1$. If $k = m$, all terms except the first contain positive powers of $z - z_1$. The first term reduces to a nonzero constant times $q(z)$, which is $\neq 0$ for $z = z_1$. Thus theorem 2.6 is proved.

Problems

24 The polynomial

$$p(z) = z^5 - z^4 - 8z^3 + 20z^2 - 17z + 5$$

has the zero $z = 1$. Determine its multiplicity.

25. What are the multiplicities of the zeros at $z = \pm i$ of the polynomial

$$p(z) = z^5 + z^4 + 2z^3 + 2z^2 + z + 1 ?$$

26. Prove: Complex conjugate zeros of real polynomials have equal multiplicities. (Hint: The derivatives of a real polynomial are real polynomials. Now use the theorems 2.5d and 2.6.)

27. Using the definition (2-38) of the derivative, prove Taylor's theorem for arbitrary polynomials. That is, show that if p is a polynomial of degree n, then for arbitrary z and h

$$p(z + h) = p(z) + \frac{h}{1!} p'(z) + \frac{h^2}{2!} p''(z) + \cdots + \frac{h^n}{n!} p^{(n)}(z).$$

(Use the representation of example 22 for the kth derivative of p.)

Recommended Reading

A more thorough treatment of complex numbers and polynomials will be found in Birkhoff and MacLane [1953].

chapter *3* difference equations

Many algorithms of numerical analysis consist in determining solutions of *difference equations*. In addition, difference equations play an important part in other branches of pure and applied mathematics such as combinatorial analysis, the theory of probability, and mathematical economics.

Many aspects of the theory of difference equations are similar to certain aspects of the theory of differential equations. We thus begin this chapter with a brief review of the idea of a *differential equation*.

3.1 Differential Equations

Suppose $f = f(x, y, z)$ is a real valued function defined for all x in an interval $I = [a, b]$, and for all y and z lying in certain sets of real numbers S_0 and S_1. The sets S_0 and S_1 may depend on x. The following problem is called a *differential equation* of the first order: To find a function $y = y(x)$, differentiable for $x \in I$, such that, for all x in I,

(i) $$y(x) \in S_0, \qquad y'(x) \in S_1;$$

(ii) $$f(x, y(x), y'(x)) = 0.$$

The essential condition here is *(ii)*; condition *(i)* is merely imposed in order that condition *(ii)* makes sense. The problem thus defined is symbolically denoted by

(3-1) $$f(x, y, y') = 0;$$

any function $y = y(x)$ satisfying the conditions *(i)* and *(ii)* is called a *solution* of the differential equation (3-1).

EXAMPLES

1. Let I, S_0, S_1 all be the sets of all real numbers, and let

$$f(x, y, z) = z - ky$$

44

where k is a constant. Every function

$$y(x) = Ce^{kx},$$

where C is an arbitrary constant, is a solution of the resulting differential equation

$$y' = ky.$$

2. Let I be the set of all reals, and let $S_0 = S_1 = [-1, 1]$. If

$$f(x, y, z) = z^2 - (1 - y^2)$$

there results the differential equation

$$y'^2 = 1 - y^2,$$

solutions of which are given by the functions

$$y(x) = \sin(x - a),$$

where a is again arbitrary.

More generally, we consider differential equations of order N, where N is a positive integer. Let $f = f(x, y_0, y_1, \ldots, y_N)$ be a real valued function defined for $x \in I$ and for all $y_0, y_1, \ldots, y_N$ in certain sets of real numbers $S_0, S_1, \ldots, S_N$. The problem of finding a function $y = y(x)$ defined for $x \in I$, having N derivatives on I, and satisfying the conditions

(*i*) $$y^{(k)}(x) \in S_k, \quad k = 0, 1, \ldots, N;$$

(*ii*) $$f(x, y(x), y'(x), \ldots, y^{(N)}(x)) = 0$$

for all x in I, is called a *differential equation of order N*, and is symbolically denoted by

$$f(x, y, y', \ldots, y^{(N)}) = 0.$$

EXAMPLE

3. Let $N = 2$, and let I, S_0, and S_2 be the set of all real numbers. If

$$f(x, y_0, y_1, y_2) = y_0 + y_2,$$

every function of the form

$$y(x) = A \cos x + B \sin x$$

where A and B are constants, is a solution of the resulting differential equation $y'' + y = 0$.

The problems studied in the theory of differential equations not only concern the analytic representation of some or all of their solutions, but also the general behavior of these solutions, especially when x tends to infinity.

3.2 Difference Equations

The fundamental problem in the theory of difference equations is in many ways similar to that of the theory of differential equations, with the exception that the mathematical object sought here is a *sequence* rather than a *function*.   From the abstract point of view, a sequence is merely a function defined on a set of integers.   More concretely, a sequence s is defined by associating with every member of a set I of integers a certain (real) number.   Traditionally, the number associated with the integer n is denoted by a symbol such as s_n and not by the usual functional notation $s(n)$.

In almost all applications, the domain of definition of a sequence is a set of *consecutive* integers, i.e., the set of all integers contained between two fixed limits, one or both of which may be infinite.   Frequently I is the set of all nonnegative integers.

Sequences can be denoted by a single letter such as s, much as functions are denoted by single letters such as f.   More commonly, however, the sequence with the general element s_n is written either as $\{s_0, s_1, s_2, \ldots\}$ or simply as $\{s_n\}$.

A sequence can be defined by giving an explicit formula for s_n, such as

$$s_n = \frac{1}{n^2 + 1}, \qquad n \geqq 27.$$

More often than not, however, the elements of a sequence are defined only implicitly.   Difference equations are among the most important tools for defining sequences.

We first explain what is meant by a *difference equation of order* 1.   Let $f = \{f_n(y, z)\}$ be a sequence of functions defined on a set I of consecutive integers and for all y and z belonging to some set of real numbers S.   The problem is to find a sequence $\{x_n\}$ of real numbers defined on a set containing I so that the following conditions are satisfied for all $n \in I$:

(*i*) $x_n \in S, \qquad x_{n-1} \in S;$

(*ii*) $f_n(x_n, x_{n-1}) = 0.$

A sequence $\{x_n\}$ satisfying these conditions is called a *solution* of the difference equation symbolized by equation (*ii*).

EXAMPLES

4.   Let I be the set of all integers.   The choice $f_n(y, z) = y - z - 1$ yields the difference equation

$$x_n - x_{n-1} = 1.$$

Obvious solutions are given by $x_n = n + c$ for every constant c.

5. Let I be the set of nonnegative integers, $f_n(y, z) = y - z - n$. There results the difference equation

$$x_n - x_{n-1} = n,$$

having (among others) the solution

$$x_n = \frac{n(n + 1)}{2}.$$

6. Let I be the set of all integers, and let $f_n(y, z) = y - qz$ where q is a nonzero constant. We obtain the difference equation

$$x_n = qx_{n-1}.$$

A solution satisfying $x_0 = 1$ is given by $x_n = q^n$.

The difference equation of order N, where N is a positive integer, is defined in a similar manner. Let $f = \{f_n(y_0, y_1, \ldots, y_N)\}$ be a sequence, defined on a set I of consecutive integers, whose elements are functions defined for y_k ($k = 0, 1, \ldots, N$) in a set of real numbers S. The problem is to find a sequence $\{x_n\}$, defined on a set containing I and satisfying the following conditions for all $n \in I$:

(*i*) $\qquad\qquad x_n \in S, \ x_{n-1} \in S, \ldots, x_{n-N} \in S;$

(*ii*) $\qquad\qquad f_n(x_n, x_{n-1}, \ldots, x_{n-N}) = 0.$

A sequence $\{x_n\}$ with these properties is again called a *solution* of the difference equation symbolized by (*ii*).

EXAMPLES

7. Let I be the set of all integers, $f_n(y_0, y_1, y_2) = y_0 - 2 \cos \varphi \, y_1 + y_2$, where φ is real. A solution of the resulting difference equation

$$x_n - 2 \cos \varphi \, x_{n-1} + x_{n-2} = 0$$

is given by $x_n = \cos(n\varphi)$.

8. Let I be the set of nonnegative integers, $f_n(y_0, y_1, y_2) = y_0 - y_1 - y_2$. Can you find a solution of the difference equation

$$x_n - x_{n-1} - x_{n-2} = 0?$$

As in the case of differential equations, the problems studied in the theory of difference equations not only concern the analytic representation of some or all solutions, but also the general behavior of these solutions, especially when n tends to infinity.

A differential equation usually has many solutions. In order to pin down a solution, we have to specify some additional property of it, such as its value, and perhaps the values of some of its derivatives, at a given point. The problem of finding a solution of the differential equation under these side conditions is called an *initial value problem*. Similarly, in order to pin down the solution of a difference equation, we have to prescribe the values of some elements of the solution $\{x_n\}$. For instance, in example 8 above, we may require that $x_0 = x_1 = 1$.

The solution of an initial value problem for a difference equation is, in a way, a trivial matter. We assume that the equation

$$f_n(y_0, y_1, \ldots, y_N) = 0$$

can be solved for y_0,

$$y_0 = g_n(y_1, y_2, \ldots, y_N).$$

The difference equation can then be written as a recurrence relation for the elements of the sequence $\{x_n\}$,

$$(3\text{-}2) \qquad x_n = g_n(x_{n-1}, x_{n-2}, \ldots, x_{n-N}).$$

Once N consecutive elements of the solution are known, further elements can be obtained by successively evaluating the functions g_n. In this manner we find for the difference equation of example 8 the solution

$$\{1, 1, 2, 3, 5, 8, 13, \ldots\}.$$

There remains the problem, however, of finding an explicit formula for x_n, and of determining *all* solutions of a given difference equation.

3.3 Linear Difference Equations of Order One

A difference equation is called *linear*, if, for each $n \in I$, the function f_n is a linear function of $y_0, y_1, \ldots, y_N$. The coefficients in that linear function may, however, depend on n. That is, for certain sequences $\{a_{0,n}\}$, $\{a_{1,n}\}, \ldots, \{a_{N,n}\}$, and $\{b_n\}$ we have

$$(3\text{-}3) \qquad f_n(y_0, y_1, \ldots, y_N) = a_{0,n}y_0 + a_{1,n}y_1 + \cdots + a_{N,n}y_N + b_n.$$

EXAMPLES

9. The difference equations considered in the examples 4 through 8 are linear.

10. The difference equation

$$x_n + 5nx_{n-1} + n^2x_{n-2} = 2$$

is linear.

11. The difference equation

$$x_n - 2x_{n-1}^2 = 0$$

is not linear.

A linear difference equation is called *homogeneous*, if $f_n(0, 0, \ldots, 0) = 0$ for all $n \in I$, i.e., if the sequence $\{b_n\}$ has zero elements only. The linear difference equations considered in the examples 6, 7, and 8 are homogeneous. The equation of example 10 is not homogeneous. Likewise, the equation of example 11 is not homogeneous, because it is not linear.

Postponing the discussion of linear difference equations of order $N > 1$ until chapter 6, we shall in the present section consider linear difference equations of order 1 only. Assuming that $a_{0,n} \neq 0$, $n \in I$, we may divide through by $a_{0,n}$ and write any such difference equation in the form (3-2), viz.,

$$(3\text{-}4) \qquad x_n = a_n x_{n-1} + b_n.$$

We shall assume that I is the set of positive integers and shall try to find a closed expression for the solution of (3-4) satisfying an arbitrary initial condition $x_0 = c$.

We first consider the homogeneous equation

$$(3\text{-}5) \qquad x_n = a_n x_{n-1}.$$

It is seen immediately that the solution satisfying $x_0 = c$ is given by

$$(3\text{-}6) \qquad x_n = c \pi_n,$$

where

$$(3\text{-}7) \qquad \pi_0 = 1, \; \pi_n = a_1 a_2 \ldots a_n, \qquad n = 1, 2, \ldots.$$

To find the solution of the nonhomogeneous equation (3-4) satisfying $x_0 = c$, we use the method of variation of constants familiar from the theory of ordinary differential equations. Thus we set

$$(3\text{-}8) \qquad x_n = c_n \pi_n,$$

where the sequence $\{c_n\}$ is to be determined. In view of $x_0 = c_0 \pi_0 = c_0$ the initial condition yields $c_0 = c$. Substituting (3-8) into (3-4) we find

$$c_n \pi_n = a_n c_{n-1} \pi_{n-1} + b_n = c_{n-1} \pi_n + b_n.$$

We assume that $a_n \neq 0$, $n = 1, 2, \ldots$, which implies that $\pi_n \neq 0$. The last relation then yields

$$c_n = c_{n-1} + \frac{b_n}{\pi_n},$$

and it follows that

$$c_n = c_0 + (c_1 - c_0) + (c_2 - c_1) + \cdots + (c_n - c_{n-1})$$

$$= c + \frac{b_1}{\pi_1} + \frac{b_2}{\pi_2} + \cdots + \frac{b_n}{\pi_n}.$$

For later reference we summarize the above as follows:

Theorem 3.3 Let $a_n \neq 0$, $n = 1, 2, \ldots$. The solution of the difference equation

$$x_n = a_n x_{n-1} + b_n$$

satisfying $x_0 = c$ is given by

(3-9) $\qquad x_n = \pi_n \left(c + \frac{b_1}{\pi_1} + \frac{b_2}{\pi_2} + \cdots + \frac{b_n}{\pi_n} \right), \qquad n = 0, 1, \ldots,$

where $\pi_0 = 1$, $\pi_n = a_1 a_2 \ldots a_n$, $\qquad n = 1, 2, \ldots$.

We observe that this solution can be considered as being composed of the sequence $\{c\pi_n\}$, which is the solution of the *homogeneous* equation having initial value c, and of the sequence

$$x_n = \pi_n \left(\frac{b_1}{\pi_1} + \frac{b_2}{\pi_2} + \cdots + \frac{b_n}{\pi_n} \right), \qquad n = 1, 2, \ldots,$$

which is the solution of the nonhomogeneous equation having initial value zero. The principle of superposition familiar from the theory of differential equations thus prevails also for difference equations.

Whether or not the solution (3-9) can be expressed in simple form depends on the possibility of expressing the products π_n and the sums c_n in simple form, much as in the case of differential equations the simplicity of the solution depends on the possibility to evaluate certain integrals.

Problems

1. Let $-1 < a < 1$. Solve the difference equation

$$x_0 = 1, \qquad x_n = a x_{n-1} + 1$$

and determine the limit of the sequence $\{x_n\}$ as $n \to \infty$.

2. Let z be an arbitrary real number, $z \neq 0$. Solve the difference equation

$$x_0 = 1, \qquad x_n = \frac{n}{z} x_{n-1} + 1.$$

Show that

$$\frac{z^n}{n!} x_n \to e^z, \qquad n \to \infty.$$

3. Let the infinite series

$$\sum_{n=0}^{\infty} b_n$$

be convergent, and let its sum be s. Show that

$$s = \lim_{n \to \infty} x_n,$$

where $\{x_n\}$ denotes the solution of the difference equation

$$x_0 = b_0, \qquad x_n = x_{n-1} + b_n.$$

4. It is shown in calculus that

$$\prod_{n=1}^{\infty} \left(1 - \frac{z^2}{n^2}\right) = \frac{\sin \pi z}{\pi z}.$$

Show that the infinite product can be obtained as $\lim_{n \to \infty} x_n$, where $\{x_n\}$ satisfies the linear and homogeneous difference equation

$$x_0 = 1, \qquad x_n = \left(1 - \frac{z^2}{n^2}\right) x_{n-1}, \qquad n = 1, 2, \ldots.$$

3.4 Horner's Scheme

Several applications of theorem 3.3 will be made in later chapters. At this point we wish to show how difference equations can be used to calculate the values of a polynomial.

Let $b_0, b_1, \ldots, b_N$ be $N + 1$ given constants, and let z be a given real number. We define

Algorithm 3.4 Calculate the numbers $x_0, x_1, \ldots, x_N$ recursively by the relations

$$(3\text{-}10) \qquad x_0 = b_0, \qquad x_n = zx_{n-1} + b_n, \qquad n = 1, 2, \ldots, N.$$

Evidently, the finite sequence $\{x_n\}$ defined in algorithm 3.4 is the solution satisfying $x_0 = b_0$ of a difference equation (3-4), where $a_n = z$, $n = 1, 2, \ldots, N$. In this special case, $\pi_n = z^n$ and hence, by virtue of theorem 3.3,

$$x_n = b_0 z^n + b_1 z^{n-1} + \cdots + b_n$$

and in particular for $n = N$,

$$x_N = b_0 z^N + b_1 z^{N-1} + \cdots + b_N.$$

We thus have obtained:

Theorem 3.4 The numbers x_n produced by algorithm 3.4 equal the values of the polynomials p_n defined by

$$p_n(x) = b_0 x^n + b_1 x^{n-1} + \cdots + b_n \qquad (n = 0, 1, \ldots, N)$$

at $x = z$.

Algorithm 3.4 may thus be regarded as a method for evaluating a polynomial. This method is generally known as *Horner's rule*. It requires n multiplications and n additions for the evaluation of a polynomial of degree n, whereas the "straightforward" method—building up the powers of x recursively by $x^n = x \cdot x^{n-1}$ and subsequently multiplying by the b_n—normally requires $2n - 1$ multiplications and n additions. Schematically, Horner's method may be indicated thus:

$$
\begin{array}{cccc}
b_0 & b_1 & b_2 \cdots & b_N \\
\downarrow & \downarrow & \downarrow & \downarrow \\
x_0 \Rightarrow & x_1 \Rightarrow & x_2 \cdots \Rightarrow & x_N
\end{array}
$$

(The symbol $\Rightarrow$ indicates multiplication by z.)

Scheme 3.4

EXAMPLE

12. To evaluate the polynomial

$$p(x) = 7x^4 + 5x^3 - 2x^2 + 8$$

at $x = 0.5$. Scheme 3.4 yields (note that the coefficient $b_3 = 0$ may not be suppressed!)

$$
\begin{array}{ccccc}
7 & 5 & -2 & 0 & 8 \\
7 & 8.5 & 2.25 & 1.125 & 8.5625.
\end{array}
$$

It follows that $p(0.5) = 8.5625$.

3.5 Binomial Coefficients

We wish to obtain a generalization of algorithm 3.4 and recall to this end some facts about binomial coefficients.

The binomial coefficients

$$\binom{n}{m} \qquad \text{(to be read: "n over m")}$$

are for integral n and m, $n \geq 0$, $0 \leq m \leq n$, defined by the expansion

$$(1 + x)^n = \binom{n}{0} + \binom{n}{1}x + \binom{n}{2}x^2 + \cdots + \binom{n}{n}x^n.$$

It is well known that

$$(3\text{-}11) \qquad \binom{n}{m} = \frac{n(n-1)(n-2)\ldots(n-m+1)}{1 \cdot 2 \cdot 3 \ldots m} = \frac{n!}{m!(n-m)!}$$

From (3-11) it follows immediately that

$$(3\text{-}12) \qquad \binom{n}{n-m} = \binom{n}{m}.$$

The identity

$$(3\text{-}13) \qquad \binom{n}{m} + \binom{n}{m+1} = \binom{n+1}{m+1}$$

likewise is easily proved. It states that if the binomial coefficients are arranged in a triangular array known as Pascal's triangle,

$$
\begin{array}{ccccccccc}
 & & & & 1 & & & & \\
 & & & 1 & & 1 & & & \\
 & & 1 & & 2 & & 1 & & \\
 & 1 & & 3 & & 3 & & 1 & \\
1 & & 4 & & 6 & & 4 & & 1 \\
\end{array}
$$

$\cdots$

then each entry in this array is equal to the sum of the two entries immediately above it. We also shall require the following slightly less obvious property of the binomial coefficients.

Theorem 3.5   For any two nonnegative integers k and $n \geq k$ the following identity holds:

$$
\binom{k}{k} + \binom{k+1}{k} + \binom{k+2}{k} + \cdots + \binom{n}{k} = \binom{n+1}{k+1}.
$$

Proof.   Keeping k fixed, we use induction with respect to n. Set

$$
x_n = \binom{k}{k} + \binom{k+1}{k} + \cdots + \binom{n}{k}.
$$

Assuming that for some integer $n - 1 \geq k$

(3-14) $$ x_{n-1} = \binom{n}{k+1}, $$

which is certainly true for $n - 1 = k$, we have, using (3-13),

$$
x_n = x_{n-1} + \binom{n}{k} = \binom{n}{k+1} + \binom{n}{k} = \binom{n+1}{k+1},
$$

proving (3-14) with n increased by one, which suffices to establish the formula for all positive integers n.

EXAMPLE

13.   For $k = 2$, $n = 5$ we get

$$
\binom{2}{2} + \binom{3}{2} + \binom{4}{2} + \binom{5}{2} = 1 + 3 + 6 + 10 = 20 = \binom{6}{3}.
$$

Problems

5. Use the definition of the binomial coefficients to prove that

$$
\binom{n}{0} + \binom{n}{1} + \binom{n}{2} + \cdots + \binom{n}{n} = 2^n.
$$

6. Obtain an alternate proof of theorem 3.5 by differentiating the identity

$$(x - 1)(1 + x + x^2 + \cdots + x^n) = x^{n+1} - 1$$

$k + 1$ times and setting $x = 1$.

7. Show by means of theorem 3.3 that the difference initial value problem

$$y_0 = 1, \qquad y_n = ny_{n-1} + n! \binom{k + n}{n}$$

has the solution

$$y_n = n!\left[\binom{k}{0} + \binom{k + 1}{1} + \binom{k + 2}{2} + \cdots + \binom{k + n}{n}\right].$$

Show that the same initial value problem is also solved by

$$y_n = n!\binom{k + n + 1}{n}$$

and hence obtain yet another proof of theorem 3.5.   (Use (3-12).)

3.6   Evaluation of the Derivatives of a Polynomial

One is frequently required not only to find the value of a polynomial, but also the values of one or several derivatives at a given point.   For instance, if the polynomial

$$p(x) = b_0 x^N + b_1 x^{N-1} + \cdots + b_N$$

is to be expanded in powers of a new variable $h = x - z$, then we have by Taylor's theorem (see Taylor [1959], p. 471)

$$p(x) = p(z + h) = c_0 h^N + c_1 h^{N-1} + \cdots + c_N,$$

where

(3-15) $$c_{N-k} = \frac{1}{k!} p^{(k)}(z), \qquad k = 0, 1, \ldots, N.$$

These coefficients could be evaluated, of course, by differentiating p analytically and evaluating the resulting polynomials by Horner's algorithm 3.4.   It turns out, however, that there is a far shorter way. To this end we consider the following extension of algorithm 3.4.

Algorithm 3.6 Let the sequence generated in algorithm 3.4 now be denoted by $\{x_n^{(0)}\}$. For $k = 1, 2, \ldots, N$, generate the sequences $\{x_n^{(k)}\}$ recursively by the difference equation

(3-16) $$x_0^{(k)} = x_0^{(k-1)}, \qquad x_n^{(k)} = zx_{n-1}^{(k)} + x_n^{(k-1)},$$
$$n = 0, 1, \ldots, N - k.$$

Each of the sequences $\{x_n^{(k)}\}$ is generated from the preceding sequence

$\{x_n^{(k-1)}\}$ just as the sequence $\{x_n^{(0)}\}$ was generated from the sequence $\{b_n\}$. However, the new sequence always terminates one step before the old sequence. Scheme 3.6 indicates the resulting two-dimensional array for $N = 4$.

$$x_0^{(0)} \quad x_1^{(0)} \quad x_2^{(0)} \quad x_3^{(0)} \quad \underline{x_4^{(0)}}$$
$$\downarrow$$
$$x_0^{(1)} \quad x_1^{(1)} \Rightarrow x_2^{(1)} \quad \underline{x_3^{(1)}}$$
$$x_0^{(2)} \quad x_1^{(2)} \quad \underline{x_2^{(2)}}$$
$$x_0^{(3)} \quad \underline{x_1^{(3)}}$$
$$\underline{x_0^{(4)}}$$

(The symbol $\Rightarrow$ indicates multiplication by z.)

Scheme 3.6

The relevance of this scheme to the problem stated above is based on the following fact:

Theorem 3.6 If p_n denotes the polynomial

$$p_n(x) = b_0 x^n + b_1 x^{n-1} + \cdots + b_n \qquad (n = 0, 1, \ldots, N)$$

then the numbers $x_n^{(k)}$ determined in algorithm 3.6 satisfy

(3-17)
$$x_n^{(k)} = \frac{1}{k!} p_{n+k}^{(k)}(z),$$

$$n = 1, 2, \ldots, N - k; \quad k = 0, 1, \ldots, N.$$

Thus, the coefficients c_{N-k} required in (3-15) are just the entries in the lower diagonal (underlined in scheme 3.6) in the array of numbers generated by algorithm 3.6.

Proof. Theorem 3.4 asserts the truth of formula (3-17) for $k = 0$. We use induction with respect to k to prove it for arbitrary k. Assuming that (3-17) is true for a certain $k \geq 0$, we can write the difference equation (3-16) defining the sequence $\{x_n^{(k+1)}\}$ as follows:

$$x_0^{(k+1)} = \frac{1}{k!} p_k^{(k)}(z), \quad x_n^{(k+1)} = z x_{n-1}^{(k+1)} + \frac{1}{k!} p_{n+k}^{(k)}(z).$$

Expressing the solution of this equation by means of formula (3-9), where

$$a_n = z, \qquad \pi_n = z^n, \qquad b_n = \frac{1}{k!} p_{n+k}^{(k)}(z),$$

we obtain

$$x_n^{(k+1)} = \frac{z^n}{k!} \{ p_k^{(k)}(z) + z^{-1} p_{k+1}^{(k)}(z) + z^{-2} p_{k+2}^{(k)}(z) + \cdots + z^{-n} p_{n+k}^{(k)}(z) \}.$$

Here we express the polynomial derivatives by means of the formula of example 22, chapter 2:

$$\frac{1}{k!} p_m^{(k)}(z) = \binom{m}{k} b_0 z^{m-k} + \binom{m-1}{k} b_1 z^{m-k-1} + \cdots + \binom{k}{k} b_{m-k}.$$

This yields the expression

$$x_n^{(k+1)} = z^n \left\{ \binom{k}{k} b_0 + z^{-1} \left[\binom{k+1}{k} b_0 z + \binom{k}{k} b_1 \right] + \cdots \right.$$

$$\left. + z^{-n} \left[\binom{n+k}{k} b_0 z^n + \binom{n+k-1}{k} b_1 z^{n-1} + \cdots + \binom{k}{k} b_n \right] \right\}.$$

By rearranging the sum by collecting terms involving like powers of z this can be transformed into

$$x_n^{(k+1)} = \left[\binom{k}{k} + \binom{k+1}{k} + \cdots + \binom{n}{k} \right] b_0 z^n$$

$$+ \left[\binom{k}{k} + \binom{k+1}{k} + \cdots + \binom{n-1}{k} \right] b_1 z^{n-1} + \cdots + \binom{k}{k} b_n.$$

By using the identity of theorem 3.5, this simplifies into

$$x_n^{(k+1)} = \binom{n+k+1}{k+1} b_0 z^n + \binom{n+k}{k+1} b_1 z^{n-1} + \cdots + \binom{k+1}{k+1} b_n$$

$$= \frac{1}{(k+1)!} p_{n+k+1}^{(k+1)}(z).$$

EXAMPLE

14. To compute the Taylor expansion of the polynomial

$$p(x) = 7x^4 + 5x^3 - 2x^2 + 8$$

at $x = 0.5$.   Continuing the scheme started in example 12, we obtain

7	5	−2	0	8
7	8.5	2.25	1.125	8.5625
7	12.0	8.25	5.25	
7	15.5	16.0		
7	19.0			
7				

We thus have

$$7x^4 + 5x^3 - 2x^2 + 8 = 7(x - 0.5)^4 + 19(x - 0.5)^3$$
$$+ 16(x - 0.5)^2$$
$$+ 5.25(x - 0.5) + 8.5625.$$

Problems

8. Find the Taylor expansion of the polynomial

$$p(x) = 4x^3 - 5x + 1$$

at $x = -0.3$.

9. Calculate $p(x)$, $p'(x)$, $p''(x)$ for $x = 1.5$, where

$$p(x) = 2x^5 - 7x^4 + 3x^3 - 6x^2 + 4x - 5.$$

PART ONE

SOLUTION OF EQUATIONS

chapter 4 iteration

In this chapter we shall begin the study of the problem of solving (non-linear) equations in one and several variables. The method of iteration is the prototype of all numerical methods for attacking this problem. It is based on the solution of a certain nonlinear difference equation of the first order. The principle of iteration is of great importance also in certain branches of theoretical mathematics such as functional analysis and the theory of differential equations.

4.1 Definition and Hypotheses

We are here concerned with the problem of solving equations of the form

$$(4\text{-}1) \qquad\qquad x = f(x),$$

where f is a given function. The method of iteration consists in executing the following algorithm:

Algorithm 4.1 Choose x_0 arbitrarily, and generate the sequence $\{x_n\}$ recursively from the relation

$$(4\text{-}2) \qquad\qquad x_n = f(x_{n-1}), \qquad n = 1, 2, \ldots.$$

At the outset, we cannot even be sure that this algorithm is well defined. (It could be that f is undefined at some point $f(x_n)$.) However, let us assume that f is defined on some closed finite interval $I = [a, b]$, and *that the values of f lie in the same interval.* Geometrically this means that the graph of the function $y = f(x)$ is contained in the square $a \leqq x \leqq b$, $a \leqq y \leqq b$ (see Fig. 4.1a).

Under this assumption, if $x_0 \in I$, we can say that all elements of the sequence $\{x_n\}$ are in I. For if some $x_n \in I$ with $n \geqq 0$, then also $x_{n+1} = f(x_n) \in I$, since f has its values in I.

A glance at figure 4.1a shows that the above hypotheses are not sufficient

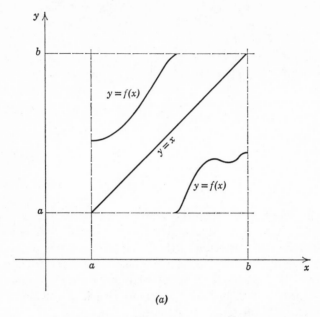

(a)

Figure 4.1

to guarantee that equation (4-1) has a solution. The graph of the function $y = f(x)$ need not intersect the graph of the function $y = x$. However, if we assume the function f to be *continuous*, then the graph shows that the equation has at least one solution. For the graph of $y = f(x)$ originates somewhere on the vertical straight line segment joining the points (a, a) and (a, b), and it ends somewhere on the straight line segment joining (b, a) and (b, b). Since the graph is now continuous, it must intersect the straight line $y = x$ $(a \leqq x \leqq b)$, perhaps at an endpoint. If s is the abscissa of the point of intersection, then

$$y = s \quad \text{and} \quad y = f(s)$$

at that point, hence $s = f(s)$, i.e., the number s is a solution of (4-1) (see Fig. 4.1b).

The above intuitive consideration can be couched in purely analytical terms, as follows. Consider the function g defined by $g(x) = x - f(x)$, $a \leqq x \leqq b$. This function is continuous on the interval $[a, b]$; moreover, since $f(a) \geqq a$, $f(b) \leqq b$, it satisfies $g(a) \leqq 0$, $g(b) \geqq 0$. By the intermediate value theorem of calculus (see Taylor [1959], p. 240) it assumes all values between $g(a)$ and $g(b)$ somewhere in the interval $[a, b]$. Therefore it must assume the value zero, say at $x = s$. This implies $0 = s - f(s)$, or $s = f(s)$. Thus the number s is the desired solution.

If an element of the sequence $\{x_n\}$ defined by algorithm 4.1 is equal to s, then all later elements will also be equal to s.   For this reason, any solution s of $x = f(x)$ is frequently called a *fixed point* of the iteration defined by the function f.

The assumptions made so far do not preclude the possibility of the existence of several, or even infinitely many, fixed points in the interval $[a, b]$ (see Fig. 4.1c).

If we wish to be sure that there is not more than one solution, we must make some assumption guaranteeing that the function f does not vary too rapidly.   We could assume, for instance, that f is differentiable, and that its derivative f' satisfies

$$(4\text{-}3) \qquad |f'(x)| \leqq L, \qquad a \leqq x \leqq b,$$

where L is some constant so that $L < 1$.   It turns out, however, that the following weaker assumption is sufficient to guarantee uniqueness: *There exists a constant $L < 1$ so that for any two points x_1 and x_2 in I the following inequality holds*:

$$(4\text{-}4) \qquad |f(x_1) - f(x_2)| \leqq L|x_1 - x_2|.$$

Any condition of the form (4-4) (whether $L < 1$ or not) is called a *Lipschitz condition*, and the constant L is called the *Lipschitz constant*.   Let us first show that condition (4-3) implies condition (4-4) with the same

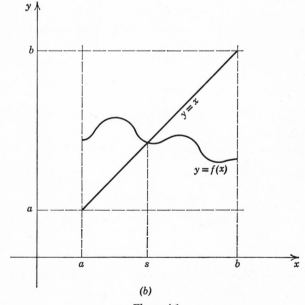

(b)

Figure 4.1

value of L. By the mean value theorem of differential calculus (see Taylor [1959], p. 240),

$$f(x_1) - f(x_2) = f'(x^*)(x_1 - x_2),$$

where x^* is a suitable point between x_1 and x_2. Relation (4-4) now follows readily by taking absolute values and using (4-3).

We now show that the Lipschitz condition (4-4) with $L < 1$ implies that equation (4-1) has at most one solution. Assume that there are two

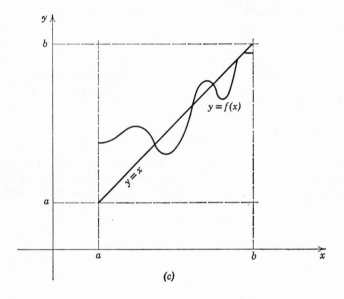

(c)

Figure 4.1

solutions s_1 and s_2, for instance. This means that the following relations both are true:

$$s_1 = f(s_1), \qquad s_2 = f(s_2).$$

Subtracting the second relation from the first, we obtain

$$s_1 - s_2 = f(s_1) - f(s_2).$$

Taking absolute values and applying (4-4) to the difference on the right, we get

$$|s_1 - s_2| = |f(s_1) - f(s_2)| \leq L|s_1 - s_2|.$$

If $s_1 \neq s_2$, we can divide by $|s_1 - s_2|$ and obtain $1 \leq L$, contradicting the assumption that $L < 1$. Thus $s_1 = s_2$, i.e., any two solutions of (4-1) are identical.

Problems

1. Show that the following functions satisfy Lipschitz conditions with $L < 1$:
   (a) $f(x) = 5 - \frac{1}{4}\cos 3x,$ $0 \leqq x \leqq 2\pi/3$;
   (b) $f(x) = 2 + \frac{1}{2}|x|,$ $-1 \leqq x \leqq 1$;
   (c) $f(x) = x^{-1},$ $2 \leqq x \leqq 3$.
2. Let m be any real number, and let $|\varepsilon| < 1$. Show that the equation

$$x = m - \varepsilon \sin x$$

   has a unique solution in the interval $[m - \pi, m + \pi]$.
3. Prove that any function satisfying a Lipschitz condition on an interval I is continuous at every point of I.
4. Construct an example showing that not every continuous function satisfies a Lipschitz condition.

4.2   Convergence of the Iteration Method

Having disposed of the theoretical preliminaries required to establish existence and uniqueness of the solution of (4-1), we now turn to the practical question of determining this solution by means of algorithm 4.1. Rather surprisingly it turns out that the assumptions which were made in §4.1 to guarantee existence and uniqueness suffice also to establish the fact that the sequence $\{x_n\}$ generated by algorithm 4.1 converges to the solution s.

Theorem 4.2   Let $I = [a, b]$ be a closed finite interval, and let the function f satisfy the following conditions:

   (i) f is continuous on I;
   (ii) $f(x) \in I$ for all $x \in I$;
   (iii) f satisfies the Lipschitz condition (4-4) with a Lipschitz constant $L < 1$.

Then for any choice of $x_0 \in I$ the sequence defined by algorithm 4.1 converges to the unique solution s of the equation $x = f(x)$.

Proof.   That the hypotheses of theorem 4.2 guarantee the existence of a unique solution s of $x = f(x)$ has already been shown in §4.1. To prove convergence of the sequence $\{x_n\}$, we shall estimate the difference $x_n - s$. By definition,

$$x_n - s = f(x_{n-1}) - s = f(x_{n-1}) - f(s)$$

and hence, by the Lipschitz condition,

$$|x_n - s| \leqq L|x_{n-1} - s|.$$

Applying the same inequality repeatedly, we find

(4-5) $$|x_n - s| = L^n|x_0 - s|.$$

Since $0 \leq L < 1$,

$$\lim_{n \to \infty} L^n = 0,$$

and it follows that

$$\lim_{n \to \infty} |x_n - s| = 0,$$

which means the same as

$$\lim_{n \to \infty} x_n = s,$$

completing the proof.

The convergence of the sequence $\{x_n\}$ is illustrated very suggestively by plotting the points (x_0, x_0), (x_0, x_1), (x_1, x_1), (x_1, x_2), (x_2, x_2), (x_2, x_3), ... in a graph of the function $y = f(x)$ (see Fig. 4.2). It is evident from the figure that convergence cannot take place in general if condition (4-4) does not hold with some $L < 1$.

EXAMPLE

1. It is desired to find a solution of the equation

$$x = e^{-x}.$$

For $0 \leq x \leq 1$, the values of the function $f(x) = e^{-x}$ lie in the interval

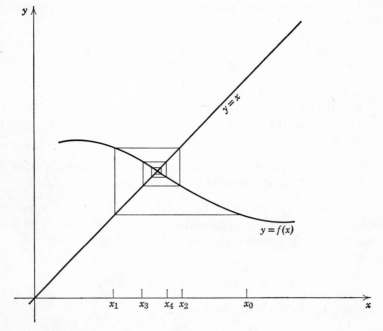

Figure 4.2

$[e^{-1}, 1]$, and thus a fortiori in $[0, 1]$. For x_1, x_2 in this interval, we have by the mean value theorem

$$|f(x_1) - f(x_2)| = |f'(x^*)||x_1 - x_2|,$$

where $f'(x^*) = -e^{-x^*}$. Since the maximum of $|f'(x)|$ for $x \in [0, 1]$ is 1, (4-4) holds only with $L = 1$, violating the condition that $L < 1$. However, let us consider the smaller interval $I = [\frac{1}{2}, \log 2]$. Since

$$\tfrac{1}{2} = e^{-\log 2} \leqq e^{-x} \leqq e^{-1/2} < \log 2$$

for $\frac{1}{2} \leqq x \leqq \log 2$, I is again mapped into I by the function f, and (4-4) now holds with $L = |f'(\frac{1}{2})| = e^{-1/2} = 0.606531$. Beginning with $x_0 = 0.5$, the first few values of the sequence $\{x_n\}$ are as follows:

Table 4.2

n	x_n	$f(x_n)$	x_n'
0	0.500000	0.606531	0.567624
1	0.606531	0.545239	0.567299
2	0.545239	0.579703	0.567193
3	0.579703	0.560065	0.567159
4	0.560065	0.571172	0.567148
5	0.571172	0.564863	0.567145
6	0.564863	0.568438	0.567144
7	0.568438	0.566410	0.567144
8	0.566410	0.567560	
9	0.567560	0.566907	
10	0.566907	0.567278	
11	0.567278	0.567067	
12	0.567067	0.567187	
13	0.567187	0.567119	
14	0.567119		

Problems

5. Kepler's equation

$$m = x - E \sin x,$$

where m and E are given and x is sought, plays a considerable role in dynamical astronomy. Solve the equation iteratively for $m = 0.8$, $E = 0.2$, by writing it in the form

$$x = m + E \sin x$$

and starting with $x_0 = m$.

6. The solution of Kepler's equation can also be represented analytically in the form

$$x = m + \sum_{n=1}^{\infty} \frac{2}{n} J_n(nE) \sin nm,$$

where J_n denotes the Bessel function of order n. Using tables of Bessel functions, check the result obtained in problem 5 and compare the amount of labor required.

7. Find the only positive solution of the equation

$$x^3 - x^2 - x - 1 = 0$$

by iteration, writing it in the form

$$x = 1 + \frac{1}{x} + \frac{1}{x^2}.$$

(Begin with $x_0 = 1$.)

8. Assume that the function f, in addition to the hypotheses of theorem 4.2, is differentiable and satisfies $f'(x) < 0$, $x \in I$. If $x_0 < s$, prove both analytically and by considering the graph of f that

$$x_0 < x_2 < x_4 < \cdots < s < \cdots < x_5 < x_3 < x_1.$$

9. Suppose the function g is defined and differentiable on the interval $[0, 1]$, and suppose that $g(0) < 0 < g(1)$, $0 < a \leq g'(x) \leq b$, where a and b are constants. Show that there exists a constant M such that the solution of the equation $g(x) = 0$ can be found by applying iteration to the function

$$f(x) = x + Mg(x).$$

10. What is the value of

$$s = \sqrt{2 + \sqrt{2 + \sqrt{2 + \cdots}}}?$$

(Hint: The number s may be considered as the limit of the sequence $\{x_n\}$ generated by algorithm 4.1, where $f(x) = \sqrt{2 + x}$, $x_0 = 0$. Show that f satisfies, in a suitable interval, the hypotheses of theorem 4.2.)

4.3 The Error after a Finite Number of Steps

No computing process can be carried on indefinitely, and in any practical application algorithm 4.1 must be artificially terminated after having computed, say, the element x_n. We are interested in finding a bound for the quantity $|x_n - s|$, that is, for the error of x_n considered as an approximation to the solution s. This bound should depend only on quantities that are known *a priori* and should not depend on a knowledge of the solution itself. (This is why a result such as (4-5) does not satisfy our purpose.)

To establish such a bound, we require the following auxiliary result: For $n = 0, 1, 2, \ldots,$

(4-6) $$|x_{n+1} - x_n| \leq L^n |x_1 - x_0|.$$

Evidently this is true for $n = 0$. Assuming the truth of (4-6) for $n = k - 1$, where k is an integer > 0, we have

$$\begin{aligned}
|x_{k+1} - x_k| &= |f(x_k) - f(x_{k-1})| \\
&\leq L|x_k - x_{k-1}| \\
&\leq L \cdot L^{k-1} |x_1 - x_0| \\
&= L^k |x_1 - x_0|,
\end{aligned}$$

establishing (4-6) for $n = k$. The truth of (4-6) for all positive integers n now follows by the principle of mathematical induction.

Let n now be a fixed positive integer, and let $m > n$. We shall find a bound for $x_m - x_n$. Writing

$$x_m - x_n = (x_m - x_{m-1}) + (x_{m-1} - x_{m-2}) + \cdots + (x_{n+1} - x_n)$$

and applying the triangle inequality (see Taylor [1959], p. 443) we get

$$|x_m - x_n| \leq |x_m - x_{m-1}| + |x_{m-1} - x_{m-2}| + \cdots + |x_{n+1} - x_n|$$

and using (4-6) to estimate each term on the right,

$$|x_m - x_n| \leq (L^{m-1} + \cdots + L^n)|x_1 - x_0|.$$

Now, since $|L| < 1$,

$$\begin{aligned}
L^{m-1} + \cdots + L^n &= L^n(1 + L + \cdots + L^{m-n-1}) \\
&\leq L^n(1 + L + L^2 + \cdots) \\
&= L^n \frac{1}{1 - L}
\end{aligned}$$

by virtue of the familiar formula for the sum of the geometric series. We thus have

$$|x_m - x_n| \leq \frac{L^n}{1 - L} |x_1 - x_0|.$$

In this relation let $m \to \infty$ while keeping n fixed. By virtue of $x_m \to s$ we obtain

Corollary 4.3 Under the conditions of theorem 4.2 the error of the nth approximation x_n defined by algorithm 4.1 is bounded as follows:

(4-7) $$|x_n - s| \leq \frac{L^n}{1 - L} |x_1 - x_0|.$$

EXAMPLE

2. The error of the final element x_{14} produced in example 1 is less than

$$\frac{L^{14}}{1-L}|x_1 - x_0| = \frac{e^{-7}}{0.393469} \times 0.106531 = 0.000247.$$

Actually, since $f' < 0$, it follows from problem 8 that the solution satisfies

$$0.567119 < s < 0.567187.$$

Problem

11. For Kepler's equation considered in problem 5, estimate the error of x_{10}.

4.4 Accelerating Convergence

Let us now assume that the function f, in addition to satisfying the hypotheses of theorem 4.2, is continuously differentiable throughout the interval I, and that the derivative f' is never zero. This means that f is either monotonically strictly increasing or monotonically strictly decreasing throughout the whole interval I. If $x_0 \neq s$, it is evident from a graph that under this condition no x_n can be equal to the exact solution s, i.e., the iteration process cannot terminate in a finite number of steps. An analytical proof of this fact is as follows: Assume the contrary, namely, that $f(x_n) = x_n$ for some n. If n is the first index for which this happens, then

$$x_n = f(x_{n-1}) = f(x_n), \qquad x_{n-1} \neq x_n,$$

and hence, by the mean value theorem (see Taylor [1959], p. 240),

$$0 = f(x_{n-1}) - f(x_n) = f'(x^*)(x_{n-1} - x_n),$$

where x^* is between x_{n-1} and x_n. Since $x_{n-1} - x_n \neq 0$, it follows that $f'(x^*) = 0$, contradicting the hypotheses that f' never vanishes.

The above implies that the error

$$d_n = x_n - s$$

is never zero. We now ask: Does the limit

$$\lim_{n \to \infty} \frac{d_{n+1}}{d_n}$$

exist, and if it does, what is its value?

Using the mean value theorem once more, we have

$$\begin{aligned}
d_{n+1} &= x_{n+1} - s \\
&= f(x_n) - s \\
&= f(s + d_n) - f(s) \\
&= f'(s + \theta_n d_n) d_n
\end{aligned}$$

where $0 < \theta_n < 1$. Let us define ε_n by

$$f'(s + \theta_n\, d_n) = f'(s) + \varepsilon_n.$$

We then have

(4-8) $$d_{n+1} = (f'(s) + \varepsilon_n)\, d_n$$

and, since $\varepsilon_n \to 0$ for $n \to \infty$ by virtue of the continuity of f',

(4-9) $$\lim_{n\to\infty} \frac{d_{n+1}}{d_n} = f'(s).$$

This equation shows that the error at the $(n + 1)st$ step is approximately equal to $f'(s)$ times the error at the nth step. As s is unknown, the limiting ratio $f'(s)$ of two consecutive errors is, of course, unknown, and all we really know is that the ratio of two consecutive errors approaches some unknown limit. We now shall show, however, how to obtain a significant improvement of the convergence of the iteration method by a judicious use of this incomplete information.

Let us heuristically proceed under the assumption that (4-8) is exact with $\varepsilon_n = 0$ for finite values of n. We then have, writing $f'(s) = A$ for brevity,

$$x_{n+1} - s = A(x_n - s)$$
$$x_{n+2} - s = A(x_{n+1} - s).$$

It is an easy matter now to eliminate the unknown quantity A and solve for s. Subtracting the first equation from the second, we obtain

$$x_{n+2} - x_{n+1} = A(x_{n+1} - x_n),$$

hence

$$A = \frac{x_{n+2} - x_{n+1}}{x_{n+1} - x_n}.$$

Solving the first equation for s and substituting for A, we get

$$s = \frac{1}{1 - A}(x_{n+1} - Ax_n)$$

$$= x_n + \frac{1}{1 - A}(x_{n+1} - x_n)$$

$$= x_n - \frac{(x_{n+1} - x_n)^2}{x_{n+2} - 2x_{n+1} + x_n}.$$

If our assumption that $\varepsilon_n = 0$ were correct, we thus could obtain the exact solution from any three consecutive iterates x_n, x_{n+1}, x_{n+2}. In reality, of course, the ε_n are not exactly zero. They are, however, ultimately small compared to $f'(s)$. We thus may hope that for n large the quantities

$$(4\text{-}10) \qquad x'_n = x_n - \frac{(x_{n+1} - x_n)^2}{x_{n+2} - 2x_{n+1} + x_n}$$

yield a better approximation to s than the quantities x_n. We are thus led to investigate the properties of the following algorithm:

Algorithm 4.4 (Aitken's Δ^2-method) Given a sequence of numbers $\{x_n\}$, generate from it a new sequence $\{x'_n\}$ by means of formula (4-10).

Formula (4-10) can be simplified somewhat by means of the difference operator Δ. If $\{x_n\}$ is any sequence, we write

$$\Delta x_n = x_{n+1} - x_n, \qquad n = 0, 1, 2, \ldots.$$

Higher powers of the operator Δ are defined recursively. For instance,

$$\Delta^2 x_n = \Delta(\Delta x_n) = \Delta x_{n+1} - \Delta x_n$$
$$= x_{n+2} - 2x_{n+1} + x_n.$$

It is now evident that formula (4-10) can be written thus:

$$(4\text{-}11) \qquad x'_n = x_n - \frac{(\Delta x_n)^2}{\Delta^2 x_n}.$$

This notation, together with the fact that algorithm 4.4 was discussed by Aitken [1926], explains its traditional name.

EXAMPLE

3. The last column of table 4.2 (see example 1) contains the accelerated Aitken values of the sequence $\{x_n\}$. It is seen that after six steps the sequence $\{x'_n\}$ has converged to the number of digits given, whereas the original sequence $\{x_n\}$ has not even nearly converged after fourteen steps.

Problem

12. The convergence behavior typified by (4-8) is sometimes characterized by the statement that "the number of correct decimal digits in x_n grows at a fixed rate." Give a quantitative interpretation of this statement, allowing you to answer the following question: As $n \to \infty$, how many steps are necessary (on the average) to reduce the error by a factor $\frac{1}{10}$?

4.5 Aitken's Δ^2-Method

After having discovered algorithm 4.4 in a heuristic manner, we now shall present a rigorous analysis of it. This analysis applies to arbitrary sequences having certain convergence properties and is not confined to sequences arising through iteration. The basic result is as follows.

Theorem 4.5   Let $\{x_n\}$ be any sequence converging to the limit s such that the quantities $d_n = x_n - s$ satisfy $d_n \neq 0$,

(4-12) $$d_{n+1} = (A + \varepsilon_n) d_n,$$

where A is a constant, $|A| < 1$, and $\varepsilon_n \to 0$ for $n \to \infty$. Then the sequence $\{x_n'\}$ derived from $\{x_n\}$ by means of algorithm 4.4 is defined for n sufficiently large and converges to s faster than the sequence $\{x_n\}$ in the sense that

(4-13) $$\frac{x_n' - s}{x_n - s} \to 0, \qquad n \to \infty.$$

Proof. Applying (4-12) twice, we have

$$d_{n+2} = (A + \varepsilon_{n+1})(A + \varepsilon_n) d_n.$$

Hence

$$\begin{aligned} \Delta^2 x_n &= x_{n+2} - 2x_{n+1} + x_n \\ &= d_{n+2} - 2d_{n+1} + d_n \\ &= [(A - 1)^2 + \varepsilon_n'] d_n, \end{aligned}$$

where

$$\varepsilon_n' = A(\varepsilon_n + \varepsilon_{n+1}) - 2\varepsilon_n + \varepsilon_n \varepsilon_{n+1}.$$

By virtue of $\varepsilon_n \to 0$ it follows that also

(4-14) $$\varepsilon_n' \to 0, \qquad n \to \infty.$$

We conclude that $(A - 1)^2 + \varepsilon_n' \neq 0$ for all sufficiently large $n, n > n_0$, say. It follows that $\Delta^2 x_n \neq 0$ for $n > n_0$; hence the sequence $\{x_n'\}$ is defined for $n > n_0$. We have

$$\Delta x_n = \Delta d_n = (A + \varepsilon_n - 1) d_n$$

and hence, subtracting s from (4-11),

$$\begin{aligned} x_n' - s &= d_n - \frac{(\Delta x_n)^2}{\Delta^2 x_n} \\ &= d_n - \frac{(A - 1 + \varepsilon_n)^2 d_n}{(A - 1)^2 + \varepsilon_n'} \\ &= \frac{\varepsilon_n' - 2\varepsilon_n(A - 1) - \varepsilon_n^2}{(A - 1)^2 + \varepsilon_n'} d_n. \end{aligned}$$

The hypothesis that $\varepsilon_n \to 0$ and (4-14) now insure that

$$\frac{x_n' - s}{d_n} = \frac{\varepsilon_n' - 2\varepsilon_n(A - 1) - \varepsilon_n^2}{(A - 1)^2 + \varepsilon_n'} \to 0,$$

as desired.

The result of theorem 4.5 is immediately applicable to sequences generated by iteration, as shown by corollary 4.5.

Corollary 4.5   Let the function f, in addition to the hypotheses of theorem 4.2, have a continuous derivative on I, and assume that $f' \neq 0$. Provided that $x_0 \neq s$, the sequence $\{x_n\}$ generated by algorithm 4.1 satisfies the hypotheses of theorem 4.5, and algorithm 4.4 thus results in a speedup of convergence.

Proof.   As was shown at the beginning of §4.4, the hypotheses of the corollary suffice not only to show that $d_n \neq 0$, $n = 0, 1, 2, \ldots$, but also that (4-8) holds, which is precisely what is needed in theorem 4.5.

Although originally motivated by the iterative procedure, the effectiveness of the Δ^2-acceleration is in no way confined to sequences generated by iteration. Some other instances where it may be applied are given in problems 15, 16, and in chapter 7.

Problems

13. Apply algorithm 4.4 to the sequences obtained in problems 5 and 7.
14. Let x_n be the nth partial sum of the infinite series $\sum_{k=0}^{\infty} a_k$,

$$x_n = \sum_{k=0}^{n} a_k.$$

Show that algorithm 4.4 in this case yields the formula

$$x_n' = x_n + \frac{a_{n+1}^2}{a_{n+1} - a_{n+2}}.$$

15. Show that the hypotheses of theorem 4.5 are satisfied if the terms a_n of the series considered in problem 14 satisfy

$$a_n = (a + \varepsilon_n)z^n,$$

where a is a constant, $|z| < 1$, and where the sequence $\{\varepsilon_n\}$ tends to zero. (Hint: Introduce the quantities

$$\delta_n = \sup_{k \geq n} |\varepsilon_k|.)$$

16. Evaluate the sum

$$\sum_{n=0}^{\infty} \frac{1}{\cosh(n \log 2)}$$

to 5 decimal places.   (Apply problem 14.)
17*. Assume the quantities ε_n in theorem 4.5 are such that the limit

(4-15) $$\lim_{n \to \infty} \frac{\varepsilon_{n+1}}{\varepsilon_n} = B$$

exists.   Show that the convergence of the sequence $\{x_n'\}$ can be sped up even further by applying algorithm 4.4 once more.

18*. Show that condition (4-15) is satisfied if the sequence $\{x_n\}$ is generated by algorithm 4.1, provided that the second derivative f'' of f exists, is continuous, and satisfies $f''(s) \neq 0$.

4.6 Quadratic Convergence

In §4.4 we had assumed that $f'(x) \neq 0$ on the interval I, and thus in particular that $f'(s) \neq 0$. We then obtained a convergence behavior characterized by relation (4-8). This is known as *linear* convergence. (The number of correct decimal places is approximately a linear function of the number of iterations performed.) Let us now investigate the asymptotic behavior of the error if $f'(s) = 0$. We first note that if this is known to be the case, then it is not necessary to verify all the hypotheses of theorem 4.2.

Theorem 4.6 Let I be an interval (finite or infinite), and let the function f be defined on I and satisfy the following conditions:

(*i*) f and f' are continuous on I;
(*ii*) the equation $x = f(x)$ has a solution s, located in the interior of I, such that $f'(s) = 0$.

Then there exists a number $d > 0$ such that algorithm 4.1 converges to s for any choice of x_0 satisfying $|x_0 - s| \leq d$.

The conclusion of the theorem can be expressed by saying that the algorithm *always* converges when the starting point is "sufficiently close" to the solution.

Proof. Let I_d denote the interval $[s - d, s + d]$. Since s is in the interior of I, I_d is contained in I if d is sufficiently small, $d \leq d_0$ say. Let L be given, $0 < L < 1$. By the continuity of f', there exists d satisfying $0 < d \leq d_0$ such that $|f'(x) - f'(s)| = |f'(x)| \leq L$ for $x \in I_d$. An application of the mean value theorem now shows that for $x \in I_d$,

$$|f(x) - s| = |f(x) - f(s)| \leq L|x - s| \leq Ld < d;$$

thus, the values taken by f in I_d lie in I_d. The hypotheses of theorem 4.2 are thus satisfied for the interval I_d, and as a consequence algorithm 4.1 converges.

Let us now assume, in addition to the hypotheses of theorem 4.6, that f'' exists, is continuous, and does not vanish on I_d. As at the beginning of §4.4, we then can show that if $x_0 \neq s$, no x_n will be accidentally equal to s, and that the iteration algorithm cannot yield the exact solution in a finite number of steps.

Using Taylor's theorem with remainder (see Taylor [1959], p. 476) we find the following expression for the error $d_{n+1} = x_{n+1} - s$:

$$
\begin{aligned}
d_{n+1} &= x_{n+1} - s \\
&= f(x_n) - f(s) \\
&= f'(s) d_n + \tfrac{1}{2} f''(s + \theta_n d_n) d_n^2.
\end{aligned}
$$

Here θ_n denotes, as usual, an unspecified number between zero and one. By virtue of our assumption that $f'(s) = 0$ the above expression simplifies, and we get

(4-16) $d_{n+1} = \tfrac{1}{2} f''(s + \theta_n d_n) d_n^2.$

Since $d_n \neq 0$ and $d_n \to 0$ for $n \to \infty$ it follows that

(4-17) $\displaystyle\lim_{n \to \infty} \frac{d_{n+1}}{d_n^2} = \tfrac{1}{2} f''(s).$

Relation (4-16) states the remarkable fact that if $f'(s) = 0$, the error at the $(n+1)st$ step is proportional to the *square* of the error at the nth step. This type of convergence behavior is known as *quadratic convergence*. It is frequently, if somewhat vaguely, described by stating that the number of correct decimal places is *doubled* at each step.

EXAMPLE

4. Let $a > 0$, and let $f(x) = \tfrac{1}{2}(x + a/x)$ for $x > 0$. The equation $x = f(x)$ has the solution $x = \sqrt{a}$. It is easily seen that $f'(\sqrt{a}) = 0$, and that $f''(x) > 0$, $x > 0$. It thus follows that the sequence defined by

$$
x_{n+1} = \frac{1}{2}\left(x_n + \frac{a}{x_n} \right)
$$

converges to $\sqrt{a}$ quadratically, provided that x_0 is sufficiently close to $\sqrt{a}$. (Actually, it can be shown that the sequence converges for every choice of $x_0 > 0$, see §4.9.) This algorithm for calculating $\sqrt{a}$ is a special case of Newton's method, which is discussed in the next section.

Problems

19. For what values of the constant M in problem 9 does the sequence defined by $x_n = f(x_{n-1})$ converge quadratically to the solution s?

20. Let the function f have a nonvanishing third derivative, and assume that $s = f(s)$, $f'(s) = f''(s) = 0$. Show that in this case the limit of d_{n+1}/d_n^3 exists for x_0 sufficiently close to s. (The convergence is called cubic in this case.)

21*. Let

$$
f(x) = \frac{x^3 + bx}{cx^2 + d}.
$$

Determine the constants b, c, d in such a manner that the sequence defined by algorithm 4.1 converges cubically to $\sqrt{z}$. Use the algorithm thus obtained to calculate $\sqrt{10}$ to ten decimal places, starting with $x_0 = 3$.

4.7 Newton's Method

The reader might well be under the impression that the discussion of quadratic convergence in the last section is without much practical value, since for an equation of the form $x = f(x)$ the condition $f'(s) = 0$ will be satisfied only by accident. However, it will now be shown that, at least for differentiable functions f, the basic iteration procedure of algorithm 4.1 can always be reformulated in such a way that it becomes quadratically convergent.

Let the function F be defined and twice continuously differentiable on the interval $I = [a, b]$, let $F'(x) \neq 0$ for $x \in I$, and let the equation

$$(4\text{-}18) \qquad\qquad F(x) = 0$$

have the solution (necessarily the *only* solution) $x = s$, where s lies in the interior of I. We have already observed that this solution can be found by applying iteration to the function

$$f(x) = x + MF(x),$$

where M is a constant that must satisfy certain inequalities (see problem 9). Unless we are lucky, the convergence of the iteration sequence thus generated is linear. We now ask: Can we determine a function h (depending on f, but easily calculable) so that the iteration sequence generated by the function

$$f(x) = x + h(x)F(x)$$

converges to s quadratically?

In view of theorem 4.6 the sole condition to be satisfied by f (in addition to the obviously satisfied condition $f(s) = s$) is $f'(s) = 0$. In view of

$$f'(x) = 1 + h'(x)F(x) + h(x)F'(x)$$

this yields

$$h'(s)F(s) + h(s)F'(s) = -1$$

or, since $F(s) = 0$,

$$h(s) = -\frac{1}{F'(s)}.$$

A simple way to satisfy this condition (we do not claim it is the only way) is to choose

$$h(x) = -\frac{1}{F'(x)}.$$

We are thus led to the following algorithm:

Algorithm 4.7   Choose x_0, and determine the sequence $\{x_n\}$ from the recurrence relation

$$(4\text{-}19) \qquad x_{n+1} = x_n - \frac{F(x_n)}{F'(x_n)}, \qquad n = 0, 1, 2, \ldots$$

Algorithm 4.7 is known as *Newton's method* or as the *Newton-Raphson method*. The convergence of Newton's method for starting values x_0 sufficiently close to s follows immediately from theorem 4.6, since the iteration function $f(x) = x - F(x)/F'(x)$ was specifically constructed so as to satisfy $f'(s) = 0$. If we assume, in addition to the hypotheses made above, that F''' exists and is continuous, then it easily follows that f'' is continuous, and hence that the convergence of the sequence defined by (4-19), if it takes place at all, is quadratic.

Formula (4-19) has a very simple graphical interpretation. We approximate the graph of the function F by its tangent at the point x_n, that is, $F(x)$ is replaced by

$$F(x_n) + (x - x_n)F'(x_n).$$

Setting this expression equal to zero and solving for x, we find equation (4-19) (see Fig. 4.7). Intuitively appealing as they may be, considerations such as these tell us nothing about the nature of convergence, nor are they easily extended to the case of systems of equations.

Figure 4.7

4.8 A Non-local Convergence Theorem for Newton's Method

The results proved in §4.7 are still unsatisfactory inasmuch convergence is proved only for starting values "sufficiently close" to the solution s. Since the exact solution is unknown, the question how to find the first approximation x_0 remains unanswered. We now shall prove a result which explicitly specifies an interval in which the first approximation may be taken. The one new hypothesis which must be made is that F'' does not change sign in the interval under consideration.

Theorem 4.8 Let the function F be defined and twice continuously differentiable on the closed finite interval $[a, b]$, and let the following conditions be satisfied:

(i) $F(a)F(b) < 0$;
(ii) $F'(x) \neq 0$, $x \in [a, b]$;
(iii) $F''(x)$ is either $\geqq 0$ or $\leqq 0$ for all $x \in [a, b]$;
(iv) If c denotes that endpoint of $[a, b]$ at which $|F'(x)|$ is smaller, then

$$\left| \frac{F(c)}{F'(c)} \right| \leqq b - a.$$

Then Newton's method converges to the (only) solution s of $F(x) = 0$ for any choice of x_0 in $[a, b]$.

Some explanation of the hypotheses is in order. Condition (i) merely states that $F(a)$ and $F(b)$ have different signs, and hence that the equation $F(x) = 0$ has at least one solution in (a, b). By virtue of condition (ii) there is only one solution. Condition (iii) states that the graph of F is either concave from above or concave from below. Condition (iv) states that the tangent to the curve $y = F(x)$ at that endpoint where $|F'(x)|$ is smallest intersects the x-axis within the interval $[a, b]$.

Proof. Theorem 4.8 covers the following four different situations:

(a) $F(a) < 0$, $F(b) > 0$, $F''(x) \leqq 0$ $(c = b)$;
(b) $F(a) > 0$, $F(b) < 0$, $F''(x) \geqq 0$ $(c = b)$;
(c) $F(a) < 0$, $F(b) > 0$, $F''(x) \geqq 0$ $(c = a)$;
(d) $F(a) > 0$, $F(b) < 0$, $F''(x) \leqq 0$ $(c = a)$.

The cases (b) and (d) are readily reduced to the cases (a) and (c), respectively, by considering the function $-F$ in place of F. (This change does not change the sequence $\{x_n\}$.) Case (c) is reduced to case (a) by replacing x by $-x$. (This changes the sequence $\{x_n\}$ into $\{-x_n\}$, and the solution s to $-s$.) It thus suffices to prove the theorem in case (a). Here the graph of F looks as given in figure 4.8.

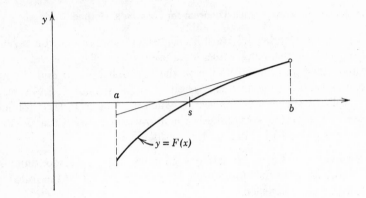

Figure 4.8

Let s be the unique solution of $F(x) = 0$. We first assume that $a \leqq x_0 \leqq s$. By virtue of $F(x_0) \leqq 0$, it is clear that

$$x_1 = x_0 - \frac{F(x_0)}{F'(x_0)} \geqq x_0.$$

We assert that $x_n \leqq s$, $x_{n+1} \geqq x_n$ for all values of n. This being true for $n = 0$, it suffices to perform the induction step from n to $n + 1$. If $x_n \leqq s$, then by the mean value theorem

$$-F(x_n) = F(s) - F(x_n) = (s - x_n)F'(x_n^*)$$

where $x_n \leqq x_{n,}^* \leqq s$. By virtue of $F''(x) \leqq 0$, F' is decreasing, hence $F'(x_n^*) \leqq F'(x_n)$

$$-F(x_n) \leqq (s - x_n)F'(x_n)$$

and

$$x_{n+1} = x_n - \frac{F(x_n)}{F'(x_n)} \leqq x_n + (s - x_n) = s.$$

Consequently, $F(x_{n+1}) \leqq 0$ and $x_{n+2} = x_{n+1} - F(x_{n+1})/F'(x_{n+1}) \geqq x_{n+1}$, completing the induction step.

Since every bounded monotonic sequence has a limit (see Taylor [1959], p. 453) it follows that $\lim_{n\to\infty} x_n$ exists and is $\leqq s$. Denoting this limit by q and letting $n \to \infty$ in the relation

$$x_{n+1} = x_n - \frac{F(x_n)}{F'(x_n)}$$

it follows by the continuity of F and F' that

$$q = q - \frac{F(q)}{F'(q)}$$

and hence that $F(q) = 0$, implying that $q = s$.

Consider now the case where $s < x_0 \leqq b$. Using once more the mean value theorem, we have $F(x_0) = F'(x_0^*)(x_0 - s)$, where $s < x_0^* < x_0$, and hence, since F' is decreasing, $F(x_0) \geqq (x_0 - s)F'(x_0)$. It follows that

$$x_1 = x_0 - \frac{F(x_0)}{F'(x_0)} \leqq x_0 - (x_0 - s) = s.$$

On the other hand $F(x_0) = F(b) - (b - x_0)F'(x_0')$ where $x_0 \leqq x_0' \leqq b$, hence

$$F(x_0) \leqq F(b) - (b - x_0)F'(b).$$

By virtue of condition (iv) of the theorem we thus have

$$x_1 = x_0 - \frac{F(x_0)}{F'(x_0)} \geqq x_0 - \frac{F(x_0)}{F'(b)} \geqq x_0 - \frac{F(b)}{F'(b)} + (b - x_0)$$

$$= x_0 - (b - a) + (b - x_0) = a.$$

Hence $a \leqq x_1 \leqq s$, and it follows by what has been proved above for the case $a \leqq x_0 \leqq s$ that the sequence $\{x_n\}$ converges to s. Thus the proof of theorem 4.8 is complete.

The literature on Newton's method is extensive. Convergence can be proved under various sets of conditions other than those of theorem 4.8, and it is also possible to give bounds for the error after a finite number of steps (see Ostrowski [1960]). The theorem given above, however, covers some of the most important special cases.

4.9 Some Special Cases of Newton's Method

We now shall give some examples for the application of theorem 4.8.

(i) *Determination of square roots.* Let c be a given number, $c > 0$, and let

$$F(x) = x^2 - c \qquad (x > 0).$$

We wish to solve the equation $F(x) = 0$, i.e., to compute $x = \sqrt{c}$. Newton's method takes the form

$$x_{n+1} = x_n - \frac{F(x_n)}{F'(x_n)}$$

$$= x_n - \frac{x_n^2 - c}{2x_n},$$

or

(4-20)
$$x_{n+1} = \frac{1}{2}\left(x_n + \frac{c}{x_n}\right).$$

We are thus led to the algorithm considered in example 4. Since $F'(x) > 0$, $F''(x) > 0$ for $x > 0$, we are in case (d) of theorem 4.8. In any interval $[a, b]$ with $0 < a < \sqrt{c} < b$ the smallest value of the slope occurs at $x = a$, and it is easily seen that condition (iv) is satisfied for every $b \geq \frac{1}{2}(a + c/a)$. Thus it follows that the sequence defined by (4-20) converges to $\sqrt{c}$ for every choice of $x_0 > 0$.

Formula (4-20) states that the new approximation is always the arithmetic mean of the old approximation and of the result of dividing c by the old approximation. For work on a desk computer it is not necessary to work with full accuracy from the beginning since every new value can be regarded as new starting value of the iteration.

EXAMPLE

5. $c = 10$, $x_0 = 3$ yields

$$
\begin{aligned}
x_0 &= 3 & c/x_0 &= 3.3 \\
x_1 &= 3.15 & c/x_1 &= 3.1746 \\
x_2 &= 3.1622 & c/x_2 &= 3.16225532 \\
x_3 &= 3.16227766 & c/x_3 &= 3.16227766
\end{aligned}
$$

Since $x_4 = x_3$ to the number of digits given, the last value is accepted as final.

(ii) *Finding roots of arbitrary order.* If $F(x) = x^k - c$, where $c > 0$ and k is any positive integer, Newton's method yields the formula

$$ x_{n+1} = x_n - \frac{x_n^k - c}{k x_n^{k-1}} $$

or

(4-21) $$ x_{n+1} = \left(1 - \frac{1}{k}\right)x_n + \frac{1}{k} c x_n^{1-k} $$

Again the conditions of theorem 4.8 are satisfied for every interval $[a, b]$ if $0 < a < \sqrt[k]{c}$ and b is sufficiently large, and the sequence defined by (4-21) converges to $\sqrt[k]{c}$ for arbitrary $x_0 > 0$.

(iii) *Finding reciprocals without division.* For a given $c > 0$ we wish to determine the number

$$ s = \frac{1}{c}. $$

This may be regarded as the solution of the equation

$$ F(x) = \frac{1}{x} - c = 0. $$

Newton's method yields

$$x_{n+1} = x_n - \frac{\dfrac{1}{x_n} - c}{-\dfrac{1}{x_n^2}}$$

$$= x_n + (1 - cx_n)x_n$$

or

(4-22) $$x_{n+1} = x_n(2 - cx_n).$$

No divisions are necessary to compute the sequence $\{x_n\}$. Since

$$F'(x) = -\frac{1}{x^2} < 0, \qquad F''(x) = \frac{2}{x^3} > 0$$

for $x > 0$, we are in case (b) of theorem 4.8, and convergence of the algorithm is assured if we can find an interval $[a, b]$ so that $a < c^{-1} < b$ and

$$\frac{F(b)}{F'(b)} = b(bc - 1) \leqq b - a.$$

The last inequality is satisfied if

$$b = \frac{1 + \sqrt{1 - ac}}{c}.$$

Since $a > 0$ may be made arbitrarily small, this means that the sequence defined by (4-22) converges to c^{-1} for any choice of x_0 such that

$$0 < x_0 < 2c^{-1}.$$

EXAMPLE

6. To calculate e^{-1}, where $e = 2.7182183$. Starting with $x_0 = 0.3$, we find

$$
\begin{aligned}
x_0 &= 0.3 & 2 - ex_0 &= 1.1846 \\
x_1 &= 0.355 & 2 - ex_1 &= 1.0350106 \\
x_2 &= 0.367429 & 2 - ex_2 &= 1.0012244 \\
x_3 &= 0.36787889 & 2 - ex_3 &= 1.00000150 \\
x_4 &= 0.36787994 & 2 - ex_4 &= 1.00000000.
\end{aligned}
$$

The quadratic nature of the convergence is quite evident in this example (doubling of the number of zeros in the second column at each step).

Problems

22. Show that the function $F(x) = x - e^{-x}$ satisfies the conditions of theorem 4.8 in the interval $[0, 1]$. Hence solve the equation by Newton's method, starting with $x_0 = 0.5$.

23. Calculate $\sqrt{\pi}$ to nine decimal places.

24. Determine a numerical value of $\frac{1}{3}$ without division, beginning a Newton iteration with $x_0 = 0.3$.

25. Show that the numbers defined by (4-20) satisfy

$$\frac{x_n - \sqrt{c}}{x_n + \sqrt{c}} = \left(\frac{x_0 - \sqrt{c}}{x_0 + \sqrt{c}}\right)^{2^n}, \qquad n = 0, 1, 2, \ldots .$$

Hence verify that the sequence $\{x_n\}$ converges to $\sqrt{c}$ quadratically for arbitrary choices of $x_0 > 0$.

26. If (4-22) is started with $x_0 = 1$, show that

$$x_n = \frac{1 - (1 - c)^{2^n}}{c}.$$

Deduce that the sequence thus generated converges for $0 < c < 2$, and that the convergence is again quadratic.

27*. How do we have to choose the function h in the formula

$$f(x) = x - \frac{F(x)}{F'(x)} + h(x)\left(\frac{F(x)}{F'(x)}\right)^2$$

such that the iteration defined by f converges cubically to a solution of $F(x) = 0$?

4.10   Newton's Method Applied to Polynomials

Newton's method is especially well suited to the problem of determining the zeros of a polynomial in view of the simple algorithm that is available for calculating both the value of a polynomial and that of its first derivative.   Let

$$p(x) = a_0 x^N + a_1 x^{N-1} + \cdots + a_N$$

be a given polynomial of degree N.   If z is any (real or complex) number, and if the constants $b_0, b_1, \ldots, b_N$ and $c_0, c_1, \ldots, c_{N-1}$ are determined from the recurrence relations† of algorithm 3.6,

(4-23) $b_0 = a_0, \qquad b_n = zb_{n-1} + a_n \qquad (n = 1, \ldots, N)$

(4-24) $c_0 = b_0, \qquad c_n = zc_{n-1} + b_n \qquad (n = 1, \ldots, N - 1)$

then we have by a special case of theorem 3.6

$$b_N = p(z), \qquad c_{N-1} = p'(z).$$

The quantities $p(z)$ and $p'(z)$ required in each step of Newton's method can

---

† We now write c_n in place of x_n to avoid confusion with the variable x.

thus be calculated very easily.   The computation proceeds as indicated in scheme 4.10.

$$a_0 \quad a_1 \quad a_2 \cdots \quad a_{N-1} \quad a_N$$

$$\downarrow \quad \downarrow \quad \downarrow \quad \quad \downarrow \quad \downarrow$$
$$b_0 \Rightarrow b_1 \Rightarrow b_2 \cdots \Rightarrow b_{N-1} \Rightarrow \underline{b_N}$$
$$\downarrow \quad \downarrow \quad \downarrow \quad \quad \downarrow$$
$$c_0 \Rightarrow c_1 \Rightarrow c_2 \cdots \Rightarrow \underline{c_{N-1}}$$

Scheme 4.10

$\rightarrow$ indicates addition, $\Rightarrow$ multiplication by z and addition.

EXAMPLE

7. To determine a zero of the polynomial

$$p(x) = x^3 - x^2 + 2x + 5$$

near $x = -1$.   (In table 4.10, the coefficients a_n, b_n, c_n are arranged in columns rather than in rows.)

Table 4.10

	a_n	b_n	c_n	p/p'
$x_0 = -1$	1	1	1	
	-1	-2	-3	
	2	4	7	0.142857
	5	1		
$x_1 = -1.142857$	1	1	1	
	-1	-2.142857	-3.285714	-0.010305
	2	4.448979	8.204076	
	5	-0.084546		
$x_2 = -1.129807$	1	1	1	
	-1	-2.129807	-3.259614	
	2	4.406241	8.089006	0.002691
	5	0.021764		
$x_3 = -1.132498$	1	1	previous	
	-1	-2.132498	value of p'	
	2	4.415050	retained!	-0.000004
	5	-0.000035		
$x_4 = -1.132494$	1	1		
	-1	-2.132494		
	2	4.415037		
	5	-0.000003		

If z is a zero of the polynomial p, then, according to theorem 2.5b, p can be represented in the form

$$(4\text{-}25) \qquad\qquad p(x) = (x - z)q(x),$$

where

$$q(x) = b_0 x^{N-1} + b_1 x^{N-2} + \cdots + b_{N-1}$$

is a certain polynomial of degree $N - 1$. Multiplying the two polynomials on the right of equation (4-25) and comparing coefficients of like powers of x, we find

$$a_0 = b_0,$$

$$a_{n+1} = -z b_n + b_{n-1}, \qquad n = 1, 2, \ldots, N.$$

Solving for b_{n+1} and replacing $n + 1$ by n, we find that the second relation is identical with (4-23). Thus we have:

Theorem 4.10 If z is a zero of the polynomial p, the coefficients $b_0, b_1, \ldots, b_{N-1}$ defined by equation (4-23) are identical with the coefficients of the polynomial $(x - z)^{-1}p(x)$.

EXAMPLE

8. Accepting $x_4 = -1.132494$ as a zero of the polynomial p considered in example 7, we have

$$q(x) = \frac{p(x)}{x + 1.132494} = x^2 - 2.132494x + 4.415037.$$

Thus, having found a zero of a polynomial p of degree N, the polynomial q whose zeros are identical with those of p save the one which has already been determined is easily constructed. The remaining zeros of p can now be found more easily as the zeros of q. The process of passing from p to q is known as *deflating p*. By successive deflations, the zeros of a given polynomial thus can be found by working with polynomials of successively lower degrees.

Unfortunately, the above process is subject to accumulation of round-off errors in view of the fact that the data of the problem (in this case, the coefficients of the given polynomial) enters the computation only at the first step. It is thus advisable to recheck each zero found by using it once more as a starting value for a Newton's process applied to the full (undeflated) polynomial p.

We mention without proof that local convergence of Newton's method can also be established for complex zeros and for polynomials with complex coefficients. However, for the determination of pairs of conjugate complex zeros of polynomials with real coefficients a more efficient method is available (see §5.6).

Problems

28. Determine the unique positive zero of the polynomial

$$p(x) = x^3 - x^2 - x - 1$$

by Newton's method.

29. Find the zero near 0.9 of the polynomial

$$p(x) = 4x^6 - 5x^5 + 4x^4 - 3x^3 + 7x^2 - 7x + 1.$$

30. Prove the relation $c_{N-1} = p'(z)$ by differentiating the recurrence relation (4-24) and observing that the b_n are functions of z.

4.11   Some Modifications of Newton's Method

Newton's method requires the evaluation of the derivative F' of the given function F. While in most textbook problems this requirement is trivial, this may not be the case in more involved situations, for instance if the function F itself is the result of a complicated computation. It therefore seems worthwhile to discuss some methods for solving $F(x) = 0$ that do not require the evaluation of F' and nevertheless retain some of the favorable convergence properties of Newton's method.

(*i*) *Whittaker's method* (Whittaker and Robinson [1928]). The simplest way to avoid the computation of F' is to replace $F'(x_n)$ in (4-19) by a constant value, say m. The resulting formula

$$(4\text{-}26) \qquad\qquad x_{n+1} = x_n - \frac{F(x_n)}{m}$$

then defines, for a certain range of values of m, a linearly converging procedure, unless we happen to pick $m = F'(s)$. If the estimate of m is good, convergence may nevertheless be quite rapid. Especially in the final stages of Newton's process it is usually not necessary to recompute F' at each step.

(*ii*) *Regula falsi.* Here the value of the derivative $F'(x_n)$ is approximated by the difference quotient

$$\frac{F(x_n) - F(x_{n-1})}{x_n - x_{n-1}}$$

formed with the two preceding approximations. There results the formula

$$(4\text{-}27) \qquad\qquad x_{n+1} = x_n - \frac{(x_n - x_{n-1})F(x_n)}{F(x_n) - F(x_{n-1})}.$$

This is identical with

$$x_{n+1} = \frac{x_{n-1}F(x_n) - x_nF(x_{n-1})}{F(x_n) - F(x_{n-1})}.$$

but for numerical purposes the "incremental" form (4-27) is preferable.

The algorithm suggested by (4-27) is known as the *regula falsi*. It is defined by a difference equation of order 2 and thus is not covered by the general theory given at the beginning of this chapter. A more detailed investigation (see Ostrowski [1960], p. 17) shows that the degree of convergence of the regula falsi lies somewhere between that of Newton's method and of ordinary iteration.

(*iii*) *Muller's method* (Muller [1956]).   The regula falsi can be obtained by approximating the graph of the function F by the straight line passing through the points $(x_{n-1}, F(x_{n-1}))$ and $(x_n, F(x_n))$. The point of intersection of this line with the x-axis defines the new approximation x_{n+1} (see Fig. 4.11).

Instead of approximating F by a linear function, it seems natural to try to obtain more rapid convergence by approximating F by a polynomial p of degree $k > 1$ coinciding with F at the points $x_n, x_{n-1}, \ldots, x_{n-k}$, and to determine x_{n+1} as one of the zeros of p. Muller has made a detailed study of the case $k = 2$ and found that this choice of k yields very satisfactory results.   Since the construction of p depends on the theory of the interpolating polynomial, we postpone the derivation of Muller's algorithm to chapter 10.

(*iv*) *Newton's method in the case* $F'(s) = 0$.   Newton's algorithm was derived in §4.7 under the assumption that $F'(x) \neq 0$, implying in particular that $F'(s) \neq 0$.   Let us now consider the general situation where

$$F(s) = F'(s) = \cdots = F^{(m-1)}(s) = 0, \; F^{(m)}(s) \neq 0,$$

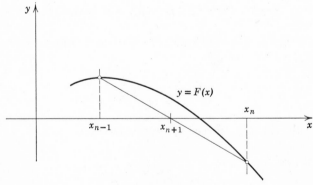

Figure 4.11

where $m \geq 1$. If we set $x = s + h$, the iteration function for Newton's process,

$$f(x) = x - \frac{F(x)}{F'(x)}$$

can be expanded in powers of h to give

$$f(s + h) = s + h - \frac{(m!)^{-1}F^{(m)}(s)h^m + O(h^{m+1})}{[(m-1)!]^{-1}F^{(m)}(s)h^{m-1} + O(h^m)}$$

$$= s + h - \frac{1}{m}h + O(h^2).$$

From this we find

$$f'(s) = \lim_{h \to 0} \frac{f(s + h) - f(s)}{h} = 1 - \frac{1}{m}.$$

Thus, if $m \neq 1$, $f'(s) \neq 0$, and the convergence fails to be quadratic. However, the above analysis shows how to modify the iteration function in order to achieve quadratic convergence. If we set

$$f(x) = \begin{cases} x - \dfrac{mF(x)}{F'(x)}, & x \neq s \\ s, & x = s \end{cases}$$

then a computation similar to the one performed above shows that $f'(s) = 0$. By theorem 4.6, the sequence defined by

(4-28) $$x_{n+1} = x_n - \frac{mF(x_n)}{F'(x_n)}, \qquad n = 0, 1, \ldots$$

converges to s quadratically, provided that x_0 is sufficiently close to s. For $m = 1$ this algorithm reduces to the ordinary Newton process.

Admittedly the above discussion is somewhat academic, because only rarely in practice we have an a priori knowledge of the fact that $F'(x) = 0$ at a solution of $F(x) = 0$. However, formula (4-28) has also been used in the early stages of Newton's process if two solutions of $F(x) = 0$ are very close together. In this case m was chosen in a heuristic fashion somewhere between 1 and 2 (see Forsythe [1958], p. 234).

Problems

31. Show that if the regula falsi is applied to the equation $x^2 = 1$, then, assuming that the errors $d_n = x_n - 1$ tend to zero, the stronger relation

$$\lim_{n \to \infty} \frac{d_{n+1}}{d_n d_{n-1}} = \frac{1}{2}$$

holds.

32. Give a closed formula for x_n if the equation $x^2 = 0$ is solved (a) by the ordinary Newton's method, (b) by the modification of Newton's method given by (4-28), and discuss the result. (Assume $x_0 = 1$ in both cases.)

33. Show that if the equation $[F(x)]^m = 0$ is solved by (4-28), there results the ordinary Newton's method for solving $F(x) = 0$.

4.12   The Diagonal Aitken Procedure

We continue to discuss the problem of achieving quadratic (i.e., Newton-like) convergence by methods not requiring the evaluation of any derivatives. We recall that none of the substitutes for Newton's method offered in the preceding section quite achieved quadratic convergence. Returning to equations written in the form

$$(4\text{-}29) \qquad\qquad x = f(x)$$

we now shall show that true quadratic convergence can be achieved without derivative evaluation by a modification of the Aitken acceleration procedure discussed in §4.4.

This modification proceeds as follows. We start out, as we do in ordinary iteration, by choosing an initial value x_0 and calculating $x_1 = f(x_0)$, $x_2 = f(x_1)$. Aitken's formula (4-11) is now applied to x_0, x_1, x_2, yielding

$$(4\text{-}30) \qquad\qquad x_0' = x_0 - \frac{(x_1 - x_0)^2}{x_2 - 2x_1 + x_0}.$$

The number $x_0' = x_0^{(1)}$ is used as a new starting value for two more iterations. Having calculated $x_1^{(1)} = f(x_0^{(1)})$, $x_2^{(1)} = f(x_1^{(1)})$, we apply Aitken's formula again, obtaining an accelerated value $x_0^{(2)}$, which in turn is used to start a new iteration, etc. If a denominator in Aitken's formula happens to be zero, we set $x_0^{(k+1)} = x_0^{(k)}$, thus in effect terminating the iteration. Schematically, the algorithm is described by the following table:

$$
\left.\begin{matrix} x_0^{(0)} \\ x_1^{(0)} \\ x_2^{(0)} \end{matrix}\right\} \nearrow
\left.\begin{matrix} x_0^{(1)} \\ x_1^{(1)} \\ x_2^{(1)} \end{matrix}\right\} \nearrow
\left.\begin{matrix} x_0^{(2)} \\ x_1^{(2)} \\ x_2^{(2)} \end{matrix}\right\} \nearrow \cdots
$$

Scheme 4.12

Since $x_1 = f(x_0)$, $x_2 = f(x_1) = f(f(x_0))$, the values $x^{(k+1)}$ can be thought of as being generated from $x^{(k)}$ in a single iteration step by means of a function F defined in terms of f as follows. We set

$$N(x) = f(f(x)) - 2f(x) + x$$

and put

$$(4\text{-}31) \qquad F(x) = \begin{cases} x - \dfrac{[f(x) - x]^2}{N(x)}, & N(x) \neq 0, \\ x, & N(x) = 0. \end{cases}$$

Thus we are led to the following formal statement of the new procedure:

Algorithm 4.12 Choose $x^{(0)}$, and determine the sequence $\{x^{(k)}\}$ recursively by

$$(4\text{-}32) \qquad x^{(k+1)} = F(x^{(k)}), \qquad k = 0, 1, 2, \ldots,$$

where F is defined by equation (4-31).

This algorithm is sometimes known as Steffensen's iteration, as it was first proposed by Steffensen [1933].

The questions arise whether Steffensen's iteration is well defined, whether the sequence $\{x^{(k)}\}$ converges to a solution of $x = f(x)$, and whether the degree of convergence is higher than linear. We shall give affirmative answers under the following hypotheses: The equation $x = f(x)$ has a solution $x = s$, and the function f is three times continuously differentiable in a neighborhood of $x = s$ and satisfies $f'(s) \neq 1$. It will be shown that these hypotheses imply that F satisfies $F(s) = s$, is twice continuously differentiable in a neighborhood of $x = s$, and satisfies $F'(s) = 0$. Quadratic convergence of the sequence $\{x^{(k)}\}$ for all $x^{(0)}$ sufficiently close to s then follows as a consequence of theorem 4.6.

As direct differentiation of F turns out to be cumbersome, we introduce an auxiliary function g by setting

$$g(h) = \begin{cases} \dfrac{f(s + h) - s}{h}, & h \neq 0, \\ f'(s), & h = 0. \end{cases}$$

The function g is still at least twice continuously differentiable near $h = 0$. The definition of g implies

$$\begin{aligned} f(s + h) &= s + hg(h), \\ f(f(s + h)) &= f(s + hg(h)) \\ &= s + hg(h)g(hg(h)). \end{aligned}$$

If $x = s + h$, it follows that

$$N(x) = f(f(x)) - 2f(x) + x = hG(h),$$

where

$$G(h) = 1 - 2g(h) + g(h)g(hg(h)).$$

Like g, the function G is twice continuously differentiable near $h = 0$; furthermore, since $g(0) = f'(s) \neq 1$,

(4-33) $$G(0) = [g(0) - 1]^2 \neq 0,$$

showing that $G(h) \neq 0$ for $|h|$ sufficiently small. Hence $N(x) \neq 0$ for $x \neq s$, $|x - s|$ sufficiently small, and by (4-31),

$$F(x) = s + h - h \frac{[g(h) - 1]^2}{G(h)}.$$

This representation of F also holds for $h = 0$; it shows that F, too, is twice continuously differentiable, and that $F(s) = s$. Furthermore,

$$F'(s) = \lim_{h \to 0} \frac{F(s + h) - s}{h}$$

$$= \lim_{h \to 0} \left\{ 1 - \frac{[g(h) - 1]^2}{G(h)} \right\}$$

$$= 1 - \frac{[g(0) - 1]^2}{G(0)} = 0,$$

by virtue of (4-33).

EXAMPLE

9. We apply Steffensen iteration to the equation $x = e^{-x}$ considered in example 1. Starting with $x^{(0)} = 0.5$, we obtain the following values (arranged in the manner of scheme 4.12)

0.500000	0.567624	0.567144	0.567143
0.606531	0.566871	0.567143	
0.545239	0.567298	0.567143.	

The values in the top row are seen to converge very rapidly.

Problems

34. Apply Steffensen iteration to the solution of Kepler's equation given in problem 5, where $m = 1$, $E = 0.8$.

35. Apply algorithm 4.12 to the equation

$$x = \frac{10}{x},$$

starting with $x = 3$. Compare the sequence $\{x^{(k)}\}$ with the sequence obtained by Newton's method for computing $\sqrt{10}$.

36. Give a somewhat simpler proof of the quadratic convergence of Steffensen's iteration by assuming that f can be expanded in powers of $h = x - s$.

37. Show that if, in addition to the hypotheses stated above, $f'(s) = 0$, then also $F''(s) = 0$. Thus in this case Steffensen's iteration converges at least cubically (see Householder [1953], p. 128).

4.13 A Non-local Convergence Theorem for Steffensen's Method†

As was the case with the corresponding result concerning Newton's method, the convergence statement concerning Steffensen's iteration proved in the last section is unsatisfactory because it guarantees convergence only for choices of $x^{(0)}$ "sufficiently close" to the solution s. We now shall prove a result which guarantees convergence no matter where the iteration is started. The extra hypothesis which will be added concerns the signs of f' and of f''.

Theorem 4.13   Let I denote the semi-infinite interval (a, ∞), and let the function f satisfy the following conditions:

(i) f is defined and twice continuously differentiable on I;
(ii) $f(x) > a$, $x \in I$;
(iii) $f'(x) < 0$, $x \in I$;
(iv) $f''(x) > 0$, $x \in I$.

Then algorithm 4.12 defines a sequence which converges to the (unique) solution s of $x = f(x)$ for any choice of the starting value $x^{(0)}$ in I.

Proof.   By virtue of the hypotheses, the graph of the function f looks as indicated in figure 4.13 (where $a = 0$); it shows that the equation $x = f(x)$ has a unique solution s.

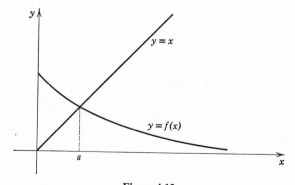

Figure 4.13

† This section may be omitted at first reading.

Let $x > s$. Then, by virtue of (iii), $f(x) < s$, and $f(f(x)) > s$. Hence, by application of the mean value theorem,

$$f(x) - s = f(x) - f(s) = f'(t_1)(x - s),$$

where $s < t_1 < x$. Furthermore,

$$\begin{aligned} f(f(x)) - s &= f(f(x)) - f(s) \\ &= f'(t_2)(f(x) - s) \end{aligned}$$

where $f(x) < t_2 < s$. We thus find

$$\begin{aligned} f(x) - x &= f(x) - s - (x - s) \\ &= [f'(t_1) - 1](x - s) \end{aligned}$$

and

$$\begin{aligned} f(f(x)) - f(x) &= f(f(x)) - s - [f(x) - s] \\ &= [f'(t_2) - 1][f(x) - s] \\ &= [f'(t_2) - 1]f'(t_1)(x - s). \end{aligned}$$

Thus the expression N in equation (4-31) is given by

$$\begin{aligned} f(f(x)) - 2f(x) + x &= f(f(x)) - f(x) - [f(x) - x] \\ &= \{[f'(t_2) - 1]f'(t_1) - [f'(t_1) - 1]\}(x - s). \end{aligned}$$

The expression inside the braces may be written

$$[f'(t_1) - 1]^2 + [f'(t_2) - f'(t_1)]f'(t_1).$$

This is positive, since by (iv), $f'(t_2) < f'(t_1)$ and hence by (iii),

$$[f'(t_2) - f'(t_1)]f'(t_1) > 0.$$

Hence $N(x) \neq 0$, and the first definition of F applies for all $x > s$. Since N is a continuous function of x, it follows that F is continuous at each point $x > s$. (Continuity at $x = s$ has already been established in the preceding section under wider assumptions.)

Using the above work, we find for $x > s$

$$F(x) - s = (1 - Q)(x - s),$$

where

(4-34) $$Q = \frac{[f'(t_1) - 1]^2}{[f'(t_1) - 1]^2 + [f'(t_2) - f'(t_1)]f'(t_1)}$$

By the above, $0 < Q < 1$, and it follows that

$$0 < F(x) - s < x - s$$

or

$$s \leq F(x) < x.$$

Thus for $x^{(0)} \geq s$, the sequence $\{x^{(k)}\}$ is decreasing and bounded below by

s. It therefore must have a limit $q \geqq s$. By the continuity of F, $F(q) = q$. This is possible only for $q = s$. Thus the relation

$$\lim_{k \to \infty} x^{(k)} = s$$

has been proved for the case $x^{(0)} > s$.

If $x^{(0)} = s$, then all $x^{(k)} = s$, and the result is trivial. Thus let now $x < s$. In that situation, $f(x) > s, f(f(x)) < s$. The above computations remain valid, with the difference that now

$$x < t_1 < s, \qquad s < t_2 < f(x).$$

We find again $N(x) \neq 0$; however, since the order of t_1 and t_2 is now reversed, the numerator in (4-34) now exceeds the denominator, and we have $Q > 1$. It follows that $F(x) > s$. Thus if $x^{(0)} < s$, then $x^{(1)} = F(x^{(0)}) > s$, and the sequence $\{x^{(k)}\}$ decreases from $k = 1$ onward. Convergence to s now follows as in the case $x^{(0)} > s$.

EXAMPLES

10. The hypotheses of theorem 4.13 are satisfied for $f(x) = e^{-x}$, $x > 0$. Steffensen iteration thus will produce the solution of $x = e^{-x}$ for any choice of the starting value $x^{(0)} > 0$.

11. Let $c > 0$, and put $f(x) = c/x$ for $x > 0$. Again this function satisfies the hypotheses of theorem 4.13, and the Steffensen iteration converges to the solution $s = \sqrt{c}$ for any choice of $x^{(0)} > 0$. Since $f(f(x)) = x$, the function F is given by

$$F(x) = x - \frac{\left(\dfrac{c}{x} - x\right)^2}{x - 2\dfrac{c}{x} + x} = \frac{1}{2}\left(x + \frac{c}{x}\right),$$

and the iteration function is identical with that given by Newton's method.

Problems

38. Prove results analogous to theorem 4.13 for the cases

(a) $\qquad\qquad 0 \leqq f'(x) < 1, \qquad f''(x) > 0;$

(b) $\qquad\qquad f'(x) > 1, \qquad f''(x) > 0.$

39. Show that the function $f(x) = A + B/x^n$ satisfies the hypotheses of theorem 4.13 for $x \geqq A > 0$, $B > 0$. Hence find the solution $s > 1$ of the equation $x^3 = x^2 + 1$.

Recommended Reading

The theory of iteration of functions of one variable is treated very thoroughly in the books by Householder [1953] and Ostrowski [1960]. Householder also gives numerous references to earlier work.

Research Problem

Find bounds (exhibiting the quadratic nature of the convergence) for the error of the approximations generated by Steffensen's iteration. (Similar bounds are known for Newton's method, see for example, Ostrowski [1960].)

chapter *5* iteration for systems of equations

In this chapter we will show how to apply the basic iteration algorithm discussed in chapter 4 and its modifications to obtain solutions of systems of equations. The equations envisaged here are nonlinear. Inasmuch as linear equations are a special case of nonlinear ones, the algorithms discussed here are naturally applicable to linear systems. However, for the reasons mentioned in the preface, the many important algorithms that are especially designed for the solution of linear systems of equations are not treated in this book.

5.1 Notation

The algorithms discussed in this chapter are, in principle, applicable to problems involving any number of equations and unknowns. However, for greater concreteness, and also in order to avoid cumbersome notation, we shall consider explicitly only the case of two equations with two unknowns. These equations will usually be written in the form

(5-1)
$$\begin{cases} x = f(x, y) \\ y = g(x, y), \end{cases}$$

where f and g are certain functions of the point (x, y) that are defined in suitable regions of the plane. Each of the two equations $x - f(x, y) = 0$ and $y - g(x, y) = 0$ defines, in general, a curve in the (x, y) plane. The problem of solving the system of equations (5-1) is equivalent to the problem of finding the point or points of intersection of these curves. It will usually be assumed, and in some cases also proved, that such a point of intersection exists. Its coordinates will be denoted by s and t. The quantities s and t then satisfy the relations

$$s = f(s, t)$$
$$t = g(s, t).$$

97

EXAMPLE

1. Let $f(x, y) = x^2 + y^2$, $g(x, y) = x^2 - y^2$. The system (4-1) reads in this case

$$x = x^2 + y^2$$
$$y = x^2 - y^2.$$

The equation $x^2 + y^2 - x = 0$ defines a circle centered at $(\frac{1}{2}, 0)$, the equation $x^2 - y^2 - y = 0$ a hyperbola centered at $(0, -\frac{1}{2})$. Both the circle and the hyperbola pass through the origin, thus our system has the obvious solution $s = t = 0$. But an inspection of the graphs shows that there must be another solution near $x = 0.8$, $y = 0.4$.

It will be convenient to employ *vector notation*. Thus we not only shall be able to simplify the writing of our equations, but also to aid the understanding of the theoretical analysis and even the programming of our algorithms. We represent the coordinates of the point (x, y) by the column vector

$$\mathbf{x} = \begin{pmatrix} x \\ y \end{pmatrix}.$$

The functions f and g then become functions of the vector $\mathbf{x}$, whose value for a particular $\mathbf{x}$ we denote by $f(\mathbf{x})$ and $g(\mathbf{x})$. If we denote by $\mathbf{f}$ the column vector with components f and g, the system (5-1) can be written more simply as follows:

(5-2) $$\mathbf{x} = \mathbf{f}(\mathbf{x}).$$

The fact that the vector

$$\mathbf{s} = \begin{pmatrix} s \\ t \end{pmatrix}$$

is a solution of equation (5-1) is expressed in the form

$$\mathbf{s} = \mathbf{f}(\mathbf{s}).$$

A vector analog of the absolute value of a number (or *scalar*, as numbers are called in this context) will be required. Clearly, the *length* of a vector is such an analog. If $\mathbf{x} = (x, y)$, we write

(5-3) $$\|\mathbf{x}\| = \sqrt{x^2 + y^2}$$

The quantity $\|\mathbf{x}\|$ is called the Euclidean norm of the vector $\mathbf{x}$. It is nonnegative, and zero only if $\mathbf{x}$ is the zero vector $\mathbf{0} = (0, 0)$. Furthermore, if the sum of two vectors and the product of a vector and a scalar are defined in the natural way, we have

(5-4) $$\|c\mathbf{x}\| = |c| \|\mathbf{x}\|$$

(5-5) $$\|\mathbf{x}_1 + \mathbf{x}_2\| \leqq \|\mathbf{x}_1\| + \|\mathbf{x}_2\|.$$

Relation (5-5) is called the *triangle inequality*. If x_1 and x_2 are two vectors, then $\|x_1 - x_2\|$ is the distance of the points whose coordinates are the components of x_1 and x_2.

We shall have occasion to consider sequences of vectors $\{x_n\}$. Such a sequence is said to converge to a vector v, if

$$\|x_n - v\| \to 0 \quad \text{for } n \to \infty.$$

The following criterion due to Cauchy is necessary and sufficient for the convergence of the sequence $\{x_n\}$ to some vector v (see Buck [1956], p. 13). Given any number $\varepsilon > 0$, there exists an integer N so that for all $n > N$ and all $m > N$

$$\|x_m - x_n\| < \varepsilon.$$

5.2 A Theorem on Contracting Maps

Iteration in several variables is defined as in the case of one variable.

Algorithm 5.2 Choose a vector x_0, and calculate the sequence of vectors $\{x_n\}$ recursively by

$$(5\text{-}6) \qquad x_n = f(x_{n-1}), \qquad n = 1, 2, 3, \ldots.$$

As in the scalar situation, there arise the questions whether the sequence $\{x_n\}$ is well defined, whether it converges, and whether its limit necessarily is a solution of the equation

$$(5\text{-}7) \qquad\qquad x = f(x).$$

All these questions are answered by the following result:

Theorem 5.2 Let R denote the rectangular region $a \leqq x \leqq b$, $c \leqq y \leqq d$, and let the functions f and g satisfy the following conditions:

(*i*) f and g are defined and continuous on R;
(*ii*) For each $x \in R$, the point $(f(x), g(x))$ also lies in R;
(*iii*) There exists a constant $L < 1$ such that for any two points x_1 and x_2 in R the following inequality holds:

$$(5\text{-}8) \qquad\qquad \|f(x_1) - f(x_2)\| \leqq L\|x_1 - x_2\|.$$

Then the following statements are true:
(a) Equation (5-7) has precisely one solution s in R;
(b) for any choice of x_0 in R, the sequence $\{x_n\}$ given by algorithm 5.2 is defined and converges to s;
(c) for any $n = 1, 2, \ldots$, the following inequality holds:

$$(5\text{-}9) \qquad\qquad \|x_n - s\| \leqq \frac{L^n}{1 - L}\|x_1 - x_0\|.$$

Condition (5-8) is again called a *Lipschitz condition*. It here expresses the fact that the mapping $x \to f(x)$ diminishes the distance between any two points in R at least by the factor L. For this reason a mapping with the property (5-8) is called a *contraction mapping*.

It should be noted that already statement (a) is not as trivial now as in the case of one variable, where the existence of a solution could be inferred from an inspection of the graph of the function f. Statement (b) guarantees convergence of the algorithm, while (c) gives an upper bound for the error after n steps.

Proof of theorem 5.2. The proof will be accomplished in several stages. From condition (*ii*) it is evident that the sequence $\{x_n\}$ is defined, and that its elements lie in R. Proceeding exactly as in the proof of (4-6) (§4.3) we now can show that (*iii*) implies

$$(5\text{-}10) \qquad \|x_{n+1} - x_n\| \leq L^n \|x_1 - x_0\|, \qquad n = 0, 1, 2, \ldots.$$

Now let n be a fixed positive integer, and let $m > n$. With a view towards applying the Cauchy criterion, we shall find a bound for $\|x_m - x_n\|$. Writing

$$x_m - x_n = (x_{n+1} - x_n) + (x_{n+2} - x_{n+1}) + \cdots + (x_m - x_{m-1})$$

and applying the triangle inequality (5-5), we obtain

$$\|x_m - x_n\| \leq \|x_{n+1} - x_n\| + \|x_{n+2} - x_{n+1}\| + \cdots + \|x_m - x_{m-1}\|$$

and, using (5-10) to estimate each term on the right,

$$(5\text{-}11) \qquad \|x_m - x_n\| \leq (L^n + L^{n+1} + \cdots + L^{m-1})\|x_1 - x_0\|$$

$$\leq \frac{L^n}{1 - L} \|x_1 - x_0\|,$$

by virtue of $0 \leq L < 1$. Since the expression on the right does not depend on m and tends to zero as $n \to \infty$, we have established that the sequence $\{x_n\}$ satisfies the Cauchy criterion. It thus has a limit s. Since R is compact, $s \in R$.

We next show that s is a solution of (5-7). By virtue of the continuity of f and g,

$$(5\text{-}12) \qquad \lim_{n \to \infty} f(x_n) = f(s),$$

and thus

$$s = \lim_{n \to \infty} x_n = \lim_{n \to \infty} x_{n+1} = \lim_{n \to \infty} f(x_n) = f(s),$$

as desired.

Uniqueness of the solution s follows from the Lipschitz condition (*iii*), exactly as it does for one variable (see the end of §4.1). Relation (5-9) finally follows by letting $m \to \infty$ in (5-11).   This completes the proof of theorem 5.2.   No use has been made of the fact that the number of equations and unknowns is two; both the theorem and its proof remain valid in a Euclidean space of arbitrary dimension, and even in some infinite-dimensional spaces.

Problems

1. Prove the relation (5-12) by means of (*iii*), without making use of the continuity of f and g.
2. Prove that condition (*iii*) (even when $L \geqq 1$) implies that both f and g are continuous at every point of R.

5.3   A Bound for the Lipschitz Constant†

We consider here the problem of verifying whether a given pair of functions (f, g) satisfies a Lipschitz condition of the form (5-8).   The corresponding condition for a single function of one variable could be very easily checked by computing the derivative (see §4.1).   If the absolute value of the derivative turned out to be bounded by a constant, then the Lipschitz condition was satisfied with that constant.   A similar criterion is available for pairs of functions of two variables.

Theorem 5.3   Let the functions f and g have continuous partial derivatives in the region R defined in theorem 5.2.   Then the inequality (5-8) holds with $L = J$, where

$$(5\text{-}13) \qquad J = \max_{(x,\, y) \in R} \sqrt{f_x^2 + f_y^2 + g_x^2 + g_y^2}$$

Proof.   Let (x_0, y_0) and (x_1, y_1) be two points in R.   We define for $0 \leqq t \leqq 1$

$$x_t = x_0 + th, \qquad y_t = y_0 + tk,$$

where

$$h = x_1 - x_0, \qquad k = y_1 - y_0$$

and set

$$f_t = f(x_t, y_t), \qquad g_t = g(x_t, y_t).$$

It is to be proved that

$$(5\text{-}14) \qquad (f_1 - f_0)^2 + (g_1 - g_0)^2 \leqq (h^2 + k^2)J^2.$$

For the proof we shall require both the Schwarz inequality for sums,

$$(5\text{-}15) \qquad (ac + bd)^2 \leqq (a^2 + b^2)(c^2 + d^2),$$

---

† A reader who is willing to accept the statement of Theorem 5.3 may omit the remainder of the section without loss of continuity.

valid for any four real numbers a, b, c, d, and the Schwarz inequality for integrals,

$$(5\text{-}16) \qquad \left(\int_a^b p(x)q(x)\, dx \right)^2 \leq \int_a^b [p(x)]^2\, dx \int_a^b [q(x)]^2\, dx,$$

valid for any two functions p and q that are integrable on the interval $[a, b]$. Proofs of these well-known inequalities are sketched in the problems 3 and 4.

By the chain rule of differentiation (see Taylor [1959], p. 590) we have

$$\frac{df_t}{dt} = hf_x + kf_y,$$

where

$$f_x = f_x(x_t, y_t), \qquad f_y = f_y(x_t, y_t),$$

and hence

$$f_1 - f_0 = \int_0^1 (hf_x + kf_y)\, dt.$$

By (5-15),

$$(hf_x + kf_y)^2 \leq (h^2 + k^2)(f_x^2 + f_y^2).$$

Hence

$$(f_1 - f_0)^2 \leq (h^2 + k^2) \left[\int_0^1 \sqrt{f_x^2 + f_y^2}\, dt \right]^2.$$

We now use (5-16) where $a = 0$, $b = 1$, $p(t) = 1$, $q(t) = (f_x^2 + f_y^2)^{1/2}$. It follows that

$$(f_1 - f_0)^2 \leq (h^2 + k^2) \int_0^1 (f_x^2 + f_y^2)\, dt.$$

In exactly the same manner we find

$$(g_1 - g_0)^2 \leq (h^2 + k^2) \int_0^1 (g_x^2 + g_y^2)\, dt.$$

Adding the last two inequalities and using $f_x^2 + f_y^2 + g_x^2 + g_y^2 \leq J^2$, we obtain (5-14).

EXAMPLE

2. Let

$$f(x, y) = A \sin x + B \cos y, \qquad g(x, y) = A \cos x - B \sin y$$

where A and B are constants. We find

$$f_x^2 + f_y^2 + g_x^2 + g_y^2 = A^2 + B^2,$$

thus (5-8) holds with $L = \sqrt{A^2 + B^2}$. The conditions of theorem 5.2

thus are satisfied, for instance for $a = -2, b = 2$, whenever $A^2 + B^2 < 1$. Convergence of the process for $A = 0.7$, $B = 0.2$, $x_0 = y_0 = 0$ is illustrated by the values given in table 5.3.

Table 5.3

n	x_n	y_n
1	0.200000	0.700000
2	0.292037	0.557203
3	0.371280	0.564599
4	0.422927	0.545289
...	...	...
28	0.526519	0.507921
29	0.526521	0.507921
30	0.526521	0.507920
31	0.526522	0.507920

Naturally, the condition of theorem 5.3 is not *necessary* for convergence of the iterative process. For instance for the problem considered in example 2 convergence also takes place for $A = B = 0.71$.

Problems

3. Prove (5-15) by observing that the equation for x,

$$(a + cx)^2 + (b + dx)^2 = 0$$

can have at most one real solution.

4. Prove (5-16) by noting that the equation in x,

$$\int_a^b (p(t) + xq(t))^2 = 0$$

can have at most one real solution. What are the conditions on p and q in order that there is a real solution?

5.4 Quadratic Convergence

Suppose the functions f and g satisfy the conditions of theorem 5.2 and have continuous derivatives up to order 2 in R. The sequence of points (x_n, y_n) defined by algorithm 5.2 then converges to a solution (s, t) of the system (5-1). What is the behavior of the errors

$$d_n = x_n - s,$$
$$e_n = y_n - t,$$

as $n \to \infty$?

An application of Taylor's theorem for functions of two variables (see Buck [1956], p. 200) shows that

$$d_{n+1} = x_{n+1} - s$$
$$= f(x_n, y_n) - f(s, t)$$
$$= f(s + d_n, t + e_n) - f(s, t)$$
$$= f_x(s, t) d_n + f_y(s, t)e_n + 0(\|\mathbf{d}_n\|^2),$$

and similarly

$$e_{n+1} = g_x(s, t) d_n + g_y(s, t)e_n + 0(\|\mathbf{d}_n\|^2).$$

Here $\mathbf{d}_n$ denotes the vector of errors,

$$\mathbf{d}_n = \begin{pmatrix} d_n \\ e_n \end{pmatrix},$$

and $0(\|\mathbf{d}_n\|^2)$ denotes a quantity bounded by $C\|\mathbf{d}_n\|^2$. Introducing the *Jacobian matrix* of the functions f and g,

$$\mathbf{J} = \begin{pmatrix} f_x & f_y \\ g_x & g_y \end{pmatrix},$$

the above relations can be written in abbreviated form as follows:

(5-17) $\mathbf{d}_{n+1} = \mathbf{J}(s, t) \mathbf{d}_n + 0(\|\mathbf{d}_n\|^2).$

Relation (5-17) is the multidimensional generalization of (4-8). If $\mathbf{J}(s, t) \neq \mathbf{0}$ (that is, if the elements of the matrix $\mathbf{J}(s, t)$ are not all zero), it shows that at each step of the iteration the error vector is approximately multiplied by a constant matrix. In this sense we again may speak of *linear convergence*. If $\mathbf{J}(s, t) = \mathbf{0}$ (that is, if all four elements of $\mathbf{J}$ are zero), then we see that the norm of the error at the $(n + 1)st$ step is of the order of the square of the norm of the error at the nth step. This is similar to what earlier has been called *quadratic convergence*.

The following analog of theorem 4.6 holds in the case where $\mathbf{J}(s, t) = \mathbf{0}$:

Theorem 5.4   Let the functions f and g be defined in a region R, and let them satisfy the following conditions:

(*i*) The first partial derivatives of f and g exist and are continuous in R.

(*ii*) The system (5-1) has a solution (s, t) in the interior of R such that $\mathbf{J}(s, t) = \mathbf{0}$.

Then there exists a number $d > 0$ such that algorithm 5.2 converges to (s, t) for any choice of the starting point within the distance d of the solution.

The conclusion can be expressed by saying that the algorithm always converges if the starting vector is "sufficiently close" to the solution vector.   The proof of theorem 5.4 is based on the fact that by virtue of the continuity of the first partial derivatives

$$\sqrt{f_x^2 + f_y^2 + g_x^2 + g_y^2} = L < 1$$

in a certain neighborhood of $(s, t) \in R$.   It then follows from theorem 5.3 that the conditions of theorem 5.2 are satisfied in that neighborhood. Further details are omitted.

5.5   Newton's Method for Systems of Equations

We now shall consider the problem of solving systems of two equations with two unknowns which are of the form

(5-18)
$$\begin{cases} F(x, y) = 0, \\ G(x, y) = 0, \end{cases}$$

where both functions F and G are defined and twice continuously differentiable on a certain rectangle R of the (x, y) plane.   We suppose that the system (5-18) has a solution (s, t) in the interior of R, and that the Jacobian determinant

(5-19)
$$D(x, y) = \begin{vmatrix} F_x(x, y) & F_y(x, y) \\ G_x(x, y) & G_y(x, y) \end{vmatrix}$$

is different from zero when $(x, y) = (s, t)$.   It then follows from a theorem of calculus (see Buck [1956], p. 216) that the system (5-18) has no solution other than (s, t) in a certain neighborhood of the point (s, t).

Newton's method for solving a single equation $F(x) = 0$ could be understood as arising from replacing $F(x + \delta)$ by $F(x) + F'(x)\delta$ and solving the equation

$$F(x) + F'(x)\delta = 0$$

for δ, thus obtaining a supposedly better approximation $x + \delta$ to s than x. We now apply the same principle to the system (5-18).   Assuming that (x, y) is a point "near" the desired solution (s, t), we replace the function $F(x + \delta, y + \varepsilon)$ by its first degree Taylor polynomial at the point (x, y), that is, by $F(x, y) + F_x(x, y)\delta + F_y(x, y)\varepsilon$.   A similar replacement is made for the function $G(x + \delta, y + \varepsilon)$.   Setting the Taylor polynomials equal to zero, we obtain a system of two linear equations for δ and ε,

(5-20)
$$\begin{cases} F_x(x, y)\delta + F_y(x, y)\varepsilon = -F(x, y), \\ G_x(x, y)\delta + G_y(x, y)\varepsilon = -G(x, y). \end{cases}$$

The determinant of this system is just the quantity $D(x, y)$ defined by (5-19).   Since D is continuous and $D(s, t) \neq 0$ by hypothesis, it follows that $D(x, y) \neq 0$ for all points (x, y) sufficiently close to (s, t). Thus for all these (x, y) the system (5-20) has a unique solution $\delta = \delta(x, y)$, $\varepsilon = \varepsilon(x, y)$. The point $(x + \delta(x, y), y + \varepsilon(x, y))$ is now chosen as the next approximation to (s, t). Algorithmically speaking, the procedure can be described as follows:

Algorithm 5.5 (Newton's method for two variables.) Choose (x_0, y_0), and determine the sequence of points (x_n, y_n) by

(5-21)
$$\begin{cases} x_{n+1} = f(x_n, y_n) \\ y_{n+1} = g(x_n, y_n), \end{cases} \quad n = 0, 1, 2, \dots,$$

where the functions f and g are defined by

$$f(x, y) = x + \delta(x, y), \qquad g(x, y) = y + \varepsilon(x, y),$$

and where δ and ε denote the solution of the linear system (5-20).

We assert that the sequence (x_n, y_n) converges quadratically to (s, t) for all (x_0, y_0) sufficiently close to (s, t). In order to verify this statement, it suffices by theorem 5.4 to show that all elements of the Jacobian matrix of the iteration functions f and g,

$$\mathbf{J}(x, y) = \begin{pmatrix} f_x(x, y) & f_y(x, y) \\ g_x(x, y) & g_y(x, y) \end{pmatrix}$$

are zero for $(x, y) = (s, t)$. Omitting arguments, we have

(5-22)
$$\begin{cases} f_x = 1 + \delta_x, & f_y = \delta_y, \\ g_x = \varepsilon_x, & g_y = 1 + \varepsilon_y. \end{cases}$$

The values of the derivatives $\delta_x, \delta_y, \varepsilon_x, \varepsilon_y$ are best determined from (5-20) by implicit differentiation. Differentiating the first of these equations, we get

$$F_{xx}\delta + F_x\delta_x + F_{xy}\varepsilon + F_y\varepsilon_x = -F_x,$$
$$F_{xy}\delta + F_x\delta_y + F_{yy}\varepsilon + F_y\varepsilon_y = -F_y.$$

Two similar relations involving the function G are obtained by differentiating the second relation. We now set $(x, y) = (s, t)$ and observe that $\delta(s, t) = \varepsilon(s, t) = 0$. We thus obtain for $(x, y) = (s, t)$

$$F_x\delta_x + F_y\varepsilon_x = -F_x,$$
$$G_x\delta_x + G_y\varepsilon_x = -G_x,$$
$$F_x\delta_y + F_y\varepsilon_y = -F_y,$$
$$G_x\delta_y + G_y\varepsilon_y = -G_y.$$

The determinant of each of these two systems of linear equations is again the Jacobian determinant $D(s, t)$ and hence is different from zero. We now easily find

$$\delta_x = -1, \qquad \delta_y = 0,$$
$$\varepsilon_x = 0, \qquad \varepsilon_y = -1.$$

According to equation (5-22), this implies that all elements of the matrix **J** are zero at the point (s, t), as desired.

For actual execution of algorithm 5.5 (although not for the above theoretical analysis) it is necessary at each step of the iteration to solve the system (5-20) for δ and ε. An application of Cramer's rule† yields

$$\delta = \frac{\begin{vmatrix} -F & F_y \\ -G & G_y \end{vmatrix}}{\begin{vmatrix} F_x & F_y \\ G_x & G_y \end{vmatrix}} = \frac{GF_y - FG_y}{F_xG_y - F_yG_x},$$

$$\varepsilon = \frac{\begin{vmatrix} F_x & -F \\ G_x & -G \end{vmatrix}}{\begin{vmatrix} F_x & F_y \\ G_x & G_y \end{vmatrix}} = \frac{FG_x - GF_x}{F_xG_y - F_yG_x}.$$

EXAMPLE

3. We solve the system considered in example 2 by writing it in the form

$$x - A \sin x - B \cos y = 0,$$
$$y - A \cos x + B \sin y = 0,$$

and applying Newton's method. The following values are obtained for $A = 0.7$, $B = 0.2$, $x_0 = y_0 = 0$:

n	x_n	y_n
1	0.6666667	0.5833333
2	0.5362400	0.5088490
3	0.5265620	0.5079319
4	0.5265226	0.5079197
5	0.5265226	0.5079197

The much greater rapidity of convergence is clearly evident.

---

† It is well known that Cramer's rule should never be used for the solution of linear systems of any sizable order. The solution of such systems is much more conveniently found by a process of elimination. For systems of small order (such as 2 or 3) Cramer's rule is perfectly applicable, however.

Problems

5. Generalizing the approach outlined in §4.7, one might try to generalize Newton's method to systems by suitably choosing functions h and k so that iteration of the functions

$$f(x, y) = x + h(x, y)F(x, y)$$
$$g(x, y) = y + k(x, y)G(x, y)$$

yields a quadratically convergent process.   Show that this is *not* possible in general.

6*. Determine the matrix $\mathbf{H} = \mathbf{H}(\mathbf{x})$ such that application of iteration to

$$\mathbf{f}(\mathbf{x}) = \mathbf{x} + \mathbf{H}(\mathbf{x})\mathbf{F}(\mathbf{x})$$

yields a quadratically convergent process.   Show that the process obtained is identical with Newton's method.

7. Find a solution near $x = 0.8$, $y = 0.4$ of the system

$$x - x^2 - y^2 = 0,$$
$$y - x^2 + y^2 = 0,$$

using Newton's method.

8. Solve by Newton's method the pair of equations

$$x + 13 \log x - y^2 = 0,$$
$$2x^2 - xy - 5x + 1 = 0,$$

starting with $x_0 = 3.4$, $y_0 = 2.2$.

9. Solve the system

$$4x^3 - 27xy^2 + 25 = 0,$$
$$4x^2 - 3y^3 - 1 = 0,$$

by Newton's method, starting with $x_0 = y_0 = 1$.

5.6   The Determination of Quadratic Factors

In this section we shall prepare the ground for the application of Newton's method to the problem of finding pairs of complex conjugate zeros of polynomials with real coefficients.   We first consider the following preliminary problem.

Given a polynomial p of degree $N \geqq 2$ with real coefficients,

$$p(x) = a_0 x^N + a_1 x^{N-1} + \cdots + a_N,$$

and a quadratic polynomial $x^2 - ux - v$, to determine constants $b_0, b_1, \ldots, b_N$ such that the identity

$$(5\text{-}23) \qquad p(x) = (x^2 - ux - v)q(x) + b_{N-1}(x - u) + b_N$$

holds, where

$$q(x) = b_0 x^{N-2} + b_1 x^{N-3} + \cdots + b_{N-2}.$$

Multiplying the polynomials on the right side of (5-23) and comparing coefficients of like powers of x, we find the following conditions on $b_0, b_1, \ldots, b_N$:

$$b_0 = a_0,$$
$$b_1 = a_1 + ub_0,$$
$$b_2 = a_2 + ub_1 + vb_0,$$

and generally for $n = 2, \ldots, N - 2$

$$(5\text{-}24) \qquad b_n = a_n + ub_{n-1} + vb_{n-2}.$$

By comparing the coefficients of x^1 and x^0 it is seen that (5-24) also holds for $n = N - 1$ and $n = N$. Furthermore, if we agree to put $b_{-1} = b_{-2} = 0$, the relation holds also for $n = 0$ and $n = 1$. Thus we find the following algorithm for determining the coefficients $b_0, b_1, \ldots, b_N$ in the representation (5-23) of the polynomial p:

Algorithm 5.6 If $a_0, a_1, \ldots, a_N$, u, v are given numbers, determine $b_0, b_1, \ldots, b_N$ from the recurrence relation $b_{-2} = b_{-1} = 0$,

$$b_n = a_n + ub_{n-1} + vb_{n-2}, \qquad n = 0, 1, \ldots, N.$$

Clearly, the coefficients $b_0, b_1, \ldots, b_N$ thus obtained are functions of the variables u and v. The reason for considering the b_n is contained in the following theorem:

Theorem 5.6 The polynomial $x^2 - ux - v$ is a quadratic factor of the real polynomial $p(x) = a_0 x^N + a_1 x^{N-1} + \cdots + a_N$ if and only if $b_{N-1} = b_N = 0$.

Proof. (a) If $b_{N-1} = b_N = 0$, then (5-23) reduces to the relation

$$p(x) = (x^2 - ux - v)q(x).$$

It shows that a zero of $x^2 - ux - v$ is also a zero of p. By considering the derivative we find that a double zero of $x^2 - ux - v$ is also a double zero of p. Thus $x^2 - ux - v$ is a quadratic factor of p.

(b) We now *assume* that $x^2 - ux - v$ is a quadratic factor. Denoting its zeros by z_1, z_2, we first assume that $z_1 \neq z_2$. We then have from (5-23), since $z_k^2 - uz_k - v = 0$ $(k = 1, 2)$

$$0 = p(z_k) = b_{N-1}(z_k - u) + b_N, \qquad k = 1, 2,$$

or, written more explicitly,

$$(z_1 - u)b_{N-1} + b_N = 0,$$
$$(z_2 - u)b_{N-1} + b_N = 0.$$

This homogeneous system of two linear equations has the determinant

$z_1 - z_2 \neq 0$, hence its only solution is $b_{N-1} = b_N = 0$. If the two zeros of the quadratic factor $x^2 - ux - v$ coincide, then $p(z_1) = p'(z_1) = 0$, hence from (5-23)

$$b_{N-1}(z_1 - u) + b_N = 0,$$
$$b_{N-1} \qquad\qquad = 0,$$

and it follows again that $b_{N-1} = b_N = 0$.

Theorem 5.6 shows that the problem of determining a quadratic factor of the polynomial p is equivalent to the problem of determining u and v such that

(5-25) $$\begin{cases} b_{N-1}(u, v) = 0, \\ b_N(u, v) = 0. \end{cases}$$

The solution of this pair of simultaneous equations by Newton's method is known as Bairstow's method.

5.7 Bairstow's Method

In order to apply Newton's method to the system (5-25) we require the partial derivatives

$$\frac{\partial b_{N-1}}{\partial u}(u, v), \qquad \frac{\partial b_{N-1}}{\partial v}(u, v),$$

$$\frac{\partial b_N}{\partial u}(u, v), \qquad \frac{\partial b_N}{\partial v}(u, v).$$

We shall obtain recurrence relations for these derivatives by differentiating the recurrence relations (5-24).

We first differentiate with respect to u and observe that $\partial b_0/\partial u = 0$. Writing

(5-26) $$c_n = \frac{\partial b_{n+1}}{\partial u}$$

for notational convenience, we obtain

$$c_0 = b_0,$$
$$c_1 = b_1 + uc_0,$$
$$c_2 = b_2 + uc_1 + vc_0,$$

and generally

$$c_n = b_n + uc_{n-1} + vc_{n-2},$$

where $n = 0, 1, 2, \ldots, N - 1$, $c_{-2} = c_{-1} = 0$. We see that the c_n are generated from the b_n exactly as the b_n were generated from the a_n. From (5-26) we have

$$\frac{\partial b_{N-1}}{\partial u} = c_{N-2}, \qquad \frac{\partial b_N}{\partial u} = c_{N-1}.$$

We next differentiate with respect to v. We observe that now $\partial b_0/\partial v = \partial b_1/\partial v = 0$. Thus, writing

(5-27) $$d_n = \frac{\partial b_{n+2}}{\partial v},$$

we obtain $d_{-2} = d_{-1} = 0$,

$$d_0 = b_0,$$
$$d_1 = b_1 + ud_0,$$
$$d_2 = b_2 + ud_1 + vd_0,$$

and generally

$$d_n = b_n + ud_{n-1} + vd_{n-2},$$

$n = 0, 1, 2, \ldots, N - 2$. These recurrence relations and initial conditions are exactly the same as those for the c_n, hence we have $d_n = c_n$, $n = 0, 1, 2, \ldots, N - 2$, and from (5-27) we obtain

$$\frac{\partial b_{N-1}}{\partial v} = c_{N-3}, \qquad \frac{\partial b_N}{\partial v} = c_{N-2}.$$

If the increments of u and v are denoted by δ and ε, respectively, their values as determined by Newton's method must satisfy

$$c_{N-2}\delta + c_{N-3}\varepsilon = -b_{N-1},$$
$$c_{N-1}\delta + c_{N-2}\varepsilon = -b_N$$

and hence are given by

(5-28) $$\delta = \frac{b_N c_{N-3} - b_{N-1} c_{N-2}}{c_{N-2}^2 - c_{N-1} c_{N-3}}, \qquad \varepsilon = \frac{b_{N-1} c_{N-1} - b_N c_{N-2}}{c_{N-2}^2 - c_{N-1} c_{N-3}}.$$

The whole procedure is summarized in

Algorithm 5.7   Given the polynomial

$$p(x) = a_0 x^N + a_1 x^{N-1} + a_2 x^{N-2} + \cdots + a_N$$

and an arbitrary tentative quadratic factor $x^2 - u_0 x - v_0$, determine a sequence $\{x^2 - u_k x - v_k\}$ of quadratic factors as follows: For each $k = 0, 1, 2, \ldots$ determine the sequence $\{b_n\} = \{b_n^{(k)}\}$ from $b_{-2} = b_{-1} = 0$,

$$b_n = a_n + u_k b_{n-1} + v_k b_{n-2}, \qquad n = 0, 1, \ldots, N$$

and the sequence $\{c_n\} = \{c_n^{(k)}\}$ from $c_{-2} = c_{-1} = 0$,

$$c_n = b_n + u_k c_{n-1} + v_k c_{n-2}, \qquad n = 0, 1, \ldots, N - 1.$$

Then set $u_{k+1} = u_k + \delta$, $v_{k+1} = v_k + \varepsilon$, where δ and ε are given by (5-28).

Schematically the algorithm can be described as follows:

$$
\begin{array}{ccc}
a_0 & b_0 & c_0 \\
a_1 \quad v \left(\begin{array}{c} b_1 \\ \end{array}\right. u \quad v \left(\begin{array}{c} c_1 \\ \end{array}\right. u \\
a_2 \longrightarrow b_2 \longrightarrow c_2 \\
\vdots & \vdots & \vdots \\
a_{N-3} & b_{N-3} & \mathbf{c}_{N-3} \\
a_{N-2} & b_{N-2} & \mathbf{c}_{N-2} \\
a_{N-1} & \mathbf{b}_{N-1} & \mathbf{c}_{N-1} \\
a_N & \mathbf{b}_N &
\end{array}
$$

Scheme 5.8

The coefficients that are needed in formula (5-28) are printed in bold face.

EXAMPLE

4. To determine a quadratic factor of

$$p(x) = x^3 - x^2 + 2x + 5$$

near $x^2 - 2x + 5$. Algorithm 5.7 yields for $u_0 = 2$, $v_0 = -5$ (watch the signs!)

n	a_n	b_n	c_n	
0	1	1	1	$3\delta + \varepsilon = 1$
1	-1	1	3	$0\delta + 3\varepsilon = 2$
2	2	-1	0	$\delta = 0.11111111$
3	5	-2		$\varepsilon = 0.66666667$

Continuing with $u_1 = u_0 + \delta = 2.11111111$, $v_1 = v_0 + \varepsilon = -4.33333333$, we find

n	a_n	b_n	c_n	
0	1	1	1	$3.222222228\delta + \varepsilon$
				$= -0.01234568$
1	-1	1.11111111	3.22222222	$2.48148148\delta + 3.22222222\varepsilon$
				$= -0.2112483$
2	2	0.01234568	2.48148148	$\delta = 0.02170139$
3	5	0.21124830		$\varepsilon = 0.08227238$

yielding $u_2 = 2.1328125$, $v_2 = -4.41560571$. Proceeding in a similar manner, we find

$$u_3 = 2.13249371, \qquad v_3 = -4.41503560,$$
$$u_4 = 2.13249369, \qquad v_4 = -4.41503564.$$

Calculating the b_n with the last values, we obtain

n	a_n	b_n
0	1	1.00000000
1	-1	1.13249369
2	2	0.00000000
3	5	0.00000000

indicating that convergence has been achieved. The two complex zeros are thus found to be

$$z_{1,2} = \frac{u}{2} \pm i\sqrt{-\left(\frac{u}{2}\right)^2 - v}$$

$$= 1.06624685 \pm i1.81056712.$$

Problems

10. Determine all zeros of the polynomial

$$p(x) = x^4 - 8x^3 + 39x^2 - 62x + 51$$

using the fact that

$$p(x) = (x^2 - 2x + 2)(x^2 - 6x + 25) + 1.$$

11. Determine quadratic factors of the polynomial

$$p(x) = 3x^6 + 9x^5 + 9x^4 + 5x^3 + 3x^2 + 8x + 5$$

near $x^2 + 1.541451x + 1.487398$ and $x^2 - 1.127178x + 0.831492$. Also determine the real zeros near -1.86 and -0.72.

5.8   Convergence of Bairstow's Method

In order to justify the application of Newton's method to the problem of solving (5-25) we have to show, according to §5.5, that the Jacobian determinant

$$(5\text{-}29) \qquad D(u, v) = \begin{vmatrix} \dfrac{\partial b_{N-1}}{\partial u}(u, v) & \dfrac{\partial b_{N-1}}{\partial v}(u, v) \\ \dfrac{\partial b_N}{\partial u}(u, v) & \dfrac{\partial b_N}{\partial v}(u, v) \end{vmatrix}$$

is different from zero for $(u, v) = (s, t)$, where $x^2 - sx - t$ is a quadratic factor of the polynomial p. One condition under which this is the case is as follows.

Theorem 5.8   Let $x^2 - sx - t$ be a quadratic factor of the polynomial p, and let its zeros z_1, z_2 be two distinct, simple zeros of p.   Then $D(s, t) \neq 0$.

Proof.   We differentiate the identity (5-23) with respect to both u and v. Since p does not depend on u or v, the result is

$$0 = -xq(x) + (x^2 - ux - v)\frac{\partial q(x)}{\partial u} + \frac{\partial b_{N-1}}{\partial u}(x - u) - b_{N-1} + \frac{\partial b_N}{\partial u},$$

$$0 = -q(x) + (x^2 - ux - v)\frac{\partial q(x)}{\partial v} + \frac{\partial b_{N-1}}{\partial v}(x - u) + \frac{\partial b_N}{\partial v}.$$

Setting here $u = s$, $v = t$, $x = z_k$ $(k = 1, 2)$ we obtain by virtue of $z_k^2 - sz_k - t = 0$ $(k = 1, 2)$ the four relations

$$(5\text{-}30) \qquad \frac{\partial b_{N-1}}{\partial u}(z_k - s) + \frac{\partial b_N}{\partial u} = z_k q_k \qquad (k = 1, 2),$$

$$(5\text{-}31) \qquad \frac{\partial b_{N-1}}{\partial v}(z_k - s) + \frac{\partial b_N}{\partial v} = q_k \qquad (k = 1, 2),$$

where $q_k = q(z_k)$, and where the derivatives are taken at $(u, v) = (s, t)$. The two relations (5-30) can be regarded as a system of two linear equations for the two unknowns $\partial b_{N-1}/\partial u$ and $\partial b_N/\partial u$ with the nonvanishing determinant $z_1 - z_2$.   We thus have

$$\frac{\partial b_{N-1}}{\partial u} = \frac{z_1 q_1 - z_2 q_2}{z_1 - z_2}, \qquad \frac{\partial b_N}{\partial u} = \frac{z_1 z_2(q_2 - q_1) + s(z_1 q_1 - z_2 q_2)}{z_1 - z_2}.$$

Solving the system (5-31) in a similar manner, we find

$$\frac{\partial b_{N-1}}{\partial v} = \frac{q_1 - q_2}{z_1 - z_2}, \qquad \frac{\partial b_N}{\partial v} = \frac{z_1 q_2 - z_2 q_1 + s(q_1 - q_2)}{z_1 - z_2}.$$

Some algebraic manipulation now yields

$$D(s, t) = \begin{vmatrix} \dfrac{\partial b_{N-1}}{\partial u} & \dfrac{\partial b_{N-1}}{\partial v} \\[2mm] \dfrac{\partial b_N}{\partial u} & \dfrac{\partial b_N}{\partial v} \end{vmatrix} = q_1 q_2 = q(z_1)q(z_2).$$

Since z_1 and z_2 are both simple zeros of p, we have $q(z_k) \neq 0$, $k = 1, 2$, and the conclusion of the theorem follows.

The theory given in §5.5 now shows that under the hypotheses of theorem 5.8, algorithm 5.7 actually defines a sequence of quadratic polynomials $\{x^2 - u_k x - v_k\}$ which converges to $x^2 - sx - t$ whenever the initial quadratic $x^2 - u_0 x - v_0$ is sufficiently close to $x^2 - sx - t$.

For most polynomials even crude approximations to quadratic factors are hard to obtain by mere inspection. In chapter 8 we shall discuss a method that will automatically produce good first approximations to quadratic factors (with complex zeros) of almost any real polynomial.

5.9   Steffensen's Iteration for Systems†

We now return to ordinary iteration as applied to systems of equations (algorithm 5.2). Our goal is to extend the Aitken-Steffensen formula (4-11) to systems of equations. As explained in §4.4, the rationale behind that formula consisted in neglecting the small term ε_n in (4-8). Proceeding in the same vein, we now assume heuristically that the asymptotic error formula (5-17) is true without the term denoted by $0(\|\mathbf{d}_n\|^2)$.

Denoting by $\{\mathbf{x}_n\}$ a sequence of vectors generated by algorithm 5.2 and by $\mathbf{s}$ a solution of $\mathbf{x} = \mathbf{f}(\mathbf{x})$, our assumption implies that

$$(5\text{-}32) \qquad \mathbf{x}_{n+1} - \mathbf{s} = \mathbf{J}(\mathbf{x}_n - \mathbf{s}),$$

for $n = 0, 1, 2, \ldots$, where $\mathbf{J} = \mathbf{J}(\mathbf{s})$ denotes the Jacobian matrix of the function $\mathbf{f}$ taken at the solution $\mathbf{s}$. The problem is to determine $\mathbf{s}$ from several consecutive iterates $\mathbf{x}_n, \mathbf{x}_{n+1}, \mathbf{x}_{n+2}, \ldots$, notwithstanding the fact that $\mathbf{J}$ is unknown.

Subtracting two consecutive equations (5-32) from each other, we find, using the symbol $\varDelta$ to denote forward differences,

$$(5\text{-}33) \qquad \varDelta\mathbf{x}_{n+1} = \mathbf{J}\,\varDelta\mathbf{x}_n, \qquad n = 0, 1, 2, \ldots.$$

We define $\mathbf{X}_n$ to be the matrix‡ with the columns $\mathbf{x}_n$ and $\mathbf{x}_{n+1}$,

$$\mathbf{X}_n = (\mathbf{x}_n, \mathbf{x}_{n+1}) = \begin{pmatrix} x_n & x_{n+1} \\ y_n & y_{n+1} \end{pmatrix}.$$

Defining $\varDelta\mathbf{X}_n$ in the obvious way, (5-33) shows that

$$\mathbf{J}\,\varDelta\mathbf{X}_n = \varDelta\mathbf{X}_{n+1}, \qquad n = 0, 1, 2, \ldots.$$

If the matrix $\varDelta\mathbf{X}_n$ is nonsingular, we can solve for $\mathbf{J}$, finding

$$(5\text{-}34) \qquad \mathbf{J} = \varDelta\mathbf{X}_{n+1}(\varDelta\mathbf{X}_n)^{-1}.$$

We now solve (5-32) for $\mathbf{s}$. Assuming that $\mathbf{I} - \mathbf{J}$ is nonsingular ($\mathbf{I}$ = unit matrix), we get

$$\begin{aligned} (\mathbf{I} - \mathbf{J})\mathbf{s} &= \mathbf{x}_{n+1} - \mathbf{J}\mathbf{x}_n \\ &= (\mathbf{I} - \mathbf{J})\mathbf{x}_n + \varDelta\mathbf{x}_n \end{aligned}$$

---

† This section may be omitted without loss of continuity.
‡ Here we use implicitly the fact that the vectors considered have two components. In the case of N components we would have to put

$$\mathbf{X}_n = (\mathbf{x}_n, \mathbf{x}_{n+1}, \ldots, \mathbf{x}_{n+N-1}).$$

and hence

$$s = x_n + (I - J)^{-1} \Delta x_n.$$

Using equation (5-34) and applying the matrix identity $(AB)^{-1} = B^{-1}A^{-1}$ we have, always proceeding in a purely formal manner,

$$
\begin{aligned}
(I - J)^{-1} &= (I - \Delta X_{n+1}(\Delta X_n)^{-1})^{-1} \\
&= ((\Delta X_n - \Delta X_{n+1})(\Delta X_n)^{-1})^{-1} \\
&= -\Delta X_n(\Delta^2 X_n)^{-1}
\end{aligned}
$$

and hence finally

$$s = x_n - \Delta X_n(\Delta^2 X_n)^{-1}\Delta x_n.$$

This formula for the exact solution has been derived under the assumption that (5-17) is true without the $O(\|d_n\|^2)$ term.   If this term is present, we still may hope that the vector

$$(5\text{-}35) \qquad x'_n = x_n - \Delta X_n(\Delta^2 X_n)^{-1}\Delta x_n$$

is closer to s than x_n, provided that the matrix $\Delta^2 X_n$ is nonsingular.   It will be noted that the formula (5-35) is built like (4-11), with the difference that certain scalars are now replaced by appropriately defined vectors and matrices.

Formula (5-35) can be used in either of two ways.   Either we can apply it to a sequence of vectors $\{x_n\}$ already constructed to obtain a sequence $\{x'_n\}$ which presumably converges to s faster.   More effectively, the formula can be used as in algorithm 4.12, as follows.

Algorithm 5.9   Choose a vector $x^{(0)}$, and construct the sequence of vectors $\{x^{(k)}\}$ as follows: For each $k = 0, 1, 2, \ldots$, set $x_0 = x^{(k)}$, calculate x_1, x_2, x_3, from

$$x_{n+1} = f(x_n), \qquad n = 0, 1, 2,$$

and let $x^{(k+1)} = x'_0$, where x'_0 is defined by (5-35).

This algorithm has not yet been fully investigated from the theoretical point of view.   As it stands, it is not even fully defined, since there is no indication of what is to be done if the matrix $\Delta^2 X_0$ is singular.   It is therefore impossible to prove that the algorithm converges, let alone that it converges quadratically.   Substantial experimental evidence, and also some theoretical considerations, seem to indicate, however, that the algorithm is indeed quadratically convergent in a large number of cases, even when ordinary iteration diverges.

EXAMPLE

5. To find the solution of the system

$$x = x^2 + y^2,$$
$$y = x^2 - y^2,$$

near $(0.8, 0.4)$. Algorithm 5.9 yields the following values:

Table 5.9

k	$x^{(k)}$	$y^{(k)}$	n	x_n	y_n
0	0.8	0.4			
			1	0.8000000	0.4800000
			2	0.8070400	0.4096000
			3	0.9253683	0.5898240
1	0.7741243	0.4194303			
			1	0.7751902	0.4233468
			2	0.7801424	0.4216974
			3	0.7864508	0.4307934
2	0.7718671	0.4196500			
			1	0.7718850	0.4196728
			2	0.7719317	0.4196813
			3	0.7720109	0.4197462
3	0.7718445	0.4196434			
			1	0.7718445	0.4196434

The fact that $x_1 = x_0$ for $k = 3$ indicates that convergence has been accomplished. It is evident in this example that the sequences $\{x_n\}$ would not converge, as they begin to diverge for each k already for small values of n.

Problems

12. Assuming (5-32) to be exact, show that applying Aitken's formula (4-11) individually to each component of x does, in general, not produce the correct solution vector s.

13*. Assuming (5-32) to be exact, show that the matrix $\Delta^2 X_n$ is singular if and only if at least one of the following situations obtains:

(*i*) $x_n = s$;
(*ii*) $x_n - s$ is an eigenvector of J;
(*iii*) the matrix J is similar to a matrix cI, where c is real.

Show that in the cases (*ii*) and (*iii*) the procedure described in problem 12 is effective.

14. Find the solution of the system considered in example 2 by means of algorithm 5.9.

Recommended Reading

The abstract background of the method of iteration is discussed in most textbooks on functional analysis; see, for example, Liusternik and Sobolev [1961], p. 27. A beautiful discussion of Newton's method for systems of equations is given by Kantorovich [1948] (see also Henrici [1962], pp. 367–371).

Research Problems

1. Formulate Newton's method for systems of equations with an arbitrary number of unknowns.
2. Generalize Bairstow's method to extract from a polynomial of degree N a factor of arbitrary degree $n < N$.
3. Discuss Newton's method in the "singular" case when the determinant (5-19) is zero at the solution (s, t).
4. Discuss experimentally the stability of algorithm 5.9 when the matrix $\Delta^2 \mathbf{X}_n$ is nearly singular.
5. Develop a theory of iteration for systems if the vectors $\mathbf{x}_n$ are formed according to

$$x_{n+1} = f(x_n, y_n),$$
$$y_{n+1} = g(x_{n+1}, y_n)$$

(i.e., the most recent information is used at each step). What is the correct formulation of the Δ^2 procedure in this case?

chapter 6 linear difference equations

Linear difference equations were first encountered in §3.3, where the main topic was the study of linear difference equations of the first order. In the present chapter, we shall consider linear difference equations of arbitrary order. The theory of such difference equations is required for the understanding of some important algorithms to be discussed in the chapters 7 and 8. Furthermore, linear difference equations are a useful tool in the study of many other processes of numerical analysis; see in particular the chapters 14 and 16. Much unnecessary complication is avoided by considering difference equations with *complex* coefficients and solutions.

6.1 Notation

We recall that a linear difference equation of order N has the form

(6-1) $$a_{0,n}x_n + a_{1,n}x_{n-1} + \cdots + a_{N,n}x_{n-N} = b_n.$$

Here $\{a_{0,n}\}$, $\{a_{1,n}\}$, ..., $\{a_{N,n}\}$ and $\{b_n\}$ are given sequences, and $\{x_n\}$ is a sequence to be determined. The difference equation (6-1) is called *homogeneous* if $\{b_n\}$ is the zero sequence, i.e., if all its elements are zero.

Although much of the subsequent theory can easily be extended to the general case, we shall be concerned exclusively with the case of linear difference equations with constant coefficients. In this case, $a_{k,n} = a_k$ for all values of n and for certain (real or complex) constants $a_0, a_1, \ldots, a_N$. (It is not required that $b_n = b$, however.) Without loss of generality we may assume that $a_0 \neq 0$, $a_N \neq 0$, for otherwise the order of the difference equation could be reduced. Dividing through by a_0 and renaming the constants and the elements of the sequence $\{b_n\}$, the linear difference equation with constant coefficients appears in the form

(6-2) $$x_n + a_1 x_{n-1} + a_2 x_{n-2} + \cdots + a_N x_{n-N} = b_n,$$

where $a_N \neq 0$.

119

We can aid the understanding by two notational simplifications. First, we shall no longer refer to a sequence by explicitly exhibiting its elements, as in the symbol $\{x_n\}$, but instead denote a sequence by a single capital letter. The nth element of a sequence X will be denoted by x_n, or sometimes also by $(X)_n$. Secondly, if $X = \{x_n\}$ is any sequence, we shall denote by $\mathscr{L}X$ the sequence whose nth element is given by

$$(\mathscr{L}X)_n = x_n + a_1 x_{n-1} + a_2 x_{n-2} + \cdots + a_N x_{n-N}.$$

With these notations, the problem of solving the difference equation (6-2) is the same as the problem of finding a sequence X such that

(6-3) $$\mathscr{L}X = B,$$

where B denotes the sequence of the nonhomogeneous terms b_n.

We note that the operator $\mathscr{L}$ defined above is a *linear* operator. Defining the product aX of a scalar a and of a sequence X by

$$(aX)_n = a(X)_n$$

and the sum of two sequences X and Y by

$$(X + Y)_n = (X)_n + (Y)_n,$$

we have for arbitrary scalars a and b and for any two sequences X and Y

(6-4) $$\mathscr{L}(aX + bY) = a\mathscr{L}X + b\mathscr{L}Y.$$

The comprehension of the above notation may be helped by considering analogous simplifications in the theory of functions. Writing X in place of $\{x_n\}$ is much like writing f in place of $f(x)$ to denote a function. The operator $\mathscr{L}$ plays a role similar to that, say, of the differentiation operator D, which associates with a function f its derivative $Df = f'$. Relation (6-4) is the analog of the familiar fact that differentiation is a linear operation, i.e., that $D(af + bg) = aDf + bDg$.

6.2   Particular Solutions of the Homogeneous Equation of Order Two

We shall consider in some detail the case $N = 2$. Here we have, for some constants a_1 and $a_2 \neq 0$,

(6-5) $$(\mathscr{L}X)_n = x_n + a_1 x_{n-1} + a_2 x_{n-2}.$$

Our first task is to find solutions of the homogeneous equation $\mathscr{L}X = 0.$†

---

† Here the symbol 0 does not denote the scalar zero, but rather the sequence whose elements are all zero. Since no misunderstanding is possible, we shall not attempt to make a graphical distinction between the two concepts.

Let us take a look at the corresponding problem in the theory of differential equations. The linear homogeneous differential equation of order 2 with constant coefficients,

$$x'' + a_1 x' + a_2 x = 0 \qquad \left(x' = \frac{dx}{dt} \right)$$

has, for suitably chosen r, solutions of the form e^{rt}. Is the same true also for the difference equation

(6-6) $$x_n + a_1 x_{n-1} + a_2 x_{n-2} = 0?$$

Replacing t by the discrete variable n, we are tempted to seek solutions of the form $x_n = e^{rn} = (e^r)^n$, or, putting $e^r = z$, of the form $x_n = z^n$. With this definition of $X = \{x_n\}$ we have

$$(\mathscr{L}X)_n = z^n + a_1 z^{n-1} + a_2 z^{n-2}$$
$$= z^{n-2}(z^2 + a_1 z + a_2).$$

This expression is 0 not only if $z = 0$—which would yield the *trivial* solution of the difference equation—but also if z is a zero of the polynomial p defined by

(6-7) $$p(z) = z^2 + a_1 z + a_2.$$

This polynomial is called the *characteristic polynomial* of the difference equation (6-6). We know from the theory of equations that p has exactly two zeros, z_1 and z_2, which may be real or complex, and which may coincide. If $z_1 \neq z_2$, then the sequences with elements z_1^n and z_2^n represent two distinct, nonzero solutions of $\mathscr{L}X = 0$.

We can also find two distinct solutions if $z_1 = z_2$. We recall that if z_1 is a zero of multiplicity > 1 of p, then by theorem 2.6 not only $p(z_1) = 0$ but also $p'(z_1) = 0$. This suggests finding a second solution by differentiation. If $(X)_n = z^n$, we have identically in z

$$(\mathscr{L}X)_n = z^n + a_1 z^{n-1} + a_2 z^{n-2}$$
$$= z^{n-2} p(z).$$

Differentiating with respect to z, we get

$$nz^{n-1} + a_1(n-1)z^{n-2} + a_2(n-2)z^{n-3}$$
$$= (n-2)z^{n-3}p(z) + z^{n-2}p'(z).$$

For $z = z_1$ the expression on the right is zero for all n, showing that the sequence with nth element nz_1^{n-1} is also a solution. We thus have obtained:

Theorem 6.2 Let a_1 and $a_2 \neq 0$ be constants, and consider the difference equation $\mathscr{L}X = 0$, where $\mathscr{L}$ is defined by (6-5). If z_1, z_2

are two distinct zeros of the characteristic polynomial, then the two sequences $X^{(1)}$, $X^{(2)}$ defined by

$$(X^{(1)})_n = z_1^n, \qquad (X^{(2)})_n = z_2^n$$

are solutions of $\mathscr{L}X = 0$. If z_1 is a zero of multiplicity 2, then the sequences defined by

$$(X^{(1)})_n = z_1^n, \qquad (X^{(2)})_n = nz_1^{n-1}$$

are solutions.

EXAMPLES

1. We consider the difference equation $x_n = x_{n-1} + x_{n-2}$. The characteristic polynomial $p(z) = z^2 - z - 1$ has the two zeros

$$z_1 = \frac{1 + \sqrt{5}}{2}, \qquad z_2 = \frac{1 - \sqrt{5}}{2},$$

thus two solutions are given by

$$(X^{(1)})_n = \left(\frac{1 + \sqrt{5}}{2}\right)^n, \qquad (X^{(2)})_n = \left(\frac{1 - \sqrt{5}}{2}\right)^n.$$

2. Consider $x_n - 2x_{n-1} + x_{n-2} = 0$. The characteristic polynomial is $p(z) = z^2 - 2z + 1$; $z_1 = 1$ is a double zero. Thus we find the two solutions

$$(X^{(1)})_n = 1^n = 1, \qquad (X^{(2)})_n = n1^{n-1} = n,$$

as can be verified directly.

6.3   The General Solution

Throughout this section, $\mathscr{L}$ will denote the difference operator defined by (6-5), where $a_2 \neq 0$. The first tool is the following:

Lemma 6.3a   If $X^{(1)}$ and $X^{(2)}$ are any two solutions of $\mathscr{L}X = 0$, and if c_1 and c_2 are any two constants, then the sequence

$$X = c_1 X^{(1)} + c_2 X^{(2)}$$

is also a solution.

Proof.   By the linearity of the operator $\mathscr{L}$,

$$\mathscr{L}X = \mathscr{L}(c_1 X^{(1)} + c_2 X^{(2)})$$
$$= c_1 \mathscr{L}X^{(1)} + c_2 \mathscr{L}X^{(2)} = 0.$$

As an exercise in the application of lemma 6.3a, we consider the problem of finding real solutions of real difference equations.   Let $\mathscr{L}$ be defined as above, where a_1 and a_2 are real.   The characteristic polynomial

$$p(z) = z^2 + a_1 z + a_2,$$

although a polynomial with real coefficients, may still have nonreal zeros z_1, z_2.   However, these zeros according to theorem 2.5d then are complex conjugate, i.e.,

$$z_2 = \bar{z}_1,$$

or, denoting by Re a and Im a the real and imaginary parts of a complex number a,

$$\text{Re } z_1 = \text{Re } z_2, \qquad \text{Im } z_2 = -\text{Im } z_1.$$

If the two zeros are nonreal, two distinct solutions are given by

$$(X^{(1)})_n = z_1^n, \qquad (X^{(2)})_n = (\bar{z}_1)^n.$$

Since the product of complex conjugate numbers is equal to the complex conjugate number of the product, we can also write

$$(X^{(2)})_n = (\overline{z_1^n}).$$

It now follows from lemma 6.3a that the two real sequences $Y^{(1)}$, $Y^{(2)}$ defined by

$$(Y^{(1)})_n = \tfrac{1}{2}[z_1^n + \overline{z_1^n}] = \text{Re } z_1^n,$$

$$(Y^{(2)})_n = \frac{1}{2i}[z_1^n - \overline{z_1^n}] = \text{Im } z_1^n,$$

are likewise solutions of the difference equation.

EXAMPLE

3.   Let $-1 < t < 1$, and consider the difference equation

(6-8) $$x_n - 2t x_{n-1} + x_{n-2} = 0.$$

The characteristic polynomial $p(z) = z^2 - 2tz + 1$ has the zeros

$$z_1 = t + i\sqrt{1 - t^2}, \qquad z_2 = t - i\sqrt{1 - t^2}.$$

If we define the angle φ by the condition

$$\cos \varphi = t \qquad (0 < \varphi < \pi)$$

then the zeros appear in the form

$$z_1 = \cos \varphi + i \sin \varphi = e^{i\varphi},$$
$$z_2 = \cos \varphi - i \sin \varphi = e^{-i\varphi}.$$

Consequently, the two solutions given by theorem 6.2 appear in the form

$$(X^{(1)})_n = (e^{i\varphi})^n = e^{in\varphi},$$
$$(X^{(2)})_n = (e^{-i\varphi})^n = e^{-in\varphi},$$

and are complex. However, in view of $e^{in\varphi} = \cos n\varphi + i \sin n\varphi$, also the sequences defined by

$$(Y^{(1)})_n = \cos n\varphi, \qquad (Y^{(2)})_n = \sin n\varphi$$

are solutions. This may be verified directly by using the addition theorems of the trigonometric functions.

It is readily seen that the elements of the sequence $Y^{(1)}$ are polynomials of degree n in the variable $t = \cos \varphi$. In fact, $(Y^{(1)})_0 = 1$, $(Y^{(1)})_1 = t$, and (6-8) shows that if this property holds for the integers $n - 2$ and $n - 1$, it holds for the integer n. Conventionally, these polynomials are denoted by $T_n(t)$ and are called Chebyshev polynomials of degree n. By the above we can also write

$$T_n(t) = \cos (n \text{ arc cos } t).$$

The Chebyshev polynomials are important in many branches of numerical analysis (see §9.4).

We return to the problem of finding *all* solutions of $\mathscr{L}X = 0$. Our second tool is the following simple observation.

Lemma 6.3b Let I be a set of consecutive integers, and let the integers m and $m - 1$ be in I. Let the sequence $B = \{b_n\}$ be defined on I. Then the difference equation $\mathscr{L}X = B$ has precisely one solution which assumes given values for $n = m$ and $n = m - 1$.

Proof. Let $X^{(1)}$ and $X^{(2)}$ be two solutions having the same values at $n = m$ and $n = m - 1$. The sequence $D = X^{(1)} - X^{(2)} = \{d_n\}$ then is a solution of $\mathscr{L}X = 0$ assuming the values 0 for $n = m$ and $n = m - 1$. If $X^{(1)}$ and $X^{(2)}$ are not identical, then $d_n \neq 0$ for some $n > m$ or some $n < m - 1$. To fix ideas, let $d_n \neq 0$ for some $n > m$. If we denote by n the smallest integer for which this is the case, then, because D is a solution,

$$d_n + a_1 d_{n-1} + a_2 d_{n-2} = 0.$$

However, since $d_{n-1} = d_{n-2} = 0$, $d_n \neq 0$, this equation reveals a contradiction. The case where some $d_n \neq 0$ with $n < m - 1$ is dealt with similarly, making use of the fact that $a_2 \neq 0$. It follows that D is the zero sequence, and hence that the sequences $X^{(1)}$ and $X^{(2)}$ are identical.

The zero sequence is a solution of $\mathscr{L}X = 0$ with the property that its elements are zero for any two consecutive values of n. Lemma 6.3b shows that this property characterizes the zero solution. In other words: *If a solution of $\mathscr{L}X = 0$ vanishes at two consecutive integers, it vanishes identically.*

Let now $X^{(1)} = \{x_n^{(1)}\}$ and $X^{(2)} = \{x_n^{(2)}\}$ be two known solutions of $\mathscr{L}X = 0$, defined for $-\infty < n < \infty$, and let $X = \{x_n\}$ be an arbitrary third solution. Is it possible to find constants c_1 and c_2 such that

$$X = c_1 X^{(1)} + c_2 X^{(2)}?$$

If that is the case, then we are entitled to call the sequence $c_1 X^{(1)} + c_2 X^{(2)}$ the *general solution* of $\mathscr{L}X = 0$, for any special solution can be obtained by assigning special values to the constants c_1 and c_2.

By lemma 6.3a, the sequence $c_1 X^{(1)} + c_2 X^{(2)}$ is in any case a solution of $\mathscr{L}X = 0$. By lemma 6.3b, this solution is identical with X if it agrees with X at two consecutive integers, n and $n - 1$, say. In order to obtain this agreement, we must be able to determine the constants c_1 and c_2 such that the two equations

(6-9)
$$\begin{cases} c_1 x_n^{(1)} + c_2 x_n^{(2)} = x_n, \\ c_1 x_{n-1}^{(1)} + c_2 x_{n-1}^{(2)} = x_{n-1}, \end{cases}$$

are satisfied. By the theory of linear equations, this system has a solution for arbitrary x_n and x_{n-1} if its determinant

$$w_n = \begin{vmatrix} x_n^{(1)} & x_n^{(2)} \\ x_{n-1}^{(1)} & x_{n-1}^{(2)} \end{vmatrix}$$

is different from zero.

The determinant w_n is called the Wronskian determinant of the sequences $X^{(1)}$ and $X^{(2)}$ at the point n. We have obtained

Theorem 6.3 Let $X^{(1)}$ and $X^{(2)}$ be two particular solutions of $\mathscr{L}X = 0$. Then every solution of $\mathscr{L}X = 0$ can be expressed in the form $c_1 X^{(1)} + c_2 X^{(2)}$ if and only if the Wronskian determinant w_n of $X^{(1)}$ and $X^{(2)}$ is different from zero for all values of n.

The requirement that $w_n \neq 0$ for *all* n is less stringent than it appears, as will be seen presently.

EXAMPLES

4. Let the two zeros z_1 and z_2 of the characteristic polynomial p of $\mathscr{L}X = 0$ be different. We calculate the Wronskian of the two solutions

$$x_n^{(1)} = z_1^n, \qquad x_n^{(2)} = z_2^n$$

given by theorem 6.2. We find

$$w_n = \begin{vmatrix} z_1^n & z_2^n \\ z_1^{n-1} & z_2^{n-1} \end{vmatrix} = (z_1 z_2)^{n-1}(z_1 - z_2).$$

Evidently $w_n \neq 0$ for all n. Hence the general solution of the difference equation is given by $c_1 z_1^n + c_2 z_2^n$.

5. If z_1 is a zero of multiplicity 2 of the characteristic polynomial, two solutions of the difference equation are given by

$$x_n^{(1)} = z_1^n, \qquad x_n^{(2)} = n z_1^{n-1}.$$

We find

$$w_n = \begin{vmatrix} z_1^n & n z_1^{n-1} \\ z_1^{n-1} & (n-1)z_1^{n-2} \end{vmatrix} = -z_1^{2n-2} \neq 0;$$

hence

$$x_n = c_1 z_1^n + c_2 n z_1^{n-1}$$

is the general solution.

6. As a somewhat more special example, we consider the real solutions of the difference equation

$$x_n - 2t x_{n-1} + x_{n-2} = 0 \qquad (-1 < t < 1)$$

found in example 3. If $t = \cos \varphi$, we were able to express these solutions in the form $x_n^{(1)} = \cos n\varphi$, $x_n^{(2)} = \sin n\varphi$. For these solutions,

$$w_n = \begin{vmatrix} \cos n\varphi & \sin n\varphi \\ \cos (n-1)\varphi & \sin (n-1)\varphi \end{vmatrix}$$

$$= \cos n\varphi \sin (n-1)\varphi - \cos (n-1)\varphi \sin n\varphi$$

$$= -\sin \varphi \neq 0.$$

Thus the general solution can be expressed in the form

$$c_1 \cos n\varphi + c_2 \sin n\varphi.$$

(Note, however, the restriction on t.)

We are now in a position to solve arbitrary initial value problems for the linear difference equation $\mathcal{L}X = 0$. All we have to do is to find two particular solutions $X^{(1)}$, $X^{(2)}$ with nonvanishing Wronskian and to determine the constants c_1 and c_2 such that the sequence $X = c_1 X^{(1)} + c_2 X^{(2)}$ satisfies the given initial conditions.

EXAMPLE

7. Let us find the solution of

$$x_n = x_{n-1} + x_{n-2}$$

satisfying the conditions $x_{-1} = 0$, $x_0 = 1$. By the examples 1 and 4, the general solution of the difference equation is

$$x_n = c_1 \left(\frac{1 + \sqrt{5}}{2} \right)^n + c_2 \left(\frac{1 - \sqrt{5}}{2} \right)^n.$$

The initial conditions yield the following conditions on c_1 and c_2:

$$c_1 + c_2 = 1,$$

$$c_1\left(\frac{1 + \sqrt{5}}{2}\right)^{-1} + c_2\left(\frac{1 - \sqrt{5}}{2}\right)^{-1} = 0.$$

We easily find the solution

$$c_1 = \frac{1 + \sqrt{5}}{2\sqrt{5}}, \qquad c_2 = -\frac{1 - \sqrt{5}}{2\sqrt{5}},$$

thus the solution of our initial value problem is given by the formula

$$x_n = \frac{1}{\sqrt{5}}\left[\left(\frac{1 + \sqrt{5}}{2}\right)^{n+1} - \left(\frac{1 - \sqrt{5}}{2}\right)^{n+1}\right].$$

It is not immediately evident from this representation that the numbers x_n all are integers. The sequence thus defined is called the Fibonacci sequence. It has many interesting number-theoretical properties.

Problems

1. Express in real terms a general solution of the following difference equations:

(a) $\qquad\qquad\qquad x_n - x_{n-2} = 0;$
(b) $\qquad\qquad\qquad x_n + x_{n-2} = 0;$
(c) $\qquad x_n + 2x_{n-1} + x_{n-2} = 0.$

2. Find a general solution of the difference equation

$$x_n + 2ix_{n-1} + x_{n-2} = 0.$$

3. Let a, b be real, $a^2 - 4b < 0$. Show that the general solution of the difference equation

$$x_n + ax_{n-1} + bx_{n-2} = 0$$

can be expressed in the form

$$x_n = r^n(c_1 \cos n\varphi + c_2 \sin n\varphi),$$

where r and φ are real.

4. Let $X = \{x_n\}$ denote the Fibonacci sequence. Show that

$$\lim_{n \to \infty} \frac{x_{n+1}}{x_n} = \frac{1 + \sqrt{5}}{2}.$$

5*. Let b, c be real. Show that a necessary and sufficient condition in order that *all* solutions of the difference equation

$$x_n + 2bx_{n-1} + cx_{n-2} = 0$$

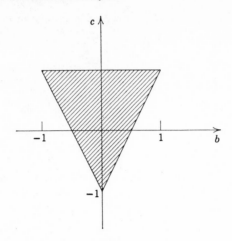

Figure 6.3

tend to zero for $n \to \infty$ is as follows: The point (b, c) lies in the interior of the triangular region of the (b, c) plane bounded by the straight lines

$$c = 1, \qquad 2b - 1 = c, \qquad -2b - 1 = c$$

(see Fig. 6.3). (Hint: Treat separately the two cases where the zeros of the characteristic polynomial are real or imaginary.)

6*. Formulate and prove results analogous to those of §6.3 for linear difference equations with variable coefficients.

7. Solve the following initial value problems for difference equations:

(a) $x_n = 3x_{n-1} - x_{n-2}, \qquad x_0 = 1, \qquad x_1 = 2;$

(b) $x_n - 2x_{n-1} + 2x_{n-2} = 0, \qquad x_0 = x_1 = 1.$

6.4 Linear Dependence

The results of §6.3 can be formulated somewhat more elegantly by introducing the concepts of linear dependence and linear independence of sequences. Two sequences $X^{(1)}$ and $X^{(2)}$ defined on a set I of integers (but not necessarily solutions of a difference equation such as $\mathscr{L}X = 0$) are called *linearly dependent* if there exist two constants c_1, c_2, not both zero, such that the sequence

$$X = c_1 X^{(1)} + c_2 X^{(2)}$$

is the zero sequence on I. If no such constants exist, the sequences are called *linearly independent*.

EXAMPLES

8. Let I be the set of integers from 1 to 20 and let

$$X^{(1)} = \{\underbrace{1, 1, \ldots, 1,}_{10 \text{ elements}} \quad \underbrace{0, 0, \ldots, 0\}}_{10 \text{ elements}}$$

$$X^{(2)} = \{0, 0, \ldots, 0, \quad 1, 1, \ldots, 1\}$$

The sequences $X^{(1)}$ and $X^{(2)}$ are independent. For assume that

$$c_1 x_n^{(1)} + c_2 x_n^{(2)} = 0$$

for $n = 1, \ldots, 20$. For $1 \leq n \leq 10$ this implies $c_1 = 0$, for $11 \leq n \leq 20$ it implies $c_2 = 0$. Thus $c_1 X^{(1)} + c_2 X^{(2)} = 0$ is possible only for $c_1 = c_2 = 0$.

9. If one of the sequences $X^{(1)}$ and $X^{(2)}$ is the zero sequence, the two sequences are always linearly dependent.

To find out whether two given sequences are independent may be difficult in general. However, if the two sequences are both solutions of the same linear difference equation $\mathscr{L}X = 0$, their linear dependence or independence is closely connected with their Wronskian determinants.

Theorem 6.4 Let $X^{(1)}$ and $X^{(2)}$ be two solutions of $\mathscr{L}X = 0$, and let $W = \{w_n\}$ be the sequence of their Wronskian determinants.

(*i*) If $X^{(1)}$ and $X^{(2)}$ are linearly dependent, then W is the zero sequence.

(*ii*) If $w_m = 0$ for some integer m, then the two solutions are linearly dependent.

An immediate consequence of theorem 6.4 is the following

Corollary 6.4 If $w_m \neq 0$ for some integer m, then $w_n \neq 0$ for all n, and the solutions $X^{(1)}$ and $X^{(2)}$ are linearly independent.

Proof of theorem 6.4. (*i*) If $X^{(1)}$ and $X^{(2)}$ are linearly dependent, then there exist, by definition, two constants c_1 and c_2, not both zero, so that

$$c_1 X^{(1)} + c_2 X^{(2)} = 0.$$

In particular, for an arbitrary integer n,

$$c_1 x_n^{(1)} + c_2 x_n^{(2)} = 0,$$
$$c_1 x_{n-1}^{(1)} + c_2 x_{n-1}^{(2)} = 0.$$

This is a homogeneous linear system of two equations with the nontrivial solution (c_1, c_2). Its determinant must therefore vanish, showing that $w_n = 0$, as required.

(*ii*) Let m be an integer such that $w_m = 0$. The homogeneous system of two linear equations with two unknowns,

$$c_1 x_m^{(1)} + c_2 x_m^{(2)} = 0,$$
$$c_1 x_{m-1}^{(1)} + c_2 x_{m-1}^{(2)} = 0,$$

then has a nontrivial solution (c_1, c_2). We define the sequence

$$X = c_1 X^{(1)} + c_2 X^{(2)}.$$

By lemma 6.3a, X is a solution of $\mathscr{L}X = 0$. By construction, this solution is zero at the two consecutive points $n = m$ and $n = m - 1$. Hence, by lemma 6.3b, X is the zero sequence. It follows that $X^{(1)}$ and $X^{(2)}$ are linearly dependent.

If A and B are any two sequences, and if c_1, c_2 are any two constants, the sequence $c_1A + c_2B$ is called a *linear combination* of the sequences A and B. Using the concept of linear dependence, the content of theorem 6.3 can now be phrased more elegantly as follows: *Every solution of $\mathscr{L}X = 0$ can be expressed as a linear combination of two fixed, linearly independent solutions.*

Problems

8. Show that if two sequences are linearly dependent, one is a constant multiple of the other.

9. Let $W = \{w_n\}$ be the sequence of Wronskian determinants of two solutions of $\mathscr{L}X = 0$. Show that W satisfies the first order difference equation

$$w_n = a_2 w_{n-1}.$$

Hence give an independent proof of the fact that either W is the zero sequence, or $w_n \neq 0$ for all n.

10. Let $X = \{x_n\}$ be a solution of $\mathscr{L}X = 0$ such that $x_n \neq 0$ for all n. Show that any solution $Y = \{y_n\}$ of the linear difference equation of order 1 with variable coefficients,

$$y_n = \frac{x_n}{x_{n-1}} y_{n-1} + a_2^n$$

satisfies $\mathscr{L}Y = 0$, and that the solutions X and Y are linearly independent.

11*. Extend the results of §6.4 to linear difference equations with variable coefficients.

6.5   The Non-homogeneous Equation of Order Two

We now shall discuss the solution of the equation $\mathscr{L}X = B$ or, more explicitly,

$$(6\text{-}10) \qquad x_n + a_1 x_{n-1} + a_2 x_{n-2} = b_n,$$

where the sequence $B = \{b_n\}$ is defined on some set I of consecutive integers. Much of the corresponding theory for differential equations again carries over. For instance we have the following result.

Theorem 6.5   Let Y be a special solution of $\mathscr{L}Y = B$, and let $X^{(1)}$ and $X^{(2)}$ be two linearly independent solutions of the corresponding homogeneous equation $\mathscr{L}X = 0$. Then every solution X of $\mathscr{L}X = B$ can be expressed in the form

$$X = c_1 X^{(1)} + c_2 X^{(2)} + Y,$$

where c_1, c_2 are suitable constants.

Proof. By hypothesis, if $Y = \{y_n\}$

(6-11) $y_n + a_1 y_{n-1} + a_2 y_{n-2} = b_n$

for all $n \in I$. If $X = \{x_n\}$ is any solution of (6-10), we obtain by subtracting (6-11) from (6-10) and setting $D = \{d_n\} = X - Y$,

$$d_n + a_1 d_{n-1} + a_2 d_{n-2} = 0.$$

Thus, the sequence D is a solution of the homogeneous equation. By theorem 6.3 it can be written in the form

$$D = c_1 X^{(1)} + c_2 X^{(2)}$$

for suitable c_1, c_2. Since $X = Y + D$, the desired result follows.

Theorem 6.5 reduces the problem of finding the general solution of the nonhomogeneous equation to the problem of finding one particular solution of it. As in the case of differential equations, such a particular solution can frequently be found by an inspired guess. For instance, if the elements of B are bq^n, where b and $q \neq 0$ are constants, a special solution of $\mathscr{L}X = B$ can frequently be found in the form $x_n = aq^n$, where a is a constant to be determined. Substituting into (6-10) yields

$$a(q^n + a_1 q^{n-1} + a_2 q^{n-2}) = bq^n,$$

or, denoting by p the characteristic polynomial of the homogeneous equation and dividing by q^n,

$$aq^{-2}p(q) = b.$$

If $p(q) \neq 0$, we find

$$a = \frac{q^2 b}{p(q)};$$

the method breaks down, however, if q is a zero of the characteristic polynomial.

Similarly, if the elements of B are polynomials in n, there often exist solutions X whose elements are polynomials of the same degree in n. These solutions can be found by the method of undetermined coefficients. Again the method may break down in exceptional cases.

EXAMPLE

10. To find a particular solution of

$$x_n - x_{n-1} - x_{n-2} = -n^2.$$

We set $x_n = an^2 + bn + c$, with constants a, b, c to be determined. Substitution yields

$$a[n^2 - (n-1)^2 - (n-2)^2] + b[n - (n-1) - (n-2)]$$
$$+ c[1 - 1 - 1] = -n^2$$

or, after simplification,

$$a(-n^2 + 6n - 5) + b(-n + 3) + c(-1) = -n^2.$$

Comparing coefficients of like powers of n, we get

$$\begin{aligned} -a &= -1, \\ 6a - b &= 0, \\ -5a + 3b - c &= 0, \end{aligned}$$

yielding $a = 1, b = 6, c = 13$. Thus we have found the solution

$$x_n = n^2 + 6n + 13.$$

Problems

12. Find general solutions of the difference equations

(a) $x_n - 5x_{n-1} + 6x_{n-2} = 2$;

(b) $8x_n - 6x_{n-1} + x_{n-2} = 2^n$;

(c) $x_n - x_{n-1} - 2x_{n-2} = n^2$.

13. Find the solution of equation (a) above that satisfies the initial condition $x_0 = 1$, $x_1 = -1$.

14. Determine a general solution of the difference equation

$$2x_n - 3x_{n-1} - 2x_{n-2} + 3 = 0.$$

What relation must hold between the values x_0 and x_1 of a particular solution $\{x_n\}$ of the above equation in order that $|x_n| \leq C$ for some constant C and for all $n > 0$?

15. Difference equations have remarkable applications in the theory of economics. Let y_n be the national income in the year n, a the marginal propensity to consume, and b the ratio of private investment to increase in consumption. Assuming that government expenditure is constant and equal to 1, a certain economic theory states that the following difference equation for y_n holds (see S. Goldberg [1958], p. 6):

$$y_n = ay_{n-1} + ab(y_{n-1} - y_{n-2}) + 1.$$

(a) Solve this equation with $a = 0.5$, $b = 1$ under the initial condition

$$y_{1946} = 2, \qquad y_{1947} = 3.$$

(b) How frequent are depressions in this economy?

(c) For what values of a, b is the economy thus described noninflationary?

6.6 Variation of Constants

The methods discussed in §6.5 for finding a particular solution of the nonhomogeneous equation are, at best, heuristic and furnish a solution only in special cases. With differential equations, the method of variation of constants permits us to find a solution of any nonhomogeneous equation if the general solution of the homogeneous equation is known (see Coddington [1962], p. 67). A similar formula exists for difference equations. For simplicity we shall consider the case in which the sequence B is defined on the set of nonnegative integers.

Theorem 6.6 Let $X^{(1)} = \{x_n^{(1)}\}$ and $X^{(2)} = \{x_n^{(2)}\}$ be two linearly independent solutions of the homogeneous equation $\mathscr{L}X = 0$, and let $W = \{w_n\}$ be the sequence of their Wronskian determinants. If $B = \{b_n\}$ is defined on the set of nonnegative integers, a solution X of $\mathscr{L}X = B$ is given by

$$(6\text{-}12) \qquad x_n = \sum_{m=0}^{n} \frac{\begin{vmatrix} x_n^{(1)} & x_n^{(2)} \\ x_{m-1}^{(1)} & x_{m-1}^{(2)} \end{vmatrix}}{w_m} b_m, \qquad n \geq 0.$$

Proof. Formula (6-12) can be verified by direct computation. A different proof, which shows how the formula is obtained, is as follows.

It is clear that, for a given difference operator $\mathscr{L}$, the elements x_n of the required solution are *linear* functions of the preceding elements of the sequence B. We may thus write

$$(6\text{-}13) \qquad x_n = \sum_{m=0}^{n} d_{n,m} b_m,$$

where the coefficients $d_{n,m}$ depend only on $\mathscr{L}$ and not on the particular sequence B. The requirement that the sequence $X = \{x_n\}$ defined by (6-13) satisfies $\mathscr{L}X = B$ leads to

$$x_n + a_1 x_{n-1} + a_2 x_{n-2} = \sum_{m=0}^{n} d_{n,m} b_m + a_1 \sum_{m=0}^{n-1} d_{n-1,m} b_m + a_2 \sum_{m=0}^{n-2} d_{n-2,m} b_m$$

$$= b_n,$$

or, collecting factors of b_m,

$$\sum_{m=0}^{n-2} (d_{n,m} + a_1 d_{n-1,m} + a_2 d_{n-2,m}) b_m$$

$$+ (d_{n,n-1} + a_1 d_{n-1,n-1}) b_{n-1} + d_{n,n} b_n = b_n.$$

This identity must hold for all $n \geq 0$, no matter how the sequence B is chosen. It follows that for each m, the coefficients of b_m on both sides must be equal. On the right, there is a nonzero coefficient only for $m = n$. This leads to the relations

(6-14a) $\qquad d_{n,m} + a_1 d_{n-1,m} + a_2 d_{n-2,m} = 0, \qquad n > m + 1,$

(6-14b) $\qquad d_{n,n-1} + a_1 d_{n-1,n-1} = 0,$

(6-14c) $\qquad\qquad d_{n,n} = 1.$

Formula (6-14a) shows that for a fixed value of m, the sequence $D = \{d_{n,m}\}$ is a solution of $\mathscr{L}D = 0$ for $n > m + 1$. Equation (6-14c) yields a first initial condition $d_{m,m} = 1$. If we impose the further initial condition $d_{m-1,m} = 0$, then (6-14b) can be replaced by (6-14a), where $n \geqq m + 1$. The sequence D is thus characterized as solving $\mathscr{L}D = 0$ for $n > m$ and satisfying the initial conditions

(6-15) $\qquad\qquad d_{m-1,m} = 0, \qquad d_{m,m} = 1.$

By theorem 6.3 there must exist constants $c_m^{(1)}$, $c_m^{(2)}$, depending only on m, such that

$$d_{n,m} = c_m^{(1)} x_n^{(1)} + c_m^{(2)} x_n^{(2)}.$$

The initial conditions (6-15) are satisfied if

$$c_m^{(1)} x_m^{(1)} + c_m^{(2)} x_m^{(2)} = 1,$$
$$c_m^{(1)} x_{m-1}^{(1)} + c_m^{(2)} x_{m-1}^{(2)} = 0.$$

The solution of this system of linear equations is readily found to be

$$c_m^{(1)} = \frac{x_{m-1}^{(2)}}{w_m}, \qquad c_m^{(2)} = -\frac{x_{m-1}^{(1)}}{w_m}.$$

We thus find

(6-16) $\qquad\qquad d_{n,m} = \frac{x_n^{(1)} x_{m-1}^{(2)} - x_n^{(2)} x_{m-1}^{(1)}}{w_m}.$

Substituting this into (6-13), we obtain (6-12).

Although theorem 6.6 does provide a solution to the nonhomogeneous equation that works in all cases, there is of course no guarantee that the sum appearing in (6-13) can be expressed in any simple form. (Neither can the integrals appearing in the variation-of-constants formula for differential equations always be expressed in closed form.) But formula (6-13) can be effective in cases where heuristic methods fail.

EXAMPLE

11. To find a particular solution of

(6-17) $\qquad\qquad x_n - 2x_{n-1} + x_{n-2} = 1.$

By example 2, two linearly independent solutions of the homogeneous equation are given by

$$x_n^{(1)} = 1, \qquad x_n^{(2)} = n.$$

Their Wronskian determinants are, by example 5, $w_n = -1$.   Formula (6-13) thus yields in view of $b_n = 1$ $(n = 0, 1, 2, \ldots)$

$$x_n = - \sum_{m=0}^{n} \begin{vmatrix} 1 & n \\ 1 & m-1 \end{vmatrix} = \sum_{m=0}^{n} (n + 1 - m).$$

Changing the index of summation from m to p, where $p = n + 1 - m$, we have

$$x_n = \sum_{p=1}^{n+1} p = 1 + 2 + 3 + \cdots + (n + 1).$$

By a well-known summation formula we obtain

$$x_n = \frac{(n + 1)(n + 2)}{2}.$$

We leave it to the reader to verify that this indeed is a solution of (6-17).

Problems

16. Let a, b be any two constants, $a \neq 0, b \neq 0$.   Find a particular solution of the difference equation

$$x_n - (a + b)x_{n-1} + abx_{n-2} = a^n.$$

(Distinguish the cases $a = b$ and $a \neq b$.)

17*. Show that formula (6-13) is valid for linear difference equations with variable coefficients.

6.7   The Linear Difference Equation of Order N

The theory developed in the sections §6.3 through §6.6 for difference equations of order two carries over, without essential change, to equations of arbitrary order.   We now consider the difference operator $\mathscr{L}$ of order N defined by

(6-18) $$(\mathscr{L}X)_n = x_n + a_1 x_{n-1} + \cdots + a_N x_{n-N},$$

where $a_1, a_2, \ldots, a_N$ are arbitrary (real or complex) constants, $a_N \neq 0$. We are interested in both the homogeneous equation

(6-19) $$\mathscr{L}X = 0,$$

where 0 denotes the null sequence, and the nonhomogeneous equation

(6-20) $$\mathscr{L}X = B,$$

where B denotes an arbitrary given sequence.

The following analogs of the results given above hold and are proved similarly.

Lemma 6.3a′   Any linear combination of two solutions of $\mathscr{L}X = 0$ is again a solution.

Lemma 6.3b′   Let I be a set of consecutive integers, let the integers $m, m - 1, \ldots, m - N + 1$ be in I, and let the sequence B be defined on I. Then the difference equation $\mathscr{L}X = B$ has precisely one solution which assumes given values for $n = m, m - 1, \ldots, m - N + 1$.

Again we have the corollary that if a solution of $\mathscr{L}X = 0$ vanishes at N consecutive integers, it vanishes identically.

Let now the sequences $X^{(1)} = \{x_n^{(1)}\}$, $X^{(2)} = \{x_n^{(2)}\}, \ldots, X^{(N)} = \{x_n^{(N)}\}$ be N solutions of $\mathscr{L}X = 0$. Their Wronskian determinant at the point n is defined by

$$
w_n = \begin{vmatrix}
x_n^{(1)} & x_n^{(2)} & \cdots & x_n^{(N)} \\
x_{n-1}^{(1)} & x_{n-1}^{(2)} & \cdots & x_{n-1}^{(N)} \\
\cdot & \cdot & \cdots & \cdot \\
x_{n-N+1}^{(1)} & x_{n-N+1}^{(2)} & \cdots & x_{n-N+1}^{(N)}
\end{vmatrix}.
$$

The following result is obtained as in §6.3:

Theorem 6.3′   Let $X^{(1)}, \ldots, X^{(N)}$ be N solutions of $\mathscr{L}X = 0$. Then every solution of $\mathscr{L}X = 0$ can be expressed as a linear combination of $X^{(1)}, \ldots, X^{(N)}$ if and only if the Wronskian determinant of these solutions is different from zero for all values of n.

N sequences $A^{(1)}, A^{(2)}, \ldots, A^{(N)}$ are called *linearly dependent* if there exist constants $c_1, c_2, \ldots, c_N$, not all zero, such that

$$
c_1 A^{(1)} + c_2 A^{(2)} + \cdots + c_N A^{(N)}
$$

is the zero sequence. If no such constants exist, the sequences are called linearly independent. As in §6.4 we can show:

Theorem 6.4′   Let $X^{(1)}, \ldots, X^{(N)}$ be N solutions of $\mathscr{L}X = 0$, and let $W = \{w_n\}$ be the sequence of their Wronskian determinants.
   (*i*) If the solutions $X^{(1)}, \ldots, X^{(N)}$ are linearly dependent, then W is the zero sequence.
   (*ii*) If W contains a zero element, then the solutions $X^{(1)}, \ldots, X^{(N)}$ are linearly dependent.

It follows that if $w_m \neq 0$ for some integer m, then $w_n \neq 0$ for all n. Thus the condition of theorem 6.3 is satisfied if the solutions $X^{(1)}, \ldots, X^{(N)}$ are linearly independent, and it follows that every solution of $\mathscr{L}X = 0$ can be expressed as a linear combination of a system of linearly independent solutions.

We now turn to the nonhomogeneous equation $\mathscr{L}X = B$. As above, we have

Theorem 6.5′ Let Y be a special solution of $\mathscr{L}Y = B$, and let $X^{(1)}, \ldots, X^{(N)}$ be a system of linearly independent solutions of the corresponding homogeneous equation $\mathscr{L}X = 0$. Then every solution X of $\mathscr{L}X = B$ can be expressed in the form

$$X = c_1 X^{(1)} + \cdots + c_N X^{(N)} + Y,$$

where $c_1, \ldots, c_N$ are suitable constants.

Particular solutions of the nonhomogeneous equation can frequently be found by guessing the general form of the solution and determining the parameters such that the equation is satisfied. A more generally applicable method is given by

Theorem 6.6′ Let $X^{(1)} = \{x_n^{(1)}\}, \ldots, X^{(N)} = \{x^{(N)}\}$ be N linearly independent solutions of the homogeneous equation $\mathscr{L}X = 0$, and let $W = \{w_n\}$ be the sequence of their Wronskian determinants. If $B = \{b_n\}$ is defined on the set of nonnegative integers, then a solution X of $\mathscr{L}X = B$ is given by

$$(6\text{-}21) \quad x_n = \sum_{m=0}^{n} \frac{\begin{vmatrix} x_n^{(1)} & x_n^{(2)} & \cdots & x_n^{(N)} \\ x_{m-1}^{(1)} & x_{m-1}^{(2)} & \cdots & x_{m-1}^{(N)} \\ \cdot & \cdot & \cdots & \cdot \\ x_{m-N+1}^{(1)} & x_{m-N+1}^{(2)} & \cdots & x_{m-N+1}^{(N)} \end{vmatrix}}{w_m} b_m.$$

Problem

18*. Let W denote the sequence of the Wronskian determinants of N solutions of $\mathscr{L}X = 0$. Find a linear difference equation of order 1 satisfied by W.

6.8 A System of Linearly Independent Solutions

To complete the discussion of the linear difference equation of order N with constant coefficients, we need to determine a system of N linearly independent solutions of the homogeneous equation $\mathscr{L}X = 0$. Special solutions of $\mathscr{L}X = 0$ can again be found by means of the characteristic polynomial

$$p(z) = z^N + a_1 z^{N-1} + \cdots + a_N$$

associated with the operator $\mathscr{L}$. If z is a zero of the characteristic polynomial, it is easy to see that the sequence $X = \{x_n\}$ defined by $x_n = z^n$ is a solution of $\mathscr{L}X = 0$, for we have

$$\begin{aligned}(\mathscr{L}X)_n &= x_n + a_1 x_{n-1} + \cdots + a_N x_{n-N} \\ &= z^n + a_1 z^{n-1} + \cdots + a_N z^{n-N} \\ &= z^{n-N} p(z) \\ &= 0.\end{aligned}$$

We now distinguish two cases.

(*i*) The polynomial p has N distinct zeros $z_1, z_2, \ldots, z_N$. Then the sequences $X^{(k)} = \{z_k^n\}$ ($k = 1, 2, \ldots, N$) represent N solutions of $\mathscr{L}X = 0$. Their Wronskian at $n = N - 1$ is

$$\begin{vmatrix} z_1^{N-1} & z_2^{N-1} & \cdots & z_N^{N-1} \\ z_1^{N-2} & z_2^{N-2} & \cdots & z_N^{N-2} \\ \cdot & \cdot & \cdot & \cdot \\ 1 & 1 & \cdots & 1 \end{vmatrix}.$$

This determinant is known to have the value

$$\prod_{m < n} (z_m - z_n) \neq 0.$$

It follows that the solutions found are linearly independent.

(*ii*) General case: The polynomial p has zeros of multiplicity > 1. The above method does not furnish sufficiently many solutions. However, further solutions can be found by differentiation. Let z be a zero of multiplicity $k + 1$ where $k > 0$. We then have

(6-22) $$p(z) = p'(z) = \cdots = p^{(k)}(z) = 0.$$

It was shown above that the sequence $X^{(0)} = \{z^n\}$ is a solution. We now assert that also the sequences $X^{(1)}, X^{(2)}, \ldots, X^{(k)}$ defined by

$$\begin{aligned} x_n^{(1)} &= nz^{n-1}, \\ x_n^{(2)} &= n(n-1)z^{n-2}, \\ &\cdot \quad \cdot \quad \cdot \quad \cdot \quad \cdot \quad \cdot \\ x_n^{(k)} &= n(n-1)\ldots(n-k+1)z^{n-k}, \end{aligned}$$

are solutions. Indeed, if $0 \leqq m \leqq k$, then

$$\begin{aligned}(\mathscr{L}X^{(m)})_n &= x_n^{(m)} + a_1 x_{n-1}^{(m)} + \cdots + a_N x_{n-N}^{(m)} \\ &= n(n-1)\ldots(n-m+1)z^{n-m} \\ &\quad + a_1(n-1)(n-2)\ldots(n-m)z^{n-m-1} \\ &\quad + \cdots \\ &\quad + a_N(n-N)(n-N-1)\ldots(n-N-m+1)z^{n-N-m} \\ &= (z^{n-N}p(z))^{(m)}.\end{aligned}$$

By the Leibnitz rule for differentiating a product (see Kaplan [1953], p. 19),

$$(z^{n-N}p(z))^{(m)} = \binom{m}{0}(n-N)(n-N-1)\ldots(n-N-m+1)z^{n-N-m}p(z)$$

$$+ \binom{m}{1}(n-N)\ldots(n-N-m+2)z^{n-N-m+1}p'(z)$$

$$+ \cdots$$

$$+ \binom{m}{m}z^{n-N}p^{(m)}(z),$$

which vanishes for all n, by (6-22).

We are thus led to the following analog of theorem 6.2:

Theorem 6.8 Let the characteristic polynomial of the Nth order equation $\mathscr{L}X = 0$ have the distinct zeros $z_1, z_2, \ldots, z_k$ ($k \leq N$), and let the multiplicity of z_i be $m_i + 1$ ($\sum m_i = N - k$). Then the sequences defined by

(6-23) $$x_n = n(n-1)\ldots(n-m+1)z_i^{n-m},$$
$$m = 0, 1, \ldots, m_i; \qquad i = 1, 2, \ldots, k$$

form a system of N linearly independent solutions of $\mathscr{L}X = 0$.

We omit the proof of the fact that the N solutions given by (6-23) are linearly independent.

EXAMPLES

12. Let

$$(\mathscr{L}X)_n = x_n - 2x_{n-2} + x_{n-4}.$$

The characteristic polynomial

$$p(z) = z^4 - 2z^2 + 1 = (z+1)^2(z-1)^2$$

has the two distinct zeros $z_1 = 1$, $z_2 = -1$, each with multiplicity 2. Theorem 6.8 thus yields the four solutions

$$x_n^{(1)} = 1, \qquad x_n^{(2)} = n, \qquad x_n^{(3)} = (-1)^n, \qquad x_n^{(4)} = (-1)^n n.$$

13. We shall show: If z is a zero of multiplicity 4 of the characteristic polynomial, then the sequence $X = \{n^3 z^n\}$ is a solution. Proof: We seek to represent X as a linear combination of the solutions given by theorem 6.8. We have

$$n(n-1)(n-2) = n^3 - 3n^2 + 2n$$
$$n(n-1) = \qquad n^2 - n$$
$$n = \qquad \qquad n$$

and hence
$$n^3 = n(n-1)(n-2) + 3n(n-1) + n.$$

Thus
$$n^3 z^n = z^3[n(n-1)(n-2)z^{n-3}] + 3z^2[n(n-1)z^{n-2}] + z[nz^{n-1}],$$

which is a combination of the desired form.

Example 13 leads us to conjecture the following fact:

Corollary 6.8 Under the hypotheses of theorem 6.8 a set of N independent solutions of $\mathscr{L}X = 0$ is also given by the sequences

(6-24) $x_n = n^m z_i^n, \qquad m = 0, 1, \ldots, m_i; \qquad i = 1, 2, \ldots, k.$

The proof that the sequences X defined by (6-24) are solutions boils down to showing that n^m can be written as a linear combination of

$$n, n(n-1), \ldots, n(n-1)\ldots(n-m+1),$$

with coefficients that are independent of n. This is readily verified by an induction argument. The proof that the N sequences given by (6-24) are linearly independent is again omitted.

EXAMPLE

14. To find the general solution of the difference equation

$$x_n - \binom{N}{1}x_{n-1} + \binom{N}{2}x_{n-2} - \cdots + (-1)^N\binom{N}{N}x_{n-N} = 0.$$

The characteristic polynomial is

$$p(z) = z^N - \binom{N}{1}z^{N-1} + \binom{N}{2}z^{N-2} - \cdots + (-1)^N.$$

As is known from the binomial theorem,

$$p(z) = (z-1)^N.$$

It follows that $z = 1$ is a zero of multiplicity N. Corollary 6.8 yields the solutions $1, n, n^2, \ldots, n^{N-1}$, and the general solution can be written in the form

$$x_n = c_0 + c_1 n + c_2 n^2 + \cdots + c_{N-1}n^{N-1}.$$

Problems

19. Let $N > 0$ be an integer. Find a general solution of the difference equation

$$x_n + x_{n-1} + x_{n-2} + \cdots + x_{n-N} = 0.$$

Deduce that for any real angle α and any integer m, $1 \le m \le N$, if $\varphi = 2\pi m/(N + 1)$,

$$\cos \alpha + \cos (\alpha + \varphi) + \cdots + \cos (\alpha + N\varphi) = 0,$$
$$\sin \alpha + \sin (\alpha + \varphi) + \cdots + \sin (\alpha + N\varphi) = 0.$$

20. Construct a difference equation that has the solutions

(a) $\qquad x_n = 1, \qquad x_n = 2^n, \qquad x_n = 3^n;$

(b) $\qquad x_n = n, \qquad x_n = n^2, \qquad x_n = n^3.$

Also find a difference equation that has both the solutions given under (a) and (b).

21*. Let $0 \le \varphi_k < 2\pi$, $k = 1, 2, \ldots, N$, $\varphi_k \ne \varphi_l$ for $k \ne l$, and let the numbers α_k be arbitrary. Show that the N sequences

$$X^{(k)} = \{e^{i(\alpha_k + n\varphi_k)}\}, \qquad k = 1, 2, \ldots, N$$

are linearly independent.

6.9 The Backward Difference Operator

An important special difference operator of the kind defined by (6-18) is the *backward difference operator*, traditionally denoted by ∇ (read "nabla" from the arabic word for harp) and defined by

(6-25) $\qquad (\nabla X)_n = x_n - x_{n-1}.$

This difference operator is of order 1. It is closely related to the forward difference operator Δ which was introduced in §4.4. In fact, we have

$$(\Delta X)_n = (\nabla X)_{n+1}.$$

Thus every relation valid for the forward difference operator can also be expressed in terms of the backward operator, and conversely. In the framework of our present notations it is a little more convenient to work with the backward operator.

Integral powers of the operator ∇ are defined inductively by the relation

(6-26) $\qquad \nabla^k X = \nabla(\nabla^{k-1} X), \qquad k = 2, 3, \ldots.$

EXAMPLE

15. $\nabla^2 X = \nabla(\nabla X)$, hence

$$\begin{aligned}
(\nabla^2 X)_n &= (\nabla X)_n - (\nabla X)_{n-1} \\
&= x_n - x_{n-1} - (x_{n-1} - x_{n-2}) \\
&= x_n - 2x_{n-1} + x_{n-2}.
\end{aligned}$$

The example suggests an explicit expression for $(\nabla^k X)_n$ in terms of binomial coefficients. In fact,

(6-27) $\qquad (\nabla^k X)_n = x_n - \binom{k}{1} x_{n-1} + \binom{k}{2} x_{n-2} - \cdots + (-1)^k \binom{k}{k} x_{n-k}.$

The proof of (6-27) is by induction with respect to k. By definition, the formula is true for $k = 1$. Assuming its truth for $k = m$, we have

$$(\nabla^{m+1}X)_n = (\nabla^m X)_n - (\nabla^m X)_{n-1}$$

$$= \left[x_n - \binom{m}{1}x_{n-1} + \binom{m}{2}x_{n-2} - \cdots + (-1)^m\binom{m}{m}x_{n-m} \right]$$

$$- \left[x_{n-1} - \binom{m}{1}x_{n-2} + \cdots + (-1)^{m-1}\binom{m}{m-1}x_{n-m} \right.$$

$$\left. + (-1)^m x_{n-m-1} \right]$$

By virtue of the identity (3-13) this expression simplifies to

$$x_n - \binom{m+1}{1}x_{n-1} + \binom{m+1}{2}x_{n-2} - \cdots + (-1)^{m+1}\binom{m+1}{m+1}x_{n-m-1},$$

which is equal to the term on the right of (6-27) when k is replaced by $m + 1$. Thus, (6-27) must be true for all positive integers k.

In practice, the operator ∇ is mainly used in connection with sequences F defined by

$$f_n = f(x_n),$$

where $x_n = nh$, h being a positive constant. One ordinarily writes ∇f_n in place of the logically more consistent, but cumbersome notation $(\nabla F)_n$. The values of successive powers of ∇ are conveniently arranged in a two-dimensional array, as in table 6.9a.

Table 6.9a

f_n			
	∇f_{n+1}		
f_{n+1}		$\nabla^2 f_{n+2}$	
	∇f_{n+2}		$\nabla^3 f_{n+3}$
f_{n+2}		$\nabla^2 f_{n+3}$	
	∇f_{n+3}		$\vdots$
f_{n+3}		$\vdots$	
	$\vdots$		
$\vdots$			

Table 6.9a is called the *difference table* of the function f, constructed with the step h. Each entry in the table is the difference of the two entries immediately to the left of it.

EXAMPLE

16. From Comrie's table of the exponential function $f(x) = e^x$ (Comrie [1961]), which has the step $h = 10^{-3}$, we can construct the following difference table (beginning at $x_n = 1.35$):

Table 6.9b

x_n	f_n	∇f_n	$\nabla^2 f_n$
1.350	3.857420		
		0.003859	
1.351	3.861285		0.000004
		0.003863	
1.352	3.865148		0.000004
		0.003867	
1.353	3.869015		

The study of properties and applications of the difference table, in particular the relation between differences and derivatives of a function, will be one of our chief concerns in part II. Here we are content with stating the following fundamental fact.

Theorem 6.9 Let the function f be defined on the whole real line, let k be a positive integer, and let $h > 0$. If $f_n = f(nh)$, a necessary and sufficient condition in order that

$$(6\text{-}28) \qquad \nabla^k f_n = 0$$

for all integers n is that $f(nh) = P(nh)$ for all n, where P is a polynomial of degree not exceeding $k - 1$.

Briefly, the theorem states that the kth differences of a function are identically zero if and only if, at the points where the differences are taken, the function agrees with a polynomial of degree $<k$.

Proof. We have to show: (a) If the kth differences are zero, then the values of f at $x = nh$ are those of a polynomial of degree $<k$; (b) If the values of f agree with those of a polynomial P of degree $<k$ at all points $x = nh$, then the kth differences are zero.

To prove (a), we note that (6-28) means that the sequence $F = \{f_n\}$ is a solution of the difference equation

$$(6\text{-}29) \qquad \nabla^k F = 0.$$

By (6-27), the characteristic polynomial of this equation is

$$p(z) = z^k - \binom{k}{1} z^{k-1} + \binom{k}{2} z^{k-2} - \cdots + (-1)^k \binom{k}{k}$$
$$= (z - 1)^k.$$

This polynomial has a single zero, of multiplicity k, at $z = 1$. By corollary 6.8, any solution of (6-29) can thus be represented in the form

$$f_n = c_1 + c_2 n + c_3 n^2 + \cdots + c_k n^{k-1}.$$

Clearly, $f_n = P(nh)$, where P is the polynomial defined by

$$P(x) = c_1 + \frac{c_2}{h} x + \frac{c_3}{h^2} x^2 + \cdots + \frac{c_k}{h^{k-1}} x^{k-1}.$$

To prove (b), let $f(x) = P(x)$ for $x = nh$, where P is a polynomial of degree $< k$,

$$P(x) = a_0 x^{k-1} + a_1 x^{k-2} + \cdots + a_{k-1}.$$

We then have

$$f_n = P(nh) = a_0(nh)^{k-1} + a_1(nh)^{k-2} + \cdots + a_{k-1}.$$

This relation shows that the sequence $F = \{f_n\}$ is a linear combination of the sequences $X^{(m)}$ defined by

$$X^{(m)} = n^m, \qquad m = 0, 1, 2, \ldots, k - 1.$$

These sequences are solutions of the difference equation $\nabla^k X = 0$, by corollary 6.8. It follows that the sequence F is a solution of the same difference equation, that is, (6-28) holds.

EXAMPLE

17. Let $P(x) = x^3 - 2x + 1$. The difference table with step $h = 1$ (begun at $x = 0$) is shown in table 6.9c.

Table 6.9c

1				
0	−1	6		
5	5	12	6	0
22	17	18	6	0
57	35	24	6	0
116	59	30	6	0
205	89	36	6	⋮
330	125	⋮	⋮	
⋮	⋮			

Problems

22. If $T = T(t)$ denotes the sequence of Chebyshev polynomials introduced in example 3, calculate

(a) $(\nabla^2 T(t))_{n+1}$,   (b) $(\nabla^4 T(t))_{n+2}$.

23. Give an explicit formula for the differences of the exponential function, $f(x) = e^x$, and show that these differences are never zero. Explain the apparent contradiction with the numerical values given in table 6.9b.

24. The first differences given in table 6.9b are very nearly equal to 10^{-3} times the average of the adjacent function values. Is this an accident?

25. Formula (6-27) expresses $(\nabla^k X)_n$ in terms of $x_n, x_{n-1}, \ldots, x_{n-k}$. Show conversely how to express x_{n-k} in terms of $(\nabla^0 X)_n, (\nabla X)_n, \ldots, (\nabla^k X)_n$.

Recommended Reading

A more thorough treatment of difference equations will be found in Milne-Thomson [1933]. Goldberg [1958] gives an enjoyable elementary account with many interesting applications.

Research Problem

Try to generalize as many results of this chapter as possible to linear difference equations with variable coefficients. Do not attempt to find solutions in explicit form.

chapter 7 Bernoulli's method

With the present chapter we return to the problem of solving nonlinear, and in particular polynomial, equations. The methods discussed in the chapters devoted to iteration are very effective, but only if a reasonable first approximation to the desired solution is known. How to obtain such a first approximation is a problem which, for equations without special properties, is of such generality that it cannot be solved by generally applicable rules or algorithms. For polynomials, however, there do exist algorithms that furnish the desired first approximation using no other information than the coefficients of the polynomial. Two such algorithms —a classical one due to D. Bernoulli and one of its modern extensions due to Rutishauser—form the subject of this and the next chapter. Bernoulli's method, in particular, is one which yields all *dominant* zeros of a polynomial. By a dominant zero we mean a zero whose modulus is not exceeded by the modulus of any other zero.

7.1 Single Dominant Zero

In chapter 6 we have seen how the general linear difference equation with constant coefficients can be solved analytically by determining the zeros of the associated characteristic polynomial. Bernoulli's method consists in reversing this procedure. The polynomial whose zeros are sought is considered the characteristic polynomial of some difference equation, and this associated difference equation is solved *numerically* by solving the recurrence relation implied by it. From this solution it is easy to extract information about the zeros of the polynomial, as we shall see.

To begin with the simplest case, let us assume that the polynomial of degree N,

$$(7\text{-}1) \qquad p(z) = a_0 z^N + a_1 z^{N-1} + \cdots + a_N,$$

146

whose coefficients may be complex, has N *distinct* zeros $z_1, z_2, \ldots, z_N$. What happens if we solve the difference equation

(7-2) $$a_0 x_n + a_1 x_{n-1} + \cdots + a_N x_{n-N} = 0$$

which has (7-1) as its characteristic polynomial? According to §6.7, the solution $X = \{x_n\}$ (whatever its starting values are) must be representable in the form

(7-3) $$x_n = c_1 z_1^n + c_2 z_2^n + \cdots + c_N z_N^n,$$

where $c_1, c_2, \ldots, c_N$ are suitable constants. To proceed further we make two assumptions:

(*i*) The polynomial p has a single dominant zero, i.e., one of the zeros— we may call it z_1—has a larger modulus than all the others:

(7-4) $$|z_1| > |z_k|, \qquad k = 2, 3, \ldots, N.$$

(*ii*) The starting values are such that the dominant zero is represented in the solution (7-3), i.e., we have

(7-5) $$c_1 \neq 0.$$

We now consider the ratio of two consecutive values of the solution sequence X. Using (7-3) we find

$$\frac{x_{n+1}}{x_n} = \frac{c_1 z_1^{n+1} + c_2 z_2^{n+1} + \cdots + c_N z_N^{n+1}}{c_1 z_1^n + c_2 z_2^n + \cdots + c_N z_N^n}.$$

By virtue of (7-5) this may be written

(7-6) $$\frac{x_{n+1}}{x_n} = z_1 \frac{1 + \dfrac{c_2}{c_1} \left(\dfrac{z_2}{z_1} \right)^{n+1} + \cdots + \dfrac{c_N}{c_1} \left(\dfrac{z_N}{z_1} \right)^{n+1}}{1 + \dfrac{c_2}{c_1} \left(\dfrac{z_2}{z_1} \right)^{n} + \cdots + \dfrac{c_N}{c_1} \left(\dfrac{z_N}{z_1} \right)^{n}}.$$

By (7-4), $|z_k/z_1| < 1$ for $k = 2, 3, \ldots, N$. It follows that

(7-7) $$\left(\frac{z_k}{z_1} \right)^n \to 0 \quad \text{as} \quad n \to \infty$$

for $k = 2, 3, \ldots, N$. The fraction multiplying z_1 thus tends to 1 as $n \to \infty$, and we find

$$\lim_{n \to \infty} \frac{x_{n+1}}{x_n} = z_1.$$

We thus have the following tentative formulation of Bernoulli's method:

Algorithm 7.1 Choose arbitrary values $x_0, x_{-1}, \ldots, x_{-N+1}$, and determine the sequence $\{x_n\}$ from the recurrence relation

$$x_n = -\frac{a_1 x_{n-1} + a_2 x_{n-2} + \cdots + a_N x_{n-N}}{a_0}, \qquad n = 1, 2, \ldots.$$

Then form the sequence of quotients

(7-8) $$q_n = \frac{x_{n+1}}{x_n}.$$

We have proved:

Theorem 7.1   If the polynomial p given by (7-1) has a single dominant zero, and if the starting values are such that (7-5) holds, then the quotients q_n are ultimately defined and converge to the dominant zero of p.

EXAMPLES

1. Applying Bernoulli's method to the polynomial

$$p(z) = z^2 - z - 1$$

with the starting values $x_0 = 1$, $x_{-1} = 0$ yields the *Fibonacci* sequence considered in example 7 of chapter 6.   Conditions (*i*) and (*ii*) are clearly satisfied here.   The ratios of consecutive elements thus converge to the dominant zero $z_1 = (1 + \sqrt{5})/2$.

2. Let

$$p(z) = 70z^4 - 140z^3 + 90z^2 - 20z + 1.$$

The difference equation (7-2) (solved for x_n) here takes the form

$$x_n = \frac{140x_{n-1} - 90x_{n-2} + 20x_{n-3} - x_{n-4}}{70}.$$

The first three columns of table 7.1 give the values of n, of the sequence x_n (started with $x_0 = 1$, $x_n = 0$, $n < 0$) and of the sequence $\{q_n\}$.   (The other columns will be explained in §7.2.)

The preceding is a mere outline of Bernoulli's method in the simplest possible case.   A number of complications have yet to be dealt with, such as the following:

1. Slow convergence.
2. Zeros of multiplicity > 1.
3. Unfortunate choice of initial values.
4. Several dominant zeros.
5. Calculation of nondominant zeros.

These questions will be dealt with in the subsequent sections.

Problems

1. Find, by Bernoulli's method, the dominant zero of the polynomial
$$p(z) = 32z^3 - 48z^2 + 18z - 1$$
to three significant digits.

Table 7.1

n	x_n	q_n	Δq_n	$\Delta^2 q_n$	$-\dfrac{(\Delta q_n)^2}{\Delta^2 q_n}$	q'_n
0	1					
1	2					
2	2.7142857					
3	3.1428571	1.1578947	−0.0910116		−0.1982597	0.9596350
4	3.3530611	1.0668831	−0.0492325	0.0417791	−0.1214233	0.9454595
5	3.4122447	1.0176506	−0.0292706	0.0199619	−0.0792746	0.9383760
6	3.3725945	0.9883800	−0.0184630	0.0108076	−0.0536856	0.9346444
7	3.2711367	0.9699170	−0.0121134	0.0063496	−0.0371658	0.9327512
8	3.1331066	0.9578036	−0.0081653	0.0039481		
9	2.9753180	0.9496383	−0.0056093	0.0025560		
10	2.8087866	0.9440290	−0.0039052	0.0017041		
11	2.6406071	0.9401238	−0.0027449	0.0011603		
12	2.4752493	0.9373789	−0.0019425	0.0008024		
13	2.3154382	0.9354364	−0.0013814	0.0005611		
14	2.1627466	0.9340550	−0.0009858	0.0003956	−0.0034633	0.9305917
15	2.0179923	0.9330692	−0.0007052	0.0002806	−0.0024890	0.9305802
16	1.8815034	0.9323640	−0.0005054	0.0001998		
17	1.7532951	0.9318586				
		. . .				. . .
		0.93057				0.93057

2. Use the value obtained in problem 1 to obtain the dominant zero to six significant digits, using either Newton's or Steffensen's method.

3. Look up the closed formula for finding the zeros of a cubic polynomial and use it to determine the dominant zero of the polynomial of problem 1.

4. What is the meaning of the phrase "the quotients are ultimately defined" in theorem 7.1? Give an example of a polynomial violating condition (i) where infinitely many of the quotients q_n are undefined.

7.2 Accelerating Convergence

Even if the conditions of convergence of Bernoulli's method are satisfied, the speed of convergence may be slow. By this we mean that the error of the approximation x_{n+1}/x_n to the zero z_1,

$$d_n = \frac{x_{n+1}}{x_n} - z_1$$

tends to zero only slowly. As in the case of iteration, it may be possible to speed up convergence by making judicious use of information about the *manner* in which d_n approaches zero. In order to discover this manner of convergence, we shall analyze the errors d_n more closely. We shall continue to make the assumptions (*i*) and (*ii*) of §7.1.   In addition, we assume that

(7-9) $$|z_1| > |z_2| > |z_k|, \qquad k = 3, 4, \ldots, N$$

(the next-to-dominant zero is the only zero of its modulus), and that

(7-10) $$c_2 \neq 0$$

in (7-3) (the next-to-dominant zero is represented in the solution $\{x_n\}$).
    Under these hypotheses, the error

$$d_n = \frac{c_1 z_1^{n+1} + c_2 z_2^{n+1} + \cdots + c_N z_N^{n+1} - z_1(c_1 z_1^n + \cdots + c_N z_N^n)}{c_1 z_1^n + c_2 z_2^n + \cdots + c_N z_N^n}$$

$$= \frac{c_2(z_2 - z_1)z_2^n + \cdots + c_N(z_N - z_1)z_N^n}{c_1 z_1^n + c_2 z_2^n + \cdots + c_N z_N^n}$$

can be written in the form

(7-11) $$d_n = A t^n (1 + \varepsilon_n),$$

where

$$A = \frac{c_2(z_2 - z_1)}{c_1}, \qquad t = \frac{z_2}{z_1},$$

and

$$1 + \varepsilon_n = \frac{1 + \dfrac{c_3(z_3 - z_1)}{c_2(z_2 - z_1)}\left(\dfrac{z_3}{z_2}\right)^n + \cdots + \dfrac{c_N(z_N - z_1)}{c_2(z_2 - z_1)}\left(\dfrac{z_N}{z_2}\right)^n}{1 + \dfrac{c_2}{c_1}\left(\dfrac{z_2}{z_1}\right)^n + \cdots + \dfrac{c_N}{c_1}\left(\dfrac{z_N}{z_1}\right)^N}.$$

By virtue of condition (7-9), we have, in addition to (7-7),

$$\left(\frac{z_k}{z_2}\right)^n \to 0 \quad \text{as} \quad n \to \infty$$

for $k = 3, 4, \ldots, N$, and the ratio on the right has the limit 1 as $n \to \infty$.
It follows that

(7-12) $$\lim_{n \to \infty} \varepsilon_n = 0.$$

As a consequence,

$$\frac{d_{n+1}}{d_n} = t\,\frac{1 + \varepsilon_{n+1}}{1 + \varepsilon_n} = t(1 + \delta_n),$$

where

$$\delta_n = \frac{\varepsilon_{n+1} - \varepsilon_n}{1 + \varepsilon_n} \to 0 \quad \text{as} \quad n \to \infty.$$

The errors d_n thus satisfy precisely the condition (4-12) of theorem 4.5 which makes Aitken's Δ^2 process effective. We thus have as an immediate consequence of theorem 4.5:

Theorem 7.2 Under the hypotheses stated at the beginning of the present section, the sequence $\{q_n'\}$ derived from the sequence $\{q_n\}$ by means of Aitken's Δ^2 formula,

$$q_n' = q_n - \frac{(\Delta q_n)^2}{\Delta^2 q_n},$$

converges faster to the dominant zero z_1 than the sequence $\{q_n\}$ in the sense that

$$\lim_{n \to \infty} \frac{q_n' - z_1}{q_n - z_1} = 0.$$

EXAMPLE

3. In table 7.1 the values q_n' are shown in the last column. Also given are the intermediate values required to calculate q_n'. The faster convergence of the sequence $\{q_n'\}$ to the exact zero $z_1 = 0.93057$ is evident.

Problems

5. Find, by Bernoulli's method speeded up by the Δ^2 process, the dominant zero of the polynomial

$$p(z) = z^4 - 7z^3 + 13z^2 - 8z + 12.$$

6. Apply the Δ^2 method to the sequence $\{q_n\}$ obtained in problem 1.

7. Explain why the Δ^2 method does not speed up appreciably the Bernoulli sequence for the polynomial

$$p(z) = z^3 - 4z^2 + 6z - 4.$$

($z = 2$ is the sole dominant zero.)

8. If suitable conditions are satisfied, the error of the sequence $\{q_n\}$ generated by Bernoulli's method tends to zero like $(z_2/z_1)^n$. How does the error of the accelerated sequence $\{q_n'\}$ tend to zero? What do you conclude about the number of steps necessary to achieve a given accuracy
(a) if $|z_1| \sim |z_2| \gg |z_3|$,
(b) if $|z_1| \gg |z_2| \sim |z_3|$?

7.3 Zeros of Higher Multiplicity

If the polynomial p has repeated nondominant zeros $z_2, \ldots, z_N$, then formula (7-3) for the general solution of the difference equation (7-2) also contains (by corollary 6.8) terms like $n^k z_2^n$. Thus the expression (7-6) contains terms like

$$n^k \left(\frac{z_2}{z_1}\right)^n \text{ in addition to } \left(\frac{z_2}{z_1}\right)^n.$$

However, these terms cannot disturb the convergence of the method, since if $|q| < 1$, then we have not only $q^n \to 0$ as $n \to \infty$ but also $n^k q^n \to 0$ for any fixed value of k.

The situation is different if the *dominant* zero has multiplicity > 1. (We still assume that there is only one dominant zero.) To fix ideas, let the multiplicity be 2. Relation (7-3) then takes the form

$$x_n = c_1 n z_1^n + c_2 z_1^n + c_3 z_3^n + \cdots,$$

where $|z_3| < |z_1|$. Thus the ratio (7-6) now becomes (still assuming $c_1 \neq 0$)

$$(7\text{-}13) \quad \frac{x_{n+1}}{x_n} = \frac{c_1(n+1)z_1^{n+1} + c_2 z_1^{n+1} + c_3 z_3^{n+1} + \cdots}{c_1 n z_1^n + c_2 z_1^n + c_3 z_3^n + \cdots}$$

$$= z_1 \frac{(n+1)c_1 + c_2}{nc_1 + c_2} \cdot \frac{1 + \dfrac{c_3}{(n+1)c_1 + c_2}\left(\dfrac{z_3}{z_1}\right)^{n+1} + \cdots}{1 + \dfrac{c_3}{nc_1 + c_2}\left(\dfrac{z_3}{z_1}\right)^n + \cdots}.$$

Convergence still takes place, but, due to the factor

$$\frac{(n+1)c_1 + c_2}{nc_1 + c_2} = 1 + \frac{1}{n + c_2/c_1}$$

at a much slower rate; the error after n steps is now of the order of $1/n$ as against $(z_1/z_2)^n$ if the dominant zero has multiplicity one. An example for this slowdown of convergence, as well as a possible remedy, is given in the following section.

Problems

9. Devise an Aitken-like acceleration scheme for the case of a single dominant zero of multiplicity 2. [Sketch of a possible solution: From (7-13) we find for the error $d_n = q_n - z_1$

$$d_n = \frac{c_1 z_1 + 0(t^n)}{c_1 n + c_2 + 0(t^n)},$$

where $t = z_3/z_1$. Neglecting $0(t^n)$ and setting $c = c_2/c_1$, we have

$$(7\text{-}14) \qquad\qquad q_n - z_1 = \frac{z_1}{n + c}.$$

The unknowns c and, if desired, n can be eliminated from consecutive relations (7-14) as in the derivation of Aitken's formula, yielding a formula for z_1.]

10. Apply the procedure devised in problem 9 to the calculation of the dominant zero of the polynomial

$$p(z) = z^4 - 4z^3 - 2z^2 + 12z + 9.$$

7.4   Choice of Starting Values

One of the conditions for convergence of algorithm 7.1 was that $c_1 \neq 0$. It can be shown by means of complex variable theory that this condition is always satisfied if the starting values are chosen as follows:

$$(7\text{-}15) \qquad x_{-N+1} = x_{-N+2} = \cdots = x_{-1} = 0, \qquad x_0 = 1.$$

A different, more sophisticated choice of starting values is defined by the following algorithm:

Algorithm 7.4   If the coefficients $a_0, a_1, \ldots, a_N$ are given, calculate $x_0, x_1, \ldots, x_{N-1}$ by the formulas

$$x_0 = -\frac{a_1}{a_0},$$

$$x_1 = -\frac{1}{a_0}(2a_2 + a_1 x_0),$$

$$x_2 = -\frac{1}{a_0}(3a_3 + a_2 x_0 + a_1 x_1),$$

and generally

$$(7\text{-}16) \quad x_k = -\frac{1}{a_0}[(k+1)a_{k+1} + a_k x_0 + a_{k-1}x_1 + \cdots + a_1 x_{k-1}],$$

$$k = 1, 2, \ldots, N-1.$$

The starting values generated by algorithm 7.4 have the following very desirable property:

Theorem 7.4   Let the polynomial $p(z) = a_0 z^N + a_1 z^{N-1} + \cdots + a_N$ have the distinct zeros $z_1, z_2, \ldots, z_M$ ($M \leq N$), and let the multiplicity of z_i be m_i ($i = 1, 2, \ldots, M$). If the starting values for Bernoulli's method are determined by algorithm 7.4, then relation (7-3) takes the form

$$(7\text{-}17) \qquad x_n = m_1 z_1^{n+1} + m_2 z_2^{n+1} + \cdots + m_M z_M^{n+1}, \qquad n = 0, 1, \ldots.$$

The proof is again most easily accomplished by complex variable theory, and is omitted here.   Relation (7-17) is remarkable for the fact that no powers of n appear, notwithstanding the possible presence of zeros of multiplicity higher than 1.   The difficulty mentioned in §7.3 thus can always be avoided by a proper choice of the starting values.   The ratio x_{n+1}/x_n then converges at a rate determined only by the magnitude of the two largest zeros.

EXAMPLE

4. We compare the sequences $\{q_n\}$ for the polynomial

$$p(z) = (z - 3)^2(z + 1)^2 = z^4 - 4z^3 - 2z^2 + 12z + 9,$$

generated by starting Bernoulli's method by (7-15) and by algorithm 7.4. The recurrence relation is in both cases

$$x_n = 4x_{n-1} + 2x_{n-2} - 12x_{n-3} - 9x_{n-4}.$$

Table 7.4

	Method (7.15)		Algorithm 7.4	
n	x_n	q_n	x_n	q_n
−3	0			
−2	0			
−1	0			
0	1		4	
1	4	4	20	5
2	18	4.5	52	2.6
3	68	3.78	164	3.15385
4	251	3.69	484	2.95122
5	888	3.54	1 460	3.01653
6	3 076	3.46	4 372	2.99452
7	10 456	3.40	13 124	3.00183
8	35 061	3.35	39 364	2.99939
9	116 252	3.32	118 100	3.00020
10	381 974	3.29	354 292	2.99993
11	1 245 564	3.26086	1 062 884	3.00002
12	4 035 631	3.24000	3 188 644	2.99999
13	13 003 696	3.22222	9 565 940	3.0000025
14	41 701 512	3.20690	28 697 812	2.9999992
		. . .		. . .
		3.00000		3.0000000

Problems

11. Use algorithm 7.4 to obtain starting values for the application of Bernoulli's method to the polynomial of problem 10. Verify relation (7-17).

12. Using Vieta's formulas, verify (7-17) for $n = 0$ and $n = 1$ in the case of an arbitrary polynomial.

13. Show that if the rational function

$$r(z) = -\frac{a_1 + 2a_2 z + \cdots + Na_N z^{N-1}}{a_0 + a_1 z + a_2 z^2 + \cdots + a_N z^N}$$

is expanded in powers of z, then the coefficients of $1, z, \ldots, z^{N-1}$ are identical with the numbers $x_0, x_1, \ldots, x_{N-1}$ defined by algorithm 7.4.

7.5 Two Conjugate Complex Dominant Zeros

The theory developed so far holds equally well whether the coefficients of the polynomial p are real or complex. However, we have always assumed that z_1 is the sole dominant zero of p. Let us now consider the case where p is a polynomial with real coefficients which has a pair of complex conjugate dominant zeros z_1 and $z_2 = \bar{z}_1$, both of multiplicity one. The remaining zeros shall satisfy

(7-18) $$|z_k| < |z_1|, \qquad k = 3, 4, \ldots, N;$$

for the purpose of our analysis we assume that the nondominant zeros, too, have multiplicity one, although this is not essential for the result.

If the starting values for the sequence $\{x_n\}$ are real, equation (7-3) takes the form

$$x_n = c_1 z_1^n + \bar{c}_1 \bar{z}_1^n + c_3 z_3^n + \cdots + c_N z_N^n.$$

Representing the complex numbers c_1 and z_1 in polar form, we write $z_1 = re^{i\varphi}$, $c_1 = ae^{i\delta}$, where $r > 0$ and $a > 0$. We may assume, furthermore, that z_1 is the zero in the upper half-plane, and consequently $0 < \varphi < \pi$. The expression for x_n now becomes

$$x_n = 2ar^n \cos(n\varphi + \delta) + c_3 z_3^n + \cdots + c_N z_N^n,$$

This may be written

(7-19) $$x_n = 2ar^n[\cos(n\varphi + \delta) + \theta_n],$$

where

$$\theta_n = \frac{c_3}{2a}\left(\frac{z_3}{r}\right)^n + \cdots + \frac{c_N}{2a}\left(\frac{z_N}{r}\right)^n.$$

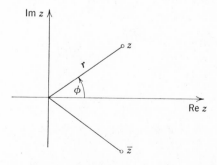

Figure 7.5

and hence, for some suitable constant C,

$$|\theta_n| \leq Ct^n,$$

where t denotes the largest of the ratios $|z_k/r|$, $k = 3, \ldots, N$. In view of (7-18), the number t is less than 1, and hence

$$(7\text{-}20) \qquad\qquad \lim_{n \to \infty} \theta_n = 0.$$

Our problem is to recover the quantities r and φ from the sequence $\{x_n\}$. To find its solution, let us begin by assuming that $\theta_n = 0$. We recall that the sequence $\{x_n\}$ with the elements

$$x_n = 2ar^n \cos(n\varphi + \delta)$$

is a solution of the difference equation

$$(7\text{-}21) \qquad\qquad x_n + Ax_{n-1} + Bx_{n-2} = 0,$$

where $B = r^2$, $A = -2r \cos \varphi$ (see problem 3, chapter 6). To determine the coefficients A and B from the known solution $\{x_n\}$, we observe that equation (7-21) together with the corresponding equation with n increased by 1,

$$x_{n+1} + Ax_n + Bx_{n-1} = 0$$

represents a system of two linear equations for the two unknowns A and B. The determinant

$$(7\text{-}22) \qquad\qquad D_n = \begin{vmatrix} x_{n-1} & x_{n-2} \\ x_n & x_{n-1} \end{vmatrix}$$

equals, by a trigonometric identity,

$$4a^2 r^{2n-2}\{\cos^2[(n-1)\varphi + \delta] - \cos(n\varphi + \delta)\cos[(n-2)\varphi + \delta]\}$$

$$= 4a^2 r^{2n-2} \sin^2 \varphi,$$

and hence is different from zero, as $0 < \varphi < \pi$. We may thus solve for A and B, finding

$$A = -\frac{E_n}{D_n}, \qquad B = \frac{D_{n+1}}{D_n},$$

where

$$(7\text{-}23) \qquad\qquad E_n = \begin{vmatrix} x_n & x_{n-2} \\ x_{n+1} & x_{n-1} \end{vmatrix}.$$

The desired quantities r and φ can now be found by

$$(7\text{-}24) \qquad r = \sqrt{B} = \sqrt{\frac{D_{n+1}}{D_n}}, \qquad \cos \varphi = -\frac{A}{2r} = \frac{E_n}{2\sqrt{D_n D_{n+1}}}.$$

The relations (7-24) solve our problem if $\{x_n\}$ is a solution of the difference equation (7-2) such that $\theta_n = 0$ in (7-19). If $\{x_n\}$ is any solution of (7-2), $\theta_n \neq 0$ in general; however, using (7-20) it is not too hard to show that

(7-25) $$\frac{D_{n+1}}{D_n} \to r^2, \qquad \frac{E_n}{2D_n} \to r \cos \varphi$$

as $n \to \infty$. We thus have obtained the convergence of the following algorithm for the determination of a pair of complex conjugate dominant zeros.

Algorithm 7.5   From the solution $\{x_n\}$ of the difference equation (7-2), calculate the determinants D_n and E_n defined by (7-22) and (7-23). With these, form the sequence of ratios D_{n+1}/D_n and $E_n/2D_n$.

The corresponding convergence theorem is as follows:

Theorem 7.5   Let the polynomial (7-1) have exactly two dominant zeros $z_{1,2} = re^{\pm i\varphi}$, both of multiplicity one, where $0 < \varphi < \pi$. If the solution of the difference equation (7-2) is such that $c_1 \neq 0$ in (7-3), then the limit relations (7-25) hold.

EXAMPLE

5.   For the polynomial

$$p(z) = 81z^4 - 108z^3 + 24z + 20$$

(exact dominant zeros: $z_{1,2} = 1 \pm i\frac{1}{3}$) the computation proceeds as in table 7.5. It is evidently unnecessary to calculate the determinants D_n and E_n from the beginning.

Algorithm 7.5 has the disadvantage of not being very accurate when φ, the argument of the dominant zero, is small. Let us assume that we have determined r accurately and $x = r \cos \varphi = \lim E_n/2D_n$ with an error dx. We then have to calculate φ from the relation

$$\cos \varphi = \frac{x}{r}$$

and find for the differential of φ

$$d\varphi = -\frac{1}{r \sin \varphi} dx.$$

For small values of φ this may be quite large even for a small value of dx.

Problems

14. Determine the dominant zeros of the polynomial

$$p(z) = z^3 - z^2 + 2$$

to three decimal places.

Table 7.5

x_n	D_n	D_{n+1}/D_n	E_n	$E_n/2D_n$
1				
1.333333				
1.777778				
2.074074				
2.123457				
1.975309				
1.580247				
0.965707				
0.178022				
−0.718589				
−1.634438				
−2.470444				
−3.124966				
−3.504914	1.229324	1.111187	2.458740	1.000037
−3.537670	1.366009	1.111125	2.732037	1.000006
−3.180991	1.517807	1.111095	3.035585	0.999990
−2.431232	1.686428	1.111115	3.372868	1.000003
−1.328033	1.873816	1.111111	3.747630	0.999999
0.045304	2.082018	1.111113	4.164035	1.000000
1.566200	2.313358		4.626705	
		. . .		. . .
		1.111111		1.000000

15. Starting from the exact representation (7-19) of x_n, prove the relations (7-25).
16. Devise a modification of Bernoulli's method for the case that the polynomial p has two real dominant zeros, both of multiplicity one, of opposite signs, and apply your algorithm to the polynomial

$$p(z) = z^4 - 2z^3 - 2z^2 + 8z - 8.$$

7.6   Sign Waves†

How can we detect a pair of conjugate complex zeros? Formula (7-19) shows that in the presence of a pair of conjugate complex dominant zeros the elements of the sequence $\{x_n\}$ behave like

$$(7-26) \qquad x_n = 2ar^n \cos{(n\varphi + \delta)}.$$

This equation implies, in particular, that the signs of the x_n oscillate. Moreover, by looking at the frequency with which these oscillations occur,

---

† This section may be omitted at first reading.

we can hope to be able to make a statement about the angle φ. Clearly, when φ is small, the "sign waves" are long, and when φ is close to π, they are short. (In the extreme case, where $\varphi = \pi$, plus and minus signs alternate in strict order.)

In order to establish a more precise result, let us assume that the polynomial p has degree 2. Equation (7-26) then is exact; we now write it in the form

$$(7\text{-}27) \qquad x_n = 2ar^n \sin\left(n\varphi + \delta + \frac{\pi}{2}\right).$$

If n were a continuous variable, the signs of x_n would change from minus to plus whenever

$$n\varphi + \delta + \frac{\pi}{2} = 2k\pi,$$

where k is any integer. Let now, for any positive integer k, n_k be the first integer following the kth change of sign from minus to plus of the sine-function in (7-27), i.e., let

$$(7\text{-}28) \qquad n_k = \frac{2k\pi - \delta - \dfrac{\pi}{2}}{\varphi} + \theta_k,$$

where $0 \leqq \theta_k < 1$. This means that for each positive integer k,

$$\text{sign } x_{n_k-1} = -1, \qquad \text{sign } x_{n_k} = 0 \quad \text{or} \quad 1.$$

Now subtract from (7-28) the corresponding relation for $k = 0$. We find, after dividing by k,

$$\frac{n_k - n_0}{k} = \frac{2\pi}{\varphi} + \frac{\theta_k - \theta_0}{k}.$$

We now consider the limit of this expression as $k \to \infty$. Since the θ_k are numbers between zero and one,

$$\lim_{k \to \infty} \frac{\theta_k - \theta_0}{k} = 0.$$

It follows that

$$T = \lim_{k \to \infty} \frac{n_k - n_0}{k}$$

exists and has the value $2\pi/\varphi$. Solving for φ, we find

$$(7\text{-}29) \qquad \varphi = \frac{2\pi}{T}.$$

The limit T appearing here has a very simple interpretation. The integer $n_k - n_{k-1}$ represents the length or period of the kth sign wave in the sequence of signs of the x_n. By virtue of the identity

$$n_k - n_0 = (n_k - n_{k-1}) + (n_{k-1} - n_{k-2}) + \cdots + (n_1 - n_0),$$

the expression $n_k - n_0$ is the sum of the periods of all sign waves from the first to the kth. Hence T is just the average period of all sign waves.

We thus have obtained the following algorithm for the determination of the arguments of a pair of complex conjugate dominant zeros.

Algorithm 7.6 In the sequence $\{x_n\}$ generated by algorithm 7.1, delete everything but the signs† of the x_n. For $k = 0, 1, 2, \ldots$, let n_k be the index of the kth + which is preceded by a −, and calculate the average value of all sign wave periods $n_k - n_{k-1}$.

Although our analysis applies only to polynomials of degree 2, the following result can be proved for polynomials of arbitrary degree (Brown [1962]).

Theorem 7.6 Under the hypotheses of theorem 7.5, the argument φ is given by (7-29), where T denotes the average sign wave period.

In electrical engineering, the quantity $2\pi/T$ is called the circular frequency of an alternating current with period T. In this sense we can say that φ is equal to the circular frequency of the sequence of signs of the x_n.

EXAMPLE

6. For the polynomial

$$p(z) = z^4 - 8z^3 + 39z^2 - 62z + 50$$
$$= (z^2 - 2z + 2)(z^2 - 6z + 25)$$

the sequence of signs of the x_n turned out as follows:

```
+ + − − − − + + + − − − + + + + − − − + + + + − − − − + + + − − − − −
        6           7             7             7
+ + + − − − + + + − − − − + + + + − − − + + + − − − − − + + + ···
    6         7               7             7
```

The average length of the periods of the full sign waves recorded above is 6.75. We thus find the approximate value

$$\varphi = \frac{2\pi}{6.75} \sim 53{,}3°.$$

The exact value is

$$\varphi = \text{arctg } \tfrac{4}{3} \sim 53{,}1°.$$

---

† A zero may be considered positive or negative.

It is only fair to point out that, in spite of the favorable showing in example 6, the convergence of algorithm 7.6 is rather slow in general. The algorithm is not useful for purposes of exact numerical computation, but it does give very quickly, with almost no computation, an idea about the location of a pair of complex conjugate zeros.

Problems

17. Bernoulli's method is applied unsuspectedly to the polynomial

$$p(z) = z^4 + 2z^3 + 4z^2 - 2z - 5.$$

Show that the polynomial has a pair of complex conjugate dominant zeros.   In which quadrants of the plane do they lie?

18. Algorithm 7.6 fails for the polynomial

$$p(z) = z^3 - 2z^2 + 2z - 1.$$

Explain!   [Hint: How many dominant zeros are there?]

19. Devise an algorithm for removing a quadratic factor $z^2 - uz - v$ from a given polynomial.   [Hint: Write $p(z) = (z^2 - uz - v)q(z)$ and compare coefficients of like powers of z, as in §4.10.]

20. Verify that $z^2 - 3.711245z + 3.728699$ is (approximately) a quadratic factor of the polynomial

$$p(z) = z^5 - 3z^4 - 20z^3 + 60z^2 - z - 78$$

and remove it from p by the algorithm devised in problem 19.

Recommended Reading

Bernoulli's method, and some extensions of it, are dealt with by Aitken [1926]; other accounts are given in Householder [1953] and Hildebrand [1956], pp. 458–462.   An entirely different procedure for determining the dominant zeros of a polynomial is known as Graeffe's method.   It is dealt with in the above standard numerical analysis texts; see also Ostrowski [1940] and Bareiss [1960].   A complete account of modern automatic procedures for polynomials is given by Wilkinson [1959].

Research Problems

1. How does the presence of more than two dominant zeros manifest itself in the sequence of signs of the x_n, and how can the arguments be recovered?

2. Suppose a polynomial has exactly three dominant zeros, one real, two complex conjugate.   Devise a modification of Bernoulli's method that deals with this situation.

chapter 8   the quotient-difference algorithm

Bernoulli's method has the disadvantage of furnishing only the dominant zeros of a polynomial. If it is desired to compute a non-dominant zero by Bernoulli's method, it is necessary first to compute all larger zeros, and then to remove them from the polynomial by the method of §4.10. Only rarely these zeros will be known exactly. Thus the successive deflations will have a tendency to falsify the remaining zeros. We now shall discuss a modern extension of Bernoulli's method, due to Rutishauser, which has the advantage of providing simultaneous approximations to *all* zeros. Since the prerequisites for this volume do not include complex function theory, we are unable to provide the proofs for the convergence theorems in this chapter. But even though its theoretical background cannot be fully exposed, we feel that Rutishauser's algorithm is of sufficient interest to warrant its presentation at this point.

8.1   The Quotient-Difference Scheme

The Quotient-Difference (QD) algorithm can be looked at as a generalization of Bernoulli's method. As in chapter 7, we are given a polynomial

$$(8\text{-}1) \qquad p(z) = a_0 z^N + a_1 z^{N-1} + \cdots + a_N$$

and form a solution of the associated difference equation

$$(8\text{-}2) \qquad a_0 x_n + a_1 x_{n-1} + \cdots + a_N x_{n-N} = 0.$$

The sequence $\{x_n\}$ may for instance be started by setting

$$(8\text{-}3) \qquad x_{-N+1} = x_{-N+2} = \cdots = x_{-1} = 0; \qquad x_0 = 1.$$

In chapter 7 we now formed the quotients

$$(8\text{-}4) \qquad q_n = \frac{x_{n+1}}{x_n} = q_n^{(1)}.$$

If the polynomial p has a single dominant zero, then, as was shown in chapter 7, the sequence $\{q_n\}$ converges to it.

The elements of the sequence $\{q_n\}$ will now be denoted by $q_n^{(1)}$; they form the first column of the two-dimensional scheme called the Quotient-Difference (QD) scheme. The elements of the remaining columns are conventionally denoted by $e_n^{(1)}, q_n^{(2)}, e_n^{(2)}, q_n^{(3)}, \ldots, e_n^{(N-1)}, q_n^{(N)}$ and are generated by alternately forming differences and quotients, as follows:

(8-5a)
$$e_n^{(k)} = (q_{n+1}^{(k)} - q_n^{(k)}) + e_{n+1}^{(k-1)},$$

(8-5b)
$$q_n^{(k+1)} = \frac{e_{n+1}^{(k)}}{e_n^{(k)}} q_{n+1}^{(k)},$$

where $k = 1, 2, \ldots, N - 1$, $n = 0, 1, 2, \ldots$. In (8-5a) we set $e_n^{(0)} = 0$ when $k = 1$. The number of q columns formed is equal to the degree of the given polynomial.

EXAMPLE

1. For $N = 4$, the general QD scheme looks as follows:

$$
\begin{array}{ccccccccc}
& q_0^{(1)} & & & & & & & \\
0 & & e_0^{(1)} & & & & & & \\
& q_1^{(1)} & & q_0^{(2)} & & & & & \\
0 & & e_1^{(1)} & & e_0^{(2)} & & & & \\
& q_2^{(1)} & & q_1^{(2)} & & q_0^{(3)} & & & \\
0 & & e_2^{(1)} & & e_1^{(2)} & & e_0^{(3)} & & \\
& q_3^{(1)} & & q_2^{(2)} & & q_1^{(3)} & & q_0^{(4)} & \\
0 & & e_3^{(1)} & & e_2^{(2)} & & e_1^{(3)} & & \\
& q_4^{(1)} & & q_3^{(2)} & & q_2^{(3)} & & q_1^{(4)} & \\
& \vdots & e_4^{(1)} & \vdots & e_3^{(2)} & \vdots & e_2^{(3)} & \vdots & \\
& & \vdots & & \vdots & & \vdots & &
\end{array}
$$

Scheme 8.1

In each column of the scheme the superscripts are constant, and in each diagonal the subscripts. The rules (8-5) can be memorized by observing that in each of the rhombus-like configurations shown in the scheme either the sums or the products of the SW and of the NE pair of elements are equal. If a rhombus is centered in a q column, sums are equal; if it is centered in an e column, products are equal. In view of this interpretation the formulas (8-5) are occasionally referred to as the *rhombus rules*.

The QD scheme can be described in yet another way if we introduce, in addition to the forward difference operator already introduced in §4.4, the quotient operator Q defined by

$$Qx_n = \frac{x_{n+1}}{x_n}.$$

The relations (8-5) then can be written more compactly thus:

$$(8\text{-}6) \qquad e_n^{(k)} = e_{n+1}^{(k-1)} + \Delta q_n^{(k)}, \qquad q_n^{(k+1)} = q_{n+1}^{(k)} Q e_n^{(k)}.$$

Here it must be understood that the operators Δ and Q act on the *sub*script.

EXAMPLE

2. We conclude this section with the numerical QD scheme for the polynomial

$$p(z) = z^2 - z - 1.$$

The sequence $\{x_n\}$ is the Fibonacci sequence (see example 7, §6.3).

Table 8.1

x_n	$e_n^{(0)}$	$q_n^{(1)}$	$e_n^{(1)}$	$q_n^{(2)}$	$e_n^{(2)}$
1	0				
		1.000000			
1	0		1.000000		
		2.000000		-1.000000	
2	0		-0.500000		-0.000001
		1.500000		-0.500001	
3	0		0.166667		-0.000001
		1.666667		-0.666669	
5	0		-0.066667		0.000002
		1.600000		-0.600000	
8	0		0.025000		0.000025
		1.625000		-0.624975	
13	0		-0.009615		-0.000049
		1.615385		-0.615409	
21	0		0.003663		-0.000171
		1.619048		-0.619243	
34	0		-0.001401		
		1.617647			
55	0				
		$\cdots$		$\cdots$	
		$\downarrow$		$\downarrow$	
		$\dfrac{1 + \sqrt{5}}{2}$		?	

Problems

1. Generate the QD scheme for the polynomial $p(z) = z^3 + 5x^2 + 9z + 5$.
2. Let $x_n = n!$, $n = 0, 1, 2, \ldots$. Determine the QD scheme corresponding to the sequence $\{x_n\}$ (a) numerically, (b) analytically. (The sequence $\{x_n\}$ does not arise as solution of a difference equation in this case.)
3. Give analytical formulas for the entries of the QD scheme, if $x_n = 1 + q^n$, where $0 < |q| < 1$. Show that

$$\lim_{n \to \infty} q_n^{(1)} = 1, \qquad \lim_{n \to \infty} e_n^{(1)} = 0, \qquad \lim_{n \to \infty} q_n^{(2)} = q,$$

and that $e_n^{(2)} = 0$ for all n.

8.2 Existence of the QD Scheme

Evidently the QD scheme fails to exist if a coefficient $e_n^{(k)}$ with $0 < k < N$ becomes zero, and it is easy to construct examples for which this actually occurs. Another, trivial, case of nonexistence of the scheme arises when a x_n becomes accidentally zero. It appears to be difficult to state explicit necessary and sufficient conditions for the existence of the scheme in terms of the polynomial p. In terms of the sequence $\{x_n\}$, a necessary and sufficient condition is that the determinants

(8-7)
$$
H_n^{(k)} = \begin{vmatrix}
x_n & x_{n+1} & \cdots & x_{n+k-1} \\
x_{n+1} & x_{n+2} & \cdots & x_{n+k} \\
\cdot & \cdot & \cdots & \cdot \\
x_{n+k-1} & x_{n+k} & \cdots & x_{n+2k-2}
\end{vmatrix}
$$

should be different from zero for $k = 1, 2, \ldots, N$ and for $n = 0, 1, 2, \ldots$. It is possible to state simple *sufficient* (but not necessary) conditions for this to be the case. Among them are the following:

(*i*) The zeros $z_1, z_2, \ldots, z_N$ of p are positive, and the sequence $\{x_n\}$ is started by algorithm 7.4.

(*ii*) The zeros $z_1, z_2, \ldots, z_N$ of p are simple (but not necessarily real) and have distinct absolute values:

(8-8)
$$
|z_1| > |z_2| > \cdots > |z_N| > 0.
$$

In case (*ii*) we can assert only that $H_n^{(k)} \neq 0$, and consequently $e_n^{(k)} \neq 0$, for all sufficiently large values of n.

There is a good deal of numerical evidence that the QD scheme exists in many cases even if neither of the above sufficient conditions is satisfied, for instance if p is a polynomial with real coefficients having pairs of complex conjugate zeros.

Problems

4. Show that

$$
q_n^{(1)} = \frac{H_{n+1}^{(1)}}{H_n^{(1)}}, \qquad e_n^{(1)} = \frac{H_n^{(2)}}{H_n^{(1)} H_{n+1}^{(1)}}, \qquad q_n^{(2)} = \frac{H_{n+1}^{(2)} H_n^{(1)}}{H_n^{(2)} H_{n+1}^{(1)}}.
$$

5. Show that the determinants $H_n^{(1)}$ and $H_n^{(2)}$ formed with the elements $x_n = 1 + q^n$, where $0 < |q| < 1$, are always different from zero.

6. Let $x_n = r^n \cos(n\varphi + \delta)$, where $0 < \varphi < \pi$. Show that the corresponding determinants $H_n^{(2)}$ are always different from zero. What are the conditions on φ and δ in order that $H_n^{(1)} \neq 0$ for all n?

8.3   Convergence Theorems

If the QD scheme exists, some remarkable statements are possible about the limits of its elements as $n \to \infty$. The simplest situation arises if the zeros of the polynomial p satisfy (8-8). We then have

Theorem 8.3a   Under the conditions just stated,

$$(8\text{-}9) \qquad \lim_{n \to \infty} q_n^{(k)} = z_k, \qquad k = 1, 2, \ldots, N,$$

i.e., the kth q-column of the QD scheme converges to the kth zero of the polynomial.

It follows from (8-9) by virtue of (8-5a) that

$$\lim_{n \to \infty} e_n^{(1)} = 0,$$

and from this we get easily by induction

$$(8\text{-}10) \qquad \lim_{n \to \infty} e_n^{(k)} = 0, \qquad k = 1, 2, \ldots, N - 1.$$

Thus, under the condition (8-8), all e-columns of the QD scheme tend to zero.

EXAMPLE

3.   In table 8.1 the column headed $q_n^{(2)}$ tends to $(1 - \sqrt{5})/2$, the smaller zero of $p(z) = z^2 - z - 1$. (Concerning the column $e_n^{(2)}$, see §8.4.)

If several zeros of p have the same absolute value (this happens, for instance, every time when a polynomial with real coefficients has a pair of complex conjugate zeros), the convergence properties of the scheme are more complicated. We still assume that the zeros are numbered such that

$$(8\text{-}11) \qquad |z_1| \geqq |z_2| \geqq |z_3| \geqq \cdots \geqq |z_N| > 0.$$

For convenience in formulating some of the conditions below, we shall put

$$|z_0| = \infty, \qquad |z_{N+1}| = 0.$$

Always assuming that the scheme exists, we then have

Theorem 8.3b   For every k such that $|z_{k+1}| < |z_k| < |z_{k-1}|$,

$$(8\text{-}12) \qquad \lim_{n \to \infty} q_n^{(k)} = z_k.$$

For every k such that $|z_k| > |z_{k+1}|$,

$$(8\text{-}13) \qquad \lim_{n \to \infty} e_n^{(k)} = 0.$$

These facts can be used in the following manner: The e columns which tend to zero (a behavior which is numerically conspicuous) divide the QD

table into subtables.   All zeros z_k whose subscripts agree with the superscripts of the q's in one subtable have the same modulus.   Thus, if a z_k is
the only zero of its modulus, this will be evident from the fact that the
corresponding subtable contains one q column only, and the value of z_k
can be obtained as the limit of that q column.

It is not yet clear how to deal with several zeros having the same
absolute value.   (Most frequently this situation occurs in connection with
complex conjugate zeros of real polynomials.)   Such zeros, too, can be
obtained from the QD table.   We first consider the general case where m
zeros $z_{k+1}, z_{k+2}, \ldots, z_{k+m}$ have the same modulus:

(8-14) $$|z_k| > |z_{k+1}| = |z_{k+2}| = \cdots = |z_{k+m}| > |z_{k+m+1}|.$$

Here it is necessary to construct polynomials $p_n^{(l)}, l = k, k+1, \ldots, k+m$,
by means of the recurrence relations

(8-15a) $p_n^{(k)}(z) = 1, \qquad n = 0, 1, 2, \ldots,$

(8-15b) $p_n^{(l)}(z) = z p_{n+1}^{(l-1)}(z) - q_n^{(l)} p_n^{(l-1)}(z),$
$$l = 1, 2, \ldots, m; \quad n = 0, 1, 2, \ldots.$$

These polynomials can again be thought as being arranged in a two-
dimensional array.   Scheme 8.3 shows a segment of this array for $m = 2$.

$$
\begin{array}{lllll}
1 & -q_n^{(k+1)} & & & \\
& z & p_n^{(k+1)}(z) & & \\
1 & & & -q_n^{(k+2)} & \\
& & z & p_n^{(k+2)}(z) & \\
& p_{n+1}^{(k+1)}(z) & & & \\
1 & & & p_{n+1}^{(k+2)}(z) & \\
& p_{n+2}^{(k+1)} & & & \\
1 & & & &
\end{array}
$$

Scheme 8.3

The zeros $z_{k+1}, z_{k+2}, \ldots, z_{k+m}$ can now be obtained from the polynomials
$p_n^{(k+m)}$ by virtue of the following theorem:

Theorem 8.3c   If the zeros satisfy (8-14), then for each fixed z

(8-16) $$\lim_{n \to \infty} p_n^{(k+m)}(z) = (z - z_{k+1})(z - z_{k+2}) \ldots (z - z_{k+m}),$$

i.e., the coefficients of the polynomials $p_n^{(k+m)}$ tend for $n \to \infty$ to the
coefficients of the polynomial with zeros $z_{k+1}, \ldots, z_{k+m}$ and leading
coefficient 1.

For $m = 1$ theorem 8.3c reduces to relation (8-3a). For $m = 2$ (the practically most frequent case) the converging polynomials are given by

$$p_n^{(k+2)}(z) = z[z - q_{n+1}^{(k+1)}] - q_n^{(k+2)}[z - q_n^{(k+1)}]$$
$$= z^2 - (q_{n+1}^{(k+1)} + q_n^{(k+2)})z + q_n^{(k+1)}q_n^{(k+2)}.$$

Relation (8-16) here means that the limits

(8-17a) $$\lim_{n \to \infty} (q_{n+1}^{(k+1)} + q_n^{(k+2)}) = A_k,$$

(8-17b) $$\lim_{n \to \infty} q_n^{(k+1)}q_n^{(k+2)} = B_k,$$

exist, and that the polynomial $z^2 - A_k z + B_k$ has the zeros z_{k+1} and z_{k+2}.

We finally mention the following fact, which could (and will) play the role of a computational check.

Theorem 8.3d   The quantities $e_n^{(N)}$ calculated from (8-5a) with $k = N$ are identically zero.

Examples illustrating the above theorems will be given in §8.5.

Problems

7. Prove theorem 8.3a in the case of a polynomial of degree $N = 2$ whose zeros satisfy $|z_1| > |z_2| > 0$.
8. Show that

$$q_n^{(1)}q_n^{(2)} = \frac{D_{n+3}}{D_{n+2}}, \qquad q_{n+1}^{(1)} + q_n^{(2)} = -\frac{E_{n+2}}{D_{n+2}},$$

where D_n and E_n denote the determinants defined by (7-22) and (7-23). Thus conclude that in the case $z_1 = \bar{z}_2$ theorem 8.3c is equivalent to theorem 7.5.
9. Obtain the two dominant complex conjugate zeros of the polynomial

$$p(z) = 81z^4 - 108z^3 + 24z + 20$$

from the QD scheme by using the relations (8-17) with $k = 0$.
10. Assuming that the quantities x_n are given by (7-17), prove theorem 8.3d for polynomials of degree $N = 1$ and $N = 2$.

8.4 Numerical Instability

As described above, the QD scheme is built up proceeding from the left to the right.   The sequence $\{x_n\}$ determines the first q column $\{q_n^{(1)}\}$; from it we obtain in succession the columns $\{e_n^{(1)}\}, \{q_n^{(2)}\}, \ldots$, by means of the relations (8-5).   The reader will be shocked to learn that this method of generating the QD scheme is not feasible in practice, because it suffers from *numerical instability* due to severe loss of *significant digits*.

The concept of numerical instability was already briefly alluded to in §1.5. In mathematical analysis, real (or complex) numbers are always conceived as being determined with infinite accuracy. Mathematically, this infinite accuracy is expressed by the Dedekind cut property (see Taylor [1959], p. 447; Buck [1956], p. 388). Numerically, the real numbers of mathematical analysis can be thought of as infinite decimal fractions. In computation a real number z is—with rare exceptions— never represented exactly, but rather approximated by some rational number z^*, e.g., by a decimal fraction with eight decimals.† The quantity $z^* - z$ is called *rounding error*, or sometimes also *absolute rounding error*, in order to distinguish it from the *relative rounding error* $|z^* - z| / |z|$. The following simple rules concerning the propagation of rounding errors follow easily from first principles:

(*i*) A sum or difference of two rounded numbers a^* and b^* has an *absolute* rounding error of the order of the sum of the *absolute* errors of a^* and b^*.

(*ii*) A product or quotient of two rounded numbers a^* and b^* has a *relative* error of the order of the sum of the *relative* errors of a^* and b^*.

The QD scheme offers an interesting illustration of these rules. To simplify matters, let us assume that the sequence $\{x_n\}$ is generated without rounding error (this is possible if p is a polynomial with integer coefficients and leading coefficient 1), and that the situation covered by theorem 8.3a obtains. If we carry t decimals, the numbers $q_n^{(1)}$ then will have (absolute) rounding errors of the order of 10^{-t}. The elements $e_n^{(1)}$, formed by differencing the $q_n^{(1)}$, will by rule (*i*) have absolute rounding errors of the same magnitude. However, since by (8-10) the $e_n^{(1)}$ tend to zero, their *relative* errors become larger and larger. Thus, by rule (*ii*), the ratios $e_{n+1}^{(1)}/e_n^{(1)}$ are formed less and less accurately, and, again by rule (*ii*), the relative error of the quantity $q_n^{(2)}$, as determined by (8-5b), increases without bound. Since $q_n^{(2)}$ tends to a nonzero limit as $n \to \infty$, the same is true for the absolute error of $q_n^{(2)}$. It is clear that this numerical instability becomes even more pronounced as k increases.

EXAMPLE

4. The loss of significant digits is illustrated already in example 2. By theorem 8.3d, the column $e_n^{(2)}$ should theoretically consist of zeros. The fact that these elements are not zero, and even increase with increasing n, shows the growing influence of rounding errors. The reader is asked to

---

† For more details the reader is referred to chapter 15. At the present stage we aim at a qualitative rather than quantitative understanding of rounding errors.

calculate the same example using numbers with ten decimals.   This will delay, but not ultimately prevent, the phenomenon of numerical instability.

The fact that the method of generating the QD scheme described in §8.1 is unstable does not, of course, prevent the theorems stated in §8.3 from being true.   These theorems concern the mathematically exact, unrounded QD scheme.   They can be used numerically as soon as we succeed in generating the QD scheme in a numerically stable manner.   One method of avoiding rounding errors, applicable to polynomials with rational coefficients, would be to perform all operations in exact rational arithmetic (see Henrici [1956]).   Fortunately, as will be seen in the following section, there is a simple way of generating a stable QD scheme also in conventional arithmetic.

8.5   Progressive Form of the Algorithm

The QD scheme can be generated in a stable manner if it is built up row by row instead of column by column, as in §8.1.   To see this, we solve each of the recurrence relations (8-5) for the south element of the rhombus involved:

(8-18a) $$q_{n+1}^{(k)} = (e_n^{(k)} - e_{n+1}^{(k-1)}) + q_n^{(k)},$$

(8-18b) $$e_{n+1}^{(k)} = \frac{q_n^{(k+1)}}{q_{n+1}^{(k)}} e_n^{(k)}.$$

Let us assume that a row of q's and a row of e's is known, each affected by "normal" rounding errors of several digits in the last place.   The new row of q's, as calculated from (8-18a), will then, by rule (i), have absolute errors of the same magnitude.   The fact that the relative errors in the e's are large (due to the smallness of the e's) is not important now.   Furthermore, the relative errors in the new row of e's determined by (8-18b) are of the same order as in the old row of e's, due to rule (ii).   While a normal amount of error propagation must be expected also in the present mode of generating the scheme, it is much less serious than when the scheme is generated column by column.

If the scheme is to be generated row by row, a first couple of rows must somehow be obtained.   The following algorithm shows how this is accomplished.

Algorithm 8.5   Let $a_0, a_1, \ldots, a_N$ be constants, all different from zero. Set

(8-19a) $q_0^{(1)} = -\dfrac{a_1}{a_0},$ $q_{1-k}^{(k)} = 0,$ $k = 2, 3, \ldots, N;$

$$(8\text{-}19b) \qquad e^{(k)}_{(1-k)} = \frac{a_{k+1}}{a_k}, \qquad k = 1, 2, \ldots, N - 1.$$

Consider the elements thus generated as the first two rows of a QD scheme, and generate further rows by means of (8-18), using the side conditions

$$(8\text{-}20) \qquad e^{(0)}_n = e^{(N)}_n = 0, \qquad n = 1, 2, \ldots.$$

As before, there is the theoretical possibility of breakdown of the scheme due to the fact that a denominator is zero.   However, we have

Theorem 8.5 If the scheme of the elements $q^{(k)}_n$ and $e^{(k)}_n$ defined by algorithm 8.5 exists, it is (for $n \geq 0$) identical with the QD scheme of the polynomial

$$p(z) = a_0 z^N + a_1 z^{N-1} + \cdots + a_N,$$

where the sequence $\{x_n\}$ is started in the manner (8-3).

The proof of theorem 8.5 requires some involved algebra and it is omitted here.   A necessary and sufficient condition for the existence of the scheme defined by algorithm 8.5 is that the determinants (8-7) be different from zero also for $n > -k$.   (Here we have to interpret $x_n = 0$ for $n < 0$.)

EXAMPLES

5. The top rows of the scheme for $N = 4$ look as follows:

	$-\dfrac{a_1}{a_0}$		0		0		0
0		$\dfrac{a_2}{a_1}$		$\dfrac{a_3}{a_2}$		$\dfrac{a_4}{a_3}$	
	$q^{(1)}_1$		$q^{(2)}_0$		$q^{(3)}_{-1}$		$q^{(4)}_{-2}$
0		$e^{(1)}_1$		$e^{(2)}_0$		$e^{(3)}_{-1}$	
	$q^{(1)}_2$		$q^{(2)}_1$		$q^{(3)}_0$		$q^{(4)}_{-1}$
0		$e^{(1)}_2$		$e^{(2)}_1$		$e^{(3)}_0$	

Scheme 8.5

6. For the polynomial

$$p(z) = 128z^4 - 256z^3 + 160z^2 - 32z + 1$$

we obtain the scheme shown in table 8.5a.

Table 8.5a

$q_n^{(1)}$	$e_n^{(1)}$	$q_n^{(2)}$	$e_n^{(2)}$	$q_n^{(3)}$	$e_n^{(3)}$	$q_n^{(4)}$
2.000000		.000000		.000000		.000000
	−.625000		−.200000		−.031250	
1.375000		.425000		.168750		.031250
	−.193182		−.079412		−.005787	
1.181818		.538770		.242375		.037037
	−.088068		−.035725		−.000884	
1.093750		.591114		.277215		.037921
	−.047596		−.016754		−.000121	
1.046154		.621956		.293848		.038042
	−.028297		−.007915		−.000016	
1.017857		.642337		.301748		.038058
	−.017857		−.003718		−.000002	
1.000000		.656476		.305464		.038060
	−.011723		−.001730		−.000000	
.988277		.666468		.307194		.038060
	−.007906		−.000798		−.000000	
.980372		.673576		.307992		.038060
	−.005432		−.000365		−.000000	
.974940		.678643		.308356		.038060
	−.003781		−.000166		−.000000	

All e columns tend to zero, thus by theorem 8.3a the polynomial has four zeros whose absolute values are different. The q columns converge to the zeros, whose exact values are as follows:

$$z_1 = 0.96194, \quad z_2 = 0.69134, \quad z_3 = 0.30866, \quad z_4 = 0.03806.$$

7. For the polynomial

$$p(z) = z^4 - 8z^3 + 39z^2 - 62z + 50$$

algorithm 8.5 yields the following QD scheme:

Table 8.5b

$q_n^{(1)}$	$e_n^{(1)}$	$q_n^{(2)}$	$e_n^{(2)}$	$q_n^{(3)}$	$e_n^{(3)}$	$q_n^{(4)}$
8.000000		.000000		.000000		.000000
	−4.875000		−1.589744		−.806452	
3.125000		3.285256		.783292		.806452
	−5.125000		−.379037		−.830296	
−2.000000		8.031220		.332033		1.636748
	20.580000		−.015670		−4.092923	
18.580000		−12.564451		−3.745220		5.729671
	−13.916921		−.004671		6.261609	
4.663079		1.347799		2.521060		−.531938
	−4.022497		−.008737		−1.321186	
.640581		5.361559		1.208612		.789248
	−33.667611		−.001970		−.862761	
−33.027030		39.027201		.347820		1.652009

We now have $e_n^{(2)} \to 0$, but $e_n^{(1)}$ and $e_n^{(3)}$ do not tend to zero. This is an indication that there are two pairs of complex conjugate zeros.   To make use of theorem 8.3c, we form the quantities

$$A_n^{(k)} = q_{n+1}^{(k+1)} + q_n^{(k+2)}, \qquad B_n^{(k)} = q_n^{(k+1)}q_n^{(k+2)}$$

for $k = 0$ and $k = 2$, obtaining the following values:

Table 8.5c

$A_n^{(0)}$	$B_n^{(0)}$	$A_n^{(2)}$	$B_n^{(2)}$
6.410256	26.282051	1.589744	0
6.031220	25.097561	1.968780	1.282051
6.015549	25.128902	1.984451	1.902439
6.010878	25.042114	1.989122	1.992225
6.002141	25.001372	1.997859	1.989741
6.000171	25.000110	1.999829	1.996637

The limits are 6, 25, 2, 2 respectively, indicating that the polynomials

$$z^2 - 6z + 25 \quad \text{and} \quad z^2 - 2z + 2$$

are quadratic factors of the given polynomial.   In fact,

$$(z^2 - 6z + 25)(z^2 - 2z + 2) = z^4 - 8z^3 + 39z^2 - 62z + 50.$$

We have yet to deal with the complication that arises if some of the coefficients $a_0, a_1, \ldots, a_N$ are zero.   In that case the extended QD scheme defined by algorithm 8.5 clearly does not exist, since some of the relations (8-19) may fail to make sense.   A possible remedy is to introduce a new variable

$$z^* = z - a$$

and to consider the polynomial

$$p^*(z^*) = p(a + z^*)$$

$$= p(a) + \frac{1}{1!} p'(a)z^* + \frac{1}{2!} p''(a)z^{*2} + \cdots + \frac{1}{N!} p^{(N)}(a)z^{*N}.$$

Here a denotes a suitably chosen parameter.   The coefficients of the polynomial p^* can easily be calculated by means of algorithm 3.6.   It can be shown that if p has some zero coefficients, then all coefficients of p^* are different from zero for sufficiently small values of $a \neq 0$.   If the zeros z_k^* of p^* have been computed, those of p are given by the formula

$$z_k = z_k^* + a.$$

EXAMPLE

8.   Let $p(z) = 81z^4 - 108z^3 + 24z + 20$.   Here $a_2 = 0$, and algorithm

8.5 cannot be started.   We form p^* with $a = 1$.   Scheme 3.6 turns out thus:

81	−108	0	24	20
81	−27	−27	−3	17
81	54	27	24	
81	135	162		
81	216			
81				

The new polynomial

$$p^*(z) = 81z^{*4} + 216z^{*3} + 162z^{*2} + 24z^* + 17$$

has all coefficients different from zero, and the first rows of its QD scheme are as follows:

$$-\frac{216}{81} \qquad 0 \qquad 0 \qquad 0$$

$$0 \qquad \frac{162}{216} \qquad \frac{24}{162} \qquad \frac{17}{24} \qquad 0$$

Problems

11. Construct the QD scheme for the polynomial

$$p(z) = 32z^3 - 48z^2 + 18z - 1$$

and determine its zeros to four significant digits.   Check your result by observing that $z = \frac{1}{2}$ is a zero.   (The convergence of the q columns may be sped up by Aitken's Δ^2-process.)

12. Determine approximate values for the zeros of the polynomial

$$p(z) = 70z^4 - 140z^3 + 90z^2 - 20z + 1.$$

Then find more exact values by Newton's method.

13. The polynomial

$$p(z) = z^5 - 3z^4 - 20z^3 + 60z^2 - z - 78$$

has two large real zeros of opposite sign, a pair of complex conjugate zeros, and a small real zero.   Find approximate values for the quadratic factors belonging to the two large real zeros and to the pair of complex zeros.

14. Prove theorem 8.5 for polynomials of degree $N = 2$.   [Hint: It suffices to show that algorithm 8.5 generates the correct values of $q_0^{(1)}$, $e_0^{(1)}$, and $q_0^{(2)}$.]

8.6 Computational Checks

Even if the QD scheme is generated by algorithm 8.5, excessively large (or small) elements may cause some loss of accuracy.   The mathematical results given below may be used for checking purposes; failure of any of these checks indicates excessive rounding error.

(*i*) Relation (8-5a) implies that the sum of the q values in any row of the scheme is constant. For the top row this sum is $-a_1/a_0$, which by Vieta's formula (see §2.5) equals the algebraic sum of the zeros of the polynomial. Thus we have

$$(8\text{-}21) \qquad q_n^{(1)} + q_{n-1}^{(2)} + \cdots + q_{n-N+1}^{(N)} = -\frac{a_1}{a_0}.$$

Note that by theorem 8.3a this relation confirms Vieta's rule for $n \to \infty$!

(*ii*) It can be shown that the product of all q elements in any diagonal sloping downward is likewise independent of n and equals the product of all zeros of the polynomials p. Thus again by Vieta,

$$(8\text{-}22) \qquad q_n^{(1)} q_n^{(2)} \ldots q_n^{(N)} = (-1)^N \frac{a_N}{a_0}.$$

It should be noted that while (8-21) checks only the additions and subtractions performed in constructing the scheme, equation (8-22) checks all operations.

(*iii*) If the QD scheme is generated by algorithm 8.5, the quantities x_n are not needed. However, we may calculate the x_n from (8-2) and should find

$$(8\text{-}23) \qquad \frac{x_{n+1}}{x_n} = q_n^{(1)}, \qquad n = 0, 1, 2, \ldots.$$

Problem

15. Prove (8-22) for the QD scheme arising from a polynomial of degree $N = 2$.

8.7 QD versus Newton

In comparison with other methods for determining the zeros of a polynomial, the QD algorithm enjoys the tremendous advantage of furnishing simultaneously approximations to all zeros of a polynomial. No information about the polynomial other than the values of its coefficients is required.

These advantages have to be paid for by the rather slow convergence of the algorithm. Since the QD method contains the Bernoulli method as a special case, the convergence can be no better than that of Bernoulli's method.   In fact it can be shown that under the hypotheses of theorem 8.3b the errors $q_n^{(k)} - z_k$ tend to zero like the larger of the ratios

$$\left(\frac{z_k}{z_{k-1}}\right)^n \quad \text{and} \quad \left(\frac{z_{k+1}}{z_k}\right)^n.$$

Even if the figures in the q columns eventually settle down, the accuracy of the zeros thus obtained is somewhat uncertain, because the large number of arithmetic operations may have contaminated the scheme with rounding error.

For the above reasons, the QD algorithm is not recommended for the purpose of determining the zeros of a polynomial with final accuracy. Instead, the following two-stage procedure is advocated:

Stage 1: Use the QD algorithm to obtain crude first approximations to the zeros, respectively to the quadratic factors containing complex conjugate zeros.

Stage 2: Using these approximations as starting values, obtain the zeros accurately by Newton's or Bairstow's method.

This combination of several methods has the advantage that the final values of the zeros are obtained from the original, undisturbed polynomial, and thus are practically free of rounding error.

The choice of the point at which to make the change-over from QD to Newton-Bairstow is, to some extent, arbitrary.   It is probably best to carry the QD scheme to a point where the division of the scheme into subschemes in the manner described after theorem 8.3b is clearly evident. On the other hand, if QD is pushed too far, a lot of computational effort may be wasted, since Newton-Bairstow usually takes only two or three steps to obtain the zeros very accurately even from mediocre first approximations.   To fuse the three algorithms into one working program constitutes a challenging but rewarding problem in machine programming which is highly recommended to the reader.   One such program is described by Watkins [1964], who also presents the results of extensive machine tests.

Problem

16. By combining QD and Newton-Bairstow, compute all zeros of the following polynomials with an error of less than 10^{-7}:

(a) $p(z) = z^4 - 8z^3 + 39z^2 - 62z + 51$;
(b) $p(z) = z^5 - 15z^4 + 85z^3 - 225z^2 + 264z - 120$;
(c) $p(z) = 4z^6 - 5z^5 + 4z^4 - 3z^3 + 7z^2 - 7z + 1$.

8.8   Other Applications

In addition to the calculation of the zeros of a polynomial, the QD

algorithm has many other applications, notably in the theory of continued fractions, in matrix computation, and in the summation of divergent series (see the references given below). It can also be used to furnish exact bounds (and not only approximations) for the location of the zeros of a polynomial. We shall mention only one further application which is related to the one discussed above.

Suppose the function f is defined by the power series

$$(8\text{-}24) \qquad f(z) = \sum_{n=0}^{\infty} a_n z^n,$$

where $a_n \neq 0$, $n = 0, 1, 2, \ldots$, and let it be known that the zeros z_k of f are real and positive, $0 < z_1 < z_2 < \cdots$.

EXAMPLE

9. The Bessel function of order zero can be defined by

$$(8\text{-}25) \qquad J_0(2\sqrt{x}) = \sum_{n=0}^{\infty} \frac{(-x)^n}{(n!)^2}$$

and has the required properties.

Obviously the QD scheme of such a function cannot be found in the ordinary way, because the horizontal rows are now infinite. However, the scheme may be generated in the following manner, as indicated by the arrows:

Scheme 8.8

Although the scheme does not terminate on the right, more and more diagonals sloping upward can be found. It can be shown that if the scheme exists,

$$\lim_{n \to \infty} q_n^{(k)} = \frac{1}{z_k}, \qquad k = 1, 2, \ldots.$$

Under certain conditions even complex conjugate zeros of transcendental functions can be found in this manner, using the method described in theorem 8.3c and in example 7.

EXAMPLE

10. For the function defined by (8-25) the coefficients a_n evidently satisfy

$$\frac{a_{n+1}}{a_n} = -\frac{1}{(n+1)^2}.$$

The first few diagonals of the QD scheme thus appear as follows:

1.000000	.000000	.000000	.000000	.000000
	$-.250000$	$-.111111$	$-.062500$	$-.040000$	
.750000	.138889	.048611	.022500	.012222
	$-.046296$	$-.038889$	$-.028929$	$-.021728$	
.703704	.146296	.058571	.029700	
	$-.009625$	$-.015570$	$-.014669$	
.694079	.140351	.059472	
	$-.001946$	$-.006597$	
.692133	.135700	
	$-.000382$	
.691751	$\vdots$	
$\vdots$	$\vdots$	
.691660	.131271	

Problems

17. Obtain an approximate value of $\sqrt{2/\pi}$ by applying the algorithm described above to the function

$$\cos \sqrt{z} = \sum_{n=0}^{\infty} \frac{(-z)^n}{(2n)!}.$$

18. Apply the above version of the QD algorithm to the problem of finding the small solutions of the transcendental equation

$$\tan z = cz$$

by setting

$$f(z^2) = \frac{\sin z}{z} - c \cos z.$$

Find the smallest positive solution for $c = 1.2$, and a pair of purely imaginary solutions for $c = 0.8$.

Recommended Reading

The QD algorithm was introduced by Rutishauser in a series of classical papers which are collected in the volume Rutishauser [1956].   A somewhat more elementary treatment is given by Henrici [1958].   A multitude of applications are discussed in Henrici [1963].

Research Problem

How can the argument of a complex zero of a real polynomial be determined from the signs of the elements of the corresponding q column? Consider the case $N = 2$ first.

PART TWO

INTERPOLATION

AND

APPROXIMATION

chapter *9* the interpolating polynomial

So far we have been concerned mainly with the problem of approximating *numbers* (such as the zeros of a polynomial or the solutions of systems of nonlinear equations). We now turn to the problem of approximating *functions* and, more generally, numbers, such as derivatives and integrals, that depend on an infinity of values of a function.

The most common method of approximating functions is the approximation by *polynomials*. Among the various types of polynomial approximation that are in use the one that is most flexible and most easily constructed (although not always the most effective) is the approximation by the *interpolating polynomial*.

9.1 Existence of the Interpolating Polynomial

Let the real function f be defined on an interval I, and let $x_0, x_1, \ldots, x_n$ be $n + 1$ *distinct* points of I. It is not assumed that these points are equidistant, nor even that they are in their natural order.

$$\begin{array}{c|c|c|c|c} & x_3 & x_1 \; x_2 & x_4 & \end{array}$$

We shall write for brevity

$$f(x_k) = f_k, \qquad k = 0, 1, \ldots, n.$$

Theorem 9.1 There exists a unique polynomial P of degree not exceeding n (the so-called Lagrangian interpolating polynomial) such that

$$(9\text{-}1) \qquad P(x_k) = f_k, \qquad k = 0, 1, \ldots, n.$$

Proof. As usual, the proofs of existence and of uniqueness require separate arguments. The *existence* of the polynomial P is proved if we can establish the existence of polynomials L_k $(k = 0, 1, \ldots, n)$ with the following properties:

(*i*) Each L_k is a polynomial of degree $\leq n$;

(*ii*) For $x = x_k$, L_k has the special value

(9-2a) $$L_k(x_k) = 1;$$

however, if $m \neq k$, then

(9-2b) $$L_k(x_m) = 0.$$

Assuming the existence of these L_k, we can set

(9-3) $$P(x) = \sum_{k=0}^{n} f_k L_k(x).$$

The function P is a sum of polynomials of degree $\leq n$ with constant factors and thus itself a polynomial of degree $\leq n$. Furthermore, if we set $x = x_m$, then by (*ii*) all L_k are zero except for the one with $k = m$, and this has the value 1. Thus we find

$$P(x_m) = f_m,$$

as required.

The polynomials L_k are called the Lagrangian interpolation coefficients. To prove the existence of L_k, observe that the product

$$\prod_{\substack{m=0 \\ m \neq k}}^{n} \frac{x - x_m}{x_k - x_m} = \frac{(x - x_0)\ldots(x - x_{k-1})(x - x_{k+1})\ldots(x - x_n)}{(x_k - x_0)\ldots(x_k - x_{k-1})(x_k - x_{k+1})\ldots(x_k - x_n)}$$

has the required properties. Indeed, as a product of $n + 1 - 1 = n$ linear factors it represents a polynomial of degree n; furthermore, if $x = x_k$, then all factors have the value 1, thus the product has the value 1 also. On the other hand, if $x = x_m$, where $m \neq k$, then the factor containing $x - x_m$ is zero, and the product vanishes. Thus, the polynomials

(9-4) $$L_k(x) = \prod_{\substack{m=0 \\ m \neq k}}^{n} \frac{x - x_m}{x_k - x_m}$$

have the required properties, and the existence of the polynomial P is proved.

In order to show the uniqueness of the interpolating polynomial, assume there exist two interpolating polynomials, P and Q, say. Then their difference $D = P - Q$, being the difference of two polynomials of degree not exceeding n, is again a polynomial of degree not exceeding n. Moreover,

$$D(x_k) = P(x_k) - Q(x_k) = f_k - f_k = 0$$

for $k = 0, 1, \ldots, n$.   The polynomial D thus has $n + 1$ zeros and hence, being a polynomial of degree $\leq n$, must vanish identically.   It follows that $P = Q$.   This completes the proof of theorem 9.1.

EXAMPLE

1.   To find the interpolating polynomial for the following x_k and f_k:

x_k	2	3	-1	4
f_k	1	2	3	4

We first calculate the Lagrangian interpolation coefficients.   Formula (9-4) yields

$$L_0(x) = \frac{(x - 3)(x + 1)(x - 4)}{(-1)3(-2)} = \tfrac{1}{6}(x - 3)(x + 1)(x - 4),$$

$$L_1(x) = \frac{(x - 2)(x + 1)(x - 4)}{1 \cdot 4 \cdot (-1)} = -\tfrac{1}{4}(x - 2)(x + 1)(x - 4),$$

$$L_2(x) = \frac{(x - 2)(x - 3)(x - 4)}{(-3)(-4)(-5)} = -\tfrac{1}{60}(x - 2)(x - 3)(x - 4),$$

$$L_3(x) = \frac{(x - 2)(x - 3)(x + 1)}{2 \cdot 1 \cdot 5} = \tfrac{1}{10}(x - 2)(x - 3)(x + 1).$$

Formula (9-3) thus yields

$$P(x) = \tfrac{1}{6}(x - 3)(x + 1)(x - 4) - \tfrac{1}{2}(x - 2)(x + 1)(x - 4)$$
$$- \tfrac{1}{20}(x - 2)(x - 3)(x - 4) + \tfrac{2}{5}(x - 2)(x - 3)(x + 1).$$

It can be verified that this polynomial has the required properties.

It will be noted that the representation of the interpolating polynomial given in the proof of theorem 9.1 does not give the polynomial in the customary form

$$P(x) = a_0 x^n + a_1 x^{n-1} + \cdots + a_n.$$

Of course, the polynomial *could* be put into the above standard form, but there usually is no particular reason for doing so.   It is well to distinguish at this point between the *function P* and the various *representations* of *P*. As a function (i.e., as a set of ordered pairs $(x, P(x))$), P is unique.   However, there may be many ways of representing P by an explicit formula. Each formula suggests a certain algorithm for calculating P.   It is not claimed that the algorithm suggested by (9-3) is the most effective from the numerical point of view.   Many other algorithms for constructing the polynomial will be discussed in the chapters 10 and 11.

Problems

1. Verify that the case $n = 1$ of (9-3) yields the familiar formula for linear interpolation.   What is the meaning of theorem 9.1 when $n = 0$?

2. Is the interpolating polynomial constructed above always of the exact degree n?
3. Show that for $x \neq x_k$, $k = 0, 1, \ldots, n$, the interpolating polynomial can be represented in the form

$$P(x) = L(x) \sum_{k=0}^{n} \frac{f_k}{(x - x_k)L'(x_k)},$$

where

$$L(x) = (x - x_0)(x - x_1) \ldots (x - x_n).$$

Verify by L'Hopital's rule (see Taylor [1959], p. 456) that the limit of the expression on the right as $x \to x_m$ is f_m.
4. Prove: If f is a polynomial of degree n or less, then $P = f$.

9.2   The Error of the Interpolating Polynomial

Since we wish to use the interpolating polynomial to approximate the function f at points which do not belong to the set of *interpolating points* x_k, we are interested in estimating the difference $P(x) - f(x)$ for $x \in I$. It is clear that without further hypotheses nothing whatever can be said about this quantity.   For we can change the function f at will at points which are not interpolating points without changing the polynomial P at all (see Fig. 9.2).

A definite statement can be made, however, if we assume a qualitative knowledge of the derivatives of the function f.

Figure 9.2

Theorem 9.2   In addition to the hypotheses of theorem 9.1, let f be $n + 1$ times continuously differentiable on the interval I. Then to each $x \in I$ there exists a point ξ_x located in the smallest interval containing the points $x, x_0, x_1, \ldots, x_n$ such that

$$(9\text{-}5) \qquad f(x) - P(x) = \frac{1}{(n + 1)!} L(x) f^{(n+1)}(\xi_x)$$

where

$$L(x) = (x - x_0)(x - x_1)\ldots(x - x_n).$$

Proof.   If x is one of the points x_k, there is nothing to prove, since both sides of (9-5) vanish for arbitrary ξ.   If x has a fixed value different from any of the points x_k, consider the auxiliary function $F = F(t)$ defined by

$$(9\text{-}6) \qquad F(t) = f(t) - P(t) - cL(t),$$

where

$$c = \frac{f(x) - P(x)}{L(x)}.$$

We have

$$\begin{aligned} F(x_k) &= f(x_k) - P(x_k) - cL(x_k) \\ &= f_k - f_k - 0 \\ &= 0, \qquad k = 0, 1, 2, \ldots, n, \end{aligned}$$

and also

$$F(x) = f(x) - P(x) - cL(x) = 0,$$

by the definition of c.   The function F thus has at least $n + 2$ distinct zeros in the interval I.   By Rolle's theorem, the derivative F' must have at least $n + 1$ zeros in the smallest interval containing x and the x_k, the second derivative must have no less than n zeros, and finally the $(n + 1)$st derivative must have at least one zero.   Let ξ_x be one such zero.   We now differentiate (9-6) $n + 1$ times and set $t = \xi_x$.   The $(n + 1)$st derivative of P is zero.   Since L is a polynomial with leading term x^{n+1}, the $(n + 1)$st derivative of cL is $c(n + 1)!$.   We thus have

$$0 = F^{(n+1)}(\xi_x) = f^{(n+1)}(\xi_x) - c(n + 1)!$$

or, remembering the definition of c and rearranging,

$$cL(x) = f(x) - P(x) = \frac{1}{(n + 1)!} L(x) f^{(n+1)}(\xi_x),$$

as was to be shown.

Equation (9-5) cannot be used, of course, to calculate the exact value of the error $f - P$, since ξ_x as a function of x is, in general, not known. (An exception occurs when the $(n + 1)$st derivative of f is constant; see below.)   However, as is shown in the examples below the formula can be used in many cases to find a *bound* for the error of the interpolating polynomial.

We also shall require the following fact.

Corollary 9.2 Under the hypotheses of theorem 9.2, the quantity $f^{(n+1)}(\xi_x)$ in (9-5) can be defined as a continuous function of x for $x \in I$.

Proof. Define the function $g = g(x)$ by

$$g(x) = \begin{cases} \dfrac{f(x) - P(x)}{L(x)}, & x \neq x_k, \quad k = 0, 1, \ldots, n, \\[2ex] \dfrac{f'(x_k) - P'(x_k)}{L'(x_k)}, & x = x_k, \quad k = 0, 1, \ldots, n. \end{cases}$$

This function is continuous for $x \neq x_k$ and, by L'Hopital's rule (see Taylor [1959], p. 456) also at the points x_k. For $x \neq x_k$,

$$f^{(n+1)}(\xi_x) = (n + 1)!g(x),$$

establishing the corollary. An application of this corollary will be made in the chapters 12 and 13.

EXAMPLES

2. *One interpolating point.* If there is only one interpolating point x_0, the interpolating polynomial reduces to the constant f_0. Formula (9-5) yields

$$f(x) - f(x_0) = (x - x_0)f'(\xi_x),$$

where ξ_x lies between x_0 and x. This is the familiar *mean value theorem* of the differential calculus.

3. *Two interpolating points.* The linear interpolating polynomial is given by

$$P(x) = \frac{(x_1 - x)f_0 + (x - x_0)f_1}{x_1 - x_0}.$$

Equation (9-5) yields the error formula

$$f(x) - P(x) = \frac{(x - x_0)(x - x_1)}{2!} f''(\xi_x).$$

What is the maximum error that can occur if we know that $|f''(x)| \leq M_2$ and x is between x_0 and x_1? The maximum of the function

$$|\tfrac{1}{2}(x - x_0)(x - x_1)|$$

between x_0 and x_1 occurs at $x = \tfrac{1}{2}(x_0 + x_1)$ and has the value $\tfrac{1}{8}(x_1 - x_0)^2$. Thus we find

$$|f(x) - P(x)| \leq \frac{(x_1 - x_0)^2}{8} M_2$$

in this case. Application: If we calculate the value of sin x from a sine table with step h, using linear interpolation, the error is bounded by $\frac{1}{8}h^2$, since $M_2 = 1$ in this case.

4. *Error in cubic interpolation.* We assume that the four interpolating points are equidistant, $x_k = x_0 + kh$, $k = 1, 2, 3$, and that x (the point where the value of the function f is sought) always lies between x_1 and x_2. We set

$$M_4 = \max_{x_0 \le x \le x_3} |f^{(4)}(x)|.$$

The interpolation error is then bounded by $(1/4!)M_4$ times the maximum of the absolute value of the function

$$L(x) = (x - x_0)(x - x_1)(x - x_2)(x - x_3)$$

in the interval $x_1 \le x \le x_2$. For reasons of symmetry this maximum occurs at $x = (x_1 + x_2)/2$ and has the value

$$[(\tfrac{3}{2}h)(\tfrac{1}{2}h)]^2 = \tfrac{9}{16}h^4.$$

It follows that the interpolation error is bounded by

$$\frac{3}{128} h^4 M_4.$$

In a sine table, for instance, using cubic interpolation and a step as large as $h = 0.1$ we get a maximum error of less than 2.5×10^{-6}.

The basic error formula (9-5) requires the knowledge of a bound of the derivatives of the function f. Such bounds can often be obtained very easily even for non-elementary functions by exploiting known functional relations.

EXAMPLE

5. The Bessel function of order zero can be defined by

$$J_0(x) = \frac{1}{\pi} \int_0^\pi \cos (x \sin t)\, dt.$$

By differentiating under the integral sign,

$$J_0'(x) = -\frac{1}{\pi} \int_0^\pi \sin t \sin (x \sin t)\, dt,$$

$$J_0''(x) = -\frac{1}{\pi} \int_0^\pi (\sin t)^2 \cos (x \sin t)\, dt,$$

etc. The integrands of all integrals which we obtain by differentiation are bounded in absolute value by 1. Thus

$$|J_0^{(n)}(x)| \le \frac{1}{\pi} \int_0^\pi 1\, dt = 1, \qquad n = 0, 1, 2, \ldots.$$

Problems

5. A table of a function of one variable is well suited for linear interpolation if the error due to interpolation does not exceed the rounding error of the entries. What is the greatest permissible step of such a "well interpolable" table of cos x as a function of the number of decimal places, (a) if x is given in radians; (b) if x is given in degrees? Make a survey of some tables accessible to you and decide whether they are well suited for linear interpolation.

6. What is the maximum value of the combined error due to linear interpolation and rounding of the formula

$$f(x) \sim \frac{x - x_0}{x_1 - x_0} f_1 + \frac{x_1 - x}{x_1 - x_0} f_0,$$

if f_1 and f_0 are known to N places, and if the products are rounded to N places? (It may be assumed that the fractions $(x - x_0)/(x_1 - x_0)$ and $(x_1 - x)/(x_1 - x_0)$ are exact decimal fractions.)

7. The function $\log_{10} (\sin x)$, where x is given in degrees, is tabulated to five decimal places with a step of $1/60$ of one degree. From what value of x on is this table well suited for linear interpolation?

8. The function $f(x) = \sqrt{x}$ is tabulated at the integers, $x = 1, 2, 3, \ldots$, giving four decimals. From what x on is this table well suited for linear interpolation?

9. The Bessel function of order n can be defined by

$$J_n(x) = \frac{1}{\pi} \int_0^{\pi} \cos (x \sin t - nt) \, dt.$$

How do we have to choose the step h of a table of J_n so that the error is less than 10^{-6}
(a) if linear interpolation is to be used?
(b) if cubic interpolation (as described in example 4) is to be used?

10. *Interpolation near the end of a table.* The fourth derivative of a function f is known to be bounded by M_4. Let P be the polynomial interpolating f at the points $x_k = kh$, $k = 0, 1, 2, 3$. Give the best possible bound for

$$\max_{x_0 \leq x \leq x_1} |f(x) - P(x)|.$$

11. Theorem 9.2 implies that if $|f^{(n+1)}(x)| \leq M_{n+1}$, $x \in I$, then, in the notation of theorem 9.2

$$|f(x) - P(x)| \leq \frac{M_{n+1}}{(n + 1)!} |L(x)|, \qquad x \in I.$$

Are there any functions f (and corresponding points in I) for which this inequality becomes an equality?

12. Let n be a positive integer. Somebody proposes to calculate the value of

e^{n+1} by constructing the polynomial P interpolating the function $f(x) = e^x$ at the points $x = 0, 1, \ldots, n$ and evaluating P for $x = n + 1$.

(a) Indicate a *lower* bound for the error $e^{n+1} - P(n + 1)$.

(b) Determine the number ξ_x of theorem 9.2, and thus obtain an exact expression for the error.

13. The function f is defined on $[0, 1]$ and is known to have a bounded second derivative. Its values are to be computed from a fixed interpolating polynomial using two interpolating points x_0 and x_1. How should one place the points x_0 and x_1 in the interval $[0, 1]$ in order to minimize the error due to interpolation?

9.3 Convergence of Sequences of Interpolating Polynomials

Let the function f be defined for $-\infty < x < \infty$, and let it and all its derivatives be bounded by one and the same constant,

$$|f^{(n)}(x)| \leq M, \qquad n = 0, 1, \ldots; \quad -\infty < x < \infty.$$

Assume one wishes to calculate $f(x)$ in the interval $[0, h]$ by means of the interpolating polynomial P of degree $2n - 1$ using the interpolating points

$$\begin{aligned} x_0 &= 0, & x_1 &= h, \\ x_2 &= -h, & x_3 &= 2h, \end{aligned}$$

$$\ldots$$

$$x_{2n-2} = -(n-1)h, \qquad x_{2n-1} = nh.$$

For what values of h does the error tend to zero as $n \to \infty$?

Obviously, the above procedure cannot be effective for unrestricted values of h, as the example $f(x) = \sin x$, $h = \pi$ shows. (All interpolating polynomials are zero in this case.) By theorem 9.2, the interpolation error of P is bounded by $M|L(x)|/(2n)!$, where

$$L(x) = [x + (n-1)h][x + (n-2)h]\ldots[x - nh].$$

The maximum of the function $|L(x)|$ on the interval $[0, h]$ occurs at the point $x = h/2$. At this point,

$$\frac{1}{(2n)!}\left|L\!\left(\frac{h}{2}\right)\right| = \frac{[(n - \frac{1}{2})h(n - \frac{3}{2})h\ldots\frac{1}{2}h]^2}{(2n)!}$$

$$= \frac{[(2n-1)(2n-3)\ldots3\cdot1]^2 h^{2n}}{2^{2n}\cdot(2n)!}$$

$$= \left[\frac{(2n)!}{2^n n!}\right]^2 \frac{h^{2n}}{2^{2n}(2n)!}$$

$$= \frac{(2n)!}{2^{4n}(n!)^2} h^{2n}.$$

Using Stirling's asymptotic formula for $n!$,

$$n! \sim \sqrt{2\pi n}\left(\frac{n}{e}\right)^{n},$$

(see Buck [1956], p. 159) we find

$$\frac{1}{(2n)!}\left|L\left(\frac{h}{2}\right)\right| \sim \frac{\sqrt{2\pi \cdot 2n}\left(\dfrac{2n}{e}\right)^{2n}}{2^{4n}2\pi n\left(\dfrac{n}{e}\right)^{2n}} \cdot h^{2n}$$

$$= \left(\frac{h}{2}\right)^{2n} \cdot \frac{1}{\sqrt{\pi n}}.$$

The last expression tends to zero if $n \to \infty$ if and only if $|h| \leq 2$. Thus the convergence of the interpolation process described above can be guaranteed only if $|h| \leq 2$.

The sequence of interpolating polynomials constructed above looks somewhat unnatural in view of the fact that we use interpolating points farther and farther removed from the interval where we wish to approximate the function f. The following question, however, is very natural: Let f be continuous on the interval $[0, 1]$ and denote by $P_n(x)$ the polynomial interpolating f at the points

$$x_k = \frac{k}{n}, \qquad k = 0, 1, \ldots, n.$$

Is it true that

(9-7) $$\lim_{n \to \infty} P_n(x) = f(x)$$

for all $x \in [0, 1]$? An important result due to Runge states that there are continuous functions for which (9-7) does not hold. (A simple example is $f(x) = |x - \frac{1}{2}|$.) Actually, the relation (9-7) even fails to hold for some functions which have derivatives of all orders.

It is important, however, to understand Runge's result correctly. The result does not mean that a continuous function cannot always be approximated by polynomials. In fact, a famous theorem due to Weierstrass (see Buck [1956], p. 39) states that every f continuous on a closed finite interval I can be approximated by polynomials to any desired accuracy. Runge's result merely states that these approximating polynomials can in general not be obtained by interpolation at uniformly spaced points.

Problems

14. *Missing entry in a table.* A function f is defined on the whole real line and satisfies

$$|f^{(m)}(x)| \leq M^m, \qquad -\infty < x < \infty; \qquad m = 0, 1, 2, \ldots$$

for some constant M.   For $n = 1, 2, \ldots$ let P_{2n-1} denote the polynomial interpolating f at the points $-n, -n + 1, \ldots, -1, 1, \ldots, n - 1, n$.   Prove that

$$\lim_{n \to \infty} P_{2n-1}(0) = f(0)$$

holds provided that $M < 2$.

15. A function f is defined for $x \geq 0$ and satisfies

$$|f^{(m)}(x)| \leq 1, \qquad x \geq 0, \qquad m = 0, 1, 2, \ldots.$$

For a fixed value of h, let P_n denote the polynomial interpolating f at the points $0, h, 2h, \ldots, nh$.   For what values of h can you guarantee that

$$\lim_{n \to \infty} P_n(x) = f(x)$$

for every fixed value of $x > 0$?

16*. Let the function f be continuous on the interval $[0, 1]$.   From the fact that such a function is *uniformly continuous* (see Buck [1956], p. 34) one can easily prove that f can be approximated to arbitrary accuracy by the piecewise linear function coinciding with f at suitable points $x_0, x_1, \ldots, x_n$.   Thus, in a sense, f can be approximated arbitrarily well by linear interpolation.   Why does this not contradict Runge's theorem?

17. A function f is defined on $[0, 1]$, and its derivatives satisfy

$$|f^{(m)}(x)| \leq m!, \qquad m = 0, 1, 2, \ldots, 0 \leq x \leq 1.$$

(Example: $f(x) = (1 + x)^{-1}$.)   Let P_n denote the polynomial interpolating f at the points $1, q, q^2, \ldots, q^n$, where q is some number such that $0 < q < 1$.   Show that

$$\lim_{n \to \infty} P_n(0) = f(0).$$

9.4   How to Approximate a Polynomial of degree n by One of Degree $n - 1$

Let Q be a polynomial of degree n with leading coefficient 1,

$$Q(x) = x^n + a_{n-1}x^{n-1} + \cdots + a_0.$$

We wish to interpolate Q in the interval $[-1, 1]$ by a polynomial P of degree $n - 1$ such that the maximum of the error $|Q(x) - P(x)|$ is minimized.   How do we have to choose the interpolating points $x_0, x_1, x_2, \ldots, x_{n-1}$, and how large is the smallest possible maximum error?

From the general error formula (9-5) we find, since $Q^{(n)}(x) = n!$,

(9-8)
$$Q(x) - P(x) = L(x)$$

where

$$L(x) = (x - x_0)(x - x_1)\ldots(x - x_{n-1}) = x^n + \cdots.$$

Our problem is thus equivalent to the problem of selecting the points $x_0, x_1, \ldots, x_{n-1}$ in such a manner that the quantity

$$\max_{-1 \leq x \leq 1} |(x - x_0)(x - x_1) \ldots (x - x_{n-1})|$$

is minimized.   Although seemingly difficult this problem can be solved explicitly.

Theorem 9.4   The best choice of the interpolating points $x_0, x_1, \ldots,$ x_{n-1} for the approximation of the polynomial $Q(x) = x^n + \cdots$ in the interval $-1 \leq x \leq 1$ by a polynomial of degree $n - 1$ is the choice for which

(9-9) $$L(x) = \frac{1}{2^{n-1}} T_n(x),$$

where T_n denotes the nth Chebyshev polynomial,†

$$T_n(x) = \cos(n \text{ arc cos } x).$$

Proof.   Let us first convince ourselves that the function L defined by (9-9) really is a polynomial of degree n with leading coefficient 1.   From the difference equation satisfied by the Chebyshev polynomials,

$$T_n(x) = 2xT_{n-1}(x) - T_{n-2}(x)$$

and from the fact that $T_0(x) = 1$, $T_1(x) = x$ it readily follows that T_n is a polynomial in x with leading coefficient 2^{n-1}.   Hence our assertion on L follows immediately.

Since we are interested in minimizing the maximum of $|L(x)|$, let us calculate the extrema of $L(x)$.   The extrema of $\cos x$ occur for $x = k\pi$, where k is an integer, hence the extrema of $L(x)$ in the interval $[-1, 1]$ occur at the points where n arc cos $x = k\pi$, i.e., for $x = t_k$, where

$$t_k = \cos \frac{k\pi}{n}, \qquad k = 0, 1, \ldots, n.$$

The values of L at these points are

$$L(t_k) = (-1)^k 2^{-n+1},$$

i.e., the extrema all have the same absolute value 2^{-n+1}, but oscillate in sign (see Fig. 9.4).

---

† See example 3, chapter 6.

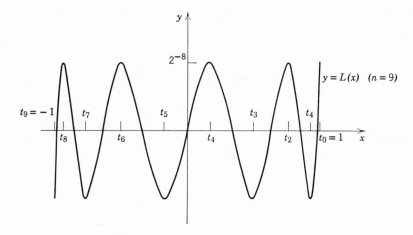

Figure 9.4   The function $L(x)$ ($n = 9$).

Now suppose there exists another polynomial $M(x) = x^n + \cdots$ for which $|M(x)|$ has a smaller maximum $m < 2^{-n+1}$ in $[-1, 1]$. Then the difference polynomial

$$D(x) = L(x) - M(x)$$

would at the $n + 1$ points t_k have the same sign as L, i.e.,

$$D(t_k) \begin{cases} > 0, & k \text{ even,} \\ < 0, & k \text{ odd.} \end{cases}$$

Since $t_0 > t_1 > t_2 > \cdots > t_n$, it would follow that D has at least n distinct zeros, namely one in each interval $[t_{k+1}, t_k]$. However, since both L and M have leading coefficient 1, it follows that D is a polynomial of degree $\leqq n - 1$, hence D cannot have n distinct zeros without vanishing identically. The assumption of the existence of a polynomial M with a maximum deviation from 0 smaller than 2^{-n+1} thus has led to a contradiction.

The interpolating points x_k for the best approximation of Q by a polynomial of lower degree are the zeros of L, that is the points $x = x_k$ satisfying

$$n \text{ arc cos } x = (k + \tfrac{1}{2})\pi, \qquad k = 0, 1, \ldots, n - 1.$$

It follows that the interpolating points are given by

$$x_k = \cos\left(\frac{2k + 1}{2n}\pi\right), \qquad k = 0, 1, \ldots, n - 1.$$

EXAMPLE

6. How can we best approximate the function

$$f(x) = x^2 + ax + b$$

in $-1 \leq x \leq 1$ by a straight line? This is the case $n = 2$ of theorem 9.4. We have

$$x_0 = \cos \frac{\pi}{4} = \frac{\sqrt{2}}{2}, \qquad x_1 = \cos \frac{3\pi}{4} = -\frac{\sqrt{2}}{2}.$$

The interpolating polynomial is given by

$$P(x) = \frac{f(x_0)(x_1 - x) + f(x_1)(x_0 - x)}{x_1 - x_0}$$

$$= \frac{(x_0^2 + ax + b)(x - x_1) + (x_1^2 + ax + b)(x_0 - x)}{x_0 - x_1}$$

$$= ax + b + \tfrac{1}{2}.$$

The maximum deviation from $x^2 + ax + b$ in $[-1, 1]$ is $\tfrac{1}{2}$, as predicted by the theory.

It is not necessary to use the interpolation points x_k in order to construct the polynomial P of best approximation. From the error formula (9-8) we find, if L is given by (9-9),

$$(9\text{-}10) \qquad P(x) = Q(x) - \frac{1}{2^{n-1}} T_n(x).$$

EXAMPLE

7. We consider once more the problem of example 6. From the recurrence relation we easily find $T_2(x) = 2x^2 - 1$, hence

$$P(x) = x^2 + ax + b - \tfrac{1}{2}(2x^2 - 1)$$
$$= ax + b + \tfrac{1}{2},$$

in accordance with the earlier result.

Relation (9-8) shows that the error curve for the best approximation of a polynomial $Q(x) = x^n + \cdots$ by a polynomial of lower degree is given by $2^{-n+1}T_n(x)$. The discussion in the proof of theorem 9.4 revealed that this curve has $n + 1$ extrema in $[-1, 1]$ with alternating signs, but all of the same absolute value. This property is shared by the polynomial P minimizing

$$\max_{-1 \leq x \leq 1} |f(x) - P(x)|$$

where f is any continuous function. The theory of such minimizing polynomials was initiated by Chebyshev (1821–1894); it plays an outstanding role in modern numerical computation.

Problems

18. Determine the polynomial of degree $\leq n - 1$ that best approximates

$$Q(x) = a_0 x^n + a_1 x^{n-1} + \cdots + a_n$$

on an arbitrary interval $a \leq x \leq b$, and show that the least value of the maximum deviation is given by

$$\frac{1}{2^{n-1}} \left(\frac{b - a}{2} \right)^n a_0.$$

[Hint: Reduce the problem to the special case considered above by introducing a new variable x^* by setting

$$x = \frac{b + a}{2} + \frac{b - a}{2} x^*.]$$

19. Determine a polynomial of degree ≤ 4 that provides the best approximation to the function $f(x) = x^5$ on the interval $[0, 4]$.

20. Approximate $f(x) = x^3$ on the interval $[0, 1]$ by a polynomial of degree 2.

21. Approximate $f(x) = x^3$ on the interval $[0, 1]$ by a polynomial of degree 1 by approximating the approximating polynomial of problem 20 by a linear polynomial.

22. Determine directly (by calculus) a linear polynomial $P(x) = ax + b$ such that the quantity

$$\max_{0 \leq x \leq 1} |x^3 - ax - b|$$

is minimized.

23. Prove the uniqueness of the solution (9-10) of the approximation problem considered at the beginning of §9.4.

Recommended Reading

A more general treatment of the error of Lagrangian interpolation is given in Ostrowski [1960], chapter 1. For a discussion of the convergence of sequences of interpolating polynomials see Hildebrand [1956], pp. 114–118. A first introduction to the theorem of Weierstrass and to the approximation of continuous functions by polynomials in general is given in Todd [1963].

Research Problems

1. Assuming that f is sufficiently differentiable, how well does the derivative of an interpolating polynomial approximate the derivative of f? (For a partial answer, see §12.1.)

2. By extending the procedure outlined in problem 21, how well can you *at least* approximate a polynomial of degree n by one of arbitrary degree $m < n$?

chapter 10 construction of the interpolating polynomial: methods using ordinates

After considering the more theoretical aspects of the interpolating polynomial in chapter 9, we shall now discuss some algorithms for actually constructing the polynomial. Many such algorithms have been devised, frequently with some special purpose in mind. There are two main categories of such algorithms: In the first category, the function f enters through its values (or "ordinates") at all interpolation points. In the second category, f enters through its value at one point, and through differences of the function values. Here we are concerned with algorithms of the first category.

10.1 Muller's Method†

For some purposes the interpolating polynomial is calculated most conveniently from the Lagrangian formula (9-4). The Lagrangian formula is especially convenient if the polynomial is to be subjected to algebraic manipulations. As an example of an application of the Lagrangian representation, we shall discuss in more detail Muller's method for solving the equation $f(x) = 0$ mentioned in §4.11.

The reader will recall that the essence of Muller's method is as follows. Assuming that three distinct approximations x_{n-2}, x_{n-1}, x_n to the desired solution s are available, we gain a new approximation by interpolating the function f at the points x_{n-2}, x_{n-1}, x_n by a (normally) quadratic polynomial P. Of the (normally) two zeros of P, one closest to x_n is selected as the new approximation x_{n+1}. The process then is continued with (x_{n-1}, x_n, x_{n+1}) in place of (x_{n-2}, x_{n-1}, x_n) and terminated as soon as $|x_{n+1} - x_n|/|x_{n+1}|$ becomes less than some preassigned number.

---

† This section may be omitted at first reading.

The Lagrangian representation of P is

$$P(x) = \frac{(x - x_{n-1})(x - x_{n-2})}{(x_n - x_{n-1})(x_n - x_{n-2})} f_n + \frac{(x - x_n)(x - x_{n-2})}{(x_{n-1} - x_n)(x_{n-1} - x_{n-2})} f_{n-1}$$

$$+ \frac{(x - x_n)(x - x_{n-1})}{(x_{n-2} - x_n)(x_{n-2} - x_{n-1})} f_{n-2}.$$

In order to write this in a more compact manner, we introduce the quantities

(10-1) $$h_n = x_n - x_{n-1}, \qquad h = x - x_n$$

and obtain

$$P(x) = P(x_n + h)$$

$$= \frac{(h + h_n)(h + h_n + h_{n-1})}{h_n(h_n + h_{n-1})} f_n - \frac{h(h + h_n + h_{n-1})}{h_n h_{n-1}} f_{n-1}$$

$$+ \frac{h(h + h_n)}{(h_n + h_{n-1})h_{n-1}} f_{n-2}.$$

Collecting terms involving like powers of h and writing

(10-2) $$q_n = \frac{h_n}{h_{n-1}}, \qquad q = \frac{h}{h_n},$$

we find

$$P(x) = P(x_n + qh_n)$$
$$= (1 + q_n)^{-1}(A_n q^2 + B_n q + C_n)$$

where

(10-3) $$\begin{cases} A_n = q_n f_n - q_n(1 + q_n)f_{n-1} + q_n^2 f_{n-2}, \\ B_n = (2q_n + 1)f_n - (1 + q_n)^2 f_{n-1} + q_n^2 f_{n-2}, \\ C_n = (1 + q_n)f_n. \end{cases}$$

Solving the quadratic equation $P(x_n + qh_n) = 0$, we find

$$x_{n+1} = x_n + h_n q_{n+1},$$

where

$$q_{n+1} = \frac{-B_n \pm \sqrt{B_n^2 - 4A_n C_n}}{2A_n}.$$

In order to avoid loss of accuracy due to forming differences, this formula is better written in the form

(10-4) $$q_{n+1} = -\frac{2C_n}{B_n \pm \sqrt{B_n^2 - 4A_n C_n}}.$$

Here the sign yielding the *smaller* value of q_{n+1}, i.e., the larger absolute value of the denominator, should be chosen.

It may happen, of course, that the square root in (10-4) becomes imaginary. If f is defined for real values only, the algorithm then breaks down, and a new start must be made. If f is a polynomial, the possibility of imaginary square roots is considered an advantage, since this will automatically lead to approximations to complex zeros.

Three starting values x_0, x_1, x_2, for the algorithm have to be provided from some other source. Muller recommends to start the algorithm by taking for P the Taylor polynomial of degree 2 of f at $x = 0$. If f is a polynomial,

$$f(x) = a_0 x^N + a_1 x^{N-1} + \cdots + a_N,$$

this can be achieved artificially by putting $x_0 = -1$, $x_1 = 1$, $x_2 = 0$, thus

(10-5) $$h_1 = 2, \qquad h_2 = -1, \qquad q_2 = -\tfrac{1}{2}$$

and setting

(10-6) $$\begin{cases} f_0 = a_N - a_{N-1} + a_{N-2}, \\ f_1 = a_N + a_{N-1} + a_{N-2}, \\ f_2 = a_N. \end{cases}$$

As soon as a zero of f has been determined, it is to be divided out by algorithm 3.4 in connection with theorem 4.10.

It follows from the work of Ostrowski ([1960], p. 86, although without reference to Muller's work) that Muller's method converges whenever the three initial approximations are sufficiently close to a simple zero of f. The degree of convergence lies somewhere between that of the regula falsi and of Newton's method. No convergence theorems in the large similar to those for the QD algorithm appear to be known. Nevertheless, the method is (in the United States) among the most popular for finding zeros of polynomials.

Problems

1. Use Muller's method to find all zeros of the polynomial

$$p(x) = 128x^4 - 256x^3 + 160x^2 - 32x + 1.$$

(Real arithmetic may be used here.)

2. Use complex arithmetic to determine all zeros of the polynomial

$$p(x) = x^4 - 8x^3 + 39x^2 - 62x + 51$$

by Muller's method.

10.2   The Lagrangian Representation for Equidistant Abscissas†

In the present section we assume that the points x_k, where the values of the function f are given, are equally spaced.   This is the case, for instance, for most mathematical tables.   If h denotes the distance between two consecutive interpolating points, we then have

$$(10\text{-}7) \qquad\qquad x_k = x_0 + kh.$$

where $k = 0, \pm 1, \pm 1, \pm 2, \ldots.$ We now introduce a new variable s by means of the relation

$$(10\text{-}8) \qquad\qquad x = x_0 + sh.$$

At $x = x_k$, s obviously has the value k.   The variable s thus measures x in units of h, starting at x_0.

We now consider the polynomial P of degree $n - m$ which interpolates the function f at the points $x_m, x_{m+1}, \ldots, x_n$.   Here m and n may be any two integers such that $n \geq m$.   (Ordinarily, we have $m \leq 0, n \geq 0.$)   By (9-4), this polynomial is given by

$$P(x) = \sum_{k=m}^{n} L_k(x) f_k,$$

where

$$L_k(x) = \prod_{\substack{q=m \\ q \neq k}}^{n} \frac{x - x_q}{x_k - x_q}.$$

We now express P in terms of the variable s defined by (10-8).   Evidently

$$x - x_q = (s - q)h,$$

and in particular,

$$x_k - x_q = (k - q)h.$$

If $P(x) = P(x_0 + sh) = p(s)$, we thus have

$$(10\text{-}9) \qquad\qquad p(s) = \sum_{k=m}^{n} l_k(s) f_k,$$

where

$$l_k(s) = \prod_{\substack{q=m \\ q \neq k}}^{n} \frac{s - q}{k - q}.$$

The remarkable fact about this representation of the Lagrangian polynomial is the independence of the functions $l_k(s)$ from h.   These functions, which may be called the normalized Lagrangian interpolation coefficients, depend only on s (the relative location of x with respect to x_0

---

† This section may be omitted at first reading.

and x_1), and, of course, on the integers m and n, which define the set of interpolating points.

EXAMPLES

1. $m = 0, n = 1$. We have

$$l_0(s) = \prod_{\substack{q=0 \\ q \neq 0}}^{1} \frac{s - q}{0 - q} = 1 - s,$$

$$l_1(s) = \prod_{\substack{q=0 \\ q \neq 1}}^{1} \frac{s - q}{1 - q} = \frac{s}{1 - 0} = s.$$

We get, of course, the formula for linear interpolation, expressed as

$$p(s) = (1 - s)f_0 + sf_1.$$

2. A case which is frequently used in practice is given by $m = -1$, $n = 2$. Here we find

$$l_{-1}(s) = \prod_{\substack{q=-1 \\ q \neq -1}}^{2} \frac{s - q}{-1 - q} = \frac{s(s - 1)(s - 2)}{(-1)(-2)(-3)} = -\frac{s(s - 1)(s - 2)}{6},$$

$$l_0(s) = \frac{(s + 1)(s - 1)(s - 2)}{1(-1)(-2)} = \frac{(s + 1)(s - 1)(s - 2)}{2},$$

$$l_1(s) = -\frac{(s + 1)s(s - 2)}{2} = l_0(1 - s),$$

$$l_2(s) = \frac{(s + 1)s(s - 1)}{6} = l_{-1}(1 - s).$$

In view of the fact that the normalized Lagrangian interpolation coefficients depend on one continuous variable only, extensive tables for them have been prepared (National Bureau of Standards [1948]). Such tables take into account symmetry properties such as the relation $l_0(s) = l_1(1 - s)$ noted above.

We note some interesting algebraic relations between the normalized interpolation coefficients. Let us consider the general case, where the interpolating points are $x_m, x_{m+1}, \ldots, x_n$. The polynomial

$$P(x) = \sum_{k=m}^{n} L_k(x)f_k,$$

using $n - m + 1$ points, will furnish an **exact** representation of the function f if f is a polynomial of degree $n - m$ or less. Thus it will be exact, in particular, for the functions

$$f(x) = \left(\frac{x - x_0}{h}\right)^q, \qquad q = 0, 1, \ldots, n - m.$$

Since $f(x) = s^q$, we have $f_k = k^q$.   Hence (10-9) yields the identities in s,

$$(10\text{-}10) \qquad \sum_{k=m}^{n} l_k(s)k^q = s^q, \qquad q = 0, 1, \ldots, n - m.$$

These identities can be regarded as a system of $n - m + 1$ equations for $n - m + 1$ unknowns $l_k(s)$.   They thus could be used to calculate the l_k numerically.

EXAMPLE

3.   For $m = 0$, $n = 2$ the relations (10-10) take the form

$$
\begin{aligned}
l_0(s) + l_1(s) \quad + l_2(s) \quad &= 1 \\
l_1(s)1 \; + l_2(s)2 \; &= s \\
l_1(s)1^2 + l_2(s)2^2 &= s^2.
\end{aligned}
$$

If f is not a polynomial of degree $\leq n - m$, the error formula (9-5) still stands.   In the present situation,

$$L(x) = \prod_{k=m}^{n} (x - x_k)$$

and thus

$$l(s) = L(x_0 + sh) = h^{n-m+1} \prod_{k=m}^{n} (s - k).$$

Thus the error formula now appears in the form

$$(10\text{-}11) \quad f(x_0 + sh) - p(s) = h^{n-m+1} \frac{f^{(n-m+1)}(\xi_s)}{(n - m + 1)!} \prod_{k=m}^{n} (s - k),$$

where ξ_s is a point between the largest and the smallest of the numbers x_m, x_n, x.

EXAMPLE

4.   If linear interpolation is used as in example 1, we have for $0 \leq s \leq 1$

$$p(s) - f(x_0 + sh) = h^2 \frac{f''(\xi_s)}{2} s(1 - s),$$

where $x_0 \leq \xi_s \leq x_1$.

Problems

3. Use normalized Lagrangian interpolation coefficients to determine $J_0(2.4068)$ by interpolation from the following values:

x	$J_0(x)$
2.1	0.16661
2.3	0.05554
2.5	-0.04838
2.7	-0.14245

4. If the interpolating points are $x_m, x_{m+1}, \ldots, x_n$, prove that

$$l_k(s) = l_{n+m-k}(n + m - s), \qquad k = m, \quad m + 1, \ldots, n.$$

5. Make a general statement about the signs of the $l_k(s)$ as a function of $m, n, k,$ and s.

6. If the interpolating points are $x_0, x_1, \ldots, x_n$, show that

$$l_k(s) = (-1)^{n-k} \binom{s}{n+1} \binom{n}{k} \frac{n+1}{s-k}, \qquad k = 0, 1, \ldots, n; \quad s \neq k.$$

7. Assuming that the interpolating points are $x_m, x_{m+1}, \ldots, x_n$, find a closed expression for the sum

$$\sum_{k=m}^{n} k^{n-m+1} l_k(s).$$

[Hint: Apply the error formula (10-11) to the function

$$f(x) = (x - x_0)^{n-m+1}.]$$

10.3 Aitken's Lemma

We now shall discuss certain algorithms that permit us to construct the interpolating polynomial recursively, without reference to the Lagrangian formula (9-4). The basic tool is a lemma which enables us to represent an interpolating polynomial of degree $d + 1$ in terms of two such polynomials of degree d.

Some special notation will be required. We again denote the points at which the function f is to be interpolated by $x_0, x_1, x_2, \ldots, x_n$, and by f_k the value of f at x_k. We shall have to consider polynomials that interpolate f at some, but not all of the points $x_0, x_1, \ldots, x_n$. If S is any nonempty subset of $\{x_0, x_1, \ldots, x_n\}$, we denote by P_S the polynomial interpolating f at those x which are in S. Thus, if S contains $k + 1$ points, P_S is the unique polynomial of degree $\leq k$ such that

$$P_S(x_i) = f_i, \qquad x_i \in S.$$

EXAMPLES

5. If S contains just one point x_i, then $P_S = f_i$.

6. $P_{\{x_1, x_2, x_5\}}$ denotes the polynomial interpolating at the points x_1, x_2, x_5.

Denoting by W the set of all interpolating points, we can state the following lemma:

Lemma 10.3 Let S and T be two proper subsets of W having all but the two points $x_i \in S$ and $x_j \in T$ in common. Then

$$(10\text{-}12) \qquad P_{S \cup T}(x) = \frac{(x_i - x)P_T(x) - (x_j - x)P_S(x)}{x_i - x_j}$$

identically in x.

Here, as usual, $S \cup T$ denotes the union of the sets S and T.

Proof.   Let the sets S and T contain $m + 1$ points each.   Both polynomials P_S and P_T interpolate at $m + 1$ points, hence are of degree $\leq m$. Denoting the expression on the right of (10-12) by P, we see that P has a degree $\leq m + 1$.   Hence if we can show that P interpolates at all points of $S \cup T$, then theorem 9.1 implies that $P = P_{S \cup T}$.

Let x_k be a point of the intersection $S \cap T$ of S and T.   By virtue of

$$P_S(x_k) = P_T(x_k) = f_k,$$

(10-12) yields

$$P(x_k) = \frac{(x_i - x_k)f_k - (x_j - x_k)f_k}{x_i - x_j}$$

$$= f_k,$$

as desired.   For $x = x_i$ we have

$$P(x_i) = \frac{-(x_j - x_i)P_S(x_i)}{x_i - x_j} = f_i,$$

and similarly for $x = x_j$

$$P(x_j) = \frac{(x_i - x_j)P_T(x_j)}{x_i - x_j} = f_j.$$

Thus P has been shown to interpolate at all points in $S \cup T$, completing the proof.

EXAMPLE

7.   If $S = \{x_0, x_2\}$, $T = \{x_2, x_5\}$, we obtain

$$P_{\{x_0, x_2, x_5\}}(x) = \frac{(x_0 - x)P_{\{x_2, x_5\}}(x) - (x_5 - x)P_{\{x_0, x_2\}}(x)}{x_0 - x_5}.$$

8.   Lemma 10.3 is already familiar if the intersection $S \cap T$ is empty. We then have, using example 5,

$$P_{\{x_i, x_j\}}(x) = \frac{(x_i - x)P_{\{x_j\}}(x) - (x_j - x)P_{\{x_i\}}(x)}{x_i - x_j}$$

$$= \frac{(x_i - x)f_j - (x_j - x)f_i}{x_i - x_j}.$$

This is the familiar formula for *linear* interpolation.

Lemma 10.3 can be used in two ways.   We may use it to get a formal *representation* for the interpolating polynomial, or we may use it to calculate the *value* of the polynomial for a given value of x.   In the latter case formula (10-12) requires dividing a sum of products by a single number, an operation that can be performed on a desk computer without writing down intermediate results.

Problems

8. Obtain the Lagrangian formula for quadratic interpolation on the set $\{x_0, x_1, x_2\}$ from the formulas for linear interpolation on the sets $\{x_0, x_1\}$ and $\{x_0, x_2\}$.

9. Prove the following generalization of lemma 10.3: Let S be an arbitrary subset of $\{x_{m+1}, x_{m+2}, \ldots, x_n\}$ and let $S_k = \{x_k, S\}$, $k = 1, 2, \ldots, m$. If $L_k(x)$ ($k = 1, 2, \ldots, m$) are the Lagrangian interpolating coefficients for interpolation on the set $\{x_1, x_2, \ldots, x_m\}$, then

$$P_{\cup S_k}(x) = \sum_{k=1}^{m} L_k(x) P_{S_k}(x).$$

10.4   Aitken's Algorithm

Lemma 10.3 enables us to generate the interpolating polynomials of higher degrees successively from polynomials of lower degrees. It still leaves us considerable freedom in the choice of the sets S and T used to finally obtain the polynomial P_W. Two standardized choices have become widely used, one named after Aitken, the other named after Neville. In both choices a triangular array of polynomials $P_{k,d}$ is generated. Here $P_{k,d}$ is a certain polynomial of degree d that interpolates on a set of $d+1$ points depending on k. Aitken's scheme is as follows:

Algorithm 10.4 For $d = 0, 1, \ldots, n$, generate the polynomials $P_{k,d}$ as follows:

$$(10\text{-}13) \qquad P_{k,0}(x) = f_k, \qquad k = 0, 1, \ldots, n;$$

$$(10\text{-}14) \qquad P_{k,d+1}(x) = \frac{(x_k - x)P_{d,d}(x) - (x_d - x)P_{k,d}(x)}{x_k - x_d},$$

$$k = d + 1, d + 2, \ldots, n.$$

The arrangement of the polynomials $P_{k,d}$ is shown in scheme 10.4.

d	0	1	2	$\cdots$	n	
x_0	$P_{0,0}$					$x_0 - x$
x_1	$P_{1,0}$	$\underline{P_{1,1}}$				$x_1 - x$
x_2	$P_{2,0}$	$P_{2,1}$	$P_{2,2}$			$x_2 - x$
$\vdots$						
x_k	$P_{k,0}$	$\underline{P_{k,1}}$	$\underline{\underline{P_{k,2}}}$			$\underline{x_k - x}$
$\vdots$						
x_n	$P_{n,0}$	$P_{n,1}$	$P_{n,2}$	$\cdots$	$P_{n,n}$	$x_n - x$

Scheme 10.4

The doubly underlined entry in scheme 10.4 is obtained by crosswise multiplication of the simply underlined entries.

Theorem 10.4   In the notation of lemma 10.3,

$$P_{k,d} = P_{\{x_0, x_1, \ldots, x_{d-1}, x_k\}},$$
$$d = 0, 1, \ldots, n; \quad k = d, d+1, \ldots, n.$$

Proof. We use induction with respect to d. By (10-13), the assertion is true for $d = 0$. Assuming it to be true for some $d \geq 0$, lemma 10.3 shows that the polynomial defined by (10-14) interpolates on the union of the sets $\{x_0, x_1, \ldots, x_{d-1}, x_d\}$ and $\{x_0, x_1, \ldots, x_{d-1}, x_k\}$ that is, on the set $\{x_0, x_1, \ldots, x_d, x_k\}$ proving our assertion for d increased by one. For $d = k = n$ we obtain

Corollary 10.4 $P_{n,n} = P_W$.

The rightmost entry in scheme 10.4 is the polynomial that interpolates on the set of *all* points $x_0, x_1, \ldots, x_n$.

EXAMPLE

9. Let $f(x) = x^4$. We wish to calculate $f(3)$ by interpolation at the points $-4, -2, 0, 2, 4$. Scheme 10.4 looks as follows:

x_k	$P_{k,0}$	$P_{k,1}$	$P_{k,2}$	$P_{k,3}$	$P_{k,4}$	$x_k - x$
-4	256					-7
-2	16	-584				-5
0	0	-192	396			-3
2	16	-24	116	-24		-1
4	256	256	116	186	81	1

Problems

10. Use Aitken's algorithm to obtain a value of $\sin \pi/4$ from the following values of the function $f(x) = \sin x\pi/2$:

x	-2	-1	0	1	2	3
$f(x)$	0	-1	0	1	0	-1

11. Use algorithm 10.4 to determine $J_0(2.4068)$ by interpolation from the values given in problem 3.

10.5   Neville's Algorithm

In Neville's use of lemma 10.3, the polynomials $P_{k,d}$ are built up in such a manner that each polynomial interpolates on a set of points with $d + 1$ *consecutive* indices. The algorithm is as follows:

Algorithm 10.5 For $d = 0, 1, \ldots, n$, construct the polynomials $P_{k,d}$ as follows:

$$(10\text{-}15) \qquad P_{k,0}(x) = f_k, \qquad k = 0, 1, \ldots, n;$$

$$(10\text{-}16) \qquad P_{k,d+1}(x) = \frac{(x_k - x)P_{k-1,d}(x) - (x_{k-d-1} - x)P_{k,d}(x)}{x_k - x_{k-d-1}},$$

$$k = d + 1, d + 2, \ldots, n.$$

The arrangement of the polynomials $P_{k,d}$ is the same as in scheme 10.4, but the doubly underlined entry is now computed from asymmetrically located entries as shown in scheme 10.5:

d	0	1	2	$\cdots$	n	
x_0	$P_{0,0}$					$x_0 - x$
x_1	$P_{1,0}$	$P_{1,1}$				$x_1 - x$
x_2	$P_{2,0}$	$P_{2,1}$	$P_{2,2}$			$x_2 - x$
$\vdots$						
x_{k-2}	$P_{k-2,0}$	$P_{k-2,1}$	$P_{k-2,2}$			$\underline{x_{k-2} - x}$
x_{k-1}	$P_{k-1,0}$	$\underline{P_{k-1,1}}$	$P_{k-1,2}$			$\underline{x_{k-1} - x}$
x_k	$P_{k,0}$	$\underline{P_{k,1}}$	$\underline{\underline{P_{k,2}}}$			$\underline{x_k - x}$
$\vdots$						
x_n	$P_{n,0}$	$P_{n,1}$	$P_{n,2}$	$\cdots$	$P_{n,n}$	$x_n - x$

Scheme 10.5

Theorem 10.5 In the notation of lemma 10.3, if the polynomials $P_{k,d}$ are generated by algorithm 10.5,

$$P_{k,d} = P_{(x_{k-d}, x_{k-d+1}, \ldots, x_k)},$$
$$d = 0, 1, \ldots, n; \quad k = d, d + 1, \ldots, n.$$

Proof. By (10-15), the assertion is true for $d = 0$. If true for some $d \geqq 0$, then it follows from (10-16) by virtue of lemma 10.3 that $P_{k,d+1}$ interpolates on the union of the sets $\{x_{k-d-1}, x_{k-d}, \ldots, x_{k-1}\}$ and $\{x_{k-d}, x_{k-d+1}, \ldots, x_k\}$, i.e., on the set $\{x_{k-d-1}, x_{k-d}, \ldots, x_k\}$, proving the assertion with d increased by one.

For $d = k = n$ we have, in particular

Corollary 10.5 $P_{n,n} = P_W$,

thus again, the rightmost polynomial in Neville's scheme is the desired polynomial interpolating at *all* points $x_0, x_1, \ldots, x_n$.

EXAMPLE

10. We again consider $f(x) = x^4$ and calculate $f(3)$ from the values at $x = -4, -2, 0, 2, 4$, using Neville's algorithm. The following scheme results:

x_k	$P_{k,0}$	$P_{k,1}$	$P_{k,2}$	$P_{k,3}$	$P_{k,4}$	$x_k - x$
-4	256					-7
-2	16	-584				-5
0	0	-24	396			-3
2	16	24	36	-24		-1
4	256	136	108	96	81	1

Problems

12. Which entries in the schemes of the polynomials $P_{k,d}$ generated by the algorithms 10.4 and 10.5 are necessarily identical?

13. Find an approximate value of $\sqrt{2}$ by interpolation, using Neville's algorithm, from the values of the function $f(x) = 2^x$ at the points $x = -2, -1, 0, 1, 2, 3$.

14. Calculate an approximate value of the infinite series

$$1 + \frac{1}{2^2} + \frac{1}{3^2} + \frac{1}{4^2} + \cdots$$

in the following manner: Let

$$f\left(\frac{1}{n}\right) = 1 + \frac{1}{2^2} + \cdots + \frac{1}{n^2} \qquad (n = 1, 2, 3, \ldots)$$

and calculate $f(0)$ by extrapolation from $f(1), f(\frac{1}{2}), f(\frac{1}{3}), \ldots$, using Neville's algorithm.

10.6 Inverse Interpolation

Interpolation (approximately) solves the problem of finding the value of $y = f(x)$ when x is given. It does *not* solve the problem of finding x when $y = f(x)$ is given. (We could, of course, replace f by the interpolating polynomial P and solve the equation $y = P(x)$ for x, but in doing so we would merely replace one problem by another problem of comparable difficulty.) The problem can be easily solved, however, by interchanging the roles of x and y. Speaking abstractly, this amounts to interpolating the *inverse function* $f^{[-1]}$ instead of f itself. Speaking concretely, it means interchanging the roles of the x_k and the f_k. Since, even for equidistant x_k, the corresponding values f_k are not equidistant, it is essential that we are able to calculate the interpolating polynomial for nonequidistant interpolating points. As an example, we consider the problem of solving $f(x) = 0$ when the function f is known at $n + 1$ distinct points x_k. If the polynomial $P(y)$ interpolating the inverse function at the points $f(x_m) = f_m$ is constructed by Aitken's algorithm and evaluated at $y = 0$, we obtain the following algorithm:

Algorithm 10.6   Let

$$X_{m,0} = x_m   (m = 0, 1, \ldots, n)$$

and form for $n = 0, 1, \ldots, m - 1$ the numbers

$$X_{m,n+1} = \frac{f_m X_{n,n} - f_n X_{m,n}}{f_m - f_n}.$$

The approximate solution is given by $X_{n,n}$. The arrangement of the triangular array of the values $X_{m,n}$ is as follows:

$$
\begin{array}{c|ccccc}
f_0 & X_{0,0} \\
f_1 & X_{1,0} & X_{1,1} \\
f_2 & X_{2,0} & X_{2,1} & X_{2,2} \\
\vdots & \cdot & \cdot & \cdot & \cdot & \cdot \\
f_n & X_{n,0} & X_{n,1} & X_{n,2} & \cdots & X_{n,n}.
\end{array}
$$

Inverse interpolation is possible only if, in the range where interpolation is used, x is a single-valued function of y. In the example depicted in figure 10.6, where this condition is not satisfied, the interpolating polynomial bears no relationship to the inverse function.

The *error* of inverse interpolation obeys the same laws as the error of ordinary interpolation. It depends on the derivatives of the inverse function $f^{[-1]}(y)$. These derivatives can be calculated, in principle at least, from the derivatives of the function f. Differentiating the identity

$$f^{[-1]}(f(x)) = x$$

we obtain

(10-17) $$f^{[-1]'}(f(x))f'(x) = 1;$$

hence

$$f^{[-1]'}(f(x)) = \frac{1}{f'(x)}.$$

Higher derivatives can be obtained by repeatingly differentiating (10-17). For instance,

$$f^{[-1]''}(f(x))[f'(x)]^2 + f^{[-1]'}(f(x))f''(x) = 0$$

shows that

$$f^{[-1]''}(f(x)) = -\frac{f''(x)}{f'(x)^3}.$$

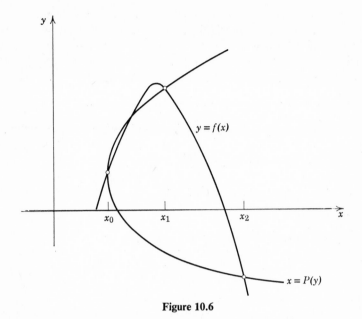

Figure 10.6

This process can be continued, but the results become more and more complicated, even if the derivatives of f are simple.

Problem

15. Using inverse interpolation, find an approximate value of the second zero of the Bessel function $J_0(x)$ if the following values are given:

x	$J_0(x)$
5.2	-0.1102904
5.4	-0.0412101
5.6	0.0269709
5.8	0.0917026

10.7 Iterated Inverse Interpolation

Solving an equation $f(x) = 0$ by simple inverse interpolation as described above is appropriate if the function f is known only at a set of discrete points x (e.g., if f is a tabulated function). If $f(x)$ can be calculated for arbitrary x, it is possible to test the result of the inverse interpolation procedure by evaluating f at the interpolated value of x. In general, $f(x)$ will not be exactly equal to 0. In this case, $f(x)$ and x are introduced as new entries in the interpolation table, and a new row of values of X is calculated by inverse interpolation. The Neville form of the interpolation table is especially appropriate here, because in it already the first entries in a new horizontal row are good approximations to the desired value of x. Beginning with two values of f, the Neville scheme is continued systematically row by row as follows:

Algorithm 10.7   Choose x_0 and x_1, and let

$$f_0 = f(x_0), \qquad X_{0,0} = x_0,$$

(10-18)
$$f_1 = f(x_1), \qquad X_{1,0} = x_1,$$

$$X_{1,1} = \frac{f_1 X_{0,0} - f_0 X_{1,0}}{f_1 - f_0}.$$

Then form the triangular array of numbers $X_{m,n}$ $(m = 2, 3, \ldots;$ $n = 0, 1, \ldots, m)$ by means of the relations

$$X_{m,0} = X_{m-1,m-1}, \qquad f_m = f(X_{m,0}),$$

(10-19)
$$X_{m,n+1} = \frac{f_m X_{m-1,n} - f_{m-n-1} X_{m,n}}{f_m - f_{m-n-1}}$$

$$n = 0, 1, \ldots, m - 1.$$

If f is sufficiently differentiable in a neighborhood of a solution s of $f(x) = 0$, if $f'(x) \neq 0$, and if x_0 and x_1 are sufficiently close to s, it is intuitively clear that the numbers $X_{n,n}$ converge to s for $n \to \infty$.

As described above, the table of the values $X_{m,n}$ extends farther and farther to the right with every new row. Ultimately, little extra accuracy will be gained from the entries far to the right, because they depend on values $X_{n,0}$ with small n which presumably are poor approximations to the desired solution. It is therefore advisable not to increase the degrees of the inverse interpolating polynomial beyond a certain degree d (say $d = 2$ or $d = 3$), that is, to truncate the table of values $X_{m,n}$ after the dth column. This means that the formulas (10-19) are only used for $m \leq d$, for $m > d$ they are to be replaced by the following:

(10-20)
$$\begin{cases} X_{m,0} = X_{m-1,d}, \qquad f_m = f(X_{m,0}), \\ X_{m,n+1} = \dfrac{f_m X_{m-1,n} - f_{m-n-1} X_{m,n}}{f_m - f_{m-n-1}}, \qquad n = 0, 1, \ldots, d - 1. \end{cases}$$

The convergence of this modified version of algorithm 10.7 is, under suitable conditions, proved by Ostrowski ([1960], chapter 13).

The case $d = 2$ of the modified algorithm 10.7 is very similar to Muller's method discussed in §10.1, except that now the inverse function rather than the function itself is interpolated by a quadratic polynomial. From the computational point of view it would even seem to be superior to Muller's method since it does not require the evaluation of square roots. However, just for this reason it lacks the advantage of automatically branching off into the complex domain if no real zeros are found.

Problems

16. Using repeated quadratic inverse interpolation, find the root of the polynomial

$$P(x) = 70x^4 - 140x^3 + 90x^2 - 20x + 1$$

located between 0.6 and 0.7. (Use Horner's scheme to evaluate the polynomial.)

17. Show that iterated *linear* inverse interpolation is identical with the regula falsi (see §4.11).

Recommended Reading

The practical aspects of interpolation are dealt with in a volume issued by the Nautical Almanac Service [1956]. The theory of a number of processes for solving $f(x) = 0$ by methods based on interpolation is dealt with very thoroughly by Ostrowski [1960].

Research Problems

1. How can the regula falsi be extended to the solution of systems of more than one equation? (For some pertinent remarks, see Ostrowski [1960], p. 146.)

2. Develop a theory for interpolating functions of two variables by bilinear polynomials of the form $a + bx + cy + dxy$.

chapter 11 construction of the interpolating polynomial: methods using differences

The representations of the interpolating polynomial discussed in chapter 10 were based directly on the values of the interpolated function. They do not convey any information, explicit or implicit, concerning the *error* of the interpolating polynomial. In this respect, the methods to be discussed in the present chapter do somewhat better. These representations are based on *differences* of the sequence of function values, and on certain properties of binomial coefficients.

11.1 Differences and Binomial Coefficients

Differences of a sequence of numbers were already defined in §4.4 and §6.9. We now introduce differences of a function f defined on a suitable interval. Let $h > 0$ be a constant. The function Δf whose value at x is given by

$$\Delta f(x) = f(x + h) - f(x)$$

is called the *first* (forward) *difference* of the function f. It obviously depends on the step h, although this fact is usually not made evident in the notation. Higher differences are defined inductively by the relation

$$\Delta^k f = \Delta(\Delta^{k-1} f), \qquad k = 2, 3, \ldots.$$

For instance,

$$\Delta^2 f(x) = f(x + 2h) - 2f(x + h) + f(x).$$

For symmetry we put

$$\Delta^0 f = f.$$

An induction argument entirely analogous to that employed in the proof of (6-27) shows that

$$\Delta^k f(x) = f(x + kh) - \binom{k}{1} f(x + (k - 1)h)$$

$$+ \binom{k}{2} f(x + (k - 2)h) + \cdots + (-1)^k f(x).$$

If, for integral k, $x_k = x_0 + kh$, and if we write

$$f(x_k) = f_k,$$

the differences thus introduced produce the same result as the difference operator Δ introduced in §4.4, if the latter is applied to the sequence of values $\{f_k\}$ of f.

It is to be expected that the differences of a function share many properties, and have many connections, with the derivatives of the function. For instance, the mean value theorem of differential calculus states that, for some ξ between x and $x + h$,

$$\Delta f(x) = h f'(\xi).$$

We shall soon become acquainted with a generalization of this relation to differences and derivatives of arbitrary order.

In differential calculus, a set of functions enjoying particularly simple properties with respect to differentiation is the set of monomials $x^n/n!$, $n = 0, 1, \ldots$. In fact,

(11-1)
$$\left(\frac{x^n}{n!}\right)' = \frac{x^{n-1}}{(n-1)!}.$$

In difference calculus, an analogous role is played by the binomial coefficients

(11-2)
$$\binom{s}{n} = \frac{s(s-1)\ldots(s-n+1)}{n!}.$$

Here s is any real (or even complex) number, and n is a positive integer. For $n = 0$, the symbol (11-2) is defined to be 1, for negative integers n, zero. It is always understood in the following that the operator Δ acts on the variable s, and that the step $h = 1$ is implied. With this understanding we have

(11-3)
$$\Delta \binom{s}{n} = \binom{s}{n-1}.$$

This is trivially true for $n \leqq 0$; for $n > 0$ we have

$$\Delta\binom{s}{n} = \binom{s+1}{n} - \binom{s}{n}$$

$$= \frac{(s+1)s(s-1)\ldots(s-n+2) - s(s-1)\ldots(s-n+1)}{n!}$$

$$= \frac{[s+1-(s-n+1)]s(s-1)\ldots(s-n+2)}{n(n-1)!}$$

$$= \binom{s}{n-1},$$

as desired.   By induction it follows immediately from (11-3) that

$$(11\text{-}4) \qquad \Delta^k\binom{s}{n} = \binom{s}{n-k}, \qquad k = 0, 1, 2, \ldots.$$

Another property of the monomials $x^n/n!$ also carries over to the binomial coefficients.   It is trivial that every polynomial of degree n can be expressed as a linear combination of the monomials

$$1, \frac{x}{1!}, \ldots, \frac{x^n}{n!}.$$

Similarly, such a polynomial can also be expressed as a linear combination of

$$1, \binom{s}{1}, \binom{s}{2}, \ldots, \binom{s}{n}.$$

In fact, a somewhat more general statement is true.   If $\{a_1, a_2, \ldots, a_n\}$ is an arbitrary set of real numbers, then a polynomial of degree n is expressible in terms of the generalized monomials

$$1, \frac{x+a_1}{1!}, \frac{(x+a_2)^2}{2!}, \ldots, \frac{(x+a_n)^n}{n!}.$$

This fact has the following analog:

Theorem 11.1   Let $a_1, a_2, \ldots, a_n$ be n arbitrary real numbers, and let p be any polynomial of degree n.   Then there exist constants A_0, $A_1, \ldots, A_n$ such that

$$(11\text{-}5) \quad p(s) = A_0 + A_1\binom{s+a_1}{1} + A_2\binom{s+a_2}{2} + \cdots + A_n\binom{s+a_n}{n}$$

identically in s.

Proof.   Evidently the statement of the theorem is true for $n = 0$; we proceed by induction with respect to n and assume that the theorem is true for some nonnegative integer $n - 1$. If

$$p(s) = b_0 s^n + b_1 s^{n-1} + \cdots + b_n,$$

then the polynomial

(11-6) $$q(s) = p(s) - b_0 n! \binom{s + a_n}{n}$$

is of degree $n - 1$, since the leading coefficient of

$$\binom{s + a_n}{n} \quad \text{is} \quad \frac{s^n}{n!}.$$

By the induction hypothesis, q can be represented in the form

$$q(s) = A_0 + A_1 \binom{s + a_1}{1} + \cdots + A_{n-1} \binom{s + a_{n-1}}{n - 1}.$$

Solving (11-6) for $p(s)$ we obtain a representation of the desired form (11-5), where $A_n = b_0 n!$

EXAMPLES

1. A special case of theorem 11.1 was used in example 13 of chapter 6, where we obtained the formula

$$s^3 = 6\binom{s}{3} + 6\binom{s}{2} + \binom{s}{1}.$$

2. The truth of corollary 6.8 (which was not proved in §6.8) follows from the special case $a_1 = a_2 = \cdots = a_n = 0$ of the above theorem 11.1.

Problems

1. Determine all functions f that are defined on the whole real line and satisfy

$$\Delta f(x) = h c f(x)$$

identically in x, where c is a constant.
2. If f and g are two differentiable functions, find a formula for $\Delta(fg)$ and derive the product rule for differentiation.
3. Formulate an algorithm for obtaining the representation (11-5) for a given polynomial $p(s) = b_0 s^n + \cdots + b_n$ and for given constants $a_1, a_2, \ldots, a_n$. (Determine A_n first.)
4. Represent the polynomials $p(s) = s^n$ $(n = 1, 2, \ldots)$ in the form (11-5), where $a_n = 1, 2, \ldots$.
5. Find a closed expression for the differences

$$\Delta^k f_0, \quad k = 0, 1, 2, \ldots,$$

if $f(x) = e^x$ and $x_0 = 0$. Show that in this case

$$\lim_{h \to 0} h^{-k} \Delta^k f_0 = f'(0).$$

11.2   Finalized Representations of Sequences of Interpolating Polynomials

We now return to the problem of constructing the polynomials interpolating a function f on a given set of points. The interpolating points are a set of equidistant points

$$x_k = x_0 + kh,$$

where the integer k may be positive or negative. As usual we write

$$f_k = f(x_k).$$

It will be convenient to express the interpolating polynomial in terms of the variable

(11-7) $$s = \frac{x - x_0}{h}.$$

Thus, if S is a set of interpolating points x_k and P_S denotes the polynomial interpolating f at the points of S, we shall define p by

$$p(s) = P_S(x) = P_S(x_0 + sh).$$

The polynomial p is characterized by the property that

$$p(k) = f_k \quad \text{whenever} \quad x_k \in S;$$

for nonintegral values of s, $p(s)$ is to be regarded as an approximation to $f(x_0 + sh)$.

Actually, we are now not merely interested in constructing a single polynomial, interpolating f on a single set S. Instead, we shall try to determine sequences of interpolating polynomials that interpolate f on a sequence of sets $S_0, S_1, S_2, \ldots$ of interpolating points. These sets are defined as follows:

Let $m_0, m_1, m_2, \ldots$ be a nonincreasing sequence of integers such that

(11-8) $$m_k - 1 \leqq m_{k+1} \leqq m_k$$

for all $k = 0, 1, 2, \ldots$, and let

$$S_k = \{x_{m_k}, x_{m_k + 1}, \ldots, x_{m_k + k}\},$$

$k = 0, 1, 2, \ldots$. The set S_k thus contains precisely $k + 1$ consecutive interpolating points, beginning with the point x_{m_k}. By virtue of (11-8), each set S_k contains the preceding set S_{k-1} and thus *all* preceding sets $S_{k-2}, \ldots, S_0$.

EXAMPLES

3. Let $m_k = 0$, $k = 0, 1, 2, \ldots$. Then

$$S_k = \{x_0, x_1, \ldots, x_k\}.$$

4. If $m_k = -k$, $k = 0, 1, 2, \ldots$, we have

$$S_k = \{x_{-k}, x_{-k+1}, \ldots, x_0\}.$$

5. Setting $m_0 = m_1 = 0$, $m_2 = m_3 = -1, \ldots$, we obtain the sets

$$S_{2k} = \{x_{-k}, x_{-k+1}, \ldots, x_k\},$$
$$S_{2k+1} = \{x_{-k}, x_{-k+1}, \ldots, x_{k+1}\}, \qquad k = 0, 1, 2, \ldots.$$

6. Setting $m_0 = 0$, $m_1 = m_2 = -1$, $m_3 = m_4 = -2, \ldots$, the sets S_k are given by

$$S_{2k} = \{x_{-k}, x_{-k+1}, \ldots, x_k\},$$
$$S_{2k+1} = \{x_{-k-1}, x_{-k}, \ldots, x_k\}.$$

By the fundamental theorem 9.1, there exists, for every $k = 0, 1, 2, \ldots$, a unique polynomial P_{S_k} of degree $\leq k$ such that

$$P_{S_k}(x_m) = f_m, \qquad x_m \in S_k.$$

If x and s are connected by (11-7), we shall write

$$p_k(s) = P_{S_k}(x).$$

We now wish to consider the following *problem*: Given a sequence of integers $\{m_k\}$ satisfying (11-8) (and hence a sequence of sets $S_0, S_1, \ldots$), determine two sequences of real numbers $\{a_k\}$ and $\{A_k\}$ such that, for *every* $n = 0, 1, 2, \ldots$,

$$(11\text{-}9) \qquad p_n(s) = A_0 + A_1 \binom{s + a_1}{1} + \cdots + A_n \binom{s + a_n}{n}.$$

identically in s.

It is not clear at all that this problem has a solution. Theorem 11.1 merely tells us that, for an arbitrary sequence $\{a_k\}$ and for every fixed integer n, constants $A_0, A_1, \ldots, A_n$ can be found such that (11-9) holds. It is to be expected, however, that if n is replaced by $n + 1$, the constants $A_0, A_1, \ldots, A_n$ already found will have to be replaced by other constants. If we wish to obtain a "finalized" representation of the sequence $\{p_n\}$ with the property that the constants A_k, once determined, remain unchanged, we can hope to do so only by a judicious choice of the sequence $\{a_n\}$.

EXAMPLE

7. Let $a_n = n$, $n = 1, 2, \ldots$. The function $f(s) = s$ is interpolated at $s = 0$ by $p_0(s) = 0$. This is a representation of the form (11-9) with $A_0 = 0$. In order to interpolate f at $s = 0$ and $s = 1$, we must take

$$p_1(s) = s = -1 + \binom{s + 1}{1}.$$

The last expression is again of the form (11-9), but we now have $A_0 = -1$.
The coefficient $A_0 = 0$ is preserved if and only if we choose $a_1 = -0$.

Let us now investigate the properties which the sequence $\{a_k\}$ must have
if the above problem is to have a solution.   For an arbitrary integer
$n \geq 0$, consider the two polynomials

$$p_n(s) = A_0 + A_1\binom{s + a_1}{1} + \cdots + A_n\binom{s + a_n}{n}$$

and

$$p_{n+1}(s) = A_0 + A_1\binom{s + a_1}{1} + \cdots + A_n\binom{s + a_n}{n} + A_{n+1}\binom{s + a_{n+1}}{n + 1}.$$

The polynomial p_n interpolates on the set S_n, p_{n+1} on the set S_{n+1}.   Since
S_n is contained in S_{n+1}, both polynomials interpolate on the set S_n.
Both thus have identical values for x_s in the set S_n.   This means that the
last term

$$A_{n+1}\binom{s + a_{n+1}}{n + 1}$$

must vanish whenever s is equal to one of the integers

(11-10) $m_n, m_n + 1, \ldots, m_n + n.$

If f is such that p_{n+1} has degree $n + 1$, then $A_{n+1} \neq 0$, and the required
condition is

(11-11) $$\binom{s + a_{n+1}}{n + 1} = 0$$

for all said integers.   The binomial coefficient in (11-11) is zero if and only
if s is one of the numbers

$$-a_{n+1}, -a_{n+1} + 1, \ldots, -a_{n+1} + n.$$

Evidently the set of these numbers coincides with the set (11-10) if and
only if

(11-12) $a_{n+1} = -m_n, \qquad n = 0, 1, 2, \ldots.$

This condition fully determines the sequence $\{a_1, a_2, \ldots\}$ as a function of
the sequence $\{m_n\}$.

There remains the problem of determining the constants A_k.   For a
fixed value of n, there certainly exist, by theorem 11.1, constants A_0,
$A_1, \ldots, A_n$ such that

$$p_n(s) = A_0 + A_1\binom{s - m_0}{1} + \cdots + A_n\binom{s - m_{n-1}}{n}.$$

The question is whether these A_k are independent of n. In order to determine A_k for $0 \leqq k \leqq n$, we form the kth difference of $p_n(s)$. By (11-4), we get

(11-13) $\Delta^k p_n(s) = A_k + A_{k+1} \binom{s - m_k}{1} + \cdots + A_n \binom{s - m_{n-1}}{n - k}.$

In this identity we set $s = m_k$. The values of p involved in forming the difference $\Delta^k p_n(s)$ then are the values $p(s)$ for $s = m_k, m_k + 1, \ldots, m_k + k$, i.e., those values of s for which $x_s \in S_k$. Since $S_k \subset S_n$, we have

$$p_n(s) = f_s$$

for these values, and hence

$$\Delta^k p_n(m_k) = \Delta^k f_{m_k}.$$

In the expression on the right of (11-13), all binomial coefficients are zero for $s = m_k$, as it follows from (11-8) that

$$0 \leqq m_k - m_{k+l} \leqq l, \qquad l = 0, 1, 2, \ldots.$$

We thus obtain

$$A_k = \Delta^k f_{m_k},$$

and it turns out that A_k is independent of n, the degree of the interpolating polynomial, as we had hoped. The polynomials p_n solving the problem posed initially thus are given by

(11-14) $p_n(s) = \sum_{k=0}^{n} \Delta^k f_{m_k} \binom{s - m_{k-1}}{k}.$

They can be generated recursively by the following simple algorithm:

Algorithm 11.2 If $\{m_k\}$ is a sequence of integers satisfying (11-8), let $p_0(s) = f_{m_0}$, and for $n = 0, 1, 2, \ldots$,

(11-15) $p_{n+1}(s) = p_n(s) + \Delta^{n+1} f_{m_{n+1}} \binom{s - m_n}{n + 1}.$

By construction, we have

$$p_n(k) = f(x_k),$$

$k = m_n, m_n + 1, \ldots, m_n + n$. We wish to find an expression for the error of $p_n(s)$ if s is not equal to one of the above values of k. This is easily possible in our new notation. According to theorem 9.2 the difference

$$f(x) - P_{S_n}(x) = f(x) - p_n(s)$$

can, if f has a continuous derivative of order $n + 1$, be written in the form

$$\frac{(x - x_{m_n})(x - x_{m_n + 1}) \cdots (x - x_{m_n + n})}{(n + 1)!} f^{(n+1)}(\xi_x),$$

where ξ_x is some point in the smallest interval containing x, x_{m_n}, and $x_{m_n + n}$. We have

$$x - x_{m_n + k} = h[s - (m_n + k)], \qquad k = 0, 1, \ldots, n.$$

The product of the factors $x - x_{m_n + k}$ appearing above thus can be written

$$h^{n+1}(n + 1)! \binom{s - m_n}{n + 1},$$

and we obtain

Theorem 11.2 Let the function f have a continuous $(n + 1)$st derivative on an interval containing the points $x = x_0 + sh$, x_{m_n}, and $x_{m_n + n}$. If $p_n(s)$ is defined by algorithm 11.2, then for a suitable point ξ_x of that interval

$$(11\text{-}16) \qquad f(x) = p_n(s) + h^{n+1} f^{(n+1)}(\xi_x) \binom{s - m_n}{n + 1}.$$

A comparison of the equations (11-15) and (11-16) shows that the correction term which has to be added to $p_n(s)$ in order to obtain the exact value of f is of the same form as the term that has to be added in order to pass from p_n to p_{n+1}, with the exception that

$$\Delta^{n+1} f_{m_n + 1} \text{ is to be replaced by } h^{n+1} f^{(n+1)}(\xi_x).$$

If the function $f^{(n+1)}$ does not change very rapidly, these two terms are of the same order of magnitude (see the problems 11 and 12). One can thus say with some justification that the error of p_n is of the order of the first omitted term in the sum (11-14). Thus, if the degree of the interpolating polynomial is not fixed beforehand, one may hope to obtain an accurate representation of f (to within rounding errors) by extending the sum (11-14) through such a value of n that the omitted terms are insignificant.

EXAMPLES

We shall construct the sequences of interpolating polynomials corresponding to the sequences $\{m_k\}$ considered in the examples 3, 4, 5, and 6.

8. For $m_n = 0$, $n = 0, 1, 2, \ldots$ we obtain the polynomials

$$p_n(s) = f_0 + \binom{s}{1} \Delta f_0 + \binom{s}{2} \Delta^2 f_0 + \cdots + \binom{s}{n} \Delta^n f_0,$$

interpolating on the sets $\{x_0, x_1, \ldots, x_n\}$.

9.   For $m_n = -n$, $n = 0, 1, 2, \ldots$ we obtain

$$p_n(s) = f_0 + \binom{s}{1} \Delta f_{-1} + \binom{s+1}{2} \Delta^2 f_{-2} + \cdots + \binom{s+n-1}{n} \Delta^n f_{-n}.$$

These polynomials p_n interpolate on the set $\{x_0, x_{-1}, x_{-2}, \ldots, x_{-n}\}$.

The formulas obtained in examples 8 and 9 are known, respectively, as the *Newton forward* and the *Newton backward formula*.

10.   Letting

$$\{m_0, m_1, m_2, \ldots\} = \{0, 0, -1, -1, \ldots\},$$

we get the polynomials

$$p_n(s) = f_0 + \binom{s}{1} \Delta f_0 + \binom{s}{2} \Delta^2 f_{-1}$$

$$+ \binom{s+1}{3} \Delta^3 f_{-1} + \binom{s+1}{4} \Delta^4 f_{-2} + \cdots$$

$$(n + 1 \text{ terms})$$

interpolating on the sets

$$\{x_{-k}, x_{-k+1}, \ldots, x_k\} \quad \text{for } n = 2k$$

and

$$\{x_{-k}, x_{-k+1}, \ldots, x_{k+1}\} \quad \text{for } n = 2k + 1.$$

11.   Taking $\{m_0, m_1, m_2, \ldots\} = \{0, -1, -1, -2, -2, \ldots\}$, we obtain the polynomials

$$p_n(s) = f_0 + \binom{s}{1} \Delta f_{-1} + \binom{s+1}{2} \Delta^2 f_{-1}$$

$$+ \binom{s+1}{3} \Delta^3 f_{-2} + \binom{s+2}{4} \Delta^4 f_{-2} + \cdots$$

$$(n + 1 \text{ terms}).$$

They interpolate on the sets $\{x_{-k}, x_{-k+1}, \ldots, x_k\}$ for $n = 2k$ and $\{x_{-k-1}, x_{-k}, \ldots, x_k\}$ for $n = 2k + 1$.

The formulas obtained in the examples 10 and 11 are known, respectively, as the *Gauss forward* and the *Gauss backward formula*.

Problems

6. Forming differences of the values of the function J_0 given in problem 15, chapter 10, find $J_0(5.5)$ by the four interpolation formulas given above.

7. Using the fact that

$$\binom{s}{m} = (-1)^m \binom{m-s-1}{m}$$

and expressing forward differences by backward differences (see §6.9), show that the Newton backward formula can be written in the form

$$p_n(s) = f_0 - \binom{-s}{1}\nabla f_0 + \binom{-s}{2}\nabla^2 f_0 - \cdots + (-1)^n\binom{-s}{n}\nabla^n f_0.$$

8. *Expressing ordinates in terms of differences.* Establish the formula

$$f_k = \sum_{m=0}^{k} \binom{k}{m}\Delta^m f_0, \qquad k = 0, 1, 2, \ldots$$

(a) by induction; (b) by considering it as a special case of the Newton formula.

9. Using the fact that the identity of problem 8 must hold for arbitrary values of $f_0, f_1, \ldots$, show that for arbitrary integers n and k such that $0 \leqq n \leqq k$

$$\sum_{m=n}^{k} (-1)^{m-n}\binom{k}{m}\binom{m}{n} = \begin{cases} 1, & n = k \\ 0, & n < k. \end{cases}$$

10. Study the convergence of the infinite series

$$\sum_{k=0}^{\infty} \Delta^k f_0 \binom{s}{k}$$

(Newton's formula extended to infinitely many terms), where $f(x) = e^x$, as it depends on x and h. (Use problem 5 and apply the ratio test.)

11. Let f be n times continuously differentiable on a suitable interval. Show that for some $\xi \in (x_0, x_n)$

$$\Delta^n f_0 = h^n f^{(n)}(\xi).$$

[Differentiate the function

$$f(x) - \sum_{k=0}^{n} \binom{s}{k}\Delta^k f_0, \qquad s = \frac{x - x_0}{h}$$

n times with respect to x and apply Rolle's theorem.]

12. As an application of the preceding problem, show that

$$\lim_{h \to 0} h^{-n}\Delta^n f_0 = f^{(n)}(x_0)$$

for any sufficiently differentiable function f.

13. Assume that the values of f_n are known only up to rounding errors ε_n, where $|\varepsilon_n| \leqq \varepsilon$. Show that the maximum error in $\Delta^k f_n$ can be as large as $2^k \varepsilon$.

11.3   Some Special Interpolation Formulas

In spite of their basic simplicity the interpolation formulas of Newton and Gauss given in §11.2 are not frequently used in practice, mainly because of their lack of formal symmetry. More frequently used in practical interpolation are certain formulas named after Stirling, Bessel, and Everett.

The elegant formulation of these formulas requires the introduction of two new operators μ and δ in addition to the forward difference operator Δ. The operator μ is defined by

(11-17) $$\mu f(x) = \frac{1}{2}\left[f\left(x + \frac{h}{2}\right) + f\left(x - \frac{h}{2}\right)\right]$$

and consequently is called the *averaging operator*. The operator δ is defined by

(11-18) $$\delta f(x) = f\left(x + \frac{h}{2}\right) - f\left(x - \frac{h}{2}\right)$$

and is called the *central difference operator*. Note that δ can always be expressed in terms of Δ, and vice versa. For instance,

$$\Delta^{2k}f_{-k} = \delta^{2k}f_0, \qquad k = 0, 1, 2, \ldots.$$

A further identity to be noted is

$$\mu\delta f_0 = \tfrac{1}{2}(\Delta f_{-1} + \Delta f_0) = \tfrac{1}{2}(f_1 - f_{-1}).$$

Stirling's formula. For a given even integer $n = 2k$ both the Gauss forward and the Gauss backward formula yield the interpolating polynomial corresponding to the set $\{x_{-k}, x_{-k+1}, \ldots, x_k\}$. Thus also their arithmetic mean must yield the same polynomial. The resulting polynomial

$$p_{2k}(s) = f_0 + \binom{s}{1}\frac{1}{2}[\Delta f_{-1} + \Delta f_0]$$

$$+ \frac{1}{2}\left[\binom{s}{2} + \binom{s+1}{2}\right]\Delta^2 f_{-1} + \binom{s+1}{3}\frac{1}{2}[\Delta^3 f_{-1} + \Delta^3 f_{-2}]$$

$$+ \cdots + \frac{1}{2}\left[\binom{s+k-1}{2k} + \binom{s+k}{2k}\right]\Delta^{2k}f_{-k}$$

can by virtue of the identity

$$\binom{s+k-1}{2k} + \binom{s+k}{2k} = \frac{s}{k}\binom{s+k-1}{2k-1} \qquad (k = 1, 2, \ldots)$$

be written in the form

(11-19) $$p_{2k}(s) = f_0 + \binom{s}{1}\left[\mu\delta f_0 + \frac{s}{2}\delta^2 f_0\right] + \cdots$$

$$+ \binom{s+k-1}{2k-1}\left[\mu\delta^{2k-1}f_0 + \frac{s}{2k}\delta^{2k}f_0\right].$$

This formula, called Stirling's formula, expresses the polynomial interpolating at an odd number of equidistant points in terms of central differences at the center point. It is preferably used for interpolation near that center point.

Bessel's formula. If n is odd, $n = 2k + 1$, the Gaussian forward formula at x_0 and the Gaussian backward formula at x_1 interpolate on the same set of points $S_{2k+1} = \{x_{-k}, x_{-k+1}, \ldots, x_{k+1}\}$. The Gaussian backward formula centered at x_1 is given by

$$p_{2k+1}(s) = f_1 + \binom{s'}{1} \Delta f_0 + \binom{s' + 1}{2} \Delta^2 f_0 + \cdots + \binom{s' + k}{2k + 1} \Delta^{2k+1} f_{-k},$$

where

$$s' = \frac{x - x_1}{h} = \frac{x - x_0 - h}{h} = s - 1.$$

Averaging this expression with the Gaussian forward formula at x_0 we get, after some simplification,

$$(11\text{-}20) \quad p_{2k+1}(s) = \mu f_{1/2} + (s - \tfrac{1}{2}) \, \delta f_{1/2}$$

$$+ \binom{s}{2} [\mu \delta^2 f_{1/2} + \tfrac{1}{3}(s - \tfrac{1}{2}) \, \delta^3 f_{1/2}] + \cdots$$

$$+ \binom{s + k - 1}{2k} \left[\mu \delta^{2k} f_{1/2} + \frac{1}{2k + 1} (s - \tfrac{1}{2}) \, \delta^{2k+1} f_{1/2} \right].$$

This formula is known as *Bessel's formula.* It expresses the interpolating polynomial for an even number of consecutive points in terms of central differences. It is preferably used for interpolation halfway between the two center points.

Everett's formula. We start from Gauss' forward formula, where n is odd, $n = 2k + 1$. Eliminating differences of odd order by use of the formula

$$\Delta^{2k+1} f_{-k} = \Delta^{2k} f_{-k+1} - \Delta^{2k} f_{-k},$$

we obtain

$$p_{2k+1}(s) = f_0 + \binom{s}{1}(f_1 - f_0) + \binom{s}{2} \Delta^2 f_{-1}$$

$$+ \binom{s + 1}{3}[\Delta^2 f_0 - \Delta^2 f_{-1}] + \binom{s + 1}{4} \Delta^4 f_{-2} + \cdots$$

$$+ \binom{s + k - 1}{2k} \Delta^{2k} f_{-k} + \binom{s + k}{2k + 1}[\Delta^{2k} f_{-k+1} - \Delta^{2k} f_{-k}].$$

Collecting equal differences, expressing them in terms of the central difference operator and using the identity

$$\binom{s+k-1}{2k} - \binom{s+k}{2k+1} = \binom{s+k-1}{2k}\left(1 - \frac{s+k}{2k+1}\right)$$

$$= \binom{t+k}{2k+1},$$

where

$$t = 1 - s,$$

we obtain the formula

$$(11\text{-}21) \quad p_{2k+1}(s) = \binom{t}{1}f_0 + \binom{t+1}{3}\delta^2 f_0 + \cdots + \binom{t+k}{2k+1}\delta^{2k}f_0$$

$$+ \binom{s}{1}f_1 + \binom{s+1}{3}\delta^2 f_1 + \cdots + \binom{s+k}{2k+1}\delta^{2k}f_1$$

due to the British astronomer Everett.

Of the three formulas given above, the highly symmetrical and elegant formula due to Everett has found great favor in practice. It has the advantage of using only differences of even order, and of furnishing an interpolation polynomial whose degree (and consequently, accuracy) is higher than the order of the highest difference employed. For instance, with a column of second differences alone we can calculate the cubic interpolating polynomial, whereas the application of all other formulas requires three difference columns. For these reasons many tables of higher transcendental functions, if they give any differences at all, give second differences only. No special tables of the Everett interpolation coefficients

$$\binom{s+k}{2k+1}, \quad k = 1, 2, \ldots,$$

are required, as these coefficients are identical with the extreme (first and last) Lagrangian interpolation coefficients interpolating on the set $x_{-k}, x_{-k+1}, \ldots, x_{k+1}$ (see §10.2).

11.4   Throwback†

Throwback of higher differences into lower differences is an extremely simple but ingenious device, due to Comrie, which enhances the accuracy of interpolation formulas without increasing the required numerical work. The idea is quite general; we explain it in the simplest possible situation.

---

† This section may be omitted at first reading.

Everett's formula for the interpolating polynomial of degree 5 may be written

$$p_5(s) = tf_0 + \binom{t+1}{3}\left\{ \delta^2 f_0 + \frac{(t+2)(t-2)}{4\cdot 5} \delta^4 f_0 \right\}$$

plus a similar term with t replaced by s and the subscript 0 replaced by 1. In the interval $0 \leq t \leq 1$ the factor

$$\frac{(t+2)(t-2)}{4\cdot 5} = \frac{t^2-4}{20}$$

varies between the narrow limits $-(4/20)$ and $-(3/20)$. Thus if we define modified second differences $\delta^2 f_k^*$ by the formula

$$\delta^2 f_k^* = \delta^2 f_k - \tfrac{7}{40} \delta^4 f_k$$

then Everett's formula with fourth differences can be approximated by the formula

$$p_5^*(s) = tf_0 + \binom{t+1}{3} \delta^2 f_0^* + sf_1 + \binom{s+1}{3} \delta^2 f_1^*$$

where $t = 1 - s$. This formula can be used in the same way as the formula involving second differences only. The error committed in replacing p_5 by p_5^* is equal to

$$\binom{t+1}{3}\left[-\frac{7}{40} - \frac{t^2-4}{20} \right] \delta^4 f_0 + \binom{s+1}{3}\left[-\frac{7}{40} - \frac{s^2-4}{20} \right] \delta^4 f_1$$

$$= \frac{1}{40}\left\{ (1-2t^2)\binom{t+1}{3} \delta^4 f_0 + (1-2s^2)\binom{s+1}{3} \delta^4 f_1 \right\}.$$

For $0 \leq s \leq 1$ (and consequently $0 \leq t \leq 1$) this turns out to be less than

$$0.00122 \max\{|\delta^4 f_0|, |\delta^4 f_1|\}.$$

Thus if one unit in the least significant digit carried in the computation is denoted by u, we have

$$|p_5^*(s) - p_5(s)| \leq \frac{u}{2}$$

already if the fourth differences are less than $400u$.

Many mathematical tables giving second differences print modified instead of ordinary second differences. In forming the modified differences, the factor $-(7/40)$ is frequently replaced by -0.184, a value suggested by Comrie from a consideration of Bessel's formula. Tables with modified second differences make it possible to calculate (with an error of less than one round-off error) the fifth degree interpolating polynomial from only one difference column, with an amount of work comparable to that for the third degree polynomial.

EXAMPLE

12. According to the tables of Jahnke and Emde [1945], $x = 11.620$ is a zero of the Bessel function $J_2(x)$. We check this statement by evaluating $J_2(11.620)$, using the following values given in the British Association tables:

x	$J_2(x)$	δ^{2*}
11.4	0.05118808	
11.5	0.02793593	
11.6	0.00461559	15622
11.7	−0.01854910	37729
11.8	−0.04133747	
11.9	−0.06353402	

With $x_0 = 11.6$, we have $s = 0.2$, $t = 0.8$

$$\binom{s+1}{3} = -0.032, \qquad \binom{t+1}{3} = -0.048,$$

yielding $J_2(11.620) = 0.00003692$. The derivative of $J_2(x)$ satisfies

$$J_2'(x) = \tfrac{1}{2}[J_1(x) - J_3(x)]$$

and thus, again from tables, has near the suspected zero the approximate value -0.23. From Newton's formula, we thus expect

$$11.62 - \frac{-0.00003692}{-0.23} = 11.61984$$

to be a more accurate value of the desired zero and indeed, Watson [1944] lists the desired zero as 11.6198412.

Problems

14. For the interpolation problem discussed in example 12, estimate
  (a) the error $J_2(x) - p_5(s)$ due to pure interpolation;
  (b) the error $p_5^*(s) - p_5(s)$ due to throwback.
  (For (a), use the integral representation of problem 9, chapter 9, to estimate the high derivative of J_2 required.)
15. Proceeding as in the derivation of Everett's formula, obtain an interpolation formula that uses only zeroth, third, sixth, . . . differences.
16. Devise a method for "throwing back the second differences into the

zeroth" in Everett's formula, and estimate the error involved. Why is the method less efficient than the one discussed in the text? When would it be useful?

17. The zeros of the Bessel function $J_0(x)$ are known to approach the points

$$x = (n - \tfrac{1}{4})\pi \qquad n = 1, 2, 3, \ldots.$$

Verify this statement by evaluating $J_0((n - \tfrac{1}{4})\pi)$, $n = 1, 2, 3, \ldots$, using a table of Bessel functions.

18. Check the values of the modified differences given in example 12 by forming ordinary second and fourth differences.

Recommended Reading

Finite difference techniques have been pushed to an especially high level in Great Britain.   Books such as Fox [1957] as well as the volumes issued by the National Physical Laboratory [1961] and by the Nautical Almanac Service [1956] contain much excellent advice on interpolation by differences.   On the whole, however, the subject of interpolation of tables is somewhat in the eclipse due to the fact that most tables have been replaced by prestored programs in digital computers.

chapter 12 numerical differentiation

Above we have used the interpolating polynomial to approximate values of a function f at points where f is not known. Another use of the interpolating polynomial, of equal or even higher importance in practice, is the imitation of the fundamental operations of calculus. In all these applications the basic idea is extremely simple: Instead of performing the operation on the function f, which may be difficult or—in cases where f is known at discrete points only—impossible, the operation is performed on a suitable interpolating polynomial. In the present chapter this program is carried out for the operation of differentiation.

12.1 The Error of Numerical Differentiation

Let f be a function defined on an interval I containing the set of points $S = \{x_0, x_1, \ldots, x_n\}$ (not necessarily equidistant) and let P_S be the polynomial interpolating f at the points of the set S. We seek to approximate

$$f'(x) \quad \text{by} \quad P_S'(x), \quad x \in I,$$

and wish to derive a formula for the error that must be expected in this approximation.

It seems natural to obtain an expression for the error $f' - P_S'$ by differentiating the error formula (9-5). If f has a continuous derivative of order $n + 1$ in I and if $x \in I$, it was shown in §9.2 that

(12-1) $$f(x) - P_S(x) = L(x)g(x),$$

where

(12-2) $$L(x) = (x - x_0)(x - x_1)\ldots(x - x_n),$$

(12-3) $$g(x) = \frac{1}{(n + 1)!} f^{(n+1)}(\xi_x),$$

ξ_x being some unspecified point in the smallest interval containing x and all the points x_i, $i = 0, 1, \ldots, n$. Corollary 9.2 shows that, although no assertion can be made about the continuity or differentiability of ξ_x as a function of x, the function g can be extended to a function that is continuous on I. A similar consideration shows that the extended function is even n times continuously differentiable on I. Hence we obtain by differentiating (12-1)

$$(12\text{-}4) \qquad f'(x) - P_S'(x) = L'(x)g(x) + L(x)g'(x).$$

If x is arbitrary, this expression is not of much use for the purpose of estimating $f' - P_S'$, since we lack a convenient explicit representation for g' such as (12-3). However, if $x = x_j$ $(j = 0, 1, \ldots, n)$ in (12-4), we obtain by virtue of $L(x_j) = 0$

$$f'(x_j) - P_S'(x_j) = L'(x_j)g(x_j).$$

Recalling that

$$L'(x_j) = \lim_{x \to x_j} \frac{\prod\limits_{i=0}^{n} (x - x_i)}{x - x_j} = \lim_{x \to x_j} \prod_{\substack{i=0 \\ i \neq j}}^{n} (x - x_i) = \prod_{\substack{i=0 \\ i \neq j}}^{n} (x_j - x_i)$$

we can state the above result as follows:

Theorem 12.1 Let the function f be continuous and $n + 1$ times continuously differentiable on an interval I containing the $n + 1$ distinct points $x_0, x_1, \ldots, x_n$, and let P_S denote the polynomial of degree $\leqq n$ interpolating f at these points. Then for each j, $j = 0$, $1, \ldots, n$ the interval spanned by the largest and the smallest of the points x_i contains a point ξ_j such that

$$(12\text{-}5) \quad f'(x_j) - P_S'(x_j) = \frac{1}{(n + 1)!} f^{(n+1)}(\xi_j) \prod_{\substack{i=0 \\ i \neq j}}^{n} (x_j - x_i).$$

Problems

1. For a sufficiently differentiable function f, $f'(0)$ is approximated by differentiating the polynomial P interpolating f at the points $0, h, 2h, \ldots,$ nh. Give a formula for the error $f'(0) - P'(0)$.

2. Indicate a *lower* bound for the error if the derivative $f'(0)$ of $f(x) = e^x$ is replaced by the derivative of the polynomial interpolating f at the points $0, 1, \ldots, n$.

3. Give a formula for the error of numerically differentiating f at $x = 0$ by differentiating the interpolating polynomial using the points $-h, 0, h$. Obtain the same error formula by subtracting the Taylor expansion for $f(-h)$ from that for $f(h)$, both terminated with the term involving h^3.

12.2 Numerical Differentiation Formulas for Equidistant Abscissas

We now shall assume that the points x_k are equidistant, $x_k = x_0 + kh$, $k = 0, \pm 1, \pm 2, \ldots$. For given m and $n > m$,

$$\left| \prod_{\substack{i=m \\ i \neq j}}^{n} (x_i - x_j) \right|$$

is smallest when x_j lies halfway between the extreme points x_m and x_n. This suggests the use of Stirling's formula (11-19)

$$p_{2k}(s) = f_0 + \binom{s}{1}\left[\mu\delta f_0 + \frac{s}{2}\delta^2 f_0\right] + \cdots$$

$$+ \binom{s+k-1}{2k-1}\left[\mu\delta^{2k-1}f_0 + \frac{s}{2k}\delta^{2k}f_0\right],$$

where $s = (x - x_0)/h$, for numerical differentiation. The derivative with respect to x at x_0 equals h^{-1} times the derivative with respect to s at $s = 0$. The derivatives of the coefficients

$$\frac{s}{2k}\binom{s+k-1}{2k-1}, \quad k = 1, 2, \ldots$$

are zero, since they contain the factor s^2. For the remaining coefficients we find

$$\frac{d}{ds}\binom{s+k-1}{2k-1}\bigg|_{s=0}$$

$$= \lim_{s\to 0}\frac{1}{s}\binom{s+k-1}{2k-1}$$

$$= \lim_{s\to 0}\frac{(s+k-1)(s+k-2)\ldots(s+1)(s-1)\ldots(s-k+1)}{(2k-1)!}$$

$$= (-1)^{k-1}\frac{[(k-1)!]^2}{(2k-1)!}.$$

The derivative of the polynomial $P_{2k}(x) = p_{2k}((x - x_0)h^{-1})$ at the central point x_0 can thus be written

$$(12\text{-}6) \quad P'_{2k}(x_0) = \frac{1}{h}\left\{\mu\delta f_0 - \frac{(1!)^2}{3!}\mu\delta^3 f_0 + \cdots\right.$$

$$\left. + (-1)^{k-1}\frac{[(k-1)!]^2}{(2k-1)!}\mu\delta^{2k-1}f_0\right\}$$

or, evaluating the numerical coefficients

$$P'_{2k}(x_0) = \frac{1}{h}\left\{\mu\delta f_0 - \tfrac{1}{6}\mu\delta^3 f_0 + \tfrac{1}{30}\mu\delta^5 f_0 - \tfrac{1}{140}\mu\delta^7 f_0 + \cdots\right\}.$$

Formulas in terms of ordinates can be found by expressing the central differences $\delta^{2k-1}f_{-1/2}$ and $\delta^{2k-1}f_{1/2}$ in the form $\sum c_n f_n$ and arranging the coefficients c_n in a table, as follows:

Table 12.2a

n	-1	0	1
$\delta f_{-1/2}$	-1	1	0
$\delta f_{1/2}$	0	-1	1
$\mu\delta f_0$	$-\frac{1}{2}$	0	$\frac{1}{2}$

Table 12.2b

n	-2	-1	0	1	2
$\delta^3 f_{-1/2}$	-1	3	-3	1	0
$\delta^3 f_{1/2}$	0	-1	3	-3	1
$\mu\delta^3 f_0$	$-\frac{1}{2}$	1	0	-1	$\frac{1}{2}$

The average of the coefficients in each column gives us the corresponding coefficient for $\mu\delta^{2k-1}f_0$. For the second and fourth degree polynomials we find in this manner

$$(12\text{-}7) \qquad P_2'(x_0) = \frac{1}{2h}(f_1 - f_{-1}),$$

$$(12\text{-}8) \qquad P_4'(x_0) = \frac{1}{h}\{\tfrac{1}{2}(f_1 - f_{-1}) - \tfrac{1}{12}(f_2 - 2f_1 + 2f_{-1} - f_{-2})\}$$

$$= \frac{1}{12h}(-f_2 + 8f_1 - 8f_{-1} + f_{-2}).$$

An expression for the error $f'(x_0) - P_{2k}'(x_0)$ is easily determined from (12-5). With $n = 2k$, and the interpolating points arranged equidistantly and symmetrically about x_0, we find

$$\frac{1}{(2k+1)!}L'(x_0) = (-1)^k \frac{(k!)^2}{(2k+1)!}h^{2k}.$$

It thus follows that

$$(12\text{-}9) \qquad f'(x_0) - P_{2k}'(x_0) = \frac{(-1)^k}{h}\frac{(k!)^2}{(2k+1)!}h^{2k+1}f^{(2k+1)}(\xi),$$

where $x_{-k} < \xi < x_k$. As in the calculation of approximate function values by algorithm 11.2, it is thus true that the error committed in differentiating Stirling's polynomial in place of the function f equals the first omitted term in the difference formula, provided that $\mu\delta^{2k+1}f_0$ is replaced by $h^{2k+1}f^{(2k+1)}(\xi)$.

Problems

4. By using the Newton forward formula, devise a formula for numerical differentiation at the beginning of a table and obtain an error formula similar to (12-9).

5. Making use of Bessel's formula, obtain a formula for numerical differentiation halfway between two entries in a table, and write the formulas resulting from the polynomials of degree one and three in terms of ordinates.

6. By differentiating Stirling's form of the interpolating polynomial twice, show that

$$f''(x_0) \approx \frac{1}{h^2}\{\delta^2 f_0 - \tfrac{1}{12}\delta^4 f_0 + \cdots\}.$$

Obtain a general formula for the coefficients on the right.

7. Suppose that, due to rounding, the values f_n are known only up to errors ε_n, where $|\varepsilon_n| \leqq \varepsilon$. What is the maximum error resulting therefrom in the formulas (12-7) and (12-8), if all arithmetic operations are performed without rounding error?

8. Suppose we calculate $J_0'(x)$ by means of (12-7) from a table of $J_0(x)$ giving six decimals. What is the smallest value of h for which we can guarantee that the maximum possible discretization error (due to replacing J_0 by P) is not exceeded by the maximum possible error due to rounding?

12.3   Extrapolation to the Limit

The formulas derived in §12.2 can also be obtained by an entirely different method which recalls the fundamental principle of numerical analysis applied already in the derivation of Aitken's Δ^2-method: Improve the accuracy of an approximation using any (possibly incomplete) knowledge of the asymptotic behavior of the error.

The simplest numerical differentiation procedure consists in

$$\text{replacing } f'(x_0) \quad \text{by} \quad \frac{1}{2h}(f_1 - f_{-1})$$

(see formula (12-7) above). We introduce an abbreviation for the expression on the right that emphasizes its dependence on the step h by defining the *basic differentiation operator* D_h as follows:

(12-10) $$D_h f(x_0) = \frac{1}{2h}[f(x + h) - f(x - h)].$$

The error formula (12-9) then states in the special case $k = 1$ that

$$(12\text{-}11) \qquad\qquad D_h f(x_0) - f'(x_0) = \tfrac{1}{6} h^2 f^{(3)}(\xi),$$

where $x_0 - h < \xi < x_0 + h$.

In order to obtain a more accurate statement about the error of $D_h f$, we use Taylor's expansion with remainder term. If the function f is sufficiently differentiable, we have for $k = 0, 1, \ldots$

$$f(x + h) = f(x) + \frac{h}{1!} f'(x) + \cdots + \frac{h^k}{k!} f^{(k)}(x) + \frac{h^{k+1}}{(k+1)!} f^{(k+1)}(\xi),$$

where ξ is a point between x and $x + h$. Writing down this expression for $k = 2m$ and $x = x_0$ and then subtracting from it the same expression with h replaced by $-h$, we obtain after dividing by $2h$

$$(12\text{-}12) \quad D_h f(x_0) = f'(x_0) + a_1 h^2 + a_2 h^4 + \cdots + a_{m-1} h^{2m-2} + R_m(h),$$

where

$$a_k = \frac{1}{(2k+1)!} f^{(2k+1)}(x_0), \qquad k = 1, 2, \ldots, m - 1,$$

$$R_m(h) = \frac{h^{2m}}{(2m+1)!} \frac{f^{(2m+1)}(\xi_1) + f^{(2m+1)}(\xi_2)}{2}.$$

Here ξ_1 is a point between x and $x + h$ and ξ_2 is between x and $x - h$. If $f^{(2m+1)}$ is continuous, it assumes every value between

$$f^{(2m+1)}(\xi_1) \quad \text{and} \quad f^{(2m+1)}(\xi_2).$$

Thus in particular for some ξ between ξ_1 and ξ_2 (and thus between $x - h$ and $x + h$)

$$f^{(2m+1)}(\xi) = \tfrac{1}{2}[f^{(2m+1)}(\xi_1) + f^{(2m+1)}(\xi_2)].$$

It follows that the remainder R_m in (12-12) can be expressed in the simpler form

$$(12\text{-}13) \qquad\qquad R_m(h) = \frac{h^{2m}}{(2m+1)!} f^{(2m+1)}(\xi).$$

With this form of the remainder, (12-12) for $m = 1$ reduces to (12-11).

In numerical applications the values of $f'(x_0)$ and of the constants $a_1, a_2, \ldots$ are of course unknown. But the mere fact that a formula of type (12-12) holds can be used to improve the accuracy of a numerical differentiation. Suppose the operator D_h is applied with two different values of h, say h and qh, where $q \neq 0, 1$. (If f is tabulated at equally spaced intervals, $q = \tfrac{1}{2}$ is a natural choice.) We then have from (12-12)

$$D_h f(x_0) = f'(x_0) + a_1 h^2 + O(h^4),$$
$$D_{qh} f(x_0) = f'(x_0) + a_1 (qh)^2 + O(h^4),$$

since $0(qh) = 0(h)$. Eliminating from this pair of equations the constant a_1 and solving for $f'(x_0)$, we find

(12-14) $$f'(x_0) = \frac{D_{qh}f(x_0) - q^2 D_h f(x_0)}{1 - q^2} + 0(h^4).$$

Using two values of the basic differentiation operator D_h (which ordinarily has an error $0(h^2)$) we thus have succeeded in deriving a differentiation formula with an error of only $0(h^4)$.

Without a more careful study of the error term we cannot assert that (12-14) is more accurate than (12-10) for any given h. However, if $f^{(5)}$ is continuous, then (12-14) is always more accurate for *sufficiently small values* of h.

In the special case $q = 2$ (12-14) takes the form

$$f'(x_0) = \frac{1}{3}\left\{\frac{4}{2h}(f_1 - f_{-1}) - \frac{1}{2\cdot 2h}(f_2 - f_{-2})\right\} + 0(h^4).$$

We thus obtain the approximate differentiation formula

$$f'(x_0) = \frac{-f_2 + 8f_1 - 8f_{-1} + f_{-2}}{12h} + 0(h^4),$$

which turns out to be identical with (12-8).

Another way to look at formula (12-14), more in the spirit of Aitken's Δ^2-process, is to consider it as a device to speed up the convergence of the basic differentiation operator D_h as $h \to 0$. The speeded up operator may be written in the form

(12-15) $$D_{qh}^* = \frac{D_{qh} - q^2 D_h}{1 - q^2}.$$

EXAMPLE

1. To find the first derivative of $J_0(x)$ at $x = 2$.

Table 12.3

h	$D_h J_0(2)$	$D_h^* J_0(2)$	$D_h^{**} J_0(2)$
0.40	$-0.56611\ 8105$		
0.20	$-0.57406\ 0360$	$-0.57670\ 7779$	
0.10	$-0.57605\ 7896$	$-0.57672\ 3741$	$-0.57672\ 4805$
0.05	$-0.57655\ 8030$	$-0.57672\ 4742$	$-0.57672\ 4808$

The exact value, to nine places, is $J_0'(2) = -0.57672\ 4808$.

Nothing prevents us from trying to further speed up the sequence of the values $D_h^* f(x_0)$. The appropriate formula can be obtained by considering the structure of the error of $D_h^* f(x_0)$. From (12-12) we find

$$D_{qh} f(x_0) = f'(x_0) + a_1 q^2 h^2 + a_2 q^4 h^4 + \cdots + a_{m-1} q^{2m-2} h^{2m-2} + R_m(qh).$$

It follows that

$$D_{qh}^* f(x_0) = f'(x_0) + a_2^*(qh)^4 + \cdots + a_{m-1}^*(qh)^{2m-2} + R_m^*(qh),$$

where

$$a_k^* = \frac{1 - q^{2-2k}}{1 - q^2} a_k,$$

$$R_m^*(qh) = \frac{R_m(qh) - q^2 R_m(h)}{1 - q^2}.$$

Thus, in particular,

$$D_h^* f(x_0) = f'(x_0) + a_2^* h^4 + 0(h^6),$$
$$D_{qh}^* f(x_0) = f'(x_0) + a_2^* q^4 h^4 + 0(h^6).$$

Eliminating a_2^* yields

(12-16) $$f'(x_0) = D_{qh}^{**} f(x_0) + 0(h^6),$$

where

(12-17) $$D_{qh}^{**} = \frac{D_{qh}^* - q^4 D_h^*}{1 - q^4}.$$

Still using the same basic differentiation operator D_h, we thus have obtained a differentiation formula with an error $0(h^6)$. Obviously the procedure can be continued, the only limits being those set by the accuracy of the values $f(x_0 + h)$ themselves. The effectiveness of the procedure is illustrated by the last column of table 12.3, where the derivative has been obtained to nine significant digits from only six values of the function.

Problems

9. Using Taylor's expansion, show that

$$\frac{1}{h^2} \delta^2 f_0 = f''(x_0) + \frac{h^2}{12} f^{(4)}(\xi),$$

where $x - h < \xi < x + h$.

10. By eliminating a_1 and a_2 in the formulas

$$D_{kh} f(x_0) = f'(x_0) + a_1(kh)^2 + a_2(kh)^4 + 0(h^6), \qquad k = 1, 2, 3,$$

obtain a differentiation formula that uses the abscissas $f_{-3}, f_{-2}, \ldots, f_3$ and has an error $0(h^6)$. Compare the result with the formula (12-6) for $k = 3$.

11. Suppose that, due to rounding, the values $D_h f(x_0)$ are known only up to rounding errors not exceeding ε/h. If the values $D_h^* f(x_0)$ and $D_h^{**} f(x_0)$ are formed with $q = \frac{1}{2}$, what are their errors due to the inaccuracies in $D_h f(x_0)$?

12.4 Extrapolation to the Limit: The General Case

Extrapolation to the limit as applied to numerical differentiation in §12.3 is a mere special case of the following general situation: An unknown quantity a_0 is approximated by a calculable quantity $A(y)$ ($y > 0$) such that

$$(12\text{-}18) \qquad \lim_{y \to 0} A(y) = a_0,$$

and it is known that there exist constants $a_1, a_2, \ldots$ and $C_1, C_2, \ldots$ such† that for $k = 1, 2, 3, \ldots$

$$(12\text{-}19) \qquad A(y) = a_0 + a_1 y + a_2 y^2 + \cdots + a_{k-1} y^{k-1} + R_k(y),$$

where

$$|R_k(y)| < C_k y^k, \qquad y > 0.$$

A triangular array of numbers $A_{m,n}$ ($m = 0, 1, 2, \ldots$; $n \leqq m$) is now formed in the following manner.

Algorithm 12.4 For two fixed constants r and y_0 ($0 < r < 1, y_0 > 0$), let for $m = 0, 1, 2, \ldots$

$$A_{m,0} = A(r^m y_0),$$

$$A_{m,n+1} = \frac{A_{m,n} - r^{n+1} A_{m-1,n}}{1 - r^{n+1}}, \qquad n = 0, 1, \ldots, m - 1.$$

The manner in which the numbers $A_{m,n}$ depend on each other is indicated in scheme 12.4.

$$
\begin{array}{ccccc}
A_{0,0} \\
A_{1,0} & A_{1,1} \\
A_{2,0} & A_{2,1} & A_{2,2} \\
A_{3,0} & A_{3,1} & A_{3,2} & A_{3,3} \\
\vdots & \vdots & \vdots & \vdots & \ddots
\end{array}
$$

Scheme 12.4

This scheme has the following interesting property.

---

† In technical language the hypothesis (12-19) means that $A(y)$ admits an asymptotic expansion for $y \to 0+$. We do *not* assume that the infinite series $a_0 + a_1 y + a_2 y^2 + \cdots$ converges.

Theorem 12.4   Let $A = A(y)$ satisfy the relations (12-19). Then for each n such that $a_{n+1} \neq 0$, the $(n+1)$st column in the scheme 12.4 converges faster to a_0 than the nth column, in the sense that

$$(12\text{-}20) \qquad \lim_{m \to \infty} \frac{A_{m, n+1} - a_0}{A_{m, n} - a_0} = 0.$$

More generally, for each fixed value of $n \geq 0$,

$$(12\text{-}21) \quad A_{m, n} = a_0 + (-1)^n a_{n+1} r^{-n(n+1)/2} (r^m y_0)^{n+1} + 0((r^m y_0)^{n+2})$$

as $m \to \infty$.

Here $0(z)$ denotes a quantity that remains bounded for $z \to 0$ when divided by z.

Proof.   We shall establish the following proposition, which is stronger than (12-21): For each fixed n, and for each $p > n$,

$$(12\text{-}22) \qquad A_{m, n} = a_0 + a_{n+1, n}(r^m y_0)^{n+1} + a_{n+2, n}(r^m y_0)^{n+2}$$
$$+ \cdots + a_{p, n}(r^m y_0)^p + 0((r^m y_0)^{p+1})$$

as $m \to \infty$, where for $q = n + 1, n + 2, \ldots$

$$(12\text{-}23) \qquad a_{q, n} = \frac{(1 - r^{1-q})(1 - r^{2-q}) \ldots (1 - r^{n-q})}{(1 - r)(1 - r^2) \ldots (1 - r^n)} a_q.$$

(Empty products are to be interpreted as 1.)

The proof is by induction with respect to n. For $n = 0$, the formulas (12-22) and (12-23) are a mere restatement of our hypothesis (12-19). Assuming that they are valid for some $n \geq 0$, it follows from algorithm 12.4 that $A_{m, n+1}$ has a representation of the form (12-22) where the coefficient of $(r^m y_0)^q$ is

$$\frac{1 - r^{n+1-q}}{1 - r^{n+1}} a_{q, n}.$$

This is zero for $q = n + 1$ and equals $a_{q, n+1}$ for $q > n + 1$, verifying (12-22) with n increased by one.

Setting $q = n + 1$ in (12-23), we obtain

$$a_{n+1, n} = \frac{(1 - r^{-n})(1 - r^{-n+1}) \ldots (1 - r^{-1})}{(1 - r)(1 - r^2) \ldots (1 - r^n)} a_{n+1}$$

$$= r^{-(1+2+\cdots+n)} \frac{(r^n - 1)(r^{n-1} - 1) \ldots (r - 1)}{(1 - r)(1 - r^2) \ldots (1 - r^n)} a_{n+1}$$

$$= (-1)^n r^{-n(n+1)/2} a_{n+1}$$

in view of the well-known formula

$$1 + 2 + \cdots + n = \frac{n(n+1)}{2}.$$

Letting $p = n + 1$ in (12-22) and using the above value of $a_{n+1,n}$, we thus obtain (12-21).

If $a_{n+1} \neq 0$, relation (12-21) may be written

$$A_{m,n} - a_0 = (-1)^n a_{n+1} r^{-n(n+1)/2} (r^m y_0)^{n+1} [1 + O(r^m y_0)].$$

Thus,

$$\frac{A_{m,n+1} - a_0}{A_{m,n} - a_0} = -\frac{a_{n+2}}{a_{n+1}} r^{-n-1} (r^m y_0)[1 + O(r^m y_0)],$$

which implies (12-20).

The technique described in §12.3, and in particular in example 1, corresponds to the special case $A(h^2) = D_h$, $r = q^2$ of algorithm 12.4.

Problems

12. A numerical computation furnished the following approximations $A(2^{-n})$ to a quantity a_0:

n	$A(2^{-n})$
0	0.000000
1	0.250000
2	0.316406
3	0.343609
4	0.356074
5	0.362055
6	0.364987
7	0.366438

Determine a_0 as accurately as you can. (Exact value:

$$a_0 = e^{-1} = 0.367879.)$$

13. Show that the hypotheses of theorem 12.4 are satisfied for the function

$$A(y) = (1 + y)^{1/y} \qquad (y > 0).$$

14. Show that the scheme generated by algorithm 12.4 is identical with the scheme that would be obtained by calculating $A(0)$ by Neville interpolation (algorithm 10.5) using the interpolating points $y_0, ry_0, r^2 y_0, \ldots$.

15. Suppose the values of the function $A(y)$ used in algorithm 12.4 are known only up to errors $\leq \varepsilon$. How large is the resulting uncertainty in the columns $A_{m,n}$? Give numerical values for the "noise amplification factor" for $n = 1, 2, 3$ and $r = 0.5$, $r = 0.25$.

16. The following relations hold for the symbol $O(z)$ introduced after theorem 12.4:

$$O(z) + O(z) = O(z);$$
$$O(cz) = O(z) \quad \text{for any constant } c.$$

From what theorems about limits do they follow?

12.5   Calculating Logarithms by Differentiation†

In this section we shall discuss a further application of algorithm 12.4 to a problem of numerical differentiation.   Let $a > 1$ be a given number. We consider the function

$$f(x) = a^x$$

and wish to evaluate $f'(0)$.   By the rules of calculus, this of course equals

$$f'(0) = \log a.$$

By carrying out the differentiation numerically, we may thus hope to obtain a method for calculating the natural logarithm of a given number.

We use the following one-sided approximation to the first derivative, viz.:

$$S(h) = \frac{f(h) - f(0)}{h}$$

$$= \frac{1}{h}(a^h - 1).$$

By the definition of the derivative,

$$\log a = f'(0) = \lim_{h \to 0} S(h).$$

This limit relation also holds if we restrict h to the discrete set of values $h = 2^{-n}$, $n = 0, 1, 2, \ldots$.   Setting

$$(12\text{-}24) \qquad s_n = S(2^{-n}) = 2^n(a^{2^{-n}} - 1)$$

we thus have

$$\log a = \lim_{n \to \infty} s_n.$$

The values $a^{2^{-n}}$ required to form the numbers s_n can easily be generated recursively by successively evaluating square roots, as follows:

$$a^{2^{-0}} = a, \qquad a^{2^{-n-1}} = \sqrt{a^{2^{-n}}}.$$

We thus have, in principle, solved our problem.

Readers who have studied §8.4 will immediately observe, however, that the algorithm thus defined is numerically unstable.   The quantity $a^{2^{-n}} - 1$ approaches zero as $n \to \infty$.   If the numbers $a^{2^{-n}}$ are computed with a fixed number of decimals, the *relative* error of $a^{2^{-n}} - 1$ will ultimately

† This section may be omitted at first reading.

become quite large. By rule (ii) of §8.4, the relative error of s_n will likewise be large, and, since the s_n approach a nonzero limit, the absolute error, too, will grow rapidly.

A procedure that is more stable numerically can be defined if we generate the s_n in a different way. Solving (12-24) for $a^{2^{-n}}$ we get

$$(12\text{-}25) \qquad a^{2^{-n}} = 1 + 2^{-n}s_n.$$

On the other hand,

$$s_{n-1} = 2^{n-1}(a^{2^{-n+1}} - 1)$$
$$= 2^{n-1}(a^{2^{-n}} + 1)(a^{2^{-n}} - 1).$$

Substituting for $a^{2^{-n}}$ the value (12-25), we have

$$s_{n-1} = 2^{n-1}(2 + 2^{-n}s_n)2^{-n}s_n$$
$$= s_n + 2^{-n-1}s_n^2.$$

Solving the quadratic for s_n and observing that $s_n > 0$, we find

$$s_n = 2^n(\sqrt{1 + 2^{-n+1}s_{n-1}} - 1).$$

To avoid loss of accuracy, we write this in the form

$$(12\text{-}26) \qquad s_n = \frac{2s_{n-1}}{1 + \sqrt{1 + 2^{-n+1}s_{n-1}}}.$$

Together with the initial condition $s_0 = a - 1$ this relation may be used to generate the sequence $\{s_n\}$ in a stable manner.†

For numerical purposes the convergence of the algorithm thus obtained, even though stable, is intolerably slow (see problem 16). If it is to be put to any practical use, we must be able to speed it up. Let us check whether the function $S(h)$ satisfies the hypotheses of theorem 12.4. Since $a^h = e^{h \log a}$ we have, using the exponential series,

$$S(h) = \log a + \frac{1}{2!}(\log a)^2 h + \frac{1}{3!}(\log a)^3 h^2 + \cdots.$$

Since this series converges for all values of h, condition (12-19) certainly holds for $A(h) = S(h)$, and theorem 12.4 is applicable. We thus obtain

---

† Relation (12-26) also provides us with an example of those relatively rare non-linear difference equations that have an explicit solution.

Algorithm 12.5 For $a > 1$, let $A_{0,0} = a - 1$, and calculate for $m = 1, 2, \ldots$

$$A_{m,0} = \frac{2A_{m-1,0}}{1 + \sqrt{1 + 2^{-m+1}A_{m-1,0}}},$$

$$A_{m,n+1} = \frac{2^{n+1}A_{m,n} - A_{m-1,n}}{2^{n+1} - 1},$$

where

(12-27) $\qquad\qquad n = 0, 1, 2, \ldots, m - 1.$

Theorem 12.4 yields in the present special case

Theorem 12.5 All columns of the scheme generated in algorithm 12.5 converge to log a, and each column converges faster than the preceding one.

One can also show that the sequence $\{A_{n,n}\}$ of diagonal elements converges to log a, and converges faster than any column.

EXAMPLE

2. For $a = 6$ algorithm 12.5 yields the following triangular array:

Table 12.5

```
5.000000
2.898980  0.797959
2.260338  1.621697  1.896277
2.008267  1.756196  1.801029  1.787422
1.895937  1.783606  1.792743  1.791559  1.791835
1.842872  1.789806  1.791873  1.791748  1.791761  1.791759
1.817076  1.791281  1.791773  1.791759  1.791759  1.791759  1.791759
```

The table shows that log $6 = 1.791759$ can be obtained to seven significant digits by the evaluation of six square roots.

If higher accuracy is desired, it may be necessary to limit the number of columns of the scheme in order to avoid build-up of rounding errors. Condition (12-27) should then be replaced by

$$n = 0, 1, \ldots, \min(m, N) - 1$$

where N is the number of columns desired.

Problems

17. Using Taylor's formula, find a *lower* bound for the error $|S(h) - \log a|$. Thus find a lower bound for the number n necessary that

$$|s_n - \log a| < 0.5 \times 10^{-6},$$

if $a = 6$.

18. Use algorithm 12.5 to calculate $\log e$ to six decimals.

19. Let $1 \leqq a \leqq e$. By obtaining explicit values for the constants C_k in (12-19) from Taylor's formula, find bounds for the errors of the quantities $A_{m,1}$ and $A_{m,2}$, considered as approximations to $\log a$.

Recommended Reading

The principle of extrapolation to the limit was first clearly stated by Richardson [1927]. Repeated extrapolation to the limit is discussed by Bauer *et al.* [1963]. Concerning its application to numerical differentiation, see also Rutishauser [1963].

Research Problem

Since every positive number can be represented in the form $e^n z$, where $e^{-1/2} \leqq z < e^{1/2} = 1.648\ldots$, it is only necessary to know $\log x$ in the interval $(1, e^{1/2})$. Make a comparative study of the computation of $\log x$ in that interval (a) by algorithm 12.5, (b) by Taylor's series.

chapter 13 numerical integration

We now turn to the problem of numerical evaluation of definite integrals. The method is the same as in chapter 12. Instead of performing the integration on the function f, which may be difficult, we perform the integration on a polynomial interpolating f at suitable points. We begin by giving a theoretical appraisal of the error committed in this approximation.

13.1 The Error in Numerical Integration

Our starting point is once again the general error formula proved in §9.2. There it was shown that if P_S interpolates f on the set of points $S = \{x_0, x_1, \ldots, x_n\}$, then

$$(13\text{-}1) \qquad f(x) - P_S(x) = L(x)g(x),$$

where

$$L(x) = (x - x_0)(x - x_1)\ldots(x - x_n),$$

and where g is a continuous function that can be expressed in the form

$$(13\text{-}2) \qquad g(x) = \frac{1}{(n+1)!}f^{(n+1)}(\xi_x),$$

ξ_x being a suitable number contained between the largest and the smallest of the numbers $x_0, \ldots, x_n$ and x. If we integrate (13-2) between two arbitrary limits a and b, we evidently have

$$\int_a^b f(x)\,dx = \int_a^b P_S(x)\,dx + R_S^{(a,b)},$$

where the integration error $R_S^{(a,b)}$ can be expressed in the form

$$(13\text{-}3) \qquad R_S^{(a,b)} = \int_a^b L(x)g(x)\,dx.$$

Let us now assume that the polynomial L does not change its sign in the interval (a, b). This will evidently be the case if and only if no interpolating point x_k is contained in the interior of (a, b). We then can apply to the integral representation (13-3) the second mean value theorem of the integral calculus (see Buck [1956], p. 58), with the result that

$$R_S^{(a, b)} = g(t) \int_a^b L(x)\, dx,$$

where t is a suitable point in (a, b). In view of the definition of g, we thus have the following result:

Theorem 13.1 Let the function f and the polynomial P satisfy the conditions of theorem 9.2. If the interval (a, b) contains no interpolating point in its interior, then

$$\text{(13-4)} \qquad \int_a^b f(x)\, dx - \int_a^b P(x)\, dx = \frac{f^{(n+1)}(\xi)}{(n+1)!} \int_a^b L(x)\, dx,$$

where ξ is a number contained between the largest and the smallest of the numbers $x_0, \ldots, x_n, a, b$.

It is clear the theorem 13.1 cannot be true if (a, b) contains an interpolating point, since it then may happen that the integral on the right of (13-4) vanishes.

EXAMPLE

1. $x_0 = -1, x_1 = 0, x_2 = 1, L(x) = x(x^2 - 1), a = -b,$

$$\int_a^b L(x)\, dx = 0.$$

Problems

1. The integral $\int_0^\pi \sin x\, dx$ is evaluated by interpolating the function $f(x) = \sin x$ at the points $x = 0$ and $x = \pi$. Calculate the bound for the error given by theorem 13.1 (using the fact that all derivatives are bounded by 1), and compare it with the actual error.

2. Dropping the assumption that the interval (a, b) contains no interpolating point, show that

$$\left| \int_a^b f(x)\, dx - \int_a^b P(x)\, dx \right| \leq \frac{M_{n+1}}{(n+1)!} \int_a^b |L(x)|\, dx$$

where $M_{n+1} = \max_{x \in I} |f^{(n+1)}(x)|$.

13.2   Numerical Integration using Backward Differences

Once again we specialize to the situation where the interpolating points x_k are equidistant, $x_k = x_0 + kh$, $k = \pm 1, \pm 2, \ldots$. We begin by deriving an integration formula which appears to be lacking in symmetry, but which for this very reason will be of use in the numerical integration of differential equations.

Let us assume that the function f is interpolated at the points x_0, $x_{-1}, \ldots, x_{-k}$, and that the integral of f is desired between the limits x_0 and x_1. Setting as before

$$s = \frac{x - x_0}{h},$$

we use the Newton backward polynomial in the form given in problem 7, chapter 11,

$$P_k(x) = \sum_{m=0}^{k} (-1)^m \binom{-s}{m} \nabla^m f_0.$$

Introducing s as variable of integration and observing that the differences are independent of s, we find

$$\int_{x_0}^{x_1} P_k(x)\, dx = h \int_0^1 \left\{ \sum_{m=0}^{k} (-1)^m \binom{-s}{m} \nabla^m f_0 \right\} ds$$

$$= h \sum_{m=0}^{k} c_m \nabla^m f_0,$$

where

(13-5) $$c_m = (-1)^m \int_0^1 \binom{-s}{m} ds, \qquad m = 0, 1, 2, \ldots.$$

We also have, in the present case

$$\frac{1}{(k+1)!} L(x) = \frac{(x - x_0)(x - x_{-1})\ldots(x - x_{-k})}{(k+1)!}$$

$$= (-1)^{k+1} h^{k+1} \binom{-s}{k+1}.$$

Since L does not vanish in the interval (x_0, x_1), and since

$$\frac{1}{(k+1)!} \int_{x_0}^{x_1} L(x)\, dx = h^{k+2} c_{k+1},$$

theorem 13.1 thus yields the formula

(13-6) $$\int_{x_0}^{x_1} f(x)\, dx = h\{c_0 f_0 + c_1 \nabla f_0 + c_2 \nabla^2 f_0 + \cdots$$
$$+ c_k \nabla^k f_0 + c_{k+1} h^{k+1} f^{(k+1)}(\xi)\},$$

where $x_{-k} < \xi < x_1$, and where the constants c_m are given by (13-5). As on several previous occasions it is seen that the error due to inter-polation equals the first omitted term in the difference formula, provided that the difference is replaced by the corresponding derivative, suitably normalized (compare similar statements in §11.2 and §12.2).

From the definition (13-5) we find

$$c_0 = \int_0^1 1 \, ds = 1, \qquad c_1 = -\int_0^1 \binom{-s}{1} ds = \tfrac{1}{2}.$$

For larger values of m, however, the c_m are more easily calculated by a method to be explained in §13.4.

In an entirely similar manner we can derive the formula

(13-7) $\displaystyle\int_{x_{-1}}^{x_0} f(x) \, dx = h\{c_0^* f_0 + c_1^* \nabla f_0 + c_2^* \nabla^2 f_0 + \cdots$

$$+ c_k^* \nabla^k f_0 + c_{k+1}^* h^{k+1} f^{(k+1)}(\xi)\},$$

where $x_{-k} < \xi < x_0$, and

(13-8) $c_m^* = (-1)^m \displaystyle\int_{-1}^0 \binom{-s}{m} ds, \qquad m = 0, 1, 2, \ldots.$

In particular we find

$$c_0^* = 1, \qquad c_1^* = -\tfrac{1}{2}.$$

Again a similar statement about the error applies.

Problem

3. Find a formula that integrates between $x_{-1/2}$ and $x_{1/2}$, using backward differences at x_0. What can you say about the error?

13.3   Numerical Integration using Central Differences

If values of f are available on both sides of the interval of integration, it seems preferable to perform the integration on a polynomial that takes into account all these values. Bessel's formula (11-20) recommends itself for the purpose of integrating between the limits x_0 and x_1. We again introduce s as a variable of integration. If s is replaced by $1 - s$, the binomial coefficients

$$\binom{s + m - 1}{2m}$$

remain unchanged, but the factors $s - \tfrac{1}{2}$ change sign. It follows that all integrals of coefficients of the form

$$(s - \tfrac{1}{2})\binom{s + m - 1}{2m}$$

vanish. If P_{2k+1} denotes the polynomial interpolating f on the set $x_{-k}, x_{-k+1}, \ldots, x_{k+1}$, we thus find

$$\int_{x_0}^{x_1} P_{2k+1}(x)\, dx = \int_{x_0}^{x_1} \left\{ \sum_{m=0}^{k} \binom{s+m-1}{2m} \mu \delta^{2m} f_{1/2} \right\} dx$$

$$= h \sum_{m=0}^{k} b_m \mu \delta^{2m} f_{1/2},$$

where

(13-9) $$b_m = \int_0^1 \binom{s+m-1}{2m} ds, \qquad m = 0, 1, 2, \ldots.$$

Since, in the present case,

$$\frac{1}{(2k+2)!} L(x) = \frac{(x - x_{-k})(x - x_{-k+1})\ldots(x - x_{k+1})}{(2k+2)!}$$

$$= h^{2k+2} \binom{s+k}{2k+2}$$

and consequently

$$\frac{1}{(2k+2)!} \int_{x_0}^{x_1} L(x)\, dx = h^{2k+3} b_{k+1},$$

theorem 13.1 yields the formula

(13-10) $$\int_{x_0}^{x_1} f(x)\, dx = h\{b_0 \mu f_{1/2} + b_1 \mu \delta^2 f_{1/2} + \cdots$$

$$+ b_k \mu \delta^{2k} f_{1/2} + b_{k+1} h^{2k+2} f^{(2k+2)}(\xi)\},$$

where $x_{-k} < \xi < x_{k+1}$.

We easily find $b_0 = 1$, $b_1 = -\frac{1}{12}$. Thus the case $k = 0$ of (13-10) yields

$$\int_{x_0}^{x_1} f(x) = \frac{h}{2}[f_0 + f_1] - \frac{h^3}{12} f''(\xi),$$

where $x_0 < \xi < x_1$. This is the familiar *trapezoidal rule* of numerical integration. More about it in §13.6!

Problems

4. By integrating Stirling's formula (11-19) between the limits x_{-1} and x_1, obtain an approximate integration formula of the form

$$\int_{x_{-1}}^{x_1} f(x)\, dx = h\{s_0 f_0 + s_1 \delta^2 f_0 + \cdots + s_k \delta^{2k} f_0 + R_{k+1}\},$$

and show that the remainder R_{k+1} is of the order of h^{2k+2}. (Theorem 13.1 is not applicable in this case, why?) In particular, show that $s_0 = 2$, $s_1 = \frac{1}{3}$ and hence obtain the approximate integration formulas

$$\int_{x_{-1}}^{x_1} f(x) \, dx = 2hf_0 + O(h^3) \qquad \text{(Midpoint rule)};$$

$$\int_{x_{-1}}^{x_1} f(x) \, dx = \frac{h}{3}(f_{-1} + 4f_0 + f_1) + O(h^5) \qquad \text{(Simpson's rule)}.$$

5. Using Taylor's expansion, show that

$$\int_{x_{-1}}^{x_1} f(x) \, dx = 2hf_0 + \tfrac{1}{3}h^3 f''(\xi), \qquad x_{-1} < \xi < x_1.$$

13.4   Generating Functions for Integration Coefficients†

We left unresolved the problem of finding numerical values of the coefficients c_m, c_m^*, and b_m introduced in the two preceding sections. Such values are conveniently found by the method of *generating functions*. The generating function of a sequence of coefficients c_m, for instance, is the function C defined by the power series

$$C(t) = \sum_{m=0}^{\infty} c_m t^m.$$

If we succeed in determining a closed formula for C, we may hope to find numerical values of the c_m in a very simple manner.

We exemplify the method with the coefficients c_m^* defined by (13-8). Their generating function is

$$C^*(t) = \sum_{m=0}^{\infty} c_m^* t^m = \sum_{m=0}^{\infty} (-1)^m t^m \int_{-1}^{0} \binom{-s}{m} ds.$$

It is easily seen that $|c_m^*| \leq 1$, $m = 0, 1, 2, \ldots$. Hence the power series converges uniformly for $|t| \leq \frac{1}{2}$, say. Interchanging summation and integration we find

$$C^*(t) = \int_{-1}^{0} \sum_{m=0}^{\infty} (-1)^m \binom{-s}{m} t^m \, ds.$$

By the general form of the binomial theorem (see Taylor [1959], p. 479),

$$\sum_{m=0}^{\infty} (-1)^m \binom{-s}{m} t^m = (1 - t)^{-s}.$$

---

† This section may be omitted at first reading.

We thus find

$$C^*(t) = \int_{-1}^{0} (1 - t)^{-s} \, ds.$$

The integration can be carried out by observing that

$$(1 - t)^{-s} = e^{-s \log (1 - t)}.$$

We thus find

(13-11)
$$C^*(t) = \frac{1}{-\log (1 - t)} [e^{-s \log (1 - t)}]^{0}_{-1}$$

$$= \frac{t}{-\log (1 - t)}.$$

Observing

$$-\frac{\log (1 - t)}{t} = 1 + \tfrac{1}{2}t + \tfrac{1}{3}t^2 + \cdots,$$

we thus have the identity

$$1 = C^*(t) \frac{-\log (1 - t)}{t}$$

$$= (c_0^* + c_1^* t + c_2^* t^2 + \cdots)(1 + \tfrac{1}{2}t + \tfrac{1}{3}t^2 + \cdots).$$

Comparing coefficients of like powers of t on both sides of this identity, we find

$$c_0^* = 1,$$

$$c_m^* + \tfrac{1}{2}c_{m-1}^* + \cdots + \frac{1}{m + 1} c_0^* = 0, \qquad m = 1, 2, \ldots.$$

These relations can readily be used to calculate the values of the coefficients c_m^* recursively.

Table 13.4a

m	0	1	2	3	4	5
c_m^*	1	$-\dfrac{1}{2}$	$-\dfrac{1}{12}$	$-\dfrac{1}{24}$	$-\dfrac{19}{720}$	$-\dfrac{3}{160}$

In a like manner, we obtain for the generating function

(13-12)
$$C(t) = \sum_{m=0}^{\infty} c_m t^m$$

of the coefficients c_m defined by (13-5) the closed expression

$$(13\text{-}13) \qquad C(t) = -\frac{t}{(1-t)\log(1-t)},$$

the recurrence relation $c_0 = 1$,

$$c_m + \tfrac{1}{2}c_{m-1} + \tfrac{1}{3}c_{m+2} + \cdots + \frac{1}{m+1}c_0 = 1, \qquad m = 1, 2, \ldots$$

and from it the numerical values

Table 13.4b

m	0	1	2	3	4	5
c_m	1	$\dfrac{1}{2}$	$\dfrac{5}{12}$	$\dfrac{3}{8}$	$\dfrac{251}{720}$	$\dfrac{95}{288}$

In order to obtain a recurrence relation for the coefficients b_m defined by (13-9), we write their generating function in the form

$$B(t) = \sum_{m=0}^{\infty} b_m (2t)^{2m} = \int_0^1 \sum_{m=0}^{\infty} \binom{s+m-1}{2m}(2t)^{2m}\, ds.$$

To evaluate it, we require the formula

$$(13\text{-}14) \qquad \sum_{m=0}^{\infty} \binom{s+m-1}{2m}(2t)^{2m} = \frac{(T+t)^{1-2s} + (T-t)^{1-2s}}{2T},$$

where

$$T = \sqrt{1+t^2}.$$

This is a result from the theory of Legendre functions (see Erdelyi [1953], equation 3.2 (14) in connection with 3.5 (12)) whose derivation cannot be given here. Some manipulation yields

$$B(t) = \sum_{m=0}^{\infty} b_m (2t)^{2m} = \frac{t}{T \log(T+t)}.$$

Since

$$\frac{d}{dt} \log(T+t) = \frac{1}{T} = 1 + \binom{-\frac{1}{2}}{1}t^2 + \binom{-\frac{1}{2}}{2}t^4 + \cdots$$

we easily find

$$t^{-1} \log(T+t) = 1 + \frac{1}{3}\binom{-\frac{1}{2}}{1}t^2 + \frac{1}{5}\binom{-\frac{1}{2}}{2}t^4 + \cdots.$$

Hence we have

$$\frac{\log (T + t)}{t} B(t) = \frac{1}{T}$$

or

$$\left[1 + \frac{1}{3} \binom{-\frac{1}{2}}{1} t^2 + \frac{1}{5} \binom{-\frac{1}{2}}{2} t^4 + \cdots \right][b_0 + 4b_1 t^2 + 16 b_2 t^4 + \cdots]$$

$$= 1 + \binom{-\frac{1}{2}}{1} t^2 + \binom{-\frac{1}{2}}{2} t^4 + \cdots.$$

Comparing coefficients, we get

$$(13\text{-}15) \quad 4^m b_m + \frac{4^{m-1}}{3} \binom{-\frac{1}{2}}{1} b_{m-1} + \cdots + \frac{1}{2m+1} \binom{-\frac{1}{2}}{m} b_0 = \binom{-\frac{1}{2}}{m},$$

$$m = 0, 1, 2, \ldots.$$

The following values are obtained:

Table 13.4c

m	0	1	2	3
b_m	1	$-\frac{1}{12}$	$\frac{11}{720}$	$-\frac{191}{60480}$

Problems

6. Find the generating function for the coefficients in the formula

$$f'(x_0) = \frac{1}{h} [a_1 \Delta f_0 + a_2 \Delta^2 f_0 + \cdots]$$

obtained by differentiating the Newton forward interpolating polynomial at $x = x_0$.

7*. Obtain the generating function for the coefficients introduced in problem 4.

8. Using generating functions, show that

$$c_m^* = c_m - c_{m-1}, \qquad m = 1, 2, \ldots.$$

13.5   Numerical Integration over Extended Intervals

In §13.2 and §13.3 we have considered the problem of evaluating the integral of a function f over an interval of length h in terms of differences calculated with the step h. Here we shall study the equally important problem of evaluating

$$I = \int_a^b f(x) \, dx,$$

where $[a, b]$ is a fixed, not necessarily short, interval as accurately as possible.   It is assumed that f is continuous on $[a, b]$ and can be evaluated at arbitrary points of that interval.   Several procedures offer themselves; we shall be able to dismiss two of them very briefly.

(*i*) *Newton-Cotes formulas*.   The most natural idea that offers itself seems to select a certain number of interpolating points within $[a, b]$, to interpolate f at these points, and to approximate the integral of f by the integral of the interpolating polynomial.   If the interpolating points divide $[a, b]$ into N equal parts, we arrive in this manner at certain integration formulas which are called the *Newton-Cotes* formulas.   Unfortunately these formulas have, for large values of N, some very undesirable properties.   In particular, it turns out that there exist functions, even analytic ones, for which the sequence of the integrals of the interpolating polynomials does not converge towards the integral of the function f.   Also, the coefficients in these formulas are large and alternate in sign, which is undesirable for the propagation of rounding error.   For these reasons, the Newton-Cotes formulas are rarely used for high values of N.   For $N = 2, 3, 4$ the formulas are identical with certain well-known integration formulas which we shall discuss below from a different point of view.

(*ii*) *Gaussian quadrature*.   One may try to avoid some of the shortcomings of the Newton-Cotes formulas by relinquishing the equal spacing of the interpolating points.   Gauss discovered that by a proper choice of the interpolating points one can construct integration formulas which, using $N + 1$ interpolating points, give the accurate value of the integral if f is a polynomial of degree $2N + 1$ or less.   These formulas turn out to be numerically stable, and they are in successful use at a number of computation laboratories.   The formulas suffer from the disadvantage, however, that the interpolating points as well as the corresponding weights are irregular numbers that have to be stored.   This practically (although not theoretically) limits the applicability of these highly interesting formulas.

In the following two sections, we shall discuss two integration schemes that are easy to use in practice.   They are (*iii*) *the Trapezoidal rule with end correction*, and (*iv*) *Romberg integration*.

Both can be regarded as more sophisticated forms of the trapezoidal rule discussed in §13.3.

13.6   Trapezoidal Rule with End Correction

As in the discussion of the Newton-Cotes formula, let us divide the interval $[a, b]$ into N equal parts of length

$$h = \frac{b - a}{N}.$$

We write

$$x_n = a + nh, \qquad n = 0, 1, \ldots, N \quad (x_N = b)$$

and evaluate the integral of f over each of the subintervals $[x_{n-1}, x_n]$ separately, using a different interpolating polynomial each time. Using the symmetrical formula (13-10), we find for the integral over the nth subinterval, if f has a continuous derivative of order $2k + 2$,

$$(13\text{-}16) \quad \int_{x_{n-1}}^{x_n} f(x)\, dx = h\{b_0\mu f_{n-1/2} + b_1\mu\delta^2 f_{n-1/2} + \cdots$$
$$+ b_k\mu\delta^{2k}f_{n-1/2} + b_{k+1}h^{2k+2}f^{(2k+2)}(\xi_n)\},$$

where $x_{n-1-k} < \xi_n < x_{n+k}$. Adding up the integrals (13-16) for $n = 1, 2, \ldots, N$, we clearly obtain, in view of $x_0 = a$, $x_N = b$

$$(13\text{-}17) \quad I = \int_a^b f(x)\, dx$$

$$= h\Bigg\{ b_0 \sum_{n=1}^{N} \mu f_{n-1/2} + b_1 \sum_{n=1}^{N} \mu\delta^2 f_{n-1/2} + \cdots$$

$$+ b_k \sum_{n=1}^{N} \mu\delta^{2k}f_{n-1/2} + b_{k+1}h^{2k+2}\sum_{n=1}^{N} f^{(2k+2)}(\xi_n) \Bigg\}$$

where $b_0 = 1$, $b_1 = -\frac{1}{12}, \ldots$, are the constants defined by (13-9) and tabulated in §13.4. Let us consider the sums on the right separately. In view of

$$\mu f_{n-1/2} = \tfrac{1}{2}(f_{n-1} + f_n)$$

the first term

$$h \sum_{n=1}^{N} \mu f_{n-1/2} = h[\tfrac{1}{2}(f_0 + f_1) + \tfrac{1}{2}(f_1 + f_2) + \cdots + \tfrac{1}{2}(f_{N-1} + f_N)]$$

clearly reduces to

$$(13\text{-}18) \quad T_N = h[\tfrac{1}{2}f_0 + f_1 + f_2 + \cdots + f_{N-2} + f_{N-1} + \tfrac{1}{2}f_N].$$

We shall call this term the *N-point trapezoidal value* of the desired integral. It is the result of evaluating the integral by the trapezoidal rule familiar from elementary calculus (see Taylor [1959], p. 515).

Even more drastic simplifications occur in the other sums on the right of (13-17). Recalling that

$$\delta^{2m}f_{n-1/2} = \delta^{2m-1}f_n - \delta^{2m-1}f_{n-1}$$

and hence

$$\mu\delta^{2m}f_{n-1/2} = \mu\delta^{2m-1}f_n - \mu\delta^{2m-1}f_{n-1}$$

we find that the remaining sums in (13-17) "telescope" as follows:

$$\sum_{n=1}^{N} \mu\delta^{2m}f_{n-1/2} = \sum_{n=0}^{N} (\mu\delta^{2m-1}f_n - \mu\delta^{2m-1}f_{n-1})$$

$$= \mu\delta^{2m-1}f_N - \mu\delta^{2m-1}f_0$$

$(m = 1, 2, \ldots, k)$. Thus, each of the sums multiplying $b_1, b_2, \ldots, b_k$ reduces to a difference of two central differences at the endpoints of the interval of integration.

In order to simplify the last term, let us denote by M the maximum and by m the minimum of the function $f^{(2k+2)}(x)$ for $x_{-k-1} \leqq x \leqq x_{N+k+2}$. The sum

$$\sum_{n=1}^{N} f^{(2k+2)}(\xi_n),$$

having $N = (b - a)/h$ terms, is then contained between the limits

$$\frac{b-a}{h} m \quad \text{and} \quad \frac{b-a}{h} M.$$

Since the continuous function $f^{(2k+2)}$ assumes all values between its extreme values, there must be a ξ in the above-mentioned interval such that

$$\frac{b-a}{h} f^{(2k+2)}(\xi) = \sum_{n=1}^{N} f^{(2k+2)}(\xi_n).$$

For that value of ξ, we thus have

$$h^{2k+2}b_{k+1} \sum_{n=1}^{N} f^{(2k+2)}(\xi_n) = (b-a)h^{2k+1}b_{k+1}f^{(2k+2)}(\xi).$$

Gathering together the above results, we have

Theorem 13.6 Let N and k be any two positive integers, and let f have a continuous derivative of order $2k + 2$ on the interval $J = [a - kh, b + kh]$. Then

(13-19) $\displaystyle\int_{a}^{b} f(x) \, dx = T_N + C_N^{(k)} + R_N^{(k)}$,

where T_N denotes the trapezoidal value of the integral defined by (13-18), $C_N^{(k)}$ denotes the "end correction"

(13-20) $C_N^{(k)} = h\{b_1(\mu\delta f_N - \mu\delta f_0) + b_2(\mu\delta^3 f_N - \mu\delta^3 f_0) + \cdots$
$$+ b_k(\mu\delta^{2k-1}f_N - \mu\delta^{2k-1}f_0)\},$$

and where, for some suitable $\xi \in J$,

(13-21) $R_N^{(k)} = h^{2k+2}b_{k+1}(b-a)f^{(2k+2)}(\xi)$.

In order to formulate the integration procedure implied in theorem 13.6 in algorithmic terms, one would have to devise a systematic method for forming the sequence of end corrections $C_N^{(k)}$ $(k = 1, 2, \ldots)$. This would best be done by first forming, in the neighborhood of the points x_0 and x_N, the two-step differences

$$\mu\delta f_n = \tfrac{1}{2}(f_{n+1} - f_{n-1})$$

and then using the identities

$$\mu\delta^{2m-1}f_n = \delta^{2m-2}(\mu\delta f_n)$$

$$= \delta^{2m-2}\left(\frac{f_{n+1} - f_{n-1}}{2}\right) \qquad (n = 0, N).$$

The coefficients b_m can be generated recursively from (13-15).

EXAMPLE

2. To evaluate $\int_0^{1.6} J_0(x)\,dx$. We choose the step $h = 0.1$, leading to $N = 16$. From a table of Bessel functions we find

$$T_{16} = 1.28934\ 6003.$$

Since $J_0(-x) = J_0(x)$, the contributions to the end correction at $x_0 = 0$ is zero. At $x_{16} = 1.6$ we find

$$
\begin{aligned}
\mu\delta f_{16} &= -0.05692\ 1406, & hb_1\mu\delta f_{16} &= 0.00047\ 4345, \\
\mu\delta^3 f_{16} &= 0.00040\ 8458, & hb_2\mu\delta^3 f_{16} &= 0.00000\ 0624, \\
\mu\delta^5 f_{16} &= -0.00000\ 3327, & hb_3\mu\delta^5 f_{16} &= 0.00000\ 0001,
\end{aligned}
$$

yielding the more accurate value

$$\int_0^{1.6} J_0(x)\,dx = 1.28982\ 0973,$$

correct to the number of places given.

Problems

9. Evaluate

$$\int_0^{\pi} \frac{\sin x}{x}\,dx$$

with an error less than 10^{-8}.

10. Devise a method, similar to the one discussed above, based on the formula obtained in problem 4. (Divide into an even number of subintervals.)

11. Using the integration formula (13-6) and a similar formula involving forward differences, obtain an end correction for the trapezoidal rule that involves values f_n satisfying $0 \leqq n \leqq N$ only.

12. Show that if the function f is periodic with period T, and if formula (13-19) is used to evaluate the integral of f over a full period, then

$$C_N^{(k)} = 0 \quad \text{for all } k \text{ and } N.$$

13. Problem 12 shows that for the integration of a sufficiently differentiable periodic function over a full period,

$$\int_a^b f(x)\, dx - T_N = 0(h^{2k})$$

for every k. Does it follow that the trapezoidal value is exact?

14. Show that the trapezoidal rule T_N yields for $N > 1$ the exact values of the integrals

$$\int_0^{2\pi} \cos x\, dx, \qquad \int_0^{2\pi} \sin x\, dx.$$

(Use problem 19, chapter 6.)

13.7 Romberg Integration

Theorem 13.6 states, in effect, that the trapezoidal approximation to $\int_a^b f(x)\, dx$ calculated with the step h,

$$A(h) = T_{N(h)},$$

where $N(h) = (b - a)h^{-1}$, satisfies

$$A(h) = a_0 - C_{N(h)}^{(k)} + 0(h^{2k+2}),$$

where a_0 is the exact value of the integral, and where $C_{N(h)}^{(k)}$ is defined by (13-20). If we could show that for every positive integer k

$$(13\text{-}22) \qquad C_{N(h)}^{(k)} = a_1 h^2 + a_2 h^4 + \cdots + a_k h^{2k} + 0(h^{2k+2}),$$

then $A(h)$ would satisfy the hypotheses for successful $k$fold extrapolation to the limit, that is, it would be of the form (12-19) where $y = h^2$. We might expect then to speed up the convergence of the trapezoidal values by an application of algorithm 12.4.

By expanding the differences appearing in (13-20) in powers of h, it is easy to see that $C_{N(h)}^{(k)}$ indeed can be expanded in the form (13-22). For instance,

$$h\mu\delta f_0 = \frac{h}{2}(f_1 - f_{-1})$$

$$= h^2 f'(x_0) + \frac{h^4}{6} f'''(x_0) + \cdots,$$

$$h\mu\delta^3 f_0 = \frac{h}{2}(f_2 - 2f_1 + 2f_{-1} - f_{-2})$$

$$= h^4 f'''(x_0) + \cdots.$$

We thus may apply algorithm 12.4, keeping in mind that $y = h^2$. The choices of the values y_0 and r are dictated by the obvious procedure to begin with a single subinterval $(N = 1)$, and then to double the number of subintervals at each step. Since $y = h^2$ this means that the ratio between consecutive values of y is $r = \frac{1}{4}$. The algorithm thus results in the triangular array

$$
\begin{array}{llll}
A_{0,0} \\
A_{1,0} & A_{1,1} \\
A_{2,0} & A_{2,1} & A_{2,2} \\
A_{3,0} & A_{3,1} & A_{3,2} & A_{3,3} \\
\cdot \quad \cdot \quad \cdot \quad \cdot \quad \cdot \quad \cdot \quad \cdot \quad \cdot \quad \cdot \quad \cdot \quad \cdot
\end{array}
$$

defined by the recurrence relations

$$(13\text{-}23) \qquad A_{m,0} = T_{2^m}, \qquad m = 0, 1, 2, \ldots,$$

$$(13\text{-}24) \quad A_{m,n+1} = \frac{4^{n+1} A_{m,n} - A_{m-1,n}}{4^{n+1} - 1}, \qquad n = 0, 1, \ldots, m - 1.$$

In order to define an economical algorithm, we note that of the ordinates necessary to compute T_{2^m} only those whose index is odd have to be freshly calculated. The others are known from $T_{2^{m-1}}$. The computation is most easily arranged by introducing besides the trapezoidal values T_N the *midpoint values*

$$M_N = h(f_{1/2} + f_{3/2} + \cdots + f_{N-1/2})$$

$$= h \sum_{n=1}^{N} f(a + (n - \tfrac{1}{2})h) \qquad \left(h = \frac{b - a}{N}\right).$$

Like the trapezoidal value, the midpoint value is an approximation to the desired integral that is in error by $O(h^2)$. We clearly have

$$T_{2N} = \frac{b - a}{2N} [\tfrac{1}{2} f_0 + f_{1/2} + f_1 + \cdots + f_{N-1} + f_{N-1/2} + \tfrac{1}{2} f_N]$$

$$= \tfrac{1}{2}(T_N + M_N).$$

Thus in the present situation algorithm 12.4 can be formulated as follows:

Algorithm 13.7 If the function f is defined on the interval $[a, b]$, generate the triangular array of numbers $A_{m,n}$ by means of the recurrence relation (13-24) and

$$A_{0,0} = T_1 = \tfrac{1}{2}(b - a)[f(a) + f(b)],$$

$$A'_{m,0} = M_{2^m} = h \sum_{n=1}^{2^m} f(a + (n - \tfrac{1}{2})h), \qquad h = 2^{-m}(b - a),$$

$$A_{m+1,0} = \tfrac{1}{2}(A_{m,0} + A'_{m,0}), \qquad m = 0, 1, 2, \ldots.$$

The hypotheses of theorem 12.4 are satisfied when f satisfies the hypotheses of theorem 13.6 for every k when N is sufficiently large. This is the case if f has derivatives of all orders on an interval containing the interval $[a, b]$ in its interior. This condition, in turn, is satisfied if f is *analytic* on the closed interval $[a, b]$ (see Buck [1956], p. 78).

Theorem 13.7 Let the function f be analytic on the closed interval $[a, b]$. Then all columns of the array generated by algorithm 13.7 converge to $\int_a^b f(x)\, dx$. If none of the coefficients a_k in (13-22) vanishes, each column converges faster than the preceding one.

The scheme generated by algorithm 13.7 is commonly known as the *Romberg* scheme (see Bauer *et al.* [1963]).

EXAMPLE

3. For the problem considered in example 2 the Romberg scheme is as follows:

Table 13.7

1.16432 1734			
1.25919 0749	1.29081 3754		
1.28220 7763	1.28988 0101	1.28981 7857	
1.28792 0410	1.28982 4626	1.28982 0927	1.28982 0976
1.28934 6003	1.28982 1201	1.28982 0973	1.28982 0973

The accuracy of extrapolation to the limit with 16 steps is about the same as applying T_{16} with "end correction." The advantage of the Romberg procedure is that no decision has to be made in advance concerning the best stepsize.

Problem 13 shows that it may happen that some or even all coefficients in the expansion (13-22) are zero. In such cases extrapolation to the limit will not speed up the convergence of the trapezoidal rule.

Problems

15. Verify experimentally that extrapolation to the limit does not speed up the convergence of the trapezoidal rule for the integral

$$\int_0^1 \sqrt{x}\, dx.$$

Can you explain why?

16. Evaluate

$$\int_0^\pi \frac{\sin x}{x}\, dx$$

with an error of less than 10^{-8}, using repeated extrapolation to the limit.

17. Show that the values $A_{m,1}$ obtained by algorithm 13.7 are identical with the values obtained by applying Simpson's rule (see problem 4) to 2^{m-1} subintervals.

18. Express the values $A_{m,2}$ in terms of the ordinates f_n. Can you recognize a familiar integration rule?

Recommended Reading

Hildebrand [1956] gives an excellent account of Gaussian quadrature in chapter 8. Many examples of the use of generating functions to obtain integration coefficients are given in Henrici [1962], chapter 5. Bauer *et al.* [1963] contains a definite treatment of Romberg integration. Milne [1949] gives numerous integration formulas not considered here and also has a general treatment of the error in numerical integration.

Research Problems

1. Make a comparative study of the effectiveness of the end correction versus repeated extrapolation to the limit.

2. Study the connection of the end correction with the Euler-MacLaurin summation formula.

chapter 14 numerical solution of differential equations

The mathematical formulation of many problems in science and engineering leads to a relation between the values of an unknown function and the value of one or several of its derivatives at the same point. Such relations are called *differential equations*. The present chapter is devoted to the problem of finding numerical values of solutions of differential equations.

14.1 Theoretical Preliminaries

Let $f = f(x, y)$ be a real-valued function of two real variables defined for $a \leqq x \leqq b$, where a and b are finite, and for all real values of y. The equation

$$(14\text{-}1) \qquad\qquad y' = f(x, y)$$

is called an *ordinary differential equation* of the first order; it symbolizes the following problem: To find a function $y = y(x)$, continuous and differentiable for $x \in [a, b]$, such that

$$y'(x) = f(x, y(x))$$

for all $x \in [a, b]$. A function y with this property is called a *solution* of the differential equation (14-1).

EXAMPLE

1. The differential equation $y' = -y$ has the solutions $y(x) = Ce^{-x}$, $C = \text{const}$.

As the above example shows, a given differential equation may have many solutions. In order to pin down a solution, one must specify its value at one point, say at $x = a$. The problem of finding a solution y of

263

(14-1) such that $y(a) = s$, where s is a given number, is called an *initial value problem* and is schematically described by the equations

(14-2)
$$\begin{cases} y' = f(x, y), \\ y(a) = s. \end{cases}$$

EXAMPLE

2. The initial value problem $y' = -y$, $y(0) = 1$ has the solution $y(x) = e^{-x}$.

In courses on differential equations much stress is placed on differential equations whose solutions can be expressed in terms of elementary functions, or of indefinite integrals of such functions. It is shown, for instance, that any differential equation of the form $y' = g(x)y + p(x)$ can be solved in this manner. The emphasis on explicitly solvable differential equations tends to create the impression that almost any differential equation can be solved in explicit form, if only the proper trick is found. Nothing could be farther from the truth, however. Most differential equations that occur in actual practice are much too complicated to admit an explicit solution; if numerical values of the solution are desired, they can only be found by special numerical methods.

EXAMPLE

3. The differential equation $y' = 1-y$ can be solved explicitly; for the equation $y' = 1-y + \varepsilon y^3 \sin x$, which for small values of ε differs only little from it, no such solution can be found.

The fact that a differential equation does not possess an explicit solution does not mean that the solution does not exist, in the mathematical sense. The following existence theorem is proved in courses on differential equations (see Coddington [1961], p. 217).

Theorem 14.1 Let the function $f = f(x, y)$ be continuous for $a \leq x \leq b$, $-\infty < y < \infty$, and let there exist a constant L such that, for any two numbers y, z and all $x \in [a, b]$,

(14-3)
$$|f(x, y) - f(x, z)| \leq L|y - z|.$$

Then, whatever the initial value s, the initial value problem (14-2) possesses a unique solution $y = y(x)$ for $x \in [a, b]$.

This theorem can be proved, for instance, by the method of successive approximations. Although this is, in a sense, a constructive method for proving the existence of a solution, the method is not suitable for the numerical computation of the solution, because it requires the evaluation of infinitely many indefinite integrals. The methods to be given below are far more economical and are therefore preferred in practice.

Condition (14-3) resembles condition (4-4) imposed on functions suitable for iteration, with the difference that the function f now depends on the additional parameter x. The condition is again called a *Lipschitz condition*.

Problems

1. Which of the following functions f satisfy a Lipschitz condition?

(a) $\qquad\qquad f(x, y) = \dfrac{y^2}{1 + y^2};$

(b) $\qquad\qquad f(x, y) = \dfrac{x^2}{1 + x^2}\, y, \qquad 0 \leqq x \leqq 1;$

(c) $\qquad\qquad f(x, y) = y^2;$

(d) $\qquad\qquad f(x, y) = \sqrt{|y|}.$

2. Show that the following condition is sufficient for f to satisfy (14-3): The partial derivative f_y exists and is continuous for $a \leqq x \leqq b$, $-\infty < y < \infty$, and there exists a constant M such that

$$|f_y(x, y)| \leqq M$$

for all values of x and y in the indicated domain.

14.2   Numerical Integration by Taylor's Expansion

Throughout the balance of the present chapter we shall assume that the function f not only satisfies the conditions of the basic existence theorem 14.1, but also that it possesses continuous derivatives with respect to both x and y of all orders required to justify the analytical operations to be performed. We shall refer to this property by the phrase "f is sufficiently differentiable."

It is a basic fact in the theory of ordinary differential equations that if f is sufficiently differentiable, all derivatives of a solution of the differential equation (14-1) are expressible in terms of the function f and its derivatives. In fact, this statement is obviously true for the first derivative. Assuming its truth for the nth derivative, we write

(14-4) $\qquad\qquad y^{(n)} = f^{(n-1)}(x, y),$

where $f^{(n-1)}$, the $(n-1)st$ total derivative of f with respect to x, is a certain combination of derivatives of f. Differentiating the identity

$$y^{(n)}(x) = f^{(n-1)}(x, y(x))$$

once more with respect to x, we have

$$y^{(n+1)}(x) = f_x^{(n-1)}(x, y(x)) + f_y^{(n-1)}(x, y(x))y'(x)$$

and thus, in view of $y'(x) = f(x, y(x))$,

$$y^{(n+1)}(x) = f^{(n)}(x, y(x)),$$

where

(14-5) $f^{(n)}(x, y) = f_x^{(n-1)}(x, y) + f_y^{(n-1)}(x, y)f(x, y).$

We thus have

Algorithm 14.2   If f is sufficiently differentiable, the nth derivative of a solution y of (14-1) is expressible in the form

$$y^{(n)}(x) = f^{(n-1)}(x, y(x)), \qquad n = 0, 1, 2, \ldots$$

where the functions $f^{(m)}$ can be calculated by means of the recurrence relation

$$f^{(0)} = f, \qquad f^{(m+1)} = f_x^{(m)} + f_y^{(m)}f, \qquad m = 0, 1, 2, \ldots.$$

In place of $f^{(1)}$ and $f^{(2)}$ we shall also write f' and f''.

EXAMPLES

4. $f' = f_x + f_y f,$
$f'' = f_{xx} + f_{xy}f + f_y f_x + (f_{xy} + f_{yy}f + f_y^2)f$
$\quad = f_{xx} + 2f_{xy}f + f_{yy}f^2 + (f_x + f_y f)f_y.$

5.   Let $f(x, y) = x^2 + y^2$.   We find

$$f'(x, y) = 2x + 2y(x^2 + y^2),$$
$$f''(x, y) = 2 + 4xy + (2x^2 + 6y^2)(x^2 + y^2).$$

In view of the fact that the derivatives of the solution of a differential equation can be determined whenever the derivatives of f can be calculated (which is, in principle, always the case if f is an elementary function of x and y), one might think of approximating the solution y of the initial value problem (14-2) by its Taylor series at $s = a$.   In view of the initial condition $y(a) = s$ this series takes the form

(14-6) $y(x) = s + \dfrac{x - a}{1!} f(a, s) + \dfrac{(x - a)^2}{2!} f'(a, s)$

$$+ \dfrac{(x - a)^3}{3!} f''(a, s) + \cdots.$$

However, the above examples suggest that unless the function f is very simple, the higher total derivatives of f rapidly increase in complexity. This circumstance makes it necessary to truncate the infinite series (14-6) already after very few terms.   This necessarily restricts the range of values of x over which the truncated series (14-6) can be expected to define a good approximation of the solution y.   One therefore will use the truncated series with a small value of $x - a$, $x - a = h$ say, and re-evaluate the derivatives $f, f', f'', \ldots$, at the point $x = a + h$.

Problems

3. Calculate the nth total derivative of f if

$$\text{(a) } f(x, y) = y + e^x, \qquad \text{(b) } f(x, y) = e^x y.$$

4. If $f(x, y) = (2y/x) - 1$, show that f'' is identically zero.   What is the explanation of this fact?

14.3   The Taylor Algorithm

In order to formalize the procedure outlined in the preceding section we introduce the following notation.   Let $h > 0$ be a constant, and set

$$x_n = a + nh, \qquad n = 0, 1, 2, \ldots.$$

We shall always denote by y_n a number intended to approximate $y(x_n)$, the value of the exact solution of the initial value problem (14-1) at $x = x_n$.   If the method of Taylor expansion is used, these values are calculated according to the following scheme: Let, for some fixed integer $p \geq 1$,

$$(14\text{-}7) \quad T_p(x, y; h) = \frac{1}{1!} f(x, y) + \frac{h}{2!} f'(x, y) + \cdots + \frac{h^{p-1}}{p!} f^{(p-1)}(x, y).$$

The numbers y_n are then calculated successively as follows:

Algorithm 14.3   For a fixed value of h, generate the sequence of numbers $\{y_n\}$ by the recurrence relation

$$(14\text{-}8a) \qquad\qquad\qquad y_0 = s,$$

$$(14\text{-}8b) \quad y_{n+1} = y_n + hT_p(x_n, y_n; h), \qquad n = 0, 1, 2, \ldots.$$

This scheme is known as the *Taylor algorithm* of order p.

EXAMPLE

6.   The Taylor algorithm of order one is particularly simple.   In view of $T_1(x, y; h) = f(x, y)$, (14-8b) then becomes

$$(14\text{-}9) \qquad\qquad\qquad y_{n+1} = y_n + hf(x_n, y_n).$$

This is also known as the *Euler method*, or as the *Euler-Cauchy* method.

Naturally we expect the values defined by (14-8) to approximate the corresponding values $y(x_n)$ of the exact solution, particularly when h is small.   To see whether this is the case, let us examine the purely academic example

$$(14\text{-}10) \qquad\qquad y(0) = 1, \qquad y' = y.$$

The exact solution, of course, is $y(x) = e^x$.   In view of

$$f(x, y) = f'(x, y) = f''(x, y) = \cdots = y,$$

the function T_p takes the simple form

$$T_p(x, y; h) = \left(\frac{1}{1!} + \frac{h}{2!} + \cdots + \frac{h^{p-1}}{p!}\right) y.$$

The recurrence relation (14-8) thus becomes

$$y_{n+1} = \left(1 + \frac{h}{1!} + \frac{h^2}{2!} + \cdots + \frac{h^p}{p!}\right) y_n.$$

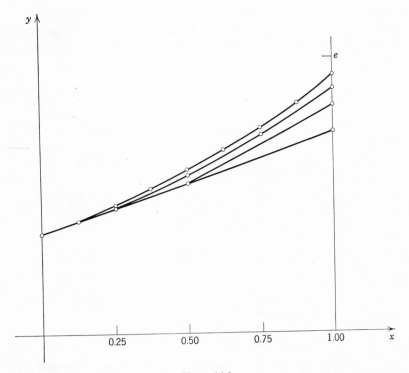

Figure 14.3

This is a difference equation of order 1 (see chapter 3); the solution satisfying the initial condition $y_0 = 1$ is given by

$$(14\text{-}11) \quad y_n = \left(1 + \frac{h}{1!} + \frac{h^2}{2!} + \cdots + \frac{h^p}{p!}\right)^n, \quad n = 0, 1, 2, \ldots$$

We wish to examine how closely y_n approximates $y(x_n) = e^{x_n}$ at a fixed point x of the interval of integration, if the approximation y_n is calculated by successively smaller integration steps h. We thus must let $h \to 0$ and $n \to \infty$ simultaneously in such a manner that $x = x_n = nh$ remains fixed. By Taylor's formula with remainder term (see Taylor [1959], p. 471)

$$e^h = 1 + \frac{h}{1!} + \frac{h^2}{2!} + \cdots + \frac{h^p}{p!} + \frac{h^{p+1}}{(p+1)!} e^{\theta h},$$

where θ is some unspecified number between 0 and 1. We now use the fact that for any two real numbers A and B such that $A \geq B \geq 0$ and for $n = 1, 2, \ldots$

$$A^n - B^n = (A - B)(A^{n-1} + A^{n-2}B + \cdots + AB^{n-2} + B^{n-1})$$
$$\leq (A - B)nA^{n-1}.$$

In particular, taking

$$A = e^h,$$

$$B = 1 + \frac{h}{1!} + \frac{h^2}{2!} + \cdots + \frac{h^p}{p!},$$

we obtain

$$y(x_n) - y_n = e^{nh} - \left(1 + \frac{h}{1!} + \cdots + \frac{h^p}{p!}\right)^n$$

$$\leq n\frac{h^{p+1}}{(p+1)!} e^{\theta h}e^{(n-1)h}$$

or, in view of $nh = x_n, 0 < \theta < 1$,

$$(14\text{-}12) \qquad |y_n - y(x_n)| \leq \frac{h^p}{(p+1)!} x_n e^{x_n}.$$

This relation shows that, at a fixed point $x_n = x$, the error in the approximation of the exact solution y by the Taylor algorithm of order p tends to zero like h^p as the stepsize h tends to zero.

The convergence if the integration steps are successively halved is illustrated in figure 14.3.

We shall now derive a similar bound for the error $y_n - y(x_n)$ of the Taylor approximation y_n to the solution y of an arbitrary initial value problem (14-2). To this end we make the following assumptions:

(i) Not only the function f, but also the function T_p defined by (14-7) satisfies a Lipschitz condition with Lipschitz constant L:

(14-13) $$|T_p(x, y; h) - T_p(x, z; h)| \leqq L|y - z|$$

for any y, z and all x and h such that $x \in [a, b]$, $x + h \in [a, b]$;

(ii) The $(p + 1)$st derivative of the exact solution y of (14-2) is continuous and hence bounded on the closed interval $[a, b]$, and

(14-14) $$|y^{(p+1)}(x)| \leqq Y_{p+1}, \qquad x \in [a, b].$$

We then have:

Theorem 14.3 Under the above assumptions (i) and (ii), the error $z_n = y_n - y(x_n)$ of the Taylor algorithm of order p is bounded as follows:

(14-15) $$|z_n| \leqq h^p \frac{Y_{p+1}}{(p + 1)!} \frac{e^{L(x_n - a)} - 1}{L}.$$

The result shows that z_n again tends to zero at least like h^p as $x_n = x$ is fixed and $h \to 0$.

Proof. By Taylor's formula with remainder, the exact solution satisfies

$$y(x_{n+1}) = y(x_n + h)$$
$$= y(x_n) + hT_p(x_n, y(x_n); h) + \frac{h^{p+1}}{(p + 1)!} y^{(p+1)}(\xi_n),$$

where ξ_n is some point between x_n and x_{n+1}. Subtracting the last relation from (14-8b), we get

(14-16) $$z_{n+1} = z_n + h[T_p(x_n, y_n; h) - T_p(x_n, y(x_n); h)]$$
$$- \frac{h^{p+1}}{(p + 1)!} y^{(p+1)}(\xi_n)$$

and hence

$$|z_{n+1}| \leqq |z_n| + h|T_p(x_n, y_n; h) - T_p(x_n, y(x_n); h)|$$
$$+ \frac{h^{p+1}}{(p + 1)!} |y^{(p+1)}(\xi_n)|.$$

Using (14-13) and (14-14), the expression on the right can be simplified, with the following result:

(14-17) $$|z_{n+1}| \leqq |z_n| + hL|z_n| + h^{p+1} \frac{Y_{p+1}}{(p + 1)!}.$$

We now make use of the following auxiliary result:

Lemma 14.3 Let the elements of a sequence $\{w_n\}$ satisfy the inequalities

$$(14\text{-}18) \qquad w_{n+1} \leqq (1 + a)w_n + B, \qquad n = 0, 1, 2, \ldots$$

where a, and B are certain positive constants, and let $w_0 = 0$. Then

$$(14\text{-}19) \qquad w_n \leqq B \frac{e^{na} - 1}{a}, \qquad n = 0, 1, 2, \ldots .$$

Proof of lemma 14.3. The relation (14-19) is evidently true for $n = 0$. Assuming its truth for some nonnegative integer n we have from (14-18), in view of $1 + a \leqq e^a$,

$$w_{n+1} \leqq (1 + a) \frac{e^{na} - 1}{a} B + B$$

$$= B \frac{(1 + a)e^{na} - 1}{a} \leqq B \frac{e^{(n+1)a} - 1}{a},$$

establishing (14-19) with n increased by one. The truth of the lemma now follows by the principle of induction.

Returning to the proof of theorem 14.3, we apply the lemma to the relation (14-17), setting $w_n = |z_n|$, $a = hL$, $B = h^{p+1}Y_{p+1}/(p + 1)!$. By virtue of (14-8a) and (14-2), $|z_0| = 0$. Thus the conclusion (14-19) applies, yielding (14-15).

Problems

5. Solve the initial value problem

$$y' = 1 - y, \qquad y(0) = 0,$$

by the Taylor algorithm of order $p = 2$, using the steps $h = 0.5$, $h = 0.25$, and $h = 0.125$, and compare the values of the numerical solution at $x_n = 1$ with the values of the exact solution.

6. Find an analytical expression for the values y_n defined by (14-9) for the initial value problem

$$y' = -\frac{2y}{1 + x}, \qquad y(0) = 1,$$

and verify the statement of theorem 14.3. [Hint: Use theorem 3.3 to solve the difference equation involved.]

14.4 Extrapolation to the Limit

The estimate for the error $z_n = y_n - y(x_n)$ given in theorem 14.3 should not be regarded as a realistic indication of the actual size of the error. It merely serves to prove the convergence of the Taylor algorithm and to indicate the order of magnitude of the error. The estimate states, in effect, that there exists a constant K so that

(14-20) $|z_n| \leq Kh^p$

for all $x_n \in [a, b]$. This relation shows that the error tends to zero as $h \to 0$. Can we make a statement about the manner in which the error tends to zero? As we have observed repeatedly, such knowledge could be helpful for the purpose of speeding up the convergence of the method as $h \to 0$.

We shall prove:

Theorem 14.4 If f is sufficiently differentiable, the errors $z_n = y_n - y(x_n)$ of the values defined by (14-8) satisfy

(14-21) $z_n = h^p z(x_n) + 0(h^{p+1})$,

where z denotes the solution of the initial value problem

(14-22)
$$
\begin{cases}
z(a) = 0, \\
z' = f_y(x, y(x))z - \dfrac{1}{(p+1)!}\, y^{(p+1)}(x).
\end{cases}
$$

Proof. We start from relation (14-16) above. By Taylor's theorem,

$$T_p(x_n, y_n; h) - T_p(x_n, y(x_n); h) = \frac{\partial T_p}{\partial y}(x_n, y(x_n); h)z_n + 0(z_n^2)$$

$$= \frac{\partial T_p}{\partial y}(x_n, y(x_n); 0)z_n + 0(z_n^2) + 0(hz_n)$$

$$= f_y(x_n, y(x_n))z_n + 0(h^{p+1}),$$

since $T_p(x, y; 0) = f(x, y)$. Also, $y^{(p+1)}(\xi_n) = y^{(p+1)}(x_n) + 0(h)$. We thus have

$$z_{n+1} = z_n + hf_y(x_n, y(x_n))z_n - \frac{h^{p+1}}{(p+1)!}\, y^{(p+1)}(x_n) + 0(h^{p+2}).$$

From this we subtract h^p times the relation

$$z(x_{n+1}) = z(x_n) + hz'(x_n) + 0(h^2)$$

$$= z(x_n) + h\left[f_y(x_n, y(x_n))z(x_n) - \frac{1}{(p+1)!}\, y^{(p+1)}(x_n) \right] + 0(h^2)$$

which follows from the definition of z. Setting

$$w_n = z_n - h^p z(x_n) \qquad (n = 0, 1, 2, \ldots)$$

we obtain

$$|w_{n+1}| \leq |w_n| + hL|w_n| + 0(h^{p+1}).$$

Since $w_0 = 0$, lemma 14.3 now yields the relation $w_n = O(h^{p+1})$ equivalent to (14-21).

In order to make explicit the dependence of the numerical values y_n on the step h with which they are calculated, we shall denote (in this section only) by $y(x; h)$ the approximation to $y(x)$ calculated with the step h. Relation (14-21) can then be written more explicitly as follows:

(14-23) $y(x, h) = y(x) + h^p z(x) + O(h^{p+1})$.

In general, both quantities $y(x_n)$ and $z(x_n)$ are unknown in this relation, the latter because it depends on the solution of a differential equation involving the unknown function y. However, the mere fact that a relation of the form (14-21) holds can be made the basis for an extrapolation to the limit procedure. Eliminating $z(x_n)$ between (14-23) and the similar relation

$$y(x, r^{-1}h) = y(x) + r^{-p}h^p z(x) + O(h^{p+1})$$

for the numerical approximation calculated with the step $r^{-1}h$, where $r \neq 1$, we find that the quantity

(14-24) $y^*(x, h) = \dfrac{y(x, h) - r^p y(x, r^{-1}h)}{1 - r^p}$

differs from $y(x)$ by only $O(h^{p+1})$. As $h \to 0$, the values $y^*(x, h)$ will thus converge to $y(x)$ faster than the values $y(x, h)$. Here r is, in principle, arbitrary; for practical reasons one usually chooses $r = \frac{1}{2}$.

Under the assumption that (14-23) holds in the generalized form

(14-25) $y(x; h) = y(x) + a_p(x)h^p + a_{p+1}(x)h^{p+1} + \cdots$
            $+ a_k(x)h^k + O(h^{k+1})$

for every $k > p$, we can speed up the values $y^*(x, h)$ once more, using (14-24) with p replaced by $p + 1$. Continuing the process systematically in the manner of algorithm 12.4, we obtain

Algorithm 14.4   For a fixed x in $[a, b]$, form the triangular array of numbers $A_{m,n}$ as follows:

$$A_{m,0} = y\left(x; \frac{x-a}{2^m}\right), \qquad m = 0, 1, 2, \ldots,$$

$$A_{m,n+1} = \frac{2^{p+n}A_{m,n} - A_{m-1,n}}{2^{p+n} - 1}, \qquad n = 0, 1, \ldots, m - 1.$$

The fact that (14-25) holds for sufficiently differentiable functions f was established by Gragg [1963]. If this is taken for granted, we can deduce as in theorem 12.4 that each succeeding column of the array $A_{m,n}$ converges faster to $y(x)$.

EXAMPLE

7. We integrate the initial value problem

$$y' = x - y^2, \qquad y(0) = 0$$

by Euler's method, using the steps $h = 0.4, 0.2, 0.1, 0.05$. The table below shows the resulting values at $x = 0.8$, and the values obtained by repeated extrapolation to the limit.

Table 14.4

h	$A_{m,0}$	$A_{m,1}$	$A_{m,2}$	$A_{m,3}$	$A_{m,4}$
0.8	0.00000				
0.4	0.16000	0.32000			
0.2	0.23682	0.31363	0.31151		
0.1	0.27201	0.30720	0.30505	0.30413	
0.05	0.28871	0.30541	0.30481	0.30478	0.30482

Problems

7. Let the initial value problem

$$y' = -y, \qquad y(0) = 1$$

be solved by the Taylor algorithm of order 1. Where does the absolute value of the error (approximately) attain its maximum value? Verify your result numerically by performing a numerical integration using the step $h = 0.1$.

8. Improve the values obtained in problem 5 by extrapolation to the limit.

9. Devise a method for extrapolation to the limit if p, the order of the method, is not known.

14.5 Methods of Runge-Kutta Type

The practical application of the Taylor algorithm described in the preceding sections is frequently tedious because of the necessity of evaluating the functions $f', f'', \ldots$ at each integration step. It therefore is a remarkable fact that formulas exist that produce values y_n of the same accuracy as some of the Taylor algorithms of order $p \geq 2$, but without requiring the evaluation of any derivatives. We mention only a few of the many available formulas of this type.

(*i*) *The simplified Runge-Kutta method.* Here we replace the function T_2 in algorithm 14.3 by K_2, where

$$(14-26) \qquad K_2(x, y; h) = \tfrac{1}{2}[f(x, y) + f(x + h, y + hf(x, y))].$$

Clearly, no evaluation of f' is necessary. Instead, the function f is evaluated twice at each step. It can be shown that

(14-27) $K_2(x, y; h) - T_2(x, y; h) = 0(h^2)$,

and that the accumulated error satisfies an inequality of the form (14-20), and, with a suitable definition of z, a relation of the form of (14-21), where $p = 2$.

(*ii*) *The classical Runge-Kutta method.* Here the function T_4 in algorithm 14.3 is replaced by K_4, a sum of four values of the function f, defined as follows:

(14-28) $K_4(x, y; h) = \frac{1}{6}[k_1 + 2k_2 + 2k_3 + k_4]$,

where

$$k_1 = f(x, y),$$

$$k_2 = f\left(x + \frac{h}{2}, y + \frac{h}{2}k_1\right),$$

$$k_3 = f\left(x + \frac{h}{2}, y + \frac{h}{2}k_2\right),$$

$$k_4 = f(x + h, y + hk_3).$$

It can be shown that

$$K_4(x, y; h) = T_4(x, y; h) + 0(h^4)$$

and that, as a consequence, the relations (14-20) and (14-21) now hold with $p = 4$. (The proofs of these statements are extremely complicated). In view of this fact, the classical Runge-Kutta method is one of the most widely used methods for the numerical integration of differential equations.

(*iii*) *A mixed Runge-Kutta-Taylor method.* If the first total derivative of f is easily evaluated, we may use in place of T_3 in algorithm 14.3 the function $G_3(x, y; h)$ defined by

(14-29) $G_3(x, y; h) = f(x, y) + \frac{h}{2}f'\left(x + \frac{h}{3}, y + \frac{h}{3}f(x, y)\right)$.

It can be shown that $G_3(x, y; h) - T_3(x, y; h) = 0(h^3)$ and that, as a consequence, (14-20) and (14-21) are true for $p = 3$.

Problems

10. Solve the initial value problem

$$y' = x - y^2, \qquad y(0) = 0$$

for $0 \leq x \leq 0.8$ by the classical Runge-Kutta method, using the step $h = 0.1$. Also, perform the same integration with the steps $h = 0.2$ and $h = 0.4$, and perform an extrapolation to the limit.

11. Establish the relation (14-27).
12. Show that for the differential equation $y' = Ay$ (A = const.) the values y_n produced by the methods K_2 and K_4 are identical, respectively, with the values produced by T_2 and T_4.
13. Prove that G_3 differs from T_3 by $O(h^3)$.

14.6   Methods Based on Numerical Integration: The Adams-Bashforth Method

All the methods discussed so far are based directly or indirectly on the idea of expanding the exact solution in a Taylor series. A different approach to the problem can be based on the idea of *numerical integration*. A solution y of (14-1) by definition satisfies the identity

$$y'(x) = f(x, y(x)).$$

Integrating between the limits x_n and x_{n+1} we obtain

(14-30) $$y(x_{n+1}) = y(x_n) + \int_{x_n}^{x_{n+1}} f(x, y(x))\, dx.$$

Let us now suppose that we have somehow already obtained approximate values $y_0, y_1, \ldots, y_n$ of the solution y at the points $x_0, x_1, \ldots, x_n$, where we again assume the points x_m to be equally spaced, $x_m = a + mh$. The approximate values of $f(x, y(x))$ at these points then are

$$f_m = f(x_m, y_m), \qquad m = 0, 1, \ldots, n.$$

If $k \leq n$, we can use these values to approximate $f(x, y(x))$ by the Newton backward polynomial

$$P_k(x) = \sum_{m=0}^{k} (-1)^m \binom{-s}{m} \nabla^m f_n, \qquad s = \frac{x - x_n}{h}.$$

Performing the integration in (14-30) on P_k in place of f, we obtain the following algorithm for computing a new value y_{n+1}:

Algorithm 14.6 (The Adams-Bashforth method.) For a given function $f = f(x, y)$, a given constant $h > 0$, a given integer $k \geq 0$, and given values $y_0, y_1, \ldots, y_k$, let $f_m = f(x_m, y_m)$ ($m = 0, 1, 2, \ldots, k$), and generate the sequence $\{y_n\}$ recursively from the formulas

(14-31) $$\begin{cases} x_{n+1} = x_n + h, \\ y_{n+1} = y_n + h[c_0 f_n + c_1 \nabla f_n + c_2 \nabla^2 f_n + \cdots + c_k \nabla^k f_n], \end{cases}$$

and

$$f_{n+1} = f(x_{n+1}, y_{n+1}) = \nabla^0 f_{n+1},$$
$$\nabla^m f_{n+1} = \nabla^{m-1} f_{n+1} - \nabla^{m-1} f_n, \qquad m = 1, 2, \ldots, k.$$

where $n = k, k + 1, \ldots$.

Here the coefficients c_m are defined by (13-5); for numerical values see table 13.4b. The working of algorithm 14.6 is illustrated by scheme 14.6 for $k = 3$.

Scheme 14.6

As soon as y_{n+1} is known, f_{n+1} can be calculated and a new diagonal of differences may be formed. The process requires exactly one evaluation of f per step, no matter how many differences are carried. This compares favorably with methods such as the classical Runge-Kutta method, which requires four evaluations.

Algorithm 14.6 does not say how to obtain the starting values $y_0, y_1, \ldots,$ y_k. This can be done by any of the methods discussed in §14.3 or §14.5; other starting methods, more in the spirit of the algorithm itself, are also known (see Collatz [1960], p. 81).

Let us now study the error $z_n = y_n - y(x_n)$ of the values defined by (14-31) under the assumption that the starting values are in error by at most δ:

(14-32) $|z_m| = |y_m - y(x_m)| < \delta, \qquad m = 0, 1, \ldots, k.$

Expressing differences in terms of ordinates, (14-31) appears in the form

$$y_{n+1} = y_n + h\{b_{k0}f_n + b_{k1}f_{n-1} + \cdots + b_{kk}f_{n-k}\},$$

where the b_{km} are certain constants, involving the c_m, that need not be specified. The corresponding relation for the exact solution is, by (13-6),

$$y(x_{n+1}) = y(x_n) + h\{b_{k0}y'(x_n) + b_{k1}y'(x_{n-1}) + \cdots + b_{kk}y'(x_{n-k})\}$$
$$+ c_{k+1}h^{k+2}y^{(k+2)}(\xi_n),$$

where ξ_n is a point between x_{n-k} and x_{n+1}. We now subtract the last two relations from each other. Observing that

$$|f_m - y'(x_m)| = |f(x_m, y_m) - f(x_m, y(x_m))|$$
$$\leqq L|y_m - y(x_m)| = L|z_m|,$$

where L denotes the Lipschitz constant of the function f, and assuming that

(14-33) $$|y^{(k+2)}(x)| \leqq Y_{k+2}, \qquad a \leqq x \leqq b,$$

we obtain

$$|z_{n+1}| \leqq |z_n| + hL\{|b_{k0}||z_n| + |b_{k1}||z_{n-1}| + \cdots + |b_{kk}||z_{n-k}|\} + |c_{k+1}|h^{k+2}Y_{k+2}.$$

Our aim is to find an explicit bound for the quantities $|z_n|$. An induction argument shows that

$$|z_n| \leqq w_n, \qquad n = 0, 1, 2, \ldots$$

where $\{w_n\}$ is any solution of the difference equation

(14-34) $$w_{n+1} = w_n + hL\{|b_{k0}|w_n + |b_{k1}|w_{n-1} + \cdots + |b_{kk}|w_{n-k}\} + |c_{k+1}|h^{k+2}Y_{k+2}$$

satisfying

(14-35) $$|w_n| \geqq \delta, \qquad n = 0, 1, \ldots, k.$$

We try to find such a solution using the principles set forth in §6.7. Since the nonhomogeneous term in (14-34) is a constant, the equation clearly has the particular solution $w_n = -C$, where

(14-36) $$C = \frac{|c_{k+1}|h^{k+1}Y_{k+2}}{LB_k},$$

(14-37) $$B_k = |b_{k0}| + |b_{k1}| + \cdots + |b_{kk}|.$$

In order to obtain a solution satisfying (14-35), we add to this solution a suitable solution of the homogeneous equation

$$w_{n+1} = w_n + hL\{|b_{k0}|w_n + |b_{k1}|w_{n-1} + \cdots + |b_{kk}|w_{n-k}\}.$$

The characteristic polynomial of the equation is

$$p(z) = z^{k+1} - z^k - hL\{|b_{k0}|z^k + \cdots + |b_{kk}|\}.$$

Evidently, $p(1) \leqq 0$. On the other hand, if $z = 1 + hLB_k$, where B_k is given by (14-37), then

$$z^{-k}p(z) = 1 + hLB_k - 1 - hL\{|b_{k0}| + \cdots + |b_{kk}|z^{-k}\}$$
$$\geqq hLB_k - hL\{|b_{k0}| + \cdots + |b_{kk}|\}$$
$$= 0.$$

It follows that for some z^* such that $1 \leqq z^* \leqq 1 + hLB_k$

$$p(z^*) = 0.$$

Thus a solution of (14-34) satisfying (14-35) is given by

$$w_n = (\delta + C)z^{*n} - C.$$

In view of

$$z^{*n} \leqq (1 + hLB_k)^n \leqq e^{(x_n - a)LB_k},$$

we finally find, remembering the definition of C,

(14-38) $$|z_n| \leqq \delta e^{(x_n - a)LB_k} + |c_{k+1}|h^{k+1} Y_{k+2} \frac{e^{(x_n - a)LB_k} - 1}{LB_k},$$

$$a \leqq x_n \leqq b.$$

In summary, we have

Theorem 14.6   If the starting values of the Adams-Bashforth method are in error by at most δ, then the errors $z_n = y_n - y(x_n)$ are bounded by (14-38), where Y_{k+2} and B_k are defined by (14-33) and (14-37).

As on earlier occasions, the estimate (14-38) should be looked at as a qualitative rather than a quantitative statement.   The important thing is that, if the starting errors are sufficiently small (namely at most $O(h^{k+1})$), the error of the Adams-Bashforth algorithm tends to zero like h^{k+1} as $h \to 0$.   Interpolating f in (14-30) by an interpolating polynomial of degree k has the same effect as expanding the solution in a Taylor polynomial of degree $k + 1$.   However, the coefficient of Y_{k+2} in (14-38) is markedly greater than the corresponding coefficient of Y_{p+1} in (14-15), on account of the fact that both

$$|c_{k+1}| > \frac{1}{(k + 2)!} \quad \text{and} \quad B_k > 1$$

for $k > 0$.

Problems

14*. Assuming that the starting values are exact, show that the errors z_n of the Adams-Bashforth method satisfy

$$z_n = z(x_n)h^{k+1} + O(h^{k+2}),$$

where z denotes the solution of the initial value problem

$$z' = f_y(x, y(x))z - c_{k+1}y^{(k+2)}(x),$$
$$z(a) = 0.$$

[Analog of theorem 14.4.]

15. Solve problem 10 by the Adams-Bashforth method with $k = 2$, determining the starting values y_{-1} and y_1 by Runge-Kutta or by a series expansion around $x = 0$.   Use the steps $h = 0.2$ and $h = 0.1$ and extrapolate to the limit at $x = 0.8$.

14.7   Methods Based on Numerical Integration: The Adams-Moulton Method

A considerable refinement and improvement of the Adams-Bashforth method can be obtained as follows: Suppose a tentative value of y_{n+1} has been obtained, for instance by the Adams-Bashforth method. We shall call this value $y_{n+1}^{(0)}$. Setting $f_{n+1}^{(0)} = f(x_{n+1}, y_{n+1}^{(0)})$, we can construct the polynomial which at the points $x_{n-k}, x_{n-k+1}, \ldots, x_n, x_{n+1}$ takes on the values $f_{n-k}, f_{n-k+1}, \ldots, f_n, f_{n+1}$. According to the Newton backward formula, this polynomial is given by

$$P_{k+1}(x) = \sum_{m=0}^{k+1} (-1)^m \binom{1-s}{m} \nabla^m f_{n+1}^{(0)},$$

where again $s = (x - x_n)/h$, and where the differences are formed with the values $f_{n+1}^{(0)}, f_n, \ldots, f_{n-k}$. Integrating between x_n and x_{n+1} we obtain a new value of y_{n+1}, to be called $y_{n+1}^{(1)}$, according to the formula

$$(14\text{-}39) \quad y_{n+1}^{(1)} = y_n + h\{c_0^* f_{n+1}^{(0)} + c_1^* \nabla f_{n+1}^{(0)} + c_2^* \nabla^2 f_{n+1}^{(0)} + \cdots \\ + c_{k+1}^* \nabla^{k+1} f_{n+1}^{(0)}\}.$$

Here the coefficients c_m^* are defined by (13-8) and are tabulated in table 13.4a.

In general, the value $y_{n+1}^{(1)}$ calculated by (14-39) will disagree with $y_{n+1}^{(0)}$. We therefore compute $f_{n+1}^{(1)} = f(x_{n+1}, y_{n+1}^{(1)})$, correct the difference table of the values of f, and reevaluate the term on the right in (14-39). A new value $y_{n+1}^{(2)}$ will result. The general step of this iteration procedure is described by the formula

$$(14\text{-}40) \quad y_{n+1}^{(i+1)} = y_n + h\{c_0^* f_{n+1}^{(i)} + c_1^* \nabla f_{n+1}^{(i)} + \cdots + c_{k+1}^* \nabla^{k+1} f_{n+1}^{(i)}\},$$

the differences on the right being formed with $f_{n+1}^{(i)} = f(x_{n+1}, y_{n+1}^{(i)})$, $f_n, \ldots, f_{n-k}$. Theoretically, the iteration with respect to i should be continued indefinitely, and the limit as $i \to \infty$ of the sequence $y_{n+1}^{(i)}$ would be accepted as the final value of y_{n+1}. In practice, of course, the iteration continues only to the point where the sequence $y_{n+1}^{(i)}$ has converged numerically in the sense that an inequality

$$\left| y_{n+1}^{(i+1)} - y_{n+1}^{(i)} \right| < \varepsilon$$

holds, where ε is some preassigned number. More frequently even, the iteration is performed only a fixed number of times, say for $i = 0, 1, 2, \ldots$, I, where I is a preassigned integer such as 2 or 3. We state the last version of the procedure as a formalized algorithm.

Algorithm 14.7 (The Adams-Moulton method.) For a given function $f = f(x, y)$, a given constant $h > 0$, given integers $k > 0$ and

$I > 0$, and given values $y_0, y_1, \ldots, y_k$, let $x_m = x_0 + mh$, $f_m = f(x_m, y_m)$ $(m = 0, 1, \ldots, k)$, and generate the sequence y_n by the following set of formulas: Form $\nabla f_k, \nabla^2 f_k, \ldots, \nabla^k f_k$, and calculate for $n = k, k + 1, \ldots$

(14-31)
$$\begin{cases} x_{n+1} = x_n + h, \\ y_{n+1}^{(0)} = y_n + h[c_0 f_n + c_1 \nabla f_n + \cdots + c_k \nabla^k f_n], \end{cases}$$

and

$$y_{n+1} = y_{n+1}^{(I)},$$

where for $i = 0, 1, \ldots, I - 1$

$$f_{n+1}^{(i)} = f(x_{n+1}, y_{n+1}^{(i)}),$$
$$\nabla^m f_{n+1}^{(i)} = \nabla^{m-1} f_{n+1}^{(i)} - \nabla^{m-1} f_n \qquad (m = 1, 2, \ldots, k + 1)$$

and

(14-40) $\quad y_{n+1}^{(i+1)} = y_n + h[c_0^* f_{n+1}^{(i)} + c_1^* \nabla f_{n+1}^{(i)} + \cdots + c_{k+1}^* \nabla^{k+1} f_{n+1}^{(i)}].$

The reader will observe that this algorithm involves three iterations: The "outer" iteration for calculating the sequence $\{y_n\}$, an inner iteration for calculating the sequence of values $\{y_{n+1}^{(i)}\}$ for each n, and a further inner iteration for calculating the differences $\nabla^m f_{n+1}^{(i)}$ for each i. (Problem 19 shows that this last iteration can be avoided, however.) Since the tentative values $y_{n+1}^{(i)}$ are "corrected" at each application of formula (14-40), this formula is called a *corrector formula*. The formula which produces a first approximation $y_{n+1}^{(0)}$ is called a *predictor formula*. The Adams-Moulton method thus belongs to the class of so-called predictor-corrector procedures. Like the Runge-Kutta method, it is one of the most reliable and most widely used procedures for the numerical integration of ordinary differential equations.

Let us convince ourselves that the sequence $\{y_{n+1}^{(i)}\}$ generated by repeated application of the corrector formula would converge for $i \to \infty$. For the purpose of analysis, we express the differences in (14-40) in terms of ordinates and observe that only the foremost values $f_{n+1}^{(i)}$ involve $y_{n+1}^{(i)}$. Setting

$$y_{n+1}^{(i)} = w_i, \qquad i = 0, 1, 2, \ldots,$$

equation (14-40) is of the form

(14-41) $\qquad\qquad w_{i+1} = F(w_i),$

where

$$F(w) = h(c_0^* + c_1^* + \cdots + c_{k+1}^*) f(x_{n+1}, w) + C,$$

C being a constant independent of w. According to theorem 4.2 the sequence $\{w_i\}$ defined by (14-41) converges—for any choice of the starting value w_0—if there exists a constant $K < 1$ such that, for any two real numbers y and z,

(14-42) $$|F(z) - F(y)| \leqq K|z - y|.$$

Problem 8 of chapter 13 shows that

(14-43) $$c_0^* + c_1^* + \cdots + c_{k+1}^* = c_{k+1},$$

where c_{k+1} is defined by (13-5). Hence if f satisfies a Lipschitz condition with Lipschitz constant L,

$$|F(z) - F(y)| = h|c_{k+1}|\,|f(x_{n+1}, z) - f(x_{n+1}, y)| \\ \leqq h|c_{k+1}|L|z - y|.$$

Thus (14-42) is shown to hold with

$$K = h|c_{k+1}|L,$$

and this is less than one whenever

(14-44) $$h < \frac{1}{|c_{k+1}|L}.$$

We thus have obtained:

Theorem 14.7   The inner iteration necessary to obtain each new value y_{n+1} in the Adams-Moulton method converges for any choice of the predicted value $y_{n+1}^{(0)}$ whenever the step h satisfies (14-44).

By theorem 4.2, the quantity

$$y_{n+1} = \lim_{i \to \infty} y_{n+1}^{(i)}$$

is a solution of the equation

(14-45) $$y_{n+1} = y_n + h[c_0^* f_{n+1} + c_1^* \nabla f_{n+1} + \cdots + c_{k+1}^* \nabla^{k+1} f_{n+1}].$$

Theoretically, we could thus define the Adams-Moulton values y_{n+1} as the solution of the non-linear difference equation (14-45). The error $z_n = y_n - y(x_n)$ of these values can be investigated by a method entirely analogous to that used in the proof of theorem 14.6. Expressing differences in terms of ordinates, we write (14-45) in the form

$$y_{n+1} = y_n + h\{b_{k+1,0}^* f_{n+1} + b_{k+1,1}^* f_n + \cdots + b_{k+1,k+1}^* f_{n-k}\}$$

Setting

(14-46) $$B_{k+1}^* = |b_{k+1,0}| + |b_{k+1,1}| + \cdots + |b_{k+1,k+1}^*|,$$

and assuming that the starting values satisfy (14-32), we can show that

(14-47) $|z_n| \leq \dfrac{1}{1 - h|c_{k+1}|L} \Big\{ \delta e^{(x_n - a)B^*_{k+1}L}$

$$+ |c^*_{k+2}| h^{k+2} Y_{k+3} \frac{e^{(x_n - a)B^*_{k+1}L} - 1}{B^*_{k+1}L} \Big\}$$

for $a \leq x_n \leq b$. Here L again denotes a Lipschitz constant for the function f. If the starting values are sufficiently accurate, then the error bound (14-47) is considerably better than the corresponding bound (14-38) for the Adams-Bashforth method using equally many points, because h^{k+1} is now replaced by h^{k+2}, and $|c^*_{k+2}| < |c_{k+1}|$, $B^*_{k+1} < B_k$.

Similar bounds can also be obtained for the more practical case where the inner iteration is only performed a finite number I of times, as indicated in algorithm 14.7. It can be shown that the above qualitative conclusions still hold when $I \geq 2$.

Problems

16. Determine the constants $b_{k,m}$ and $b^*_{k+1,m}$ for $k = 0, 1, 2, 3$ and calculate the values of the constants B_k and B^*_{k+1}.
17. Repeat problem 15, using the Adams-Moulton procedure with $k = 2$.
18. Give a proof of (14-47) along the lines of the proof of theorem 14.6.
19. Show that, by virtue of (14-43), the values $y^{(i)}_{n+1}$ defined in algorithm 14.7 can be calculated more simply from the relation

$$y^{(i+1)}_{n+1} = y^{(i)}_{n+1} + hc_{k+1}[f(x_{n+1}, y^{(i)}_{n+1}) - f(x_{n+1}, y^{(i-1)}_{n+1})], \qquad (i \geq 1).$$

14.8   Numerical Stability

In order to bring the discussions of the two preceding sections to a more concrete level, we now shall determine explicitly the numerical solutions of the initial value problem

(14-48) $\begin{cases} y(0) = 1, \\ \quad y' = Ay \end{cases}$

(exact solution: $y(x) = e^{Ax}$) by several methods based on numerical integration.

We begin with the Adams-Bashforth method (algorithm 14.6) for $k = 1$. Since $c_0 = 1$, $c_1 = \frac{1}{2}$, (14-31) yields the recurrence relation

$$y_{n+1} = y_n + h(f_n + \tfrac{1}{2}\nabla f_n)$$
$$= y_n + h(\tfrac{3}{2}f_n - \tfrac{1}{2}f_{n-1})$$

or, since in the present case $f_n = f(x_n, y_n) = Ay_n$,

(14-49) $$y_{n+1} = y_n + Ah(\tfrac{3}{2}y_n - \tfrac{1}{2}y_{n-1}).$$

This is a linear difference equation of order two with constant coefficients. Its characteristic polynomial

$$p(z) = z^2 - (1 + \tfrac{3}{2}Ah)z + \tfrac{1}{2}Ah$$

has the zeros

$$z_1 = \tfrac{1}{2} + \tfrac{3}{4}Ah + \sqrt{\tfrac{1}{4} + \tfrac{1}{4}Ah + \tfrac{9}{16}(Ah)^2}$$

and, by Vieta

$$z_2 = \frac{Ah}{2z_1}.$$

These zeros are certainly distinct for sufficiently small values of h. By §6.3 the general solution is thus given by

$$y_n = c_1 z_1^n + c_2 z_2^n,$$

where c_1 and c_2 are two arbitrary constants. Determining these constants in such a manner that the solution satisfies $y_0 = 1$, we obtain

(14-50) $$y_n = (1 - c_2)z_1^n + c_2 z_2^n,$$

where c_2 is a function of the as yet unspecified value y_1,

(14-51) $$c_2 = \frac{y_1 - z_1}{z_2 - z_1}.$$

As in §14.3, we now shall study the behavior of y_n as $h \to 0$ and $n \to \infty$ while $nh = x$ remains fixed. We begin by expressing z_1^n in such a way that this behavior becomes evident. Expanding the square root in powers of Ah (see Taylor [1959], §15.10) we find

$$z_1 = 1 + Ah + \tfrac{1}{2}(Ah)^2 - \tfrac{1}{4}(Ah)^3 + 0(h^4).$$

By virtue of

$$e^{Ah} = 1 + Ah + \tfrac{1}{2}(Ah)^2 + \tfrac{1}{6}(Ah)^3 + 0(h^4)$$

this may be written

(14-52) $$z_1 = e^{Ah} - \tfrac{5}{12}(Ah)^3 + 0(h^4)$$

or, since $e^{Ah} = 1 + 0(h)$,

$$z_1 = e^{Ah}[1 - \tfrac{5}{12}(Ah)^3 + 0(h^4)].$$

By virtue of $nh = x$ it follows that

$$z_1^n = e^{Ax}[1 - \tfrac{5}{12}xA^3h^2 + 0(h^3)].$$

Since $z_2 = 0(h)$, $z_2^n = 0(h^n)$ is very small compared with z_1^n. We thus obtain from (14-50), neglecting less important terms,

(14-53) $$y_n \sim e^{Ax} - \tfrac{5}{12}A^3 x e^{Ax} h^2 - c_1 e^{Ax}.$$

Here the first term is clearly the desired exact solution. The second term arises as a result of approximating the integral in (13-6) by a discrete formula. In the general case it would be

$$-c_{k+1}A^{k+2}xh^{k+1}e^{Ax}.$$

The third term is a function of the choice of our second starting value y_1. It would be zero if we succeeded in choosing $y_1 = z_1$. It is small but different from zero, if we take $y_1 = e^{Ah}$, the value of the exact solution at x_1. The significant fact is that both errors, the one due to discretization as well as the starting error, contain the factor e^{Ax}. This is particularly important when A is negative, e.g., when $A = -1$. In this case, the errors do not grow indefinitely; the discretization error, for instance, grows up to $x = 1$ and then tends to zero, like the solution itself.

Let us now examine the integration of the same problem by a different integration formula. As the error of the interpolating polynomial is smallest near the median interpolating point, one is always tempted to use symmetric central difference formulas for numerical integration. To consider the simplest case, let us integrate the identity

$$y'(x) = f(x, y(x))$$

between the limits x_{n-1} and x_{n+1}, using the midpoint rule (see problem 4, chapter 13) to approximate the integral. There results the formula

$$(14\text{-}54) \qquad\qquad y_{n+1} = y_{n-1} + 2hf_n.$$

This formula could be used, in principle, much like the Adams-Bashforth formula. For the special initial value problem (14-48) we obtain the difference equation

$$y_{n+1} = 2Ahy_n + y_{n-1}.$$

Its characteristic polynomial

$$p(z) = z^2 - 2Ahz - 1$$

has the two distinct zeros

$$z_1 = Ah + \sqrt{1 + (Ah)^2}$$

and

$$z_2 = -\frac{1}{z_1}.$$

All solutions satisfying $y_0 = 1$ can thus again be represented in the form (14-50).

For the purpose of exploring the asymptotic behavior of the solution y_n as $h \to 0$ while $nh = x$ remains fixed, we again expand z_1 in powers of h. Using the binomial formula (see Taylor [1959], p. 479) we obtain

$$z_1 = 1 + Ah + \tfrac{1}{2}(Ah)^2 + 0(h^4)$$

or, by comparison with the exponential series,

$$z_1 = e^{Ah} - \tfrac{1}{6}(Ah)^3 + 0(h^4).$$

Proceeding as above, we thus find

$$z_1^n = e^{Ax}[1 - \tfrac{1}{6}xA^3h^2 + 0(h^3)]$$

and

$$z_2^n = (-z_1)^{-n} = (-1)^n e^{-Ax}[1 + \tfrac{1}{6}xA^3h^2 + 0(h^3)].$$

It is seen that z_1^n and z_2^n have the same order of magnitude, and that the term $c_2 z_2^n$ can now no longer be neglected. We thus find from (14-50), up to less significant terms,

(14-55) $y_n \sim e^{Ax} - \tfrac{1}{6}A^3 x e^{Ax} h^2 + c_2 e^{Ax} + c_2(-1)^n e^{-Ax}.$

In the leading term we again recognize the desired solution of the continuous problem. The second term represents the genuine discretization error, due to the approximation of an integral by a discrete formula. This term is smaller than the corresponding term in (14-53), emphasizing the greater accuracy of central difference formulas. The last two terms are "starting" errors; they owe their presence to the fact that $y_1 \neq z_1$ in general. In particular both terms are present if we take $y_1 = e^{Ah}$, the exact value. These starting errors would not be of much concern if it were not for the fact that the second term $(-1)^n c_2 e^{-Ax}$, shows a behavior whose character is exactly opposite to that of the exact solution. If A is negative, this term will grow at an exponential rate and, no matter how small initially, overshadow all other terms if x is sufficiently large.

EXAMPLE

8. Table 14.8 shows some values of the errors $z_n = y_n - e^{-x_n}$ of the numerical approximations to the solution of $y' = -y$, $y(0) = 1$ obtained by the formulas (14-49) and (14-54) with the step $h = 0.1$.

While for small values of x the Adams-Bashforth method has the larger errors (due to the fact that the discretization error is larger) we have at $x = 5$ reached a point where the error of the midpoint formula is larger by a factor 100, due to the exponentially growing oscillatory component in (14-55).

The presence of oscillatory error terms that grow relative to the exact solution represents a special kind of numerical instability that is typical

Table 14.8

x_n	$10^5 z_n$ Adams	$10^5 z_n$ Midpoint
0.0	0	0
0.1	0	0
0.2	38	30
0.3	70	21
0.4	90	51
⋮		
5.0	15	1129
5.1	14	− 1385
5.2	12	1406
5.3	11	− 1665
5.4	11	1739

for a number of formulas for integrating differential equations. This phenomenon of numerical instability can be traced to the fact that the characteristic polynomial of the linear difference equation arising from integrating $y' = Ay$ has several zeros of approximate modulus one. This, in turn, will always be the case if the identity $y'(x) = f(x, y(x))$ is integrated over an interval whose length exceeds one integration step.

Problems

20. Carry out the above investigation for the integration algorithm based on Simpson's formula

$$y_{n+1} = y_{n-1} + h(\tfrac{1}{3}f_{n+1} + \tfrac{4}{3}f_n + \tfrac{1}{3}f_{n-1}).$$

Show, in particular, that the starting error now has a component of the form $(-1)^n c_2 e^{-Ax/3}$.

21. Integrating Bessel's interpolating polynomial between the limits x_{-1} and x_2, obtain the following formula for integration:

$$y_{n+2} = y_{n-1} + \tfrac{3}{8}h(f_{n+2} + 3f_{n+1} + 3f_n + f_{n-1}).$$

22*. Investigate the stability of the formula obtained in the preceding problem.
23. In constructing table 14.8, y_1 was chosen as the exact value e^{-h}. Show experimentally that, due to rounding errors, the phenomenon of numerical instability occurs also for $y_1 = z_1 = -h + \sqrt{1 + h^2}$, where theoretically $c_2 = 0$.

Recommended Reading

A large variety of methods for integrating differential equations is discussed in Milne [1953]. Collatz [1960] contains a wealth of valuable information. The phenomenon of numerical instability of algorithms for the solution of initial value problems was first discussed by Rutishauser [1952] in a brief but classical paper. A comprehensive treatment of errors and numerical stability will be found in Henrici [1962, 1963]. For the numerical solution of boundary value problems and partial differential equations, which had to be ignored here for reasons of space, we refer to the excellent treatises by Fox [1957] and Forsythe and Wasow [1960].

Research Problem

Study the effectiveness of *repeated* extrapolation to the limit in the numerical solution of differential equations. In particular, compare the accuracy obtained with repeated extrapolation to the limit in the Euler method with that given by the Runge-Kutta method and the Adams-Moulton method, using the same number of evaluations of f.

PART THREE

COMPUTATION

chapter 15 number systems

All numbers that have occurred so far in the theoretical discussions in this book were real (or complex) numbers in the strict mathematical sense. That is, they were to be conceived as infinite decimal fractions, or as Dedekind cuts. For the purposes of computation such numbers have to be approximated by real numbers of a rather special type, such as terminating decimal fractions, or other rational numbers. The present chapter is devoted to a study of the number systems that can be used for the purposes of computation.

15.1 Representation of Integers

Let us take a look at our conventional number system. What do we mean by a symbol such as 247? Evidently

$$247 = 2 \cdot 100 + 4 \cdot 10 + 7$$
$$= 2 \cdot 10^2 + 4 \cdot 10^1 + 7 \cdot 10^0.$$

The number 247 is represented as a polynomial in the base 10, with integral coefficients between 0 and $9 = 10 - 1$.

There is no intrinsic reason why 10 should be used as a base; the number of fingers may have to do with it. There is evidence that in cultures different from ours other number systems have been used. The French word *quatre-vingts* for the number 80 indicates a system with base 20. (Maybe the French counted with their toes as well as with their fingers.) In New Zealand, words for 11^2 and 11^3 have been found. The Babylonian astronomers used a sexagesimal system, i.e., a system with the base 60. A trace of this can be found in our dividing the circumference of the circle into 360 degrees. Also mixed systems, although mathematically much less satisfying, are in use, such as the Anglo-Saxon system for measuring length, and the English monetary system.

In electronic computation, the digits of an integer are represented by various states of a physical quantity, such as an electric current. The technically simplest situation arises when there are only two states to be represented, such as the state "no current" and the state "a unit current." For this reason, modern electronic computers work internally almost exclusively with the base 2. The resulting number system is called the *binary number system.* In this system, only the digits 0 and 1 occur. In order to distinguish them from decimal digits, we shall underline them. Thus, if a given nonnegative integer N is in the binary system represented in the form

$$(15\text{-}1) \qquad N = a_n 2^n + a_{n-1} 2^{n-1} + \cdots + a_1 2 + a_0$$

where the a_1 are either zero or one, it will be written in the form

$$a_n a_{n-1} \ldots a_1 a_0.$$

EXAMPLE

1. $1 = \underline{1}$, $2 = \underline{10}$, $3 = \underline{11}$, $\underline{101} = 5$, $8 = \underline{1000}$, $\underline{1010} = 10$.

If we wish to communicate with a computer working in the binary system, we (or the computer) must be able to convert a number from the decimal to the binary system and conversely. To convert from binary to decimal, we regard the number N given by (15-1) as the value of the polynomial

$$P(x) = a_n x^n + a_{n-1} x^{n-1} + \cdots + a_1 x + a_0$$

for $x = 2$. To evaluate $P(2)$, we may use algorithm 3.4. (Note that the coefficients of the polynomial are numbered differently now.) It follows that if we calculate the numbers b_k recursively by

$$(15\text{-}2) \quad b_0 = a_n, \qquad b_k = a_{n-k} + 2b_{k-1} \qquad (k = 1, 2, \ldots, n),$$

then $b_n = P(2) = N$.

EXAMPLE

2. To express the number $N = \underline{11111001111}$ in decimal. The Horner scheme yields

k	0	1	2	3	4	5	6	7	8	9	10
a_{n-k}	1	1	1	1	1	0	0	1	1	1	1
b_k	1	3	7	15	31	62	124	249	499	999	1999

It follows that $N = 1999$.

To convert a given integer from decimal to binary, we make use of the fact that the *last* binary digit a_0 of an integer N is zero if and only if N is even.   The second binary digit a_1 is zero if and only if $(n - a_0)/2$ is even, and so on.   This leads to the following scheme:

Algorithm 15.1   To find the binary representation (15-1) of a given positive integer N let

$$(15\text{-}3) \qquad \begin{cases} N_0 = N, \\ N_{k+1} = \dfrac{N_k - a_k}{2}, & k = 0, 1, 2, \ldots \end{cases}$$

where

$$(15\text{-}4) \qquad a_k = \begin{cases} 1, & \text{if } N_k \text{ is odd,} \\ 0, & \text{if } N_k \text{ is even.} \end{cases}$$

Continue until $N_k = 0$.

EXAMPLE

3. To express $N = 1999$ in binary form.   Algorithm 15.1 yields the scheme

k	0	1	2	3	4	5	6	7	8	9	10
N_k	1999	999	499	249	124	62	31	15	7	3	1
a_k	1	1	1	1	0	0	1	1	1	1	1

It follows that $1999 = \underline{11111001111}$.   (Note that the *least* significant digits are obtained first.)   The scheme is an exact reversal of the scheme of example 2.

Problems

1. Express the numbers 1685, 1770, 1882 in the binary system.
2. What are the decimal values of the binary numbers $\underline{1'000}$, $\underline{1'000'000}$, $\underline{1'000'000'000}$?
3. What is, for $N \to \infty$, the ratio of the number of digits in the binary and the decimal representation of an integer N?
4. State the rules for the conversion of a decimal integer N into the ternary system, and vice versa.   Express 10^n in the ternary system ($n = 1, 2, 3$).
5. What is the representation of the positive integer N in the number system to the base N?

15.2   Binary Fractions

A *binary fraction* is a series of the form

$$(15\text{-}5) \qquad z = \sum_{k=1}^{\infty} a_{-k} 2^{-k},$$

where the coefficients $a_{-1}, a_{-2}, \ldots$ are either zero or one. The series (15-5) always converges, because it is majorized by the geometric series

$$\sum_{k=1}^{\infty} 2^{-k} = \frac{1}{2} \frac{1}{1 - \frac{1}{2}} = 1.$$

The sum z of (15-5) will also be denoted by

$$z = 0.a_{-1}a_{-2}a_{-3}\ldots.$$

The binary fraction (15-5) is said to *terminate* if, for some integer n, $a_k = 0, k > n$.

The following theorem is fundamental, but will not be proved:

Theorem 15.2a   Any real number z such that $0 < z \leqq 1$ can be represented in a unique manner by a nonterminating binary fraction.

If we drop the condition that the binary fraction shall not terminate, then the representation may not be unique; for instance, the binary fractions

$$0.1 \quad \text{and} \quad 0.01111\ldots$$

both represent the number 0.5.

A terminating binary fraction $z = 0.a_{-1}a_{-2}\ldots a_{-n}$ can be regarded as the value of the polynomial

$$P(x) = a_{-1}x + a_{-2}x^2 + \cdots + a_{-n}x^n$$

at $x = \frac{1}{2}$ and thus can be evaluated by algorithm 3.4 (Horner's scheme) as follows: Let

$$b_0 = a_{-n}, \qquad b_k = a_{-n+k} + \tfrac{1}{2}b_{k-1}, \qquad k = 1, 2, \ldots, n,$$

where $a_0 = 0$. Then $b_n = z$.

EXAMPLE

4. To express $z = 0.00110011$ in decimal. Horner's scheme yields

k	a_{n-k}	b_k
0	1	1
1	1	1.5
2	0	0.75
3	0	0.375
4	1	1.1875
5	1	1.59375
6	0	0.796875
7	0	0.3984375
8	0	0.19921875

It follows that $z = 0.19921875$.

Another method for converting a terminating binary fraction consists in converting the integer

$$2^n z = a_{-1} 2^{n-1} + a_{-2} 2^{n-2} + \cdots + a_{-n}$$

and dividing the result by 2^n.

Except in special circumstances, non-terminating binary fractions cannot be converted into terminating decimal fractions. To get an approximate decimal representation, we truncate an infinite binary fraction after the nth digit and convert the resulting terminating fraction. The error in this approximation will be less than 2^{-n}.

The inverse problem of converting a given (decimal) fraction into a binary fraction is solved by the following algorithm:

Algorithm 15.2   For a real number z such that $0 \leq z \leq 1$, calculate the sequences $\{z_k\}$ and $\{a_{-k}\}$ recursively by the relations

$$
\begin{cases}
z_1 = z; \\[4pt]
a_{-k} = \begin{cases} 1, & \text{if } 2z_k > 1, \\ 0, & \text{if } 2z_k \leq 1, \end{cases} \\[12pt]
z_{k+1} = 2z_k - a_{-k}, \qquad k = 1, 2, \ldots.
\end{cases}
$$

(15-6)

Theorem 15.2b   For the sequence $\{a_{-k}\}$ defined by (15-6),

$$z = 0.a_{-1}a_{-2}a_{-3}\ldots.$$

Proof. According to theorem 15.2a, z has a nonterminating binary representation of the form

$$z = 0.b_{-1}b_{-2}b_{-3}\ldots;$$

we have to show that

(15-7) $b_{-k} = a_{-k}, \qquad k = 1, 2, \ldots,$

where a_{-k} is defined by (15-6). Incidentally we shall also show that

(15-8) $z_k = 0.b_{-k}b_{-k-1}b_{-k-2}\ldots, \qquad k = 1, 2, \ldots.$

The simultaneous proof of the two assertions is by induction. Clearly, (15-8) is true for $k = 1$. Let us assume that (15-7) and (15-8) are true for the integers $k - 1$ and k, where $k \geq 1$. We then have

$$2z_k = b_{-k} + 0.b_{-k-1}b_{-k-2}\ldots.$$

Since the binary fraction on the right is positive and bounded by one, it follows that $2z_k > 1$, and hence $a_k = 1$, if and only if $b_k = 1$. This establishes (15-7), and, by the second formula (15-6), (15-8) with k increased by one.

EXAMPLE

5. To express $z = \frac{1}{5}$ as a binary fraction.   We have

k	z_k	$2z_k$	a_{-k}
1	0.2	0.4	0
2	0.4	0.8	0
3	0.8	1.6	1
4	0.6	1.2	1
5	0.2		

Since $z_k = 0.2$ has occurred before, the periodic† binary fraction

$$0.2 = 0.001100110011\ldots = 0.\overline{0011}$$

results.   (The period is indicated by a cross-bar.)

It is now easy to represent any nonnegative number in the binary system. If z is such a number, let $[z]$ be the greatest integer not exceeding z. According to §15.1 we can write

$$[z] = \sum_{k=0}^{n} a_k 2^k,$$

where the a_k are either zero or one.   For the fractional part we have, by (15-5)

$$z - [z] = \sum_{k=1}^{\infty} a_{-k} 2^{-k}$$

with the same limitation on the a_k.   Thus

$$z = [z] + (z - [z]) = \sum_{k=-n}^{\infty} a_{-k} 2^{-k}$$

$$= a_n a_{n-1} \ldots a_0 . a_{-1} a_{-2} \ldots .$$

To convert a binary number into a decimal or vice versa, we must convert the integral and the fractional part by themselves.

Problems

6. Give the binary value of π, correct to 12 binary digits after the binary point.

7. Express the binary numbers (a) $0.\overline{10101}$, (b) $0.\overline{10101}$ as ratios of two integers.

8. Determine the representation of $\frac{1}{3}$ in the number systems to the base (a) 2, (b) 5, (c) 7.

---

† It is shown in number theory that every rational fraction can be represented by an infinite binary fraction that is ultimately periodic.

9. Devise an algorithm that yields directly the binary representation of the square root of a given positive binary number. Use your algorithm to determine the binary representations of $\sqrt{2}$, $\sqrt{\pi}$, $\sqrt{5}$, and check your result by converting the known decimal representations of these numbers.

15.3 Fixed Point Arithmetic

As mentioned earlier, in most digital computing machines today numbers are internally represented in the binary system. Each element of a computer can assume only a finite number of (recognizable and reproducible) states, and each computer has only finitely many elements. It is thus clear that only finitely many different numbers can be represented in a computer. A number that can be represented exactly in a given computer is called a *machine number*. All other numbers can be represented in the computer only, at best, approximately. There are two principal ways in which a given number z can be represented. They are known as the *fixed point* and as the *floating point* representation of z.

In fixed point operation, the machine numbers are terminating binary fractions of the form

$$(15\text{-}9) \qquad \pm \sum_{k=1}^{t} a_{-k} 2^{-k}$$

where t is an integer that is either fixed for a given machine ($t = 35$ for the IBM 7090, $t = 48$ for the CDC 1604) or, in some cases, can be selected by the user (e.g., on the IBM 1620). The numbers used by the machine can also be described as the set of numbers $n \cdot 2^{-t}$, where n is an integer, $|n| < 2^t$. The density of machine numbers is uniform in the interval $(-1, 1)$ and zero outside this interval.

If z is any real number, we shall denote by z^* one of the (at most two) terminating binary fractions of the form (15-9) for which $|z - z^*|$ is a minimum. If the interval

$$R = [-1 + 2^{-t-1}, 1 - 2^{-t-1}]$$

is called the *range* of the machine, then

$$(15\text{-}10) \qquad |z - z^*| \leqq 2^{-t-1} \quad \text{for all } z \in R,$$

that is, any real number within the range of the machine can be approximately represented by a machine number z^* with an error of at most 2^{-t-1}. Any of the (at most two) representations z^* of a number z will be called a *correctly rounded fixed point representation of z*.

If a and b are two numbers within the range of the machine, the numbers $a \pm b$ do not necessarily belong to the range. If they do not belong to the range we say that *overflow* occurs. The ever-present possibility of overflow is one of the serious disadvantages of fixed point arithmetic.

The above remark shows very clearly that even if the data of a computational problem are within range, we can usually not be sure that all intermediate results fall within the range. It is frequently possible, however, to obtain a (possibly very crude) a priori estimate of the size of the intermediate results. One then may try to reformulate the problem (for instance by introducing new units of measurement) in such a manner that the data as well as the intermediate and final results are within range. This reformulation is known as *scaling*. The frequent necessity of scaling is a further disadvantage of fixed point arithmetic.

Let us now consider the accuracy of the arithmetical operations in fixed point arithmetic. If a and b are two machine numbers, and if $a + b$ is within range, then it is clear that $a + b$ is also a machine number. That is, *addition* can be performed without error in a fixed point machine, i.e., we have

(15-11) $$(a + b)^* = a + b, \quad \text{if } a + b \in R.$$

The same is not true of *multiplication*, however. If a and b are two machine numbers, then ab is, in general, not a machine number. However $ab \in R$, hence there exists a correctly rounded machine value of ab, and we have

(15-12) $$|(ab)^* - ab| \leq 2^{-t-1}.$$

The *ratio* a/b of two machine numbers is, in general, not in the range of the machine. (The probability for this to be the case is only 50 per cent—a further disadvantage of fixed point arithmetic.) If it is, we again have

$$|(a/b)^* - a/b| \leq 2^{-t-1},$$

independently of the size of $|a/b|$.

Many machines have built-in subroutines for calculating values of elementary functions such as $\sin x$ or $\sqrt{x}$. It is clear that even if the argument x is a machine number, the value of the function is, in general, not. In the case of the sine function, the best we can hope for in general is a correctly rounded value of $\sin x$, but even this ideal is seldom attained. The author knows of a machine where $\sqrt{0}$ was 2^{-t}.

Problems

10. Devise an algorithm for forming the sum of two positive machine numbers of the form (15-9).

11. Reformulate the algorithm obtained in problem 9 in such a manner that it yields, for every nonnegative machine number x, a correctly rounded value of $\sqrt{x}$.

12. Devise an algorithm that yields the correctly rounded product of two machine numbers a and b.

15.4 Floating Point Arithmetic

In floating point operation, the set of machine numbers consists of 0 and of the set of all numbers of the form

$$(15\text{-}13) \qquad\qquad z = \pm m2^p$$

where m is a terminating binary fraction,

$$m = \sum_{k=1}^{t} a_{-k} 2^{-k}, \qquad \tfrac{1}{2} \leqq m < 1$$

normalized by the condition $a_{-1} = 1$, and where p is an integer ranging between $-P$ and P, say. The integers t and P are normally fixed for a given machine. (On the IBM 7090 computer, $t = 27$, $P = 128$.) The binary fraction m is called the *mantissa* and the integer p the *exponent* of the floating number (15-13). The machine numbers now cover a much wider range than in fixed point arithmetic. We again denote, for any real z and for a given machine, by $z^{\oplus}$ any of the at most two numbers of the form (15-13) for which $|z - z^{\oplus}|$ is minimized. We now define the range of the machine to be the interval

$$R = [-2^P(1 - 2^{-t-1}), \ 2^P(1 - 2^{-t-1})].$$

If $z \in R$, $|z| \geqq 2^{-P-1}$, we can define $z^{\oplus}$ by

$$(15\text{-}14) \qquad\qquad z^{\oplus} = \text{sign } z \cdot m \cdot 2^p$$

where

$$p = [\log_2 |z|] + 1, \qquad m = (2^{-p}|z|)^*.$$

Here $\log_2$ denotes the logarithm to the base 2, $[x]$ denotes the greatest integer not exceeding x, and the * refers to correct rounding in fixed point arithmetic. Any of the (at most two) values $z^{\oplus}$ will be called a correctly rounded floating representation of z. If $|z| < 2^{-P-1}$, we set $z^{\oplus} = 0$. If $|z| \geqq 2^{-P-1}$, we evidently have

$$|z - z^{\oplus}| \leqq 2^p 2^{-t-1}$$
$$= 2^{p-1} 2^{-t}$$
$$= 2^{[\log_2 |z|]} 2^{-t}$$
$$\leqq 2^{\log_2 |z|} 2^{-t}$$

and hence

$$(15\text{-}15) \qquad\qquad |z - z^{\oplus}| \leqq 2^{-t}|z|.$$

This relation shows:

Theorem 15.4 If, for a given floating point machine, $z \in R$, $|z| \geq$ 2^{-P-1}, then the relative error of the correctly rounded floating representation $z^{\oplus}$ of z is at most 2^{-t}.

For $z \to 0$ the relative error tends to ∞, as in fixed point arithmetic.

Since machines with floating arithmetic can handle very large numbers with a small relative error, scaling is, in general, not necessary, and the possibility of overflow is minimal. For these reasons, floating arithmetic is almost universally used today. The FORTRAN system, for instance, employs floating arithmetic.

Let us examine briefly the accuracy of the basic arithmetic operations in floating point arithmetic. If a and b are two floating machine numbers, and if $a + b$ is in the range of the machine, then, unlike the fixed point case, $a + b$ is not necessarily a machine number. Thus we must also expect rounding errors in addition. If

$$a = \pm m2^p, \qquad b = \pm n2^q,$$

and if $p \geq q$, we have

$$a + b = \pm m2^p \pm n2^q$$
$$= (\pm m \pm n2^{q-p})2^p.$$

Here $|\pm m \pm n2^{q-p}| < 2$; thus we have, at worst,

$$(a + b)^{\oplus} = \left(\frac{\pm m \pm n2^{q-p}}{2}\right)^* 2^{p+1}$$

and hence

$$|(a + b)^{\oplus} - (a + b)| \leq 2^{-t-1}2^{p+1}$$
$$= 2^{-t+1}2^{\log_2|a|}$$

and consequently

(15-16) $$|(a + b)^{\oplus} - (a + b)| \leq 2^{-t+1}|a|.$$

Thus the error of the machine value of a sum (or difference) is at most 2^{-t+1} times the absolute value of the larger summand.

The *product ab* of two machine numbers a and b is now (contrary to fixed-point arithmetic) not always a number in the range of the machine. If the absolute value of the product lies in the interval $[2^{-P}, 2^P]$, we find by considerations similar to those just given that

(15-17) $$|(ab)^{\oplus} - ab| \leq 2^{-t}|ab|.$$

Similarly we find for division, if a/b is in the range of the machine,

(15-18) $$\left|\left(\frac{a}{b}\right)^{\oplus} - \frac{a}{b}\right| \leq 2^{-t}\left|\frac{a}{b}\right|.$$

Concerning built-in subroutines for elementary functions, the remarks made above apply also to machines with floating point arithmetic.

Multiple precision arithmetic. As was noted above, both fixed point numbers and the mantissae of floating numbers are represented in the machine in the form $N \times u$, where the number $u = 2^{-t}$ may be called the *basic unit* of the machine, and where N is an integer, $|N| < 2^t$. For some machines and/or some problems this approximation is not sufficiently accurate. In such cases one can increase the accuracy by working instead with numbers of the form

$$(15\text{-}19) \qquad N_1 u + N_2 u^2 + \cdots + N_q u^q,$$

where the N_k are integers satisfying $0 \leq N_k < u^{-1}$, $k = 1, 2, \ldots, q$. This enlargement of the set of available machine numbers is called working with *q-fold precision*. Double precision ($q = 2$) is fairly common; on some machines, its use is encouraged by built-in circuitry to facilitate arithmetical operations with multiple precision numbers of the form (15-19). Multiple precision with $q > 2$ is normally restricted to special experimental programs. From a mathematical point of view, multiple precision is equivalent to single precision with t replaced by qt.

Problems

13. Prove the inequalities (15-17) and (15-18).
14. Assume that in the approximate formula of numerical differentiation

$$D_h f(x_0) = \frac{f_1 - f_{-1}}{2h},$$

f_1 and f_{-1} are known only with errors $\leq 2^{-16}$, whereas h is an exact binary number.
(a) If floating operations are used, how big is (at most) the resulting error in $D_h f(x_0)$?
(b) If the function to be differentiated is $f(x) = J_0(x)$, for which value of h is the maximum error in the numerical value of $J_0'(x)$ due to rounding equal to the maximum error due to numerical differentiation?
(c) For which value is the sum of the two errors a minimum?

Suggested Reading

Wilkinson [1960] gives a careful account of rounding errors in the elementary arithmetic operations. For a wealth of detail from the point of view of computer technology see Speiser [1961].

Research Problem

Assume that in a fixed point machine it is possible to identify both the more and the less significant half of the exact value of the product of two machine numbers. Formulate an algorithm for obtaining the correctly rounded value of the product of any two complex numbers whose real and imaginary parts are machine numbers.

chapter 16 propagation of rounding error

16.1 Introduction and Definitions

The process of replacing a real number z by a machine number z^* or $z^\oplus$ is called *rounding*. The difference $z^* - z$ or $z^\oplus - z$ is called *rounding error*. Due to rounding, the final result of a numerical computation usually differs from the theoretically correct result. The difference of the numerical result and the theoretically correct result is called the *accumulated rounding error*. In order to distinguish them from the accumulated rounding error, the rounding errors committed at each step of a computation will also be called the *local rounding errors*. Except in simple cases, the accumulated rounding error is not merely the sum of the local errors. Each local rounding error is propagated through the remaining part of the computation, during which process its influence on the accumulated rounding error may either be amplified or diminished.

Different numerical procedures for solving the same theoretical problem (such as integrating a differential equation) may show a different behavior with respect to the propagation of local rounding error. This varying sensitivity with regard to rounding off operations is frequently referred to as the *numerical stability* of the process. In chapter 8 we noted that the numerical stability even of one and the same numerical procedure (the QD algorithm) can depend strongly on the way the arithmetical operations are performed.

In the present chapter we shall study the propagation of local rounding error in some simple but typical cases.

16.2 Finite Differences

As a first example we consider a case where the accumulated rounding error is due exclusively to errors in the data of the computation; all intermediate arithmetic operations are performed exactly. Let $x_n =$

302

$a + nh$, $n = 0, 1, 2, \ldots$, let f be a given function, and let $f_n = f(x_n)$. We consider the effect of replacing the exact values f_n by machine values f_n^* on the differences of the sequence of values f_n.

In fixed point arithmetic, we clearly have

(16-1) $$f_n^* = f_n + \varepsilon_n, \qquad n = 0, 1, 2, \ldots$$

where the local rounding errors ε_n satisfy

(16-2) $$|\varepsilon_n| \leqq \varepsilon = \tfrac{1}{2}u, \qquad n = 0, 1, 2, \ldots$$

u being the basic unit of the machine (or the table of f). According to (6-27)

$$\Delta^k f_n = \sum_{m=0}^{k} (-1)^{k-m} \binom{k}{m} f_{n+m},$$

$$\Delta^k f_n^* = \sum_{m=0}^{k} (-1)^{k-m} \binom{k}{m} f_{n+m}^*.$$

Hence, in view of (16-1), if we denote by $r_n^{(k)}$ the accumulated rounding error in the kth difference,

$$r_n^{(k)} = \Delta^k f_n^* - \Delta^k f_n = \Delta^k (f_n^* - f_n)$$

$$= \sum_{m=0}^{k} (-1)^{k-m} \binom{k}{m} \varepsilon_{n+m}.$$

It follows by (16-2) that

$$|r_n^{(k)}| \leqq \sum_{m=0}^{k} \binom{k}{m} |\varepsilon_{n+m}|$$

$$\leqq \varepsilon \sum_{m=0}^{k} \binom{k}{m}.$$

In view of

$$\sum_{m=0}^{k} \binom{k}{m} = (1 + 1)^k = 2^k,$$

we obtain for $r_n^{(k)}$ the bound

(16-3) $$|r_n^{(k)}| \leqq 2^k \varepsilon.$$

This bound cannot be improved in general; equality holds whenever

$$\varepsilon_{n+m} = (-1)^m \varepsilon.$$

EXAMPLE

1. We consider an excerpt of a table of sines, tabulated with a step $h = 0.01$ to six decimal places. In view of

$$\Delta^k y_n = h^k y^{(k)}(\xi), \qquad x_n < \xi < x_{n+k}$$

(see problem 11, chapter 11), the exact differences satisfy

$$|\Delta^k y_n| \leq 10^{-2k}, \qquad k = 0, 1, 2, \ldots$$

and are zero from Δ^4 on to the number of digits given. The following table shows the numerical differences $\Delta^k y_n^*$:

Table 16.1

x_n	$y_n^* = (\sin x_n)^*$	Δy_n^*	$\Delta^2 y_n^*$	$\Delta^3 y_n^*$	$\Delta^4 y_n^*$	$\Delta^5 y_n^*$
0.25	0.247 404					
0.26	0.257 081	9677				
0.27	0.266 731	9650	-27	2		
0.28	0.276 356	9625	-25	-4	-6	
0.29	0.285 952	9596	-29	1	5	11
0.30	0.295 520	9568	-28	-1	-2	-7
0.31	0.305 059	9539	-29	-2	-1	1
0.32	0.314 567	9508	-31	-1	1	2
0.33	0.324 043	9476	-32	0	1	0
0.34	0.333 487	9444	-32	-1	-1	-2
0.35	0.342 898	9411	-33			

The example shows that the local rounding errors ε_n, although hardly noticeable in the function values f_n themselves, show up very strongly in the higher differences. The propagation of rounding error is real.

Problems

1. A tablemaker wishes to add, in a table of $f(x) = J_0(x)$ giving eight decimal digits after the decimal point, values of $\delta^2 f_n$ and $\delta^4 f_n$ that differ from the exact values by at most $0.6 \cdot 10^{-8}$. To what accuracy does $J_0(x)$ have to be calculated? Does the result depend on the step h or on the function f?

2. *The impossibility of making a correctly rounded table.* A recurrent nightmare of tablemakers is the following situation. Assume a table of a function f is to be prepared, giving six digits after the decimal point. For a certain value of x_n, a very accurate computation yields

$$f(x_n) = 0.123456499996,$$

with an uncertainty of $7 \cdot 10^{-12}$. Should this value be rounded up or down? A classical result in number theory states that if α is an irrational number (such as $\sqrt{2}$ or e), the numbers

$$\alpha n - [\alpha n], \qquad n = 0, 1, 2, \ldots$$

come arbitrarily close to every number in the interval $(0, 1)$. Show that this result implies the following: Given any two positive integers N and M, and any finite procedure for calculating square roots, there always exists an interval such that it is impossible to construct a correctly rounded table of the function $f(x) = \sqrt{2}\, x$ with the step 10^{-M} in that interval, giving N digits after the decimal point.

16.3   Statistical Approach

Example 1 above shows that the propagated rounding error in a table of differences can be considerable.   It also shows that the errors in the differences probably rarely have the maximum values given by (16-3) (8 and 16 for the last two difference columns).   This is due to the fact that consecutive local rounding errors ε_n only rarely have the maximum value permitted by (16-2) and, in addition, occur with strictly alternating signs such as $\varepsilon, -\varepsilon, \varepsilon, -\varepsilon, \ldots$.   Such an occurrence would contradict the intuitive notion that the local rounding errors are, somehow, distributed in a random fashion.

It is plain that, on a given machine and for a given problem, the local rounding errors are not, in fact, random variables.   If the same problem is run on the same machine a number of times, there will result always the same local rounding errors, and therefore also the same accumulated error.   We may, however, adopt a stochastic *model* of the propagation of rounding error, where the local errors are treated *as if they were* random variables.   This stochastic model has been applied in the literature to a number of different numerical problems and has produced results that are in complete agreement with experimentally observed results in several important cases.

The most natural assumption concerning the local rounding error in the stochastic model seems to be the following: We assume that the local rounding errors are uniformly distributed between their extreme values $-\varepsilon$ and ε.   The probability density $p(x)$—defined as $(\Delta x)^{-1}$ times the probability that the error lies between x and $x + \Delta x$—of this random distribution is given by

(16-4) $$p(x) = \begin{cases} 0, & x < -\varepsilon, \\ c, & -\varepsilon \leqq x \leqq \varepsilon, \\ 0, & x > \varepsilon. \end{cases}$$

The constant c is determined by the condition that the sum of all probabilities, that is, the integral

$$\int_{-\infty}^{\infty} p(x)\, dx$$

equals 1.   This yields the value

$$c = \frac{1}{2\varepsilon}$$

in (16-4) (see Fig. 16.3a).

(a)

(b) Normal probability distribution

Figure 16.3

For theoretical purposes it is more convenient to assume that the local rounding errors are *normally distributed*. The normal distribution is defined by the probability density

(16-5)
$$p(x) = \frac{1}{\sqrt{2\pi}\,\sigma}\, e^{-(x^2/2\sigma^2)}.$$

Here σ is a parameter, called the *standard deviation* of the distribution, that measures the spread of the distribution. For small values of σ the distribution is narrowly concentrated around $x = 0$, with a sharp peak at $x = 0$. For large values of σ the distribution is flattened out (see Fig. 16.3b).

The absolute value of a normally distributed random variable exceeds σ in only 31.7 per cent of all cases and 2.576σ in only 1 per cent of all cases.

Both distributions considered above have mean value 0. For a random variable ξ with arbitrary probability density $p(x)$, the *mean or expected value* is defined by

(16-6)
$$E(\xi) = \int_{-\infty}^{\infty} xp(x)\, dx.$$

The *standard deviation* is defined as the square root of the *variance* of ξ, which in turn is defined as the mean of the square of the deviation of ξ from its mean. Thus, if $\mu = E(\xi)$,

(16-7) $\qquad \text{var} (\xi) = \int_{-\infty}^{\infty} (x - \mu)^2 p(x) \, dx; \qquad \text{s.d. } (\xi) = \sqrt{\text{var} (\xi)}.$

EXAMPLES

2. The variance of the distribution defined by (16-4) is

$$\int_{-\varepsilon}^{\varepsilon} x^2 \frac{1}{2\varepsilon} \, dx = \frac{\varepsilon^2}{3}.$$

3. The variance of the normal distribution is

$$\frac{1}{\sqrt{2\pi} \, \sigma} \int_{-\infty}^{\infty} x^2 e^{-x^2/2\sigma^2} \, dx = \frac{2\sigma^2}{\sqrt{\pi}} \int_{0}^{\infty} t^{1/2} e^{-t} \, dt = \sigma^2.$$

Thus, if we wish the distributions (16-4) and (16-5) to have the same standard deviation, we must choose

$$\sigma = \frac{\varepsilon}{\sqrt{3}}.$$

If $\xi_1, \xi_2, \ldots, \xi_m$ are random variables with means $\mu_1, \mu_2, \ldots, \mu_m$, and if $a_1, a_2, \ldots, a_m$ are arbitrary constants, the quantity

(16-8) $\qquad \xi = a_1 \xi_1 + a_2 \xi_2 + \cdots + a_m \xi_m$

is again a random variable, and its mean is given by

(16-9) $\qquad E(\xi) = a_1 \mu_1 + a_2 \mu_2 + \cdots + a_m \mu_m.$

The importance of the normal probability distribution (16-5) is based on the following fact: If the variables $\xi_1, \xi_2, \ldots, \xi_m$ are *independent* (i.e., if the value of any ξ_i has no bearing on the value of any other ξ_j), and if they are normally distributed with standard deviations $\sigma_1, \sigma_2, \ldots, \sigma_m$, then the variable defined by (16-8) is also normally distributed, and its standard deviation is given by

(16-10) $\qquad \text{s.d. } (\xi) = \sqrt{a_1^2 \sigma_1^2 + a_2^2 \sigma_2^2 + \cdots + a_m^2 \sigma_m^2}.$

In a limiting sense, the above statement is also true if the random variables ξ_j themselves are not normally distributed.

Let us now apply the above results to the problem of forming differences considered in §16.2. Assuming that the local rounding errors ε_n are independent, normally distributed random variables with mean zero and standard deviation σ, we find that $r_n^{(k)}$ is a normally distributed variable with variance

$$\text{var}\,(r_n^{(k)}) = \sigma^2 \sum_{m=0}^{k} \binom{k}{m}^2.$$

Comparing coefficients of x^k in the identity

$$\left[1 + \binom{k}{1}x + \cdots + \binom{k}{k}x^k\right]\left[\binom{k}{k} + \binom{k}{k-1}x + \cdots + \binom{k}{0}x^k\right]$$
$$= 1 + \binom{2k}{1}x + \binom{2k}{2}x^2 + \cdots + \binom{2k}{2k}x^{2k},$$

we find that

$$\sum_{m=0}^{k}\binom{k}{m}^2 = \binom{2k}{k} = \frac{(2k)!}{(k!)^2}.$$

We thus obtain

$$\text{var}\,(r_n^{(k)}) = \frac{(2k)!}{(k!)^2}\,\sigma^2,$$

$$\text{s.d.}\,(r_n^{(k)}) = \frac{\sqrt{(2k)!}}{k!}\,\sigma.$$

In order to obtain an intuitive notion of the size of the coefficient appearing here, we approximate the factorials by Stirling's formula (see §9.3):

$$\frac{(2k)!}{(k!)^2} \sim \frac{\sqrt{4\pi k}\left(\dfrac{2k}{e}\right)^{2k}}{2\pi k\left(\dfrac{k}{e}\right)^{2k}} = \frac{2^{2k}}{\sqrt{\pi k}}.$$

This yields

(16-11) $$\text{s.d.}\,(r_n^{(k)}) \sim \frac{2^k\sigma}{\sqrt[4]{\pi k}} = \frac{2^k\varepsilon}{\sqrt{3}\sqrt[4]{\pi k}}$$

in the case of the rectangular distribution (16-4). This relation shows that the ratio of the standard deviation and the theoretical maximum $2^k\varepsilon$ is not as small as might be expected.

EXAMPLE

4. Twenty-four consecutive values of the exponential function given in Comrie's table (Comrie [1961]) gave the following experimental values of the standard deviations of the differences $\Delta^k y_n$ (in units of the least significant digit):

Table 16.3

k	3	4	5	6
experimental s.d.	1.31	2.28	4.22	7.64
theoretical s.d. (16-11)	1.29	2.42	4.57	8.78

Problem

3. For n given machine numbers $a_1, a_2, \ldots, a_n$ the sums

$$s_k = a_1^2 + a_2^2 + \cdots + a_k^2,$$
$$s_k' = s_1 + s_2 + \cdots + s_k \qquad (k = 1, 2, \ldots, n)$$

are formed by means of the recurrence relations

$$s_0 = 0, \quad s_k = s_{k-1} + a_k^2; \quad s_0' = 0, \quad s_k' = s_{k-1}' + s_k$$

$(k = 1, 2, \ldots, n)$. What is the resulting standard deviation in s_n and s_n', if the rounding errors at each step are considered independent random variables with the distribution (16-4)? What are the theoretically possible maximum errors?

16.4   A Scheme for the Study of Propagated Error

In the example considered above, the accumulated error was due exclusively to the rounding of the initial data of the computation. All intermediate computations were performed exactly. We shall now discuss a scheme of fairly wide applicability which permits us to take into account rounding in the intermediate results.

Many numerical algorithms consist in generating a sequence of numbers $q_0, q_1, q_2, \ldots$ that are defined by recurrence relations of the form

$$(16\text{-}12) \qquad q_n = Q_n(q_0, q_1, q_2, \ldots, q_{n-1}), \qquad n = 1, 2, \ldots.$$

In actual numerical computation not the numbers q_n are generated, but certain machine numbers $\tilde{q}_n$ (not necessarily the correctly rounded values q_n^*!), which satisfy the recurrence relations

$$(16\text{-}13) \qquad \tilde{q}_n = \tilde{Q}_n(\tilde{q}_0, \tilde{q}_1, \ldots, \tilde{q}_{n-1}), \qquad n = 1, 2, \ldots.$$

Here the symbols $\tilde{Q}_n$ denote rounded and otherwise approximated values of the functions Q_n. Instead of working with relation (16-13), which is difficult mathematically, we write (16-13) in the form

$$(16\text{-}14) \qquad \tilde{q}_n = Q_n(\tilde{q}_0, \tilde{q}_1, \ldots, \tilde{q}_{n-1}) + \varepsilon_n.$$

We consider this relation as the *definition* of the local rounding error ε_n. Thus,

$$\varepsilon_n = \tilde{Q}_n(\tilde{q}_0, \tilde{q}_1, \ldots, \tilde{q}_{n-1}) - Q_n(\tilde{q}_0, \tilde{q}_1, \ldots, \tilde{q}_{n-1}).$$

By analyzing the computational process used to evaluate Q_n, some statement can usually be made about size and distribution of the ε_n.

Let now the accumulated rounding errors r_n be defined by

$$(16\text{-}15) \qquad r_n = \tilde{q}_n - q_n, \qquad n = 0, 1, 2, \ldots.$$

By subtracting (16-12) from (16-14) we find

$$r_n = Q_n(\tilde{q}_0, \tilde{q}_1, \ldots, \tilde{q}_{n-1}) - Q_n(q_0, q_1, \ldots, q_{n-1}) + \varepsilon_n$$

or, using the mean value theorem,

$$(16\text{-}16) \qquad r_n = Q_n^{(0)}r_0 + Q_n^{(1)}r_1 + \cdots + Q_n^{(n-1)}r_{n-1} + \varepsilon_n,$$

where $Q_n^{(k)}$ denotes a partial derivative,

$$Q_n^{(k)} = \frac{\partial Q_n}{\partial q_k}, \qquad k = 0, 1, \ldots, n - 1,$$

taken at some point between $(q_0, q_1, \ldots, q_{n-1})$ and $(\tilde{q}_0, \tilde{q}_1, \ldots, \tilde{q}_{n-1})$.

If the functions Q_n are linear in the q_k, the partial derivatives $Q_n^{(k)}$ do not depend on the previous rounding errors $r_0, r_1, \ldots, r_{n-1}$, and (16-16) then represents a *linear* difference equation for the quantities r_n. If the $Q_n^{(k)}$ are constants, and if $Q_n^{(k)} = 0$ for $k < n - m$, then (16-16) is a difference equation of order m with constant coefficients and can be solved by the method by §6.7 and §6.8. There results a solution of the form

$$(16\text{-}17) \qquad r_n = \sum_{m=0}^{n} d_{nm}\varepsilon_m,$$

where the coefficients d_{nm} themselves satisfy a certain difference equation.

A solution of the form (16-17) also must exist in the general case of a recurrence relation of the form (16-12) with linear functions Q_n, since all ε_m enter into (16-16) only linearly. In order to determine the coefficients d_{nm} we substitute (16-17) into (16-16). There results

$$r_n = Q_n^{(0)}d_{00}\varepsilon_0$$
$$+ Q_n^{(1)}(d_{10}\varepsilon_0 + d_{11}\varepsilon_1)$$
$$+ Q_n^{(2)}(d_{20}\varepsilon_0 + d_{21}\varepsilon_1 + d_{22}\varepsilon_2)$$
$$+ \cdots$$
$$+ Q_n^{(n-1)}(d_{n-1,0}\varepsilon_0 + d_{n-1,1}\varepsilon_1 + \cdots + d_{n-1,n-1}\varepsilon_{n-1})$$
$$+ \varepsilon_n.$$

The expression on the right must be identical with (16-17) for all possible values of $\varepsilon_0, \varepsilon_1, \ldots, \varepsilon_n$. It follows that the coefficients of corresponding ε_m must be equal. Comparing the coefficients of ε_n we immediately find

$$(16\text{-}18) \qquad d_{n,n} = 1, \qquad n = 0, 1, 2, \ldots,$$

and hence, comparing the coefficients of $\varepsilon_{n-1}, \varepsilon_{n-2}, \ldots, \varepsilon_0$,

$$(16\text{-}19) \quad \begin{cases} d_{n,n-1} = Q_n^{(n-1)} \\ d_{n,n-2} = Q_n^{(n-1)}d_{n-1,n-2} + Q_n^{(n-2)} \\ \quad . \quad . \quad . \quad . \quad . \quad . \quad . \quad . \quad . \\ d_{n,0} = Q_n^{(n-1)}d_{n-1,0} + Q_n^{(n-2)}d_{n-2,0} + Q_n^{(1)}d_{1,0} + Q_n^{(0)} \end{cases}$$

These relations have the form of difference equations for the d_{nm} with respect to the first subscript and can be solved in special cases.

We summarize the above result as follows:

Theorem 16.4 If (16-12) is a linear algorithm, i.e., if

(16-20) $\qquad q_n = Q_n^{(0)}q_0 + Q_n^{(1)}q_1 + \cdots + Q_n^{(n-1)}q_{n-1} + p_n$

for certain constants $Q_n^{(k)}$ and p_n $(n = 0, 1, 2, \ldots; \; k = 0, 1, \ldots, n - 1)$, then the dependence of the accumulated rounding errors on the local rounding errors is given by (16-17), where the coefficients d_{nm} are determined by (16-19).

The coefficients d_{nm} may be called *influence coefficients*, because they indicate the influence of the local errors on the accumulated error.

Once the influence coefficients have been calculated, the relation (16-17) may be used to make either a deterministic or a probabilistic statement about the accumulated rounding error. Assuming

(16-21) $\qquad |\varepsilon_m| \leqq \varepsilon, \qquad m = 0, 1, 2, \ldots$

we find

(16-22) $\qquad |r_n| \leqq \varepsilon \sum_{m=0}^{n} |d_{nm}|, \qquad n = 0, 1, 2, \ldots.$

The bound on the right is attained for $\varepsilon_m = \varepsilon$ sign d_{nm} and thus cannot be improved. Assuming that the local errors are independent random variables with

(16-23) $\qquad E(\varepsilon_m) = \mu, \qquad \text{var}(\varepsilon_m) = \sigma^2, \qquad m = 0, 1, 2, \ldots$

we find for the random variables r_n, using (16-9) and (16-10)

(16-24) $\qquad \begin{cases} E(r_n) = \mu \sum\limits_{m=0}^{n} d_{nm}, \\[2mm] \text{var}(r_n) = \sigma^2 \sum\limits_{m=0}^{n} d_{nm}^2, \qquad n = 0, 1, 2, \ldots. \end{cases}$

In the case where the expected values and variances of the local errors depend on m (which is the appropriate assumption for floating point arithmetic) the assumptions (16-21) are to be replaced by

(16-25) $\qquad E(\varepsilon_m) = \mu_m, \qquad \text{var}(\varepsilon_m) = \sigma_m^2, \qquad m = 0, 1, 2, \ldots,$

yielding

$$E(r_n) = \sum_{m=0}^{n} \mu_m d_{nm},$$

$$\text{var}(r_n) = \sum_{m=0}^{n} \sigma_m^2 d_{nm}^2.$$

In a qualitative sense, the above results remain even true when the functions Q_n are not linear. The derivatives $Q_n^{(k)}$ in (16-16) are then evaluated at $(q_0, q_1, \ldots, q_{n-1})$, and terms of higher order in Taylor's expansion are neglected. This can frequently be justified if an a priori bound for the accumulated errors r_n is known.

16.5   Applications

We now shall apply the results of §16.4 to a number of special algorithms. Most of these have already been discussed in preceding chapters. For the sake of simplicity we shall assume that fixed point arithmetic is used. The hypotheses (16-21) and (16-23) are then appropriate. In many cases the results remain qualitatively true for floating point arithmetic.

(*i*) *Evaluation of a sum.* We begin by considering the extremely simple example of evaluating numerically the sum

$$S = \sum_{n=1}^{N} a_n,$$

where $a_1, a_2, \ldots, a_N$ are given real numbers. This can be put into algorithmic form by setting

(16-27) $\begin{cases} q_0 = 0, \\ q_n = q_{n-1} + a_n, & n = 1, 2, \ldots, N. \end{cases}$

Clearly, $q_N = S$. We thus have

$$Q_n(q_0, q_1, \ldots, q_{n-1}) = q_{n-1} + a_n.$$

In actual computation, in place of the exact numbers q_n numerical values $\tilde{q}_n$ are generated according to the scheme

(16-28) $\begin{cases} \tilde{q}_0 = 0, \\ \tilde{q}_n = \tilde{q}_{n-1} + a_n^*. \end{cases}$

(In floating arithmetic, the second of the relations (16-28) would have to be replaced by $q_n = (q_{n-1} + a^{\oplus})^{\oplus}$.) According to our scheme, we replace the second relation (16-28) by

$$\tilde{q}_n = \tilde{q}_{n-1} + a_n + \varepsilon_n,$$

showing that the local error ε_n is given by

$$\varepsilon_n = a_n^* - a_n$$

and thus, in fixed point binary arithmetic, satisfies (16-21) with $\varepsilon = 2^{-t-1}$, or (16-23) with

(16-29) $\mu = 0, \qquad \sigma^2 = \tfrac{1}{12} 2^{-2t}.$

In view of

$$Q_n^{(k)} = 0, \qquad k = 0, 1, 2, \ldots, n - 2,$$
$$Q_n^{(n-1)} = 1,$$

the relations (16-19) reduce to

$$d_{n,n-1} = 1, \qquad d_{n,k} = d_{n-1,k}, \qquad n > k$$

and thus yield $d_{n,k} = 1$, $n \geq k$. Relation (16-17) thus shows that

$$(16\text{-}30) \qquad r_n = \sum_{m=1}^{n} \varepsilon_m.$$

(In the present simple example this result could have been obtained directly, see problem 3.) We thus find from (16-22) and (16-24)

$$(16\text{-}31) \qquad |r_n| \leq n\varepsilon, \qquad \text{s.d. } (r_n) = \sqrt{n}\, \sigma.$$

The result shows that while the theoretically greatest possible error in a sum of n terms grows like n, the standard deviation grows only like $\sqrt{n}$.

(*ii*) *Iteration.* We next consider the algorithm of solving the equation

$$x = f(x)$$

by determining the limit of the sequence $\{x_n\}$ defined by algorithm 4.1:

$$x_n = f(x_{n-1}).$$

Here the functions Q_n in (16-12) are given by

$$Q_n(q_0, q_1, \ldots, q_{n-1}) = f(q_{n-1}).$$

To simplify matters we shall consider only the idealized situation where

$$f(x) = ax + b$$

and where a and b are constant machine numbers. For convergence we must assume (see theorem 4.2) that $|a| < 1$. On the machine, the theoretical recurrence relation

$$q_n = aq_{n-1} + b$$

is replaced by

$$\tilde{q}_n = (a\tilde{q}_{n-1})^* + b.$$

Writing the latter relation in the form

$$\tilde{q}_n = a\tilde{q}_{n-1} + b + \varepsilon_n,$$

we see that

$$\varepsilon_n = (a\tilde{q}_{n-1})^* - a\tilde{q}_{n-1}.$$

Thus, in fixed point arithmetic, (16-21) again holds with $\varepsilon = 2^{-t-1}$, and (16-23) with the values (16-29).   In view of

$$Q_n^{(k)} = 0, \qquad k = 0, 1, \ldots, n - 2,$$
$$Q_n^{(n-1)} = a,$$

the recurrence relations (16-19) simplify to

$$d_{nn} = 1, \qquad d_{n,m} = a d_{n-1,m} \qquad (n > m \geqq 0)$$

and permit the immediate solution

$$d_{nm} = a^{n-m}, \qquad n = m, m + 1, \ldots.$$

It follows that

$$r_n = \sum_{m=0}^{n} a^{n-m} \varepsilon_m.$$

In view of $|a| < 1$ we thus find

$$(16\text{-}32) \qquad |r_n| \leqq \varepsilon \frac{1 - |a|^{n+1}}{1 - |a|} \leqq \frac{1}{1 - |a|} \varepsilon$$

and for the stochastic model

$$(16\text{-}33) \qquad \mathrm{var}\,(r_n) = \sigma^2 \frac{1 - a^{2n+2}}{1 - a^2} \leqq \sigma^2 \frac{1}{1 - a^2}.$$

The bounds (16-32) and (16-33) are remarkable for the fact that they are independent of n, the number of iteration steps.   An algorithm with this property must be called *stable* under any reasonable definition of this term.   Newton's method in particular, which corresponds to the case $a = 0$ of the above simplified model, enjoys an extreme degree of stability.

(*iii*) *Generating* cos $n\varphi$ *and* sin $n\varphi$ *by recurrence relations.*   As our next example, we consider the algorithm for generating the sequences {cos $n\varphi$} and {sin $n\varphi$} by the algorithm suggested by example 3, §6.3.   (These sequences are required, e.g., for computing the sums of Fourier series.) The difference equation

$$(16\text{-}34) \qquad t_n - 2 \cos \varphi t_{n-1} + t_{n-2} = 0$$

has the solutions $t_n = \cos n\varphi$ and $t_n = \sin n\varphi$ and can therefore be used to generate these functions recursively if the values of cos φ and sin φ are known.   Here the theory of §16.4 applies with

$$Q(t_0, t_1, \ldots, t_{n-1}) = 2 \cos \varphi t_{n-1} - t_{n-2}.$$

In numerical computation, (16-34) is replaced by

$$(16\text{-}35) \qquad \tilde{t}_n = (2 \widetilde{\cos \varphi} \tilde{t}_{n-1})^* - \tilde{t}_{n-2},$$

where $\widetilde{\cos\varphi}$ denotes a machine value of $\cos\varphi$. Writing (16-35) in the form

$$\tilde{t}_n = 2\cos\varphi\tilde{t}_{n-1} - \tilde{t}_{n-2} + \varepsilon_n,$$

we see that

$$\varepsilon_n = (2\widetilde{\cos\varphi}\tilde{t}_{n-1})^* - 2\cos\varphi\tilde{t}_{n-1}.$$

Adding and subtracting $2\widetilde{\cos\varphi}\tilde{t}_{n-1}$, we also have

$$\varepsilon_n = (2\widetilde{\cos\varphi}\tilde{t}_{n-1})^* - 2\widetilde{\cos\varphi}\tilde{t}_{n-1} + 2(\widetilde{\cos\varphi} - \cos\varphi)\tilde{t}_{n-1}.$$

Here we see that ε_n is due to two sources: (a) rounding the product $2\widetilde{\cos\varphi}\tilde{t}_{n-1}$; (b) replacing $\cos\varphi$ by $\widetilde{\cos\varphi}$. Both errors can be estimated and permit us to make assumptions such as (16-21) and (16-23).

To determine the d_{nm}, we observe that

$$Q_n^{(k)} = 0, \qquad k = 0, 1, \ldots, n - 3,$$
$$Q_n^{(n-2)} = -1,$$
$$Q_n^{(n-1)} = 2\cos\varphi.$$

The relations (16-19) thus yield

$$(16\text{-}36) \qquad \begin{cases} d_{mm} = 1, \\ d_{m+1,m} = 2\cos\varphi, \\ d_{mm} = 2\cos\varphi d_{n-1,m} - d_{n-2,m}, \qquad n \geqq m + 2. \end{cases}$$

These equations show that, for a fixed value of m, the quantities d_{nm} themselves are a solution of the difference equation (16-34), with the initial values given at $n = m$ and $n = m + 1$. We thus must have

$$d_{nm} = A_m \cos n\varphi + B_m \sin n\varphi, \qquad n = m, m + 1, \ldots,$$

where A_m and B_m are to be determined from the first two relations (16-36). Some algebra yields (if $0 < \varphi < \pi$)

$$A_m = -\frac{\sin(m-1)\varphi}{\sin\varphi}, \qquad B_m = \frac{\cos(m-1)\varphi}{\sin\varphi},$$

and we thus get, after some further simplification,

$$d_{nm} = \frac{\sin(n - m + 1)\varphi}{\sin\varphi}, \qquad n \geqq m.$$

Since $\varepsilon_0 = 0$, the general theory thus yields

$$r_n = \sum_{m=1}^{n} \frac{\sin(n - m + 1)\varphi}{\sin\varphi} \varepsilon_m.$$

Using the crude estimate $|\sin (n - m + 1)\varphi| \leq 1$, we thus have

$$|r_n| \leq \frac{n\varepsilon}{\sin \varphi}, \qquad n = 1, 2, \ldots.$$

Using the known formula

$$\sum_{m=1}^{n} (\sin \varphi)^2 = \frac{n}{2} + \frac{1}{4} - \frac{\sin (2n + 1)\varphi}{4 \sin \varphi},$$

we get for the variance the expression

$$\text{var}\,(r_n) = \sigma^2 \sum_{m=1}^{n} \left(\frac{\sin (n - m + 1)\varphi}{\sin \varphi}\right)^2$$

$$= \frac{\sigma^2}{(\sin \varphi)^2} \left[\frac{n}{2} + \frac{1}{4} - \frac{\sin (2n + 1)\varphi}{4 \sin \varphi}\right].$$

As in the algorithm for finding the sum of n numbers, the standard deviation of the accumulated error grows only like $\sqrt{n}$, while the rigorous estimate grows like n. This relatively high stability of the recursive method for generating $\cos n\varphi$ and $\sin n\varphi$ (or, what amounts to the same, the Chebyshev polynomials) has been observed experimentally (Lanczos [1955]).

(*iv*) *Horner's scheme.* We next consider the propagation of error in the evaluation of a polynomial by Horner's scheme (algorithm 3.4), assuming that the coefficients $a_0, a_1, \ldots, a_N$ of the polynomial and the value of the variable x are machine numbers. The scheme then consists in generating a finite sequence of numbers $q_0, q_1, \ldots, q_N$ by the formulas

(16-37) $$\begin{cases} q_0 = a_0, \\ q_n = a_n + xq_{n-1}, \qquad n = 1, 2, \ldots, N; \end{cases}$$

the desired value is q_N. The functions Q_n are evidently given by

$$Q_n(q_0, q_1, \ldots, q_{n-1}) = a_n + xq_{n-1}.$$

In numerical work, the second relation (16-37) is replaced by $\tilde{q}_n = a_n + (x\tilde{q}_{n-1})^*$. If the last term is written as $a_n + x\tilde{q}_{n-1} + \varepsilon_n$, we see that, as in (*ii*) above, the local rounding error equals the rounding error in the fixed point multiplication $x\tilde{q}_{n-1}$. Thus the assumptions (16-21) and (16-23) are again justified with $\varepsilon = 2^{-t-1}$, $\mu = 0$, $\sigma^2 = \frac{1}{12}2^{-2t}$. We now have

$$Q_n^{(k)} = 0, \qquad k = 0, 1, \ldots, n - 2,$$
$$Q_n^{(n-1)} = x,$$

and thus find, as above,

$$d_{nm} = x^{n-m}, \qquad n \geq m \geq 0.$$

Since $\varepsilon_0 = 0$ we thus have

$$r_n = \sum_{m=1}^{n} x^{n-m} \varepsilon_m$$

and find in the usual way

$$|r_n| \leqq \begin{cases} \dfrac{|x|^n - 1}{|x| - 1}\, \varepsilon, & x \neq 1, \\[2mm] n\varepsilon, & x = 1, \end{cases}$$

and, under the statistical hypothesis,

$$\text{s.d. } (r_n) = \begin{cases} \sqrt{\dfrac{x^{2n} - 1}{x^2 - 1}}\, \sigma, & x \neq 1, \\[2mm] \sqrt{n}\, \sigma, & x = 1. \end{cases}$$

Thus, for the evaluation of high degree polynomials in fixed point arithmetic, Horner's scheme is unstable when $|x| > 1$ and stable when $|x| < 1$.

(*v*) *Numerical integration of differential equations.* We finally consider the numerical integration of the simple but typical initial value problem

$$y' = Ay, \qquad y(0) = 1,$$

where A is a real constant, $A \neq 0$, (a) by Euler's method; (b) by the integration scheme based on the midpoint formula discussed in §14.8. The approximate values generated by Euler's method satisfy

$$y_0 = 1,$$
$$y_n = y_{n-1} + Ahy_{n-1}, \qquad n = 1, 2, \dots.$$

This is an algorithm of the form (16-12) where $Q_n^{(k)} = 0$ ($k = 0, 1, \dots, n - 2$), $Q_n^{(n-1)} = 1 + Ah$. If the local errors are defined by

$$\tilde{y}_n = \tilde{y}_{n-1} + Ah\tilde{y}_{n-1} + \varepsilon_n,$$

we find, by computations similar to the ones carried out earlier, that the accumulated error $r_n = \tilde{y}_n - y_n$ can be expressed in the form

$$r_n = \sum_{m=1}^{n} (1 + Ah)^{n-m} \varepsilon_m.$$

We thus obtain

$$|r_n| \leqq \frac{(1 + Ah)^n - 1}{hA}\, \varepsilon,$$

$$\text{var } (r_n) = \frac{(1 + Ah)^{2n} - 1}{2Ah + h^2 A^2}\, \sigma^2.$$

Some simplification is possible by observing that for $h \to 0$, $nh = x$ fixed and positive, $(1 + Ah)^n = e^{Ax} + O(h)$. We thus find

(16-38)
$$|r_n| \leq \frac{\varepsilon}{h} \left[\frac{e^{Ax} - 1}{A} + O(h) \right],$$

$$\text{var} (r_n) = \frac{\sigma^2}{h} \left[\frac{e^{2Ax} - 1}{2A} + O(h) \right].$$

These relations show that Euler's method is numerically *stable* if $A \leq 0$, provided that h is sufficiently small. The method is *unstable* if $A > 0$, but this instability is not serious, since then the solution itself grows exponentially. Analogous statements hold for all methods based on Taylor's expansion, and also for all Adams' methods.

If the midpoint rule is used, the values y_n satisfy

$$y_0 = 1, \qquad y_1 = e^{Ah} \text{ (ideally)}$$
$$y_n - y_{n-2} = 2hAy_{n-1}, \qquad n \geq 2.$$

This is of the form (16-12) where

$$Q_n(y_0, y_1, \ldots, y_{n-1}) = 2hAy_{n-1} + y_{n-2}.$$

A consideration similar to that under (*iii*) above shows that the coefficients d_{nm} satisfy, for a fixed value of m, the difference equation

(16-39) $$d_{nm} - 2hAd_{n-1,m} - d_{n-2,m} = 0 \qquad (n \geq m + 2)$$

and the starting conditions

(16-40) $$d_{mm} = 1, \qquad d_{m+1,m} = 2Ah.$$

The characteristic polynomial p of (16-39) is given by

$$p(z) = z^2 - 2hAz - 1;$$

its two zeros are

$$z_1 = Ah + \sqrt{1 + (Ah)^2} = e^{Ah} + O(h^2),$$
$$z_2 = -z_1^{-1}.$$

The solution d_{nm} of (16-39) satisfying (16-40) is found to be

$$d_{nm} = \frac{z_1^{n-m+1} - z_2^{n-m+1}}{z_1 - z_2}.$$

A somewhat elaborate but elementary computation using the approximations (see §14.8)

$$z_1^n = e^{Ax} + O(h), \qquad z_2^n = (-1)^n e^{-Ax} + O(h),$$

valid for $h \to 0$, $nh = x$ fixed and positive, shows that

$$(16\text{-}41) \qquad |r_n| \leq \varepsilon \sum_{m=0}^{n} |d_{nm}| = \frac{\varepsilon}{h} \left[\frac{\cosh Ah - 1}{2A} + 0(h) \right],$$

and, if var $(\varepsilon_m) = \sigma^2$,

$$(16\text{-}42) \qquad \text{var } (r_n) = \frac{\sigma^2}{h} \left[\frac{\cosh 2Ax - 1}{4A} + 0(h) \right].$$

These relations confirm the result of §14.8 that the midpoint formula is always unstable, also when $A < 0$. It produces exponential growth of the rounding error also when the exact solution is exponentially decreasing. It is clear that such a method cannot be used for the numerical integration of a differential equation such as $y' = -y$. In a qualitative sense, this negative result is true for all methods based on numerical integration where the numerical integration is performed over an interval comprising several steps. Simpson's rule, in particular, if applied to the numerical solution of differential equations, also suffers from this kind of instability, see problem 11.

Problems

4. In floating arithmetic it is frequently permissible to replace the statistical hypotheses (16-23) by

$$(16\text{-}43) \qquad E(\varepsilon_m) = \mu q_m, \qquad \text{var } (\varepsilon_m) = \sigma^2 q_m^2,$$

where μ and σ are again constants. Discuss the propagation of error in the computation of the sum

$$(16\text{-}44) \qquad q_n = a_1 + a_2 + \cdots + a_n,$$

where $a_i > 0$, $i = 1, 2, \ldots$, by the algorithm described under (*i*) above, if floating arithmetic is used. Show that, contrary to the fixed point arithmetic case, the propagated error depends on the order of the terms in (16-44), and that both the maximum error and the standard deviation are minimized if the terms are summed in increasing order.

5. Discuss the propagation of rounding error if the geometric series $\sum_{n=0}^{\infty} a^n$, where $|a| < 1$, is summed in floating point arithmetic, generating a^n by the formula $a^n = a(a^{n-1})$. Is the resulting process numerically stable?

6. The Fibonacci numbers (see example 7, §6.3) are generated from their recurrence relation

$$x_0 = x_1 = 1, \qquad x_n = x_{n-1} + x_{n-2}$$

in floating arithmetic. Assuming that the relations (16-43) hold with

$q_n = x_n$, what is the standard deviation of the numerical value $\tilde{x}_n$ for large values of n? If the $\tilde{x}_n$ are used to compute the number

$$\frac{1 + \sqrt{5}}{2} = \lim_{n \to \infty} \frac{\tilde{x}_{n+1}}{\tilde{x}_n},$$

is this a stable process?

7*. (Generalization of problem 6.) Discuss the propagation of rounding error in Bernoulli's method for determining a single dominant zero of a polynomial whose coefficients are exact machine numbers. Discuss both floating and fixed point arithmetic.

8. Discuss the propagation of rounding error in algorithm 5.6 for extracting a quadratic factor, assuming fixed point arithmetic.

9. Let, for non-integral $s > 0$, the binomial coefficients $q_n = \binom{s}{n}$ be generated by the recurrence relation

$$q_0 = 1, \qquad q_n = \frac{s - n + 1}{n} q_{n-1}, \qquad n = 1, 2, \ldots .$$

Assuming fixed point arithmetic, show that

$$\operatorname{var}(r_n) = \sigma^2 S_n(s),$$

where

$$S_n(s) = \left[\binom{s}{n} \right]^2 \sum_{m=1}^{n} \left[\binom{s}{m} \right]^{-2}.$$

(It can be shown that $S_n(s) = n/(3 + 2s) + 0(1)$ as $n \to \infty$.)

10. Study the propagation of rounding error in algorithm 12.4 (repeated extrapolation to the limit), if the same error distribution (16-23) is assumed in the zeroth column $A_{m,0}$ and in the relations defining the elements of the $(m + 1)$st column in terms of those of the mth column.

11. Show that if the problem discussed under (v) above is solved by Simpson's formula

$$y_{n+1} - y_{n-1} = \frac{h}{3}(f_{n+1} + 4f_n + f_{n-1})$$

in fixed point arithmetic, the standard deviation of the accumulated rounding error behaves for x large like $\cosh\left(\frac{1}{3}Ax\right)$.

Recommended Reading

The detailed study of the propagation of rounding error in numerical computation is of recent origin. The classical paper is by Rademacher [1948]. Very detailed accounts of the propagation of error in a large number of methods for solving ordinary differential equations are given in the author's books [1962, 1963].

Research Problems

1. Make a study, both experimental and (as far as possible) theoretical, of the propagation of error in the Quotient-Difference algorithm.
2. Discuss the stability of Horner's scheme in floating point arithmetic.
3. The hypotheses underlying the statistical theory of propagation of rounding error have been criticized as unreliable (Huskey [1949]).   Carry out some statistical experiments on rounding error propagation and compare the results with the theoretical results given above.   (See the author's books quoted above for some ideas on how to perform such experiments.)

bibliography

This list of books and papers contains the titles quoted in the text; it is not intended to be complete in any sense of the word. More complete bibliographies on many topics of numerical analysis will be found in some of the references given below; see in particular Hildebrand [1956] and Todd [1962].

Aitken, A. C. [1926]: On Bernoulli's numerical solution of algebraic equations, *Proc. Roy. Soc. Edinburgh*, **46**, 289–305.

Bareiss, E. H. [1960]: Resultant procedure and the mechanization of the Graeffe process, *J. Assoc. Comp. Mach.*, **7**, 346–386.

Bauer, F. L., H. Rutishauser, and E. Stiefel [1963]: New aspects in numerical quadrature, *Proc. of Symp. in Appl. Math.*, vol. 15: *High speed computing and experimental arithmetic*, American Mathematical Society, Providence, R.I.

Birkhoff, G., and S. MacLane [1953]: *A survey of modern algebra*, rev. ed., Macmillan, New York.

Brown, K. M., and P. Henrici [1962]: Sign wave analysis in matrix eigenvalue problems, *Math. of Comput.*, **16**, 291–300.

Buck, R. C. [1956]: *Advanced Calculus*, McGraw-Hill, New York, Toronto, London.

Coddington, E. A. [1961]: *An introduction to ordinary differential equations*, Prentice-Hall, Englewood Cliffs, N.J.

Comrie, L. J. [1961]: *Chambers's shorter six-figure mathematical tables*, W. R. Chambers Ltd., Edinburgh and London.

Erdelyi, A. (ed.) [1953]: *Higher transcendental functions*, vol. 1, McGraw-Hill, New York, Toronto, London.

Forsythe, G. E. [1958]: Singularity and near singularity in numerical analysis, *Amer. Math. Monthly*, **65**, 229–240.

—— and W. Wasow [1960]: *Finite difference methods for partial differential equations*, Wiley, New York.

Fox, L. [1957]: *The numerical solution of two-point boundary problems in ordinary differential equations*, Clarendon, Oxford.

Goldberg, S. [1958]: *Introduction to difference equations*, Wiley, New York.

Henrici, P. [1956]: A subroutine for computations with rational numbers, *J. Assoc. Comput. Mach.*, **3**, 10–15.

—— [1958]: The quotient-difference algorithm, *Nat. Bur. Standards Appl. Math. Series*, **49**, 23–46.

322

Henrici, P. [1962]: *Discrete variable methods in ordinary differential equations*, Wiley, New York.

—— [1963]: *Error propagation for difference methods*, Wiley, New York.

—— [1963a]: Some applications of the quotient-difference algorithm, *Proc. Symp. Appl. Math.*, vol. 15, *High speed computing and experimental arithmetic*, American Mathematical Society, Providence, R.I.

Hildebrand, F. B. [1956]: *Introduction to numerical analysis*, McGraw-Hill, New York, Toronto, London.

Householder, A. S. [1953]: *Principles of numerical analysis*, McGraw-Hill, New York and London.

Huskey, H. D. [1949]: On the precision of a certain procedure of numerical integration, with an appendix by Douglas R. Hartree, *J. Res. Nat. Bur. Stand.*, **42**, 57–62.

Jahnke, E., and F. Emde [1945]: *Tables of functions with formulae and curves*, Dover, New York.

Kantorovich, L. V. [1948]: Functional analysis and applied mathematics, *Uspekhi Mat. Nauk.*, **3**, 89–185. Translated by C. D. Benster and edited by G. E. Forsythe as *Nat. Bur. Stand. Rept.* No. 1509.

Kaplan, W. [1953]: *Advanced Calculus*, Addison-Wesley, Cambridge.

Lanczos, C. [1955]: Spectroscopic eigenvalue analysis, *J. Wash. Acad. Sci.*, **45**, 315–323.

Liusternik, L. A., and W. I. Sobolev [1960]: *Elemente der Funktionalanalysis* (translated from the Russian). Akademieverlag, Berlin.

McCracken, D. D. [1961]: *A guide to FORTRAN programming*, Wiley, New York.

—— [1962]: *A guide to ALGOL programming*, Wiley, New York.

Milne, W. E. [1949]: *Numerical Calculus*, Princeton University Press, Princeton, N.J.

—— [1953]: *Numerical solution of differential equations*, Wiley, New York.

Milne-Thomson, L. M. [1933]: *The calculus of finite differences*, Macmillan, London.

Muller, D. E. [1956]: A method for solving algebraic equations using an automatic computer, *Math. Tables Aids Comput.*, **10**, 208–215.

National Physical Laboratory [1961]: *Modern Computing Methods* (Notes on Applied Science No. 16), 2nd ed., H.M. Stationery Office, London.

Naur, P. et al. [1960]: Report on the algorithmic language ALGOL 60, *Comm. Assoc. Comp. Mach.*, **3**, 299–314.

Nautical Almanac Office [1956]: *Interpolation and allied tables*, H.M. Stationery Office, London.

Ostrowski, A. [1940]: Recherches sur la méthode de Graeffe et les zéros des polynomes et les séries de Laurent, *Acta Math.*, **72**, 99–257.

—— [1960]: *Solution of equations and systems of equations*, Academic Press, New York.

Rademacher, H. [1948]: On the accumulation of errors in processes of integration on high-speed calculating machines. Proceedings of a symposium on large scale digital calculating machinery, *Annals Comput. Labor. Harvard Univ.*, **16**, 176–187.

Richardson, L. F. [1927]: The deferred approach to the limit, I—Single lattice, *Trans. Roy. Soc. London*, **226**, 299–349.

Rutishauser, H. [1952]: Ueber die Instabilität von Methoden zur Integration gewöhnlicher Differentialgleichungen, *Z. angew. Math. Physik*, **3**, 65–74.

—— [1956]: *Der Quotienten-Differenzen-Algorithmus*. Mitteilungen aus dem Institut für angew. Math. No. 7. Birkhäuser, Basel and Stuttgart.

Rutishauser, H. [1963]: Ausdehnung des Rombergschen Prinzips, *Numer. Math.*, **5**, 48–53.

Schwarz, H. R. [1962]: An Introduction to ALGOL, *Comm. Assoc. Comp. Mach.*, **5**, 82–95.

Sokolnikoff, I. S., and R. M. Redheffer [1958]: *Mathematics of Physics and modern Engineering*, McGraw-Hill, New York.

Speiser, A. P. [1961]: *Digitale Rechenanlagen*, Springer, Berlin.

Steffensen, J. F. [1933]: Remarks on iteration, *Skand. Aktuar. Tidskr.*, **16**, 64–72.

Taylor, A. E. [1959]: *Calculus with analytic geometry*, Prentice-Hall, Englewood Cliffs, N.J.

Todd, J. (ed.) [1962]: *Survey of numerical analysis*, McGraw-Hill, New York.

—— [1963]: *Introduction to the constructive theory of functions*, Birkhäuser, Basel and Stuttgart.

Watkins, B. O. [1964]: Roots of a polynomial using the QD method. To be published.

Watson, G. N. [1944]: *A treatise on the theory of Bessel functions*, 2nd. ed., University Press, Cambridge.

Whittaker, E. T., and G. Robinson [1924]: *The calculus of observations*, Blackie, London.

Wilkinson, J. H. [1959]: The evaluation of the zeros of ill-conditioned polynomials, *Numer. Math.*, **1**, 150–180.

—— [1960]: Error analysis of floating-point computation, *Numer. Math.*, **2**, 319–340.

—— [1963]: *Rounding errors in algebraic processes*, National Physical Laboratory Notes on Applied Science No. 32, H.M. Stationery Office, London.

INDEX

ANSWERS FOR PROBLEMS

Chapter 1

1) If $n > 1$ is the given integer, divide n by all integers m from 2 to the greatest integer not exceeding $\sqrt{n}$. n is prime if no such m divides n without remainder.

2) Algorithm infinite because $\sqrt{2}$ irrational, hence decimal fraction neither terminating nor periodic.

3) Existence of $\sqrt{a}$ for real $a > 0$; proof of the fact that every bounded monotone sequence has a limit; existence of supremum and infimum of a bounded set of real numbers.

Chapter 2

1) a) $-\frac{1}{2} + i\frac{\sqrt{3}}{2}$ b) -4 c) $\cos 2\varphi + i \sin 2\varphi$
d) $\cos\varphi + i \sin\varphi$ e) 1 .

2) Not defined for $z = -1$, $z = 0$.

3)
$$s = \frac{1 - z^{n+1}}{1 - z}$$

4) a) 2, $\varphi = -\frac{\pi}{2} + 2k\pi$ b) 10, $\varphi = 126°45' + k\,360°$
c) $2^{-1/2}$, $\varphi = \frac{\pi}{4} + 2k\pi$.

5) $\arg\omega = \frac{2\pi}{3} + 2k\pi$, $|\omega| = \sqrt[3]{1} = 1$

8) If $k = 1$, then locus is imaginary axis. If $k \neq 1$, let
$$q = \frac{1 + k^2}{1 - k^2} .$$
The equation is
$$z\,\bar{z} - q(z + \bar{z}) + 1 = 0$$
or in real form
$$x^2 + y^2 - 2qx + 1 = 0$$
(circle with center at (q, 0) and radius $q^2 - 1$).

9) $i^n = (-1)^m$ if $n = 2m$
          $i^n = i$ if $n = 4m + 1$
          $i^n = -i$ if $n = 4m + 3$

10) $z = e^{ik\varphi}$, $k = 1, 2, \ldots, n$, where
$$\varphi = \frac{2\pi}{n + 1} .$$

11) $A_n = \dfrac{1 - r\cos\varphi - r^{n+1}\cos(n+1)\varphi + r^{n+2}\cos n\varphi}{1 - 2r\cos\varphi + r^2}$

$B_n = \dfrac{r\sin\varphi - r^{n+1}\sin(n+1)\varphi + r^{n+2}\sin n\varphi}{1 - 2r\cos\varphi + r^2}$

12) a) $\pm 1 \pm i$

  b) $\exp i(\frac{\pi}{12} + n\frac{\pi}{3})$, $n = 0, 1, \ldots , 5$

  c) $\sqrt{3}$, $\dfrac{-\sqrt{3} + i3}{2}$, $\dfrac{-\sqrt{3} - i3}{2}$.

13) $\cos 4\varphi = 8(\cos\varphi)^4 - 8(\cos\varphi)^2 + 1$

14) $\sqrt{x + iy} =$

$$\pm\left[\sqrt{\frac{x + \sqrt{x^2 + y^2}}{2}} + (\mathrm{sign}\, y)i\sqrt{\frac{-x + \sqrt{x^2 + y^2}}{2}}\right]$$

15) $\frac{1}{64}(\cos 7\varphi - \cos 5\varphi - 3\cos 3\varphi + 3\cos\varphi)$

18) a) ellipse with semiaxes $|a + b|$ and $|a - b|$

  b) parabolic arc $x = 2y^2 - 1$, $-1 \leqq y \leqq 1$.

22) a) $\pm 1 \pm 2i$ b) $\pm 2 \pm i$ c) $\pm 1 \pm 2i$, $\pm 2 \pm i$

23) $a_1 = a_2 = a_3 = 0$, $a_4 = 4$.

24) three.

25) two.

Chapter 3

1) $x_n = \dfrac{1 - a^{n+1}}{1 - a}$, $\lim\limits_{n\to\infty} x_n = \dfrac{1}{1 - a}$

2) $x_n = \dfrac{n!}{z^n}(1 + z + \frac{z^2}{2!} + \ldots + \frac{z^n}{n!})$

3) $x_n = b_0 + b_1 + \ldots + b_n =$ n-th partial sum of series.

4) $x_n = \prod\limits_{k=1}^{n}(1 - \frac{z^2}{k^2})$

8) $p(x) = 2.392 - 3.92(x + 0.3) - 3.6(x + 0.3)^2 + 4(x + 0.3)^3$

9) $P(1.5) = -22.625$, $P'(1.5) = -37.625$, $P''(1.5) = -39$

Chapter 4

1) a) $|f'(x)| = |\frac{3}{4}\sin x| \leqq \frac{3}{4}$, thus $L = \frac{3}{4}$

  b) $|f'(x)| = \frac{1}{2}$, thus $L = \frac{1}{2}$

  c) $|f'(x)| = \dfrac{1}{x^2}$, thus $|f'(x)| \leqq \frac{1}{4}$ for $x \geqq 2$,

    thus $L = \dfrac{1}{4}$

2) $f(x) = m - \varepsilon \sin x$ maps $[m - \pi , m + \pi]$ into itself and satisfies Lipschitz condition with $L = |\varepsilon| < 1$.

3) $f(x) = \sqrt{x}$, $0 \leq x \leq 1$. f' is unbounded!

5) $x = 0.96433388$

7) $x_{32} = 1.839287$

9) Any M such that $-\frac{2}{b} < M < 0$ will do.

10) $s = 2$. For $x \geq 0$, $y \geq 0$, $|f(x) - f(y)| \leq \frac{1}{2\sqrt{2}} |x - y|$.

11) $|x_{10} - s| \leq 1.8 \times 10^{-8}$.

13) Prob. 7: $x'_{15} = 1.839286$, Prob. 5: $x'_3 = 0.964318$

16) 2.766204

19) $M = - \frac{1}{g'(s)}$

20) $\lim_{n \to \infty} \frac{d_{n+1}}{d_n^3} = \frac{f'''(s)}{6}$

21) $f(x) = x \frac{x^2 + 3z}{3x^2 + z}$; $x_1 = 3.16216216$, $x_2 = 3.162277660$

22) $x = 0.5671433$

23) $\sqrt{\pi} = 1.772453851$

24) $x_0 = 0.3$, $x_1 = 0.33$, $x_2 = 0.3333$, $x_3 = 0.33333333$, ... (x_n has 2^n 3's).

27) $h(x) = - \frac{1}{2} \frac{F''(x)}{F'(x)}$

28) $x = 1.8392867$

29) $x = 0.9024738$

32) $x_n = 2^{-n}$; $x_n = 0$, $n = 1$

34) 1.782191

35) 3.16227766 (sequence identical with that obtained by Newton's method, if starting values are the same).

39) $s = 1.4655712$

Chapter 5

7) $x = 0.7718445$, $y = 0.4196434$

8) $x = 4.9322865$, $y = 5.0673188$

9) $x = 1.0309038$, $y = 1.0033246$

10) $3.0053220 \pm i\, 3.9963692$, $0.9946779 \pm i\, 1.0248789$.

11) Quadratic factors $x^2 + 1.5415682\, x + 1.4873158$, $x^2 - 1.1272386\, x + 0.8316443$, real zeros $- 1.8620342$, -0.7236362.

Chapter 6

1) a) $x_n = c_1 + c_2(-1)^n$

   b) $x_n = c_1 \cos\frac{n\pi}{4} + c_2 \sin\frac{n\pi}{4}$

   c) $x_n = (-1)^n(c_1 + c_2 n)$

2) $x_n = c_1 \left[-i(1 - \sqrt{2})\right]^n + c_2 \left[-i(1 + \sqrt{2})\right]^n$

3) $x_n = r^n(c_1 \cos n\varphi + c_2 \sin n\varphi)$, where

   $r = \sqrt{b}$, $\varphi = \text{arctg} \dfrac{\sqrt{4b - a^2}}{a}$

7) a) $x_n = \dfrac{1 + \sqrt{5}}{2\sqrt{5}} (\dfrac{3 + \sqrt{5}}{2})^n + \dfrac{\sqrt{5} - 1}{2\sqrt{5}} (\dfrac{3 - \sqrt{5}}{2})^n$

   b) $x_n = 2^{n/2} \cos\frac{n\pi}{4}$ is solution of $x_n - 2x_{n-1} + 2x_{n-2} = 0$

12) a) $x_n = c_1 3^n + c_2 2^n + 1$

    b) $x_n = c_1 2^{-n} + c_2 4^{-n} + \dfrac{4}{21} 2^n$

    c) $x_n = c_1 2^n + c_2 (-1)^n - \dfrac{1}{2}n^2 - \dfrac{5}{2}n - 4$

13) $x_n = - 2 \times 3^n + 2 \times 2^n + 1$

14) $x_n = c_1(\dfrac{3 + \sqrt{17}}{4})^n + c_2(\dfrac{3 - \sqrt{17}}{4})^n + 1$;

    $x_1 - 1 = (x_0 - 1)\dfrac{3 - \sqrt{17}}{4}$.

15) $y_n = 2 \left[1 + 2^{-n'/2} \sin\dfrac{n'\pi}{4}\right]$, $n' = n - 1946$;

every 8 years; if a and b are non-negative, the condition

is $a \leqslant 1$, $ab \leqslant 1$.

16) $x_n = \dfrac{na^{n-1}}{a - b}$, if $b \neq a$; $x_n = \dfrac{1}{2} n^2 a^n$, if $b = a$.

20) a) $x_n - 6x_{n-1} + 11x_{n-2} - 6x_{n-3} = 0$

    b) $x_n - 4x_{n-1} + 6x_{n-2} - 4x_{n-3} + x_{n-4} = 0$

    c) $x_n - 9x_{n-1} + 32x_{n-2} - 58x_{n-3} + 57x_{n-4}$

       $- 29x_{n-5} + 6x_{n-6} = 0$

22) $(\nabla^2 T(t))_{n+1} = 2(t - 1)T_n(t)$,

    $(\nabla^4 T(t))_{n+2} = 4(t - 1)^2 T_n(t)$.

23) $\nabla^k f(x) = (1 - e^{-h})^k e^x$.

25) $x_{n-k} = \displaystyle\sum_{m=0}^{k} (-1)^m \binom{k}{m} \nabla^m x_n$

Chapter 7

1) $x = 0.933$

2) $x = 0.933012$

5) $z = 4.189791$

6) $x_9' = 0.933013$, $x_{10}' = 0.933011$

7) $|z_2| = |z_3|$ $(= \sqrt{2})$ (compare condition $|z_2| > |z_3|$ at top of p. 150)

10) Dominant zero has multiplicity 2 .

16) Dominant zeros are $z = \pm 2$.

17) In the left half-plane.

18) All three zeros are dominant.

Chapter 8

1) Scheme cannot be generated in a stable manner. If constructed according to §8.5, scheme is stable and yields the zeros $z = 2 \pm i$, $z = 1$.

2) $e_n^{(k)} = 1$, $n \geq 0$, $k > 0$; $q_n^{(k)} = n + k$, $n \geq 0$, $k > 0$.

3)
$$q_n^{(1)} = \frac{1 + q^{n+1}}{1 + q^n} \quad , \quad e_n^{(1)} = \frac{(1 - q)^2 \, q^n}{(1 + q^n)(1 + q^{n+1})} \quad ,$$

$$q_n^{(2)} = \frac{q(1 + q^n)}{1 + q^{n+1}} \quad ,$$

9) $z = 1 \pm i \frac{1}{3}$

11) $z_1 = 0.933013$, $z_2 = 0.500000$, $z_3 = 0.066987$.

12) 0.9305682, 0.6699905, 0.3300095, 0.0694318 .

13) Real zeros: 4.70967, -4.41484, 1.00608, quadratic factor has zeros $1.85562 \pm i0.534194$.

16) a) $3.0053221 \pm i\, 3.9963933$, $0.9446779 \pm i\, 1.0248789$

b) 5.7074300, $1.0725870 \pm i\, 0.4775376$, $3.5736981 \pm i\, 0.1.5751498$

c) 0.1700599, 0.9024738, $0.7351475 \pm i\, 0.9018407$, $-0.6464144 \pm i\, 0.8862372$.

Chapter 9

2) No; if $f(x) = c$, the polynomial $P(x) = c$ interpolates at arbitrarily many points.

7) From $x = 1^\circ$ 42' onward.

8) From $x = 16$ onward.

9) a) $h \leq 0.003$ b) $h = 0.08$ suffices.

10) $\left|f(x) - P(x)\right| \leq 0.063\, h^4\, M_4$, $0 \leq x \leq h$.

11) The error is at least 1; Error $= (e - 1)^{n+1}$.

13) Choose $x_0 = \dfrac{2 - \sqrt{2}}{4}$, $x_1 = \dfrac{2 + \sqrt{2}}{4}$, then
$$\max_{0 \leq x \leq 1} \left|L(x)\right| = \frac{1}{8} \ .$$

15) For $h < 1$.

18) $P(x) = Q(x) - \left(\dfrac{b-a}{2}\right)^n a_0 \cos\left(n \arccos\dfrac{2x-b-a}{b - a}\right) 2^{-n+1}$;

$$\left|P(x) - Q(x)\right| \leq \left(\dfrac{b - a}{2}\right)^n \left|a_0\right| 2^{-n+1} \ .$$

19) $P(x) = 10x^4 - 35x^3 + 50x^2 - 25x + 2$

20) $P(x) = \dfrac{3}{2}x^2 - \dfrac{9}{16}x + \dfrac{1}{32}$ ($\left|\text{error}\right| \leq \dfrac{1}{32}$)

21) $P^*(x) = \dfrac{15}{16} x - \dfrac{5}{32}$ ($\left|\text{error}\right| \leq \dfrac{3}{16} + \dfrac{1}{32} = \dfrac{7}{32} = \dfrac{1}{4.571}$)

22) $P(x) = x - \dfrac{1}{3\sqrt{3}}$ ($\left|\text{error}\right| \leq \dfrac{1}{3\sqrt{3}} = \dfrac{1}{5.196}$)

Chapter 10

1) See example 8-6.

2) See problem 8-16a.

3) (as stated) $J_0(2.4068) \sim -0.00101$
   (corrected) $J_0(2.4048) \sim 0.00002$

10) $f(\frac{1}{2}) \sim 0.6718$

11) See problem 10-3

13) $\sqrt{2} \sim \dfrac{1449}{1024} = 1.415\ldots$

14) Ten extrapolated terms give only 1.646109.

15) $x = 5.5200299$

Chapter 11

1) Define f arbitrarily for $0 \leqq x < h$ and set (for $hc \neq 1$) $f(x + nh) = (1 + hc)^n f(x)$, $0 \leqq x < h$, $n = 0, \pm 1, \pm 2, \ldots$. For $hc = -1, f(x) = 0$ is the only solution.

5) $\Delta^n e^x = (e^h - 1)^n e^x$. Use $\dfrac{e^h - 1}{h} \to 1$.

10) Convergent for $h < \log 2$.

Chapter 12

1) $f'(0) - P'(0) = \dfrac{1}{n + 1} f^{(n+1)}(\xi_0)(-h)^n$, $0 \leqq \xi_0 \leqq nh$.

2) By preceding problem, error is at least $\dfrac{1}{n + 1}$.

3) $f'(0) = \dfrac{f(h) - f(-h)}{2h} + \dfrac{h^2}{6} f''(\xi)$, $-h < \xi < h$.

4) $P'_k(x_0) = \dfrac{1}{h} \left[\Delta f_0 - \dfrac{1}{2} \Delta^2 f_0 + \dfrac{1}{3} \Delta^3 f_0 - \ldots + \dfrac{(-1)^{k-1}}{k} \Delta^k f_0 \right]$.

7) (12-7): $\dfrac{\varepsilon}{h}$, (12-8): $\dfrac{3\varepsilon}{h}$.

8) $h = 0.0145$.

11) $1.667 \dfrac{\varepsilon}{h}$ and $1.889 \dfrac{\varepsilon}{h}$.

17) $n = 22$.

Chapter 13

1) actual error = 2; error bound = $\dfrac{\pi^3}{12} = 2.583\ldots$

6) $\sum\limits_{k=1}^{\infty} a_k t^k = \log(1 + t)$

9) 1.85193704

Chapter 14

1) a) yes, $L = 1$ b) yes, $L = 1$ c) no d) no

3) a) $f^{(n)}(x,y) = y + (n + 1)e^x$

  b) $f^{(n)}(x,y) = P_n(e^x) y$, where P_n = polynomial of degree n satisfying recurrence relation $P_1(z) = z$, $P_{n+1}(z) = z \left[P'_n(z) + P_n(z) \right]$.

5)

h	solution
0.5	0.81250
0.25	0.71710
0.125	0.67314

8) Twice extrapolated value 0.65524.

11)

h	y_n
0.4	0.304405
0.2	0.304588
0.1	0.304599

Extrapolated value: 0.304600.

Chapter 15

1) <u>11010010101</u>, <u>11011101010</u>, <u>11100111010</u>.

2) $8 = 2^3$, $64 = 2^6$, $512 = 2^9$.

3) $1/\log 2 = 3.3219\ldots$.

4) $10 = \underline{101}$, $100 = \underline{10201}$, $1000 = \underline{1101001}$.

5) $N = \underline{10}$

6) $\pi = \underline{11.001001000100}$

7) a) $\frac{21}{32}$ b) $\frac{21}{31}$

8) a) $\frac{1}{3} = \underline{0.\overline{01}}$ b) $\frac{1}{3} = \underline{0.\overline{13}}$ c) $\frac{1}{3} = \underline{0.\overline{2}}$

9) $\sqrt{2} = \underline{1.01101010\ldots}$, $\sqrt{\pi} = \underline{1.1100010\ldots}$,

$\sqrt{5} = \underline{10.001111000\ldots}$

Chapter 16

1) 3.75×10^{-10} ; No.

Praise for *The Kitchen Shrink*

"Dr. Dora Calott Wang skillfully uses the literary form of the memoir to argue that the for-profit insurance industry is taking over health care."
—*Albuquerque Journal*

"In *The Kitchen Shrink,* Dora Wang shows us what impersonal statistics already have shown: That in the United States, unique among nations in making health care about profit, it is now virtually impossible to get adequate psychiatric care. Dr. Wang conveys these cold truths in warm stories of human lives caught in the balance, including stories of her own personal evolution as a psychiatrist. By making the lives at stake palpable, Wang moves us to get involved in addressing our current health care crisis."
—Jodi Halpern, M.D., Ph.D., author of
From Detached Concern to Empathy: Humanizing Medical Practice

"What a wonderful book, so full of heart and wisdom and generosity. I wish everyone in the country would read it."
—Karen Joy Fowler, author of *The Jane Austen Book Club*

"A beautifully written memoir about the author's frustration with the transformation of the profession of medicine into the business of health care, and the unraveling of the doctor-patient. . . . A thoroughly compelling message: without an ethical commitment to the value of every life, 'the very humanity of our society' is at stake." —*Kirkus Reviews* (starred review)

"In a memoir that reads like a quest, psychiatrist Wang reports a decades-long mission to discover or, rather, rediscover the profession to which she once aspired and that is currently becoming more and more obscured by the burgeoning so-called health care industry. Her personal story dovetails with an account of a medical profession floundering under an ever-increasing avalanche of paperwork, driven by and a consequence of the profit motive. This all began, she says, in the 1980s with deregulation, and it represents a 180-degree reversal of previously held notions about the medical profession, from a time when 'courts repetitively ruled that it was "against sound public policy" for companies to seek profit from medical care.' Insisting that for-profit medical care is counterintuitive to good medical care, this daughter of an economics professor notes that good medical care lessens the need for itself and does not look for repeat business. That the current health-care crisis has caused anguish and even physical illness in Wang and her like-minded peers registers palpably." —*Booklist*

continued . . .

"An intimate, thoughtful memoir that documents Wang's experiences navigating the American medical system, fighting for her patients' best interests, and protecting her own mental and physical health. Part memoir, part rallying cry, this compelling book lends a profoundly human face to American health care, which, as its author so aptly observes, has become more about business than humanity."
—*New Mexico Magazine*

"Psychiatrist Dora Calott Wang says that, like most physicians these days, she practices 'a strange new kind of doctoring.' It's the kind of doctoring in which life-and-death decisions are made less often by doctors and patients and more frequently by the managed health care industry."
—*Pasatiempo Magazine*

"Dora Wang's *The Kitchen Shrink* is really two books. The first is a fascinating account of a young woman's medical school education, written with wit and empathy; the second, her personal struggles with the changes in her profession, the different forms of managed care, and other payment schemes that bring new insight into the health care debate. Dora Wang's is a fresh voice and one that commands our attention."
—David Musto, M.D., Yale School of Medicine

"Dr. Wang never lets readers forget that the medical profession didn't always operate the way it does now. Doctors once cared and worried about patients, paid home visits, made themselves available 24/7. Clearly a challenging labor of love, this life-crammed book arrives right on time. Dora Wang's insights into modern health care remind us that nothing trumps loving care or mutually shared doctor-patient compassion and concern. Savor this intimate, wise read."
—Al Young, California Poet Laureate Emeritus

"In this thoroughly engaging memoir, we accompany Dr. Dora Calott Wang as she and her patients grapple with disruptive upheavals that have profoundly impacted medical care of the past several decades. We travel alongside her through university medical centers, major health facilities, and private practices. In profoundly moving, humane life-and-death stories, Dr. Wang raises very large questions about how the health insurance business and for-profit forces have impacted not just medicine, but our humanity, and what type of society we've become."
—Joel Yager, M.D., UCLA David Geffen School of Medicine, Professor Emeritus of Psychiatry

RHEAD BOOKS
lished by the Penguin Group
guin Group (USA) Inc.
5 Hudson Street, New York, New York 10014, USA
nguin Group (Canada), 90 Eglinton Avenue East, Suite 700, Toronto, Ontario M4P 2Y3, Canada
division of Pearson Penguin Canada Inc.)
enguin Books Ltd., 80 Strand, London WC2R 0RL, England
Penguin Group Ireland, 25 St. Stephen's Green, Dublin 2, Ireland (a division of Penguin Books Ltd.)
Penguin Group (Australia), 250 Camberwell Road, Camberwell, Victoria 3124, Australia
(a division of Pearson Australia Group Pty. Ltd.)
Penguin Books India Pvt. Ltd., 11 Community Centre, Panchsheel Park, New Delhi—110 017, India
Penguin Group (NZ), 67 Apollo Drive, Rosedale, North Shore 0632, New Zealand
(a division of Pearson New Zealand Ltd.)
Penguin Books (South Africa) (Pty.) Ltd., 24 Sturdee Avenue, Rosebank, Johannesburg 2196,
South Africa

Penguin Books Ltd., Registered Offices: 80 Strand, London WC2R 0RL, England

While the author has made every effort to provide accurate telephone numbers and Internet addresses at the time of publication, neither the publisher nor the author assumes any responsibility for errors, or for changes that occur after publication. Further, the publisher does not have any control over and does not assume any responsibility for author or third-party websites or their content.

The excerpt on pp. 163–164 from *The Art of War* by Sun Tzu is quoted from the 1988 Shambhala Publications edition, translated by Thomas Cleary.

First Riverhead hardcover edition: April 2010
First Riverhead trade paperback edition: May 2011
Riverhead trade paperback ISBN: 978-1-59448-517-6

The Library of Congress has catalogued the Riverhead hardcover edition as follows:

Wang, Dora.
The kitchen shrink : a physician's story of changing times / Dora Calott Wang.
        p.   cm.
    ISBN 978-1-59448-753-8
    1. Wang, Dora.   2. Physicians—United States—Biography.   I. Title
    R154.W188A3   2010   2009047768
    610.92—dc22
    [B]

PRINTED IN THE UNITED STATES OF AMERICA

10 9 8 7 6 5 4 3 2 1

*Penguin is committed to publishing works of quality and integrity.
In that spirit, we are proud to offer this book to our readers;
however, the story, the experiences, and the words
are the author's alone.*

The Kitchen Shrin

A Psychiatrist's Reflections on Healing in a Changing World

Dora Calott Wang, M.D.

RIVERHEAD BOOKS
New York

For Physicians

λαμπάδια ἔχοντες διαδώσουσιν ἀλλήοις

Those having torches will pass them on to others.

Contents

Prologue

Everything now seems to be about Zoe, even the kitchen sink, which I fill with warm water for her bath this spring afternoon. I lean my face into gentle steam and linger my fingers on the soft hills of her baby feet. In her face as small as the palm of my hand, I see my past and all my future.

Sleepy days and interrupted nights blur into a hazy new life, but I still make it once in a while to the university where I'm the psychiatrist for the medical hospital. After a grand rounds lecture last week, lights flickered on after an hour of slides. Fellow physicians smiled and hugged me. "Dora, how's your baby? Dora, when are you coming back to work?" What was I to say—that on my bookshelves at home I've cleared away textbooks with chapters I've written, psychiatry lectures I've given, my stethoscope and blood-pressure cuff, to make room for baby bottles and hooded towels?

But it's not just that my life has changed. Medicine and psychiatry have changed.

When I chose medicine for my career, it felt such a noble profession devoted to healing the sick and guarding the sanctity of human life. But now health care seems just another business.

Behind me on my kitchen table, next to unread medical journals and a red rattle, is a tall pile of worn pages—the book I've been trying to write since I began my career in the early 1990s. It started as a self-help book about new medications, new therapies, and patients who got better. But after long days at work, I'd come home, switch on my desk lamp, and in its soft quieting light, I'd write about patients who didn't get better. These were not self-help stories, but stories I couldn't keep from writing.

Years passed. I went from job to job where my task was to prescribe medications only, not what I expected I'd be doing as a psychiatrist. Health care issues increasingly made national headlines. Dusty piles of pages accumulated on my desk, yet I wasn't writing self-help stories.

After Zoe was born on a snowy November morning, everything looked new in baby's light. In those wintry first days of my new life, of feedings, sleep and tired moments in between, I took a good look at the book I'd been trying to write. Surrounded by pages on the floor as my baby slept, I finally saw what I had written through the years.

I saw my story, a doctor working in the medical profession as it became the health care industry.

When I was a child, my doctor lived in my neighborhood and made house calls. We had devoted, lifelong relationships with our personal physicians. But the insurance company has long replaced the doctor as a patient's primary medical relationship. Even my profession of psychiatry, the medical specialty that once healed through the doctor-patient relationship only, now seems an impersonal assembly line.

I'd nearly discarded the story of my patient Selena. But now I understand why I couldn't stop writing about her. By writing her story

I realized that I fought not just for her life, but for my own life, a way of practicing medicine centered on science, the doctor-patient relationship, and on the everyday practice of our highest human values.

I now see what I've been writing these years, beneath the quiet light of my desk lamp.

My book turns out to be the story of my career as a physician and psychiatrist—which also is the story of the remarkable changes that have occured in American medicine.

Curtains lift in a springtime breeze. Out the kitchen window, I see Gabriel, a stout, red-bearded young doctor with a steady strength in his step. He stands on my back porch, a notebook in his hand. On his belt hang a hospital beeper, a cell phone, and a PalmPilot.

I scoop Zoe from the sink. I pull open my back door, Zoe in my arms, bundled in a towel the color of blooming lavender fields.

"Dr. Wang, I'm sorry. I'll come back later," Gabriel says.

I look into his eyes that are looking at my baby. I feel his air of authority. Dr. Gabriel Schwartz, a resident in training, looks like a psychiatrist. And me? I'm now a housewife in a ponytail and black velour sweats.

"Come in, Gabriel. Let me get you a drink."

In my kitchen, Gabriel contemplates the photos on my fridge—newborn Zoe swaddled in hospital blankets, my parents resting on lawn chairs surrounded by peach blossoms, in-laws and friends, all fastened by magnets from pharmaceutical corporations. A Paxil notepad reminds me to pick up *laundry detergent, baby shampoo, fusilli, basil*. A lime-green Effexor clip holds emergency phone numbers. Beneath a sky-blue Zoloft magnet, Chris and I honeymoon in Aloha shirts. His Mediterranean curls are wild in tropical humidity.

"I started Paolo on Celexa." Gabriel sips a raspberry spritzer. "He's depressed and wants to stop his transplant medicines. His new kidney would fail and it would be passive suicide."

"Why Celexa?" I ask. "Do we know how it affects renal transplant patients?" We walk to the library, now more a nursery, a room stocked with medical books, novels, Chris's books on architecture and urbanism, and lately, diapers and chew toys.

I can't help thinking: Gabriel's patient needs my old-fashioned talk-therapy skills. But tomorrow will be another patient I'll want to help, then another. In my years as chief of the Psychiatry Consultation-Liaison Service at the University of New Mexico Hospital, I saw more than a thousand new patients each year. Weekly psychotherapy was a mathematical impossibility.

So I have gotten good at letting go.

The patient's health insurance won't cover psychiatry visits to prevent organ rejection, even though they paid for a new organ, even if they'll pay for intensive medical care when Paolo goes into kidney failure again and again. So Gabriel assumed Paolo's case as part of his training, free of charge.

Gabriel sips his drink. He strokes his auburn hair and beard. "Celexa. It's only been on the market a few months. I'll do a literature search."

Medicines are tested only by their pharmaceutical makers before FDA approval, I remind Gabriel. Celexa is so new it can't have been tested yet in transplant patients. I'd switch the patient to Zoloft. I feel like John Houseman in *The Paper Chase*. I am also reaching for a diaper.

Zoe smiles. I breathe in her scent, of powder-fresh baby soap and the sugar musk of milk.

When I was a resident in training, I visited my professor Dr. Martha Kirkpatrick weekly at her home. After "funny dinners," as she called them, sometimes of chicken quickly microwaved and yellow bulb tomatoes from her garden, we'd walk down a path to her home office, a white stand-alone cube with an orange door surrounded by flowers and vines. Here the deep healing of a patient's mind and body occurred without machines or medicines, but through the doctor-patient relationship, with the doctor as the instrument of change. In Martha's office overlooking the tranquil, blue Pacific, I once told her, "I started my patient Eric on Prozac."

"Dora, why did you medicate him?" Her eyes looked puzzled. Sunset glinted from her gray hair.

In the early 1990s, psychiatrists still mostly asked "Why medication?" not "Which medication?" But the 1990s was the Decade of the Brain, when science and technology became conventionally applied toward understanding human minds, once considered too nebulous, or too sacred, to probe in this way. Insurance companies also started calling the shots, preferring to pay psychiatrists to prescribe medications, leaving psychotherapy for counselors, if at all. It was a perfect storm. Martha griped about "the end of medicine" and "the end of psychiatry." I wrote her off as eccentric. But all of my jobs since finishing my training in 1994 have been to prescribe medications, only.

It wasn't just psychiatry that changed, but how we see ourselves and our own minds, how we view the medical profession and the ancient art of healing the human body.

Sunset glimmers upon the Sandia Mountains as Chris pulls his car into our driveway. I bundle Zoe and dash outside.

"We're running out of diapers," I call, instead of, *I just need to get out of the house.*

Minutes later, we hit rush-hour traffic. Across three lanes of unmoving cars is my hospital, a seven-story concrete tower and a triangular addition with black glass windows.

My hospital—and I will always call it "my hospital"—is the lifeline trauma center for all New Mexico, parts of Texas, Arizona, Oklahoma, and Colorado, the Navajo Nation, nineteen Pueblos, and two Apache reservations. Yet all of our neurosurgeons are gone, again, and we have no pediatric ENT doctor. To make ends meet, the hospital proposed cutting care to the Indian Health Service. But the IHS still owns the hospital's land, they reminded us. This was originally an Indian hospital.

And yet . . . health care everywhere seems to be forgetting its original purpose.

"Why does everyone get lost in hospitals?" I ask Chris, an architect who reads societies by their buildings.

"Hospitals never make sense," Chris says. "They change constantly to accommodate more people, new technologies. But hospitals are unique. You can't just shut them down, tell patients to wait until after remodeling to have their heart attacks and broken legs. Hospitals are too expensive to knock down, too unique to recycle into anything else. So we just keep adding and adding, until the buildings make no sense."

"Kind of like our health care system itself," I laugh.

Out the window, past the traffic, I look at my hospital and I remember.

Here I was a recruited participant in the lives of strangers, a witness and navigator of life's dilemmas, a prescriber of wonder drugs and a handyman of emotions. My hospital is not just a place of sickness, healing, birth, death, and all that's in between. It's a place of stories. Here are the rooms where I approached patients in their beds, the hallways where I talked with families, the nurses' stations where lives were revealed in binder charts and on glowing computer screens, the conference rooms where I fought that fate might have a good outcome.

When all is done, when all is quiet, a hospital is a place of stories, and among the stories this hospital holds is my own.

Part One

A Strange New Kind
of Doctoring

2001–2002

Chapter One

At the University Hospital

JANUARY 2001

Earlier today, when the sun was high in New Mexico's ocean-dome sky, teams of young men and women in white coats walked down hospital corridors. They rustled from patients' rooms, chatting, fumbling, instruments and charts in hand.

Illness was revealed from symptoms, stories unfolded. Lives changed.

I walked with my Psychiatry Consultation-Liaison Service, a plainclothes team of psychiatry and medical residents, psychologists, nurses, and students. We visited with patients, discerned how emotional states intertwined with their medical illnesses, then in hallway conversations or around conference tables littered with papers and food, we coordinated with medical and surgical doctors.

Now the hospital readies for night, even if it will never really sleep.

On 7-East, empty chairs sit beneath fluorescent lights at the nurses' station. A young woman in a sweater and blue scrubs keeps watch beside video monitors and an intercom.

The linoleum floor is quiet of footsteps when I walk toward my last patient for the day. As I enter her room, sunset's bright light warms my skin.

A girl sits in bed with eyes fixed on the TV high in a corner of the room. Brown hair frames her yellowing face, as if a bulb is lit inside. Beneath blankets, her belly bulges as though she is pregnant. But from her jaundiced skin I know that she is in liver failure. I visualize her anatomy, her abdomen filling with fluid.

"I'm Dr. Wang," I say, my clipboard against my chest. "I'm the psychiatrist in the medical hospital. You must be Selena. Can you tell me why you're here?" It's a standard, easy way to start an interview late in the day.

She turns and looks at me with dark yellow eyes. "The liver transplant service is gone. But this is still where I come when I'm sick." Her voice surprises me, the high, sweet voice of a child, even if she is eighteen.

"I know you had a liver transplant when you were twelve. How has it been, taking medicines every day?"

"Medicines remind me that I'm sick. I just want to be a normal teenager."

"You know, it's the medicines that keep you well."

"I know. But I'm so tired. And it's been so hard without my mom."

On her nightstand is a framed photograph of a small girl with rose-colored cheeks and braided pigtails, smiling in the arms of a woman in a white linen dress. Behind them, a bright summer's lawn stretches. The woman's hair has the same treble-clef wave framing Selena's face now. Rosary beads drape the photo.

Out the window, the Sandia Mountains span our city. They glow watermelon red at sunset, the color that inspired Spanish explorers centuries ago to give them the name we still use today.

The earth's shadow moves rapidly up the Sandias, folding our city in dusk.

As the medical hospital's psychiatrist for adults (there's also a child psychiatrist), I had worked closely with the liver transplant team. Over coffee and stacks of papers, together we examined lives hanging on the hope of a new liver. The work was never easy. The liver transplant surgeons and internists knew our leukemia patient in heart failure wouldn't survive an organ transplant. As the psychiatrist, I broke the news to him. We thought the history professor a good transplant candidate—until I discovered he hadn't really stopped drinking. A Vietnam vet slept in his truck clutching a loaded rifle, and transplant medications would make him even more edgy. Yet could we deny him more life because patriotic duty broke his brain? We listed him. I'd handle whatever psychiatric problems worsened.

But when the liver transplant service closed, all patients met the same fate. A leather-faced man said with a single tear, "Move to another state? Wait, and maybe get a new liver to save my life? Or I could just go fishing."

In a hospital full of stories, reasons circulated—lack of funds, lack of livers, lack of doctors. Even as health care costs rise, resources at our hospital only dwindle.

Now except for me, the psychiatrist, the liver-transplant doctors are gone.

Patients whose lives waited on the hope of a new organ, or whose bodies were already kept alive by a stranger's gift inside, now rely on primary-care doctors. Selena was lucky when Dr. Indigo, a gastroenterologist, took her case.

Dr. Indigo (as I'll call him) asked me to consult on Selena. He explained over the phone that she was a child when she received a liver transplant for idiopathic liver failure. *Idiopathic* means that even with all our medical knowledge, we still can't say why something goes wrong. "She's noncompliant with her medicines," he said, "like she's suicidal. She'll die if we don't treat her depression."

Beneath fluorescent lights at the nurses' station, I flip through Selena's chart.

Andi slides into a chair beside me, her red hair glinting, the gold scarf around her neck still perfect at the end of the day. Andi is a kidney-transplant nephrologist. And now she's our hospital's only transplant internist.

"Selena—she's one of the *liver orphans* I really worry about," she says.

I page Dr. Indigo to discuss Selena.

He never calls back. I go ahead and order a low dose of the antidepressant Effexor, 25 milligrams, just half a tablet a day.

The Sandia Mountains are silver beneath a bright moon and stars when I climb into my car in the parking structure. On my drive home, patches of white snow shine in moonlight by the side of the road.

At home, Chris takes my face in his hands and kisses my lips. His breath is tender, his wavy hair soft on my face. In our coats and gloves, we walk down Mountain Road, a major thoroughfare, but once a dirt path traveled by the original dwellers of this land to quiet volcanoes in the west, centuries before Francisco Coronado arrived in 1540, seeking but never finding the legendary Seven Golden Cities of Cíbola.

In Old Town plaza, our breaths rise in hazy lamplight. We pass a mural of the twelve Spanish families who arrived in 1706 on horseback and in wagons to build this town for Spain, long before New Mexico became part of the United States in 1912.

The plaza is quiet. The tourists are gone. In the warm nave of San Felipe Church, we walk past rows of pews to the altar. We light candles and put them in sand alongside others burning in pinpoint brightnesses, each flame a solitary wish.

Chris and I kneel and pray for a baby, someone who will join us more than we are now, with hands held, fingers intertwined.

In the heat of candlelight on Chris's face, I feel warm, even on this winter night.

My mornings are busy with duties in the Psychiatric Emergency Service, the faculty clinic, and the transplant service that now only does kidneys. I also do lectures, teaching, meetings, research, publishing, committee work, and coverage for colleagues when they're away.

It's always lunchtime when I arrive in the medical hospital for my main responsibility as chief of the Psychiatry Consultation-Liaison Service. It's always dark when I drive home.

The Sandias are bright in midday sun when I walk into the Psych Consult Service offices on the fourth floor of the medical hospital. At the round table beside the window, I sit down, pop open my Styrofoam box from the cafeteria, and put my fork into red chile enchiladas.

Janet, our psychologist, runs the service in the mornings, when I am seeing patients elsewhere. Her strawberry-blond hair is long, over a blue sweater. She looks at me with turquoise eyes. "It's a good day for sitting rounds." I know this means that we have too many patients today for walking rounds.

Jude, our psychiatry resident these three months, sits down beside me. He smooths his blond hair and plucks at clear noodles with chopsticks. He begins with Nellie, who had cardiac bypass surgery and now sees monkeys crawling through hospital windows. The cardiothoracic surgeons asked us to treat her new schizophrenia. But schizophrenia doesn't just begin in fifty-eight-year-old women. Jude and I noticed an infected toe, no doubt the cause of her delirium and hallucinations. This morning, Jude navigated egos and transferred Nellie to ID, the infectious disease service.

"Another casualty of assembly-line medicine, where each doctor cares for one body part," Jude says. He can hardly believe the humanity he sees here. A woman raised in a dungeon as the family sex slave. An old man who can't remember his own name but who arrived in our ER with a wristband from an Oregon hospital.

Janet speaks next. "Silvia was asleep in her apartment when an intruder stabbed her forty times." We talk about Silvia. Then we talk about her other patients.

Kathryn, our psych nurse, adjusts her cat's-eye reading glasses. She reports that Deborah is status-post her second heart transplant from a California medical center. She's hospitalized with us for organ rejection. Our surgeons wonder how she'll take her antirejection medications regularly, since she's homeless.

"Why has she gotten two new hearts, but no home?" Jude asks with wide green eyes.

I think about it. I want to give my best answer. "Beats me," I finally say.

We rush through updates and discussions for ten other patients. We gather our clipboards, ready to see patients.

Becky, our medical student, finishes her sandwich. She stows her thermos into her book bag. Buttoning her sweater over her blue oxford shirt, she turns to me.

"About Silvia, who was stabbed in her sleep," she says. "I live alone, too, with just my baby daughter." Her eyes search mine.

I remember when I was a student, when tragedies like these were still new. Life's spectrum used to happen at home, where we were born, grew old, fought illness, and faced death. Now these milestones happen in hospitals, where clinicians like us are put suddenly into the most intimate moments of the lives of strangers.

Here in the hospital, the newly injured, quadriplegic, blinded, or widowed say, *If only I'd left a moment earlier . . . a moment later . . . If I hadn't run the yellow light . . . Why? . . . There must be a reason.*

"Life is ultimately beyond our control, often simply random," I say to Becky. "Appreciate, celebrate each moment."

We disperse to see patients.

The next morning, snow flutters outside the windows of the faculty psychiatry clinic. Patients come and go from the chair next to my desk for their thirty-minute medication visits. I squeeze in whatever quick psychotherapy I can. *Schedule two activities a week you look forward to, four pleasurable things a day.* Or, *It's hard not to be stressed with the turnover in your workplace.* Never mind uncovering subconscious motivations. There's no time. The subconscious seems to be disappearing from psychiatry.

Again, it's lunch when I arrive in the hospital for rounds, afternoon when I see patients, evening when I reach Selena's room.

Even though antidepressants take weeks to begin working (if they'll work), I search Selena's face for signs of lifting depression—more expression, maybe a smile. Instead, the yellow in her eyes has deepened.

Thursday, after a busy morning in the Psychiatric Emergency Service, I learn it's Munchausen day in the hospital. Patients come in clusters. We can never explain why one week our service is filled with car accident victims, the next week with women named Benita who live in trailers, or today with Munchausen patients.

A young nursing student insisted yesterday, "Something's growing inside me, for God's sake! Open me up or I'll sue!" The surgeons operated. They found nothing abnormal.

Today, she stands on her bed, Venus rising from a foam of bedsheets. She flings open her hospital gown. On her naked body, staples hold together a pink wound, like a zipper down her belly. "Look what you've done to me. I'm going to sue!" The surgeons, internists, and hospital administrators all turn their heads to me—psych consults.

When I finally return to the Psych Consult office, Kathryn's face is as gray as the Sandias out the window.

"Victoria is dead," she whispers.

"Victoria, the baby daughter of that Munchausen patient, Freddie?" Janet asks.

"He tried to get her admitted at another hospital," Kathryn says. "She wasn't. She died that night."

I remember when Victoria was born in our hospital last year to a teenaged mother and a young father with Munchausen syndrome. The young man kept getting hospitalized for knee infections that our orthopedic surgeons thought had to be self-induced. No one really understands why these patients make themselves ill, maybe not even the patients themselves. Pediatrics feared Munchausen by proxy, that

Victoria's father might harm not just himself but the baby as well. They watched the infant closely.

Kathryn sits down on a sofa beneath a window. The sun is setting. The Sandias cast reddish hues on her gray hair.

"I didn't think Victoria had a chance in the world," she says. "But still, I hoped."

By Friday, Nellie's hallucinations are gone, thanks to antibiotics for her foot infection. Most of our patients, including Silvia, are discharged. In our decentralized system, "Venus," I'm sure, will show up at another hospital to be cut open anew.

On 7-East, Selena's eyes have grown an even deeper yellow.

In the evening, while the sky is still blue and stars begin to glimmer, we arrive at Becky's house in a neighborhood of horse farms and orchards along the Rio Grande. Janet, now in jeans and Birkenstocks, lays a steaming pot of green chile stew on the kitchen counter. Kathryn brings shish kebabs of melon balls and mint leaves. Her husband, Tomas, holds her hand. Chris and I have made quesadillas filled with arugula and pears.

Music plays, Gershwin, with smoldering, dancing horns. The moon rises. We eat, laugh, and tell stories.

A car door slams. Footsteps climb the stairs. It's Kurt, in jeans and a blue beret, with four bottles of wine in one arm, and the picnic basket of wineglasses he keeps in his VW Bug. Janet's eyes sparkle. She rises, kisses him.

"God, I've been indoors all day," Kurt sighs. He pours wine for us, then leaves.

Out the window, the Sandias look a close relative of the moon above. On the front lawn, Kurt lights a camping stove. A blue flame illuminates his face.

Soon Chris and Tomas are also outside. They stand near the flame, sipping wine, talking, laughing.

Slowly, we all go outside. We skewer shrimp to hold over the stove. We warm our hands.

"Here's to Victoria." I lift my glass.

"Victoria." Other glasses rise. The faces of my friends glow in the soft light of the fire. We are silent for a moment, together.

The moon grows hazy behind a thin circle of fog. A soft mist drizzles.

We pull our coats around us, laugh, tell stories, at the end of this long week, in this brief respite before another.

Chapter Two

Selena's Problem

In Selena's room the next week, the IV machine hums and the TV laugh track chatters.

I look into her yellow eyes. "Your mother just passed away?"

Tears stain her cheeks. "Four months ago. They said it was an accidental overdose. But how do they know it was an accident?"

"Four months ago?" I hand tissues to her.

Selena is mourning her mother's death? Why didn't I know this? Jude is assigned to Selena. Jude. He's so overwhelmed by this hospital, he's thinking about seminary school. But it's not Jude's fault I've grown so distant from patients, supervising others and only glimpsing myself, my thousand new patients a year.

"My mom left us when I was twelve," Selena weeps. "She came back to take care of me after my transplant. Then she left again. Me and my little brothers begged her to stay. Maybe if I was a better daughter, if I didn't get sick. Maybe she could have stayed home."

I feel water rising into my eyes. In all my years as a physician, now, for the first time, I am with a patient weeping.

Selena grabs a tissue, hands it to me. Her hand brushes mine. Her skin is too soft, like a wilting flower.

"You loved your mother. You must have been the best thing she had." I dig my fingernails into my arm to regain my psychiatrist's voice. "You're feeling survivor guilt, a natural reaction when you lose someone you love. It doesn't mean you did anything wrong. It just means you care."

As the psychiatrist in a medical hospital, I myself am no stranger to survivor guilt.

"Yes," Selena says, "but now I can finally be with my mom."

At the nurses' station, on the glowing computer screen, I see that Selena's liver tests, SGOT and SGPT, are rising, corresponding with her yellowing skin and growing belly.

The problem, it turns out, is grief and a mother's death, something Effexor can't fix. Is my Effexor only worsening her liver failure?

I page Dr. Indigo. I scribble in Selena's chart. He doesn't call back, so I go ahead and write the order myself to stop her antidepressant: "D/C Effexor."

Over the next days, yellow fades from Selena's body. She grows more active, and in the evenings, she chats with nurses and holds the elbows of elderly patients to guide their way.

By Friday, pages rustle and binders click. Nurses and residents gather Selena's discharge papers.

"Jude, make sure she sees a good psychotherapist," I say. "She needs help with grief."

"Hen hao"—he always surprises me with his Mandarin—"righto."

I'll never know if my Effexor worsened Selena's liver failure, or if it would have happened this way regardless. But my mother taught me, as her parents taught her—it's a Chinese saying that if you save a life, it's yours to guard always.

Each week, I continue my work in the hospital, the faculty clinic, the transplant clinic, and in the Psychiatric Emergency Service.

In the mornings, snow lies in white patches. By the time I walk to the hospital in noontime sun, puddles sit on sidewalks.

During sitting rounds over lunch, Janet discusses Leonard, who is admitted for spontaneous bacterial peritonitis, something that happens to patients in kidney failure. "Spontaneous," like "idiopathic," means we just can't explain it.

"Dora, I want to know what you think about him," Janet says. "The medical team finds him odd, and they can't say why. All I can do is agree—he's odd, and I can't say why."

In his room, Leonard is a tall man, judging from his appearance beneath hospital blankets. He has a long, horsey face and odd blinking expressions.

After talking with him, I find Janet. "I think he's schizotypal personality. You know, Axis II, Cluster A. He's not schizophrenic, but I'll bet there's schizophrenia in his family."

"He says there isn't," Janet says.

But later in the week, Leonard's brother, an upright version of our patient, invites me to a Mardi Gras party. "Clothing optional. I vant to drink your blood. I'll be a vampire. My sis will be there. You're a shrink, you'll like her. She's schizophrenic, no costume needed."

"I guess you were right," Janet laughs. "And it looks like Leonard is the most normal one."

Soon Selena returns with yellow skin and glowing eyes.

"Her Prograf level is low," Jude says to me in the hallway outside her room. "She's been noncompliant with her meds again."

"And the psychotherapy for grief and medication compliance?"

"It never happened."

I don't bother asking why, not with all the cracks in our system, all the details that go wrong every day if not for us checking, checking, following up again and again.

When my duties are done in the evening, I go to Selena's room. Out her window, the Sandias are bright in the moonlight.

"Selena, you mind if I pull up a chair?"

Eyelashes blink around yellow eyes. She puts down her comic book, turns off the TV. The IV machine hums in rhythm with her voice.

"My dad. He never counted on being a single parent. I want him to have a life, too." She explains that he's always at the office, doing accounting, something like that. She tries to help at home, but she gets too sick. She doesn't want to lose her dad, too.

"Selena. Tell me. How do you feel about your mother's death?"

Selena doesn't know the secrets our hospital keeps, like the file of a woman hospitalized over the years for overdoses and car accidents while drunk. The woman worried about her teenaged daughter, who had a liver transplant. Selena's mother, whom I never met but whose records I read, grieved her own mother, who died in a car accident. She tried to forget the only way she knew, by drowning her sorrows in alcohol and drugs.

"Sometimes I wonder"—Selena wipes her eyes—"why fight so hard, when now I can just be with my mom?"

"I can't imagine what it's like, losing your mom. But I watch people get through grief all the time. Your life will never be the same. But it won't always feel this hard."

Tears streak her cheeks like dew on a browning daffodil. She turns toward the window, and the Sandias in moonlight.

At the nurses' station, Isela, the ward's head nurse, wears pink scrubs and white shoes with thick soles. She motions to me. In the nurses' break room, she points to photos on the refrigerator door. Selena with long brown hair in pigtails, grinning, her arms around a white teddy bear. Selena in a cap and gown, her braces gleaming.

"I've known her since she was a little girl," Isela says, "since her transplant. I love her. Patients like her are why I became a nurse."

By Friday, the yellow fades from Selena's skin.

I never take care of my psych consult patients after they leave the hospital. My medical school mentor, Dr. Robert Byck, did, as Yale's consultation-liaison psychiatrist in the 1980s. But in 2001, women give birth and are discharged the same day. Chests are cracked open for heart surgery and patients go home the next day. Discharges are earlier and riskier, and there are so many more of them, so many more patients, and so much less time. I always say good-bye to patients with an unsettling feeling of unfinished work. But for one patient, Selena, can I do it the way it used to be done?

I stand at Selena's door.

She packs her photograph, rosary beads, and comic books into a suitcase. She lays her palm on the bed and smooths the sheets.

"Selena, will you come see me every week? Even when you're not hospitalized?"

She looks down and smiles. "Yes."

In the kidney transplant offices the next week, a stylish young woman arrives with a bounce in her walk. She wears platform boots, and a gray coat over a flowered dress. Her hair swings in a ponytail with blue ribbons.

"Selena?" I ask.

"You only know me in the hospital. Outside the hospital, I'm different, just a normal teenager." Her eyes are soft, the whites shine.

In a windowless office I've borrowed from the transplant social worker (my own office has only one chair and is set up for paperwork, not patients), Selena smiles, sits on the sofa, and smooths her dress. Her face is lit in soft lamplight.

"My mom," she says in her child's voice. "This drunk driver hit us from nowhere. I was in the backseat. When I came to, my mom was sobbing, shaking my grandma. She blamed herself because she was driving. She couldn't get over it. That's when she left us." Everything happened when she was twelve, the liver transplant as well. All Selena remembers is that she got sick, and the next thing, she was waking up in the hospital, Isela telling her that she had a new liver. Her mom was there, too.

"She came back to take care of me after my transplant. Slept in the hospital on a pull-out chair. Then she left again. She couldn't get over my grandma." Selena weeps.

I see the pattern.

Daughters grieving mothers, grief outweighing the will for life itself.

Every week in the windowless transplant offices, Selena comes to see me. But one sunny winter afternoon the next month, Selena doesn't show up.

Beneath fluorescent lights, I write notes and look up labs. Andi sits beside me, doing the same. Finally, I pick up the phone.

Selena answers. "Sorry, Dr. Wang. I'm too yellow today to leave home."

"Have you been taking your medicine?"

"My little brothers say I'm lazy because I'm not cooking or cleaning today."

"Selena, you're sick, not lazy."

She weeps, chokes back tears.

"Selena. Promise me you'll take your medicine. Promise you'll come see me tomorrow."

"I will. Thank you, Dr. Wang."

Andi looks up from the computer screen. "Isn't there anyone who can help this child?"

"Andi, what do you think of calling a meeting of everyone involved with Selena's care?"

The next week, in a windowless conference room, the kidney transplant team convenes. Gale, our transplant social worker, walks toward me in a red-checkered dress and white tennis shoes. "Dr. Wang, I want you to meet the social worker from Selena's insurance company."

A tall woman with teased red hair holds out her hand. "I'm Fiona, a clinical social worker. I've been reading your notes. I wanted to come to your meeting."

"Terrific," I say, and shake her hand. "We need all the help we can get."

At the end of the gray oblong conference table, a nervous-looking blond man thumbs his portfolio. He wears a pin-striped suit, and a white, starched shirt. It's the first time I've seen Selena's father.

"Mr. Naranja"—I hold out my hand—"I'm Dr. Wang. Pleased to meet you."

He shakes my hand briskly, then keeps thumbing his folder.

I put my hand in my pocket and walk toward Andi. I sit down beside her.

"Dr. Andi Gris and I called this meeting," I begin, "because we're all concerned about Selena. Every time she's hospitalized for organ rejection, it puts her life more in danger."

"How come more isn't being done for her?" Her father looks at me.

Silence.

Gale comes to my aid. "Transplant patients all need support. And Selena is just a teenager. She can't even drive in her condition, and buses take all day. Is there anybody who can at least drive her to appointments?"

"If someone could encourage her to take her medicines every day, it would make a huge difference," I add.

"I'm a single father with a demanding job and three kids. I can only afford to live on the westside, so just driving myself to work takes an hour each way. She's an adult now. She needs to be be responsible for herself."

"If she keeps going into organ rejection, she'll need a second liver transplant," I continue, "but she won't even be considered unless family can care for her afterward. But if she has that support now, we can avoid another transplant."

"I'm doing everything I can. I'm barely surviving. You're the medical professionals," he says. "Isn't there anything more you can do?"

I look at Andi and Isela. They look at me.

"A big problem," I continue, "is that Selena is a liver transplant patient. And there is no liver transplant service anymore. All of us here are now part of the kidney transplant service."

"Then whose job is it?" he asks, still fidgeting with his portfolio.

"Whose job is it?" Andi says. "That's a good question."

Selena still hasn't arrived. I pick up the phone and call her.

"Selena? It's Dr. Wang."

"Hi."

"The meeting has started. Gale sent a taxi for you. Did it get there?"

"I sent the taxi away. I wanted to go with my dad. That's what's important. Please understand, Dr. Wang."

"You sent the taxi away?"

"Well . . ."

The redheaded insurance rep clasps her hands like a stone. "At what point do you give up?"

"We don't ever give up on patients," Andi says.

I sit down beside Andi, and I nod proudly in agreement.

In the early spring, leaves reappear on trees. Snow melts from the Sandias. I pack away my winter jackets and I fill my closet with linen blouses and T-shirts for sunny weekends.

When Selena and I walk out of Gale's office one spring afternoon, Isela is waiting. "Come on, Selena. You ready for lunch?"

Selena and Isela walk down the hall, laughing, talking, Selena's ponytail swinging.

At the nurses' station, I finish paperwork. On Selena's billing form, the diagnosis I want to list is: *needs a mother*. But that's not a diagnosis, not a problem her health insurance company would ever reimburse.

Evenings grow hot.

Summer brings weekends of music, salsa at the museum beneath stars, and outdoor concerts in the civic center. Summer means farmer's markets, city pools, fireworks lighting the night, and lazy hot mornings.

In the hospital's cool corridors, I walk past patients' rooms and realize Selena hasn't been hospitalized for months.

She no longer blames herself for her mother's addiction. She sees that as a child, there was little she could've done about it. She's stopped blaming herself for her own illness, too, and recognizes all she's done, stepping into her mother's role for her brothers, while caring for her own illness.

Without surgery or additional medications, but thanks to psychotherapy, something I no longer really do, and our doctor-patient relationship, Selena has been well.

After a summer's visit to an aunt in California, Selena returns calm and happy.

"It's so different there. The kids have a mom. Everyone eats together. My cousins spend their time reading, drawing, praying."

"How did you feel, being there?"

"I think I could remember to take my medications if I lived there," she says, eyes looking downward. "My aunt asked me to live with them."

Together, we investigate liver transplant programs near her aunt's home. Selena orders a catalogue for the local community college.

At night, Selena and her new boyfriend lie in her backyard, looking at stars, making plans.

But it turns out to be me, not Selena, who goes to California next.

On a Saturday morning in July, I walk with my neighbor Teresa to the local farmer's market. She wears a large hat with sunglasses over her green eyes and fair skin. As we walk past yard sales and kids manning a lemonade stand, my pager buzzes. The number is unfamiliar, but I recognize the area code, 310, as West Los Angeles.

We return to Teresa's house. I use her phone to dial the number on my pager.

"Bao Bao." It's my mom. She always calls me this name Chinese people call babies. "Your daddy is having a stroke. This morning, he was mumbling. I thought it was toothpaste. I told him, '*Aiya*, spit it out.' He still did not talk right, so I got mad at him. He still did not talk right. I called Dr. Abi. Dr. Abi told me, 'Go to the emergency room right away.' He was here when we arrived. *Aiya*, Dr. Abi. He is so good."

"Dr. John Abi is with you in the ER on a Saturday morning?"

"So you don't have to worry. You are busy. Dr. Abi is here."

Minutes later, I'm driving to the airport, a hastily packed bag beside me. Monday I'll call my vice chair. I'll take care of my patients by phone. I'll do the best I can.

What is more important than my father?

Three hours later, I walk into the UCLA emergency room in Los Angeles. It's been ten years since I was a resident here. Alarms ring. Monitors beep. Automatic doors swing. Yet I feel calm in this familiar place. No one greets me. No one recognizes me. But from my words—*My father just had a CVA, I'm looking for him*—the ER staff know I'm one of them.

In a makeshift room walled by white curtains is the man who used to pick me up from school when it was too hot to walk home. When I was little, I thought my father walked across oceans. It turned out to be a narrow portion of a river, but that's how I saw him, someone who could do anything.

Sitting next to him is the woman who held me through long nights when allergies made me wheeze for breath. She used to wear hairpieces, eyeliner, and Jackie O suits. She was the most beautiful woman in the world.

My parents are old now, their bodies frail versions of what they once were.

I walk to my father's gurney. I take his hand.

In the next forty-eight hours, four medical teams are responsible for my father's care—the ER team who admitted him, Saturday's covering neurology team, Sunday's covering neurology team, and finally, the attending neurology team Monday morning. Add to that, the consulting team from cardiology, the consulting team from endocrinology, and their covering teams. Each shift, Dad has a new head nurse, registered nurse, licensed vocational nurse, and *care partner,* a nonmedical person who comes most often to bring water, change sheets, ask if there's anything Dad needs.

Communications pass through notes, if legible, and hurried words during sign-outs.

My mom and I sleep on sofas in his room. We sit at his bedside all day, every day.

So I'm the one who discovers that in addition to new weakness on Dad's left side, he has an *acalcula,* a new inability to do math. What an ironic loss for a former economics professor, as if a higher power mandates that now that he's seventy-six, it's finally time for Dad to stop managing accounts, time to hand over his real estate business to my brother, Dave, at last, time to slow down.

In the early morning, or is it still really night, I pull myself from the stiff vinyl sofa.

I follow Dr. Abi out of the room.

This strange angel in full dark beard and soft black sweater doesn't feel like an interruption from sleep. His voice is distinctive, humble, with the sounds of his Persian homeland that he left so long ago, a voice almost any doctor or nurse in this hospital knows.

"Sweetheart, your father will not get his angiogram this morning." John's stethoscope is clasped around his neck. It snakes down his body into his pocket.

"I've been concerned about fluid overload when he gets hydrated for the test," I say as I rub sleep from my eyes.

"It's not that, sweetie. He is taking glucophage. It is not good with the contrast dye. He will need to wait another day for the scan. I already wrote to hold the glucophage today."

"And you postponed the angiogram?"

"I did."

Drug interactions can have dire, even lethal consequences. I take John's hands into mine. "Thank you, John, for catching it."

He shrugs his shoulders, pats me on the head, and walks into another patient's room. At the nurses' station, where the clock reads two forty-five a.m., a woman in maroon scrubs says to me, "Dr. Abi is my doctor, too. He's the doctor for so many of the staff. He helps us at night, too, when we nurses know that new interns and residents have ordered the wrong thing."

"Especially now, in July, the start of the new year," I joke with her.

"So we wait until Dr. Abi comes at night," she says. "The other docs don't get offended when he changes orders."

"Everyone respects Dr. Abi," I say. "Thank you also for watching after my dad."

"It's why I'm here."

Finally, I corner Dad's always hurried attending neurologist two days later, after Dad's postponed angiogram is done. He is a young man in a long white coat, fashionable wire-rimmed glasses, and a stiff manner.

"What do you think caused my father's stroke?" I ask.

"According to the scan, he hasn't had a stroke. But the usual causes for stroke are hypertension, diabetes—"

"I know," I interrupt. "What I'm thinking is that when he was admitted, his heart rate was in the forties."

"Heart rate in the forties?" he exclaims. "I never heard that!"

"Trust me. I was here. His heart rate was in the forties. Could that have caused an underperfusion of his brain, leading to a stroke?"

"Underperfusion in that manner wouldn't cause a stroke. Also, technically, he hasn't had a stroke."

"So, what's happened to my dad?"

"It's inconclusive."

Even nonmedical people might tell by my father's new limp and the drooping of his entire left side that he's had a stroke. But this young doctor, going by tests, despite the patient's physical exam, says it's inconclusive.

Dr. John Abi, in the early mornings, is the one physician who sees Dad each day, aside from myself.

"He may have a sick cardiac sinus," John says. "Watch his heart rate. He'll get a pacemaker if it falls into the thirties."

"Thank you, John. Again."

Five days after his admission, when Dad is discharged with no diagnosis and no useful plans from the neurology team, my family heeds Dr. Abi's informal advice. My brother, Dave, buys a heart-rate monitor. Mom straps it onto Dad's wrist. She watches it, day and night.

Back in Albuquerque, I buy my first cell phone. I don't want to waste a moment if my dad needs me.

Week after week, I sit in Gale's windowless office, listening, talking with Selena.

Two months later, just before Labor Day weekend, my mother calls late at night.

"Bao Bao, I've been watching Daddy's heart rate. It is thirty-five. I want to get him to UCLA, but he won't go."

"Get him in the car. Make him lie down in the backseat. Get him to UCLA right away."

"*Aiya!* He won't go!" she says. "He tells me to let him sleep. I called Dr. Abi—oh, wait a minute. He is already calling me back on the other line. Bao Bao, I call you back."

I hang up the phone and walk to my closet. I throw sweats and toiletries into my red overnight bag. The phone rings again. It's Mom.

"Oh, Dr. Abi. He is so good. He told me, get him in the car and bring him in right away. Don't let him sleep. Dr. Abi will meet us in the emergency room."

"Dr. Abi will meet you in the ER? At ten p.m. on a Friday night?"

"Dr. Abi is there. You know he will be there all night. So you don't have to come. You are busy."

Immediately, of course, I book the first flight in the morning for L.A. I'd get in my car and drive, except I wouldn't get there any sooner.

The next morning in Los Angeles, I arrive at my father's bed, which is surrounded by machines and monitors in the cardiac care unit. I kiss his forehead. I hug my mother. They tell me that Dr. Abi is in the hospital, tending to him, even if the CCU is in charge.

Other doctors come and go in a hazy Labor Day weekend parade. Someone orders a temporary pacemaker for Dad. Someone else tells us, yes, it is a sick cardiac sinus.

There's a robot in the hospital. RONI (or, Robot of the Neuro

ICU) transmits videos of patients to a doctor at home. Patients talk to the robot, and the doctor onscreen on the robot's face. I take pictures of the five-foot-six metallic man on wheels, and his wife, an electronic female robot.

In the dark early mornings, Dr. Abi always visits, in person, in a black sweater and slacks, his stethoscope snaked down his body.

"John, I heard that you're the doctor for a lot of the staff," I say.

"If you don't care for the caretakers, nothing works." He shrugs.

The hospital troops return four days and nights later, after the Labor Day weekend. Dad gets his pacemaker, a St. Jude Medical model 5336, serial number 563291.

I first heard about Dr. John Abi when I was a resident at UCLA. Colleagues called him UCLA's finest physician. Over the years, I've watched UCLA's best cardiologists, endocrinologists, and other specialists defer to the knowledge and judgment of this English-educated physician who is devoted to this hospital, its patients, its staff, and to the art and science of medicine. He's a definite factor in UCLA's consistent ranking as one of the nation's best hospitals.

Now I know another reason why so many consider Dr. John Abi UCLA's finest physician.

A doctor needs to be there. All else follows.

With his heart rate in the thirties, my father's life couldn't have waited until the morning shift. A 40-hour workweek covers but a fraction of the 168-hour week, and the many moments when an urgent medical need might occur.

Doctors never used to sign off. Doctors once delivered patients from the womb, then cared for them through their lives. Physicians were awakened at night to go to their patients' homes, or to receive patients into their own homes.

Like family, the doctor-patient relationship was once a faithful one, until death did us part.

Dr. John Abi is a "last doctor" of sorts, still always present for patients in his clinic, in the ER, and on the ward, like all physicians of another time.

I am grateful he has been at my father's side.

But because I've been at my father's side, I haven't been at Selena's.

In Albuquerque, Selena is hospitalized for the first time in months. She went running in the mountains on a summer day. Her leg was scratched by thistles or thorns, nothing serious for most of us. But Selena's immune system is suppressed by transplant medications. Welts appeared on her leg. Dr. Indigo prescribed an antibiotic— which Selena didn't take. So now Selena is hospitalized for sepsis, an infection spread through her body.

I sit down at Selena's bedside. Red welts are on her leg. In my mind, I see welts on her liver, too.

"Dr. Wang, I'm sorry." Her eyes are deep yellow.

"Selena, why didn't you take the antibiotic?"

"I didn't have the money." She looks away, ashamed.

"But you have medical insurance."

"My insurance didn't cover it."

"What?" I am unable to hide my disdain. For me the mission of medicine is far above fleabite details as this. I don't know that soon I'll see these fleabite details as the largest, most central problem in American medicine.

Selena hears the disappointment in my voice. She begins to cry.

I hang my head to fight back my own tears.

Andi and I agree that it's time to seek a second liver transplant for
Selena. We telephone a medical center that I will call McMed University, because outside this story, no such place exists to my knowledge.

"There's a lot of good in this young lady," I tell McMed's transplant coordinator, "a lot in her that's worth saving."

"And who are you?" the voice on the phone asks. "Are you her
doctor?"

"Yes. I'm her psychiatrist."

Silence.

I explain that our liver transplant service is closed. And so it's me,
the psychiatrist calling, the only physician left of what was the liver
transplant service.

"We already know this case," the voice says. "The insurance company read your progress notes and called to forewarn us. This patient
is *noncompliant*. She doesn't take her medications."

The insurance company called to forewarn them?

"Even a juvenile delinquent gets a fresh start at eighteen," I say.
"We forgive kids who have stolen or murdered when they turn eighteen. Surely we can give Selena another chance. She's been the woman
of her house, taking care of her family as just a child herself. What
teenager takes medicines on her own or gets to doctor appointments
on her own?"

"There was a meeting," the voice says, "and the patient didn't even
show up."

I remember the meeting, and the redheaded insurance rep asking, "At what point do you give up?" Andi and I said proudly that
we never give up on patients. I assumed the insurance rep was fighting as hard for Selena's life as we were. Now I remember that she

also said, "We have to keep resources in mind. It's my job to educate physicians."

"Besides," the voice says, "if her family won't help, there's no use doing another transplant."

The Sandias are dark when I arrive at Selena's bedside. I take her yellowing hand into mine.

"You know, Selena, a lot of people want to help you through another transplant."

"My mom took care of me the first time," she weeps. Her words slur, a sign of worsening liver failure and rising ammonia levels in her blood.

"Some of the 7-East nurses want to travel with you to get the transplant, then take care of you afterward." Even Jude contemplates a leave of absence to tend to her.

"Thank you, Dr. Wang. Please understand. I only want family."

Fall arrives. The air cools. On the state fairgrounds and in parking lots across the city, green chiles roast in metal drums turning over fire. Ash floats, along with the charry pepper scent.

Evenings, I glimpse Selena playing checkers with ward clerks, walking with her IV pole to the fridge, and helping other patients.

Weeks pass. Outside Selena's window, the sun rises and sets on the Sandias. The yellow in Selena's eyes deepens.

On an evening when trees sway in cold wind, Selena is wheeled to the ICU, to a windowless room where the light is always the same.

She grows delirious. Dreams, reality, past and present all blur for her. But she still recognizes me. "Dr. Wang, don't forget to take out the garbage. It's Wednesday. Don't forget."

I hold her soft yellow hands, wrinkled and bruised from IVs.

Kaliani, my new medical student, stands next to me, with sad eyes. She's the daughter of two physicians, with her mother's dark eyes and her father's long surgeon's fingers. She makes me think of the children I don't have.

Over the next days, Selena's eyes grow even brighter, but the light in them that is Selena dims.

On a cold autumn day, Kaliani and I sit in the strange blended light of our new temporary office just outside the hospital. Janet had announced one day that we'd be trading office space with the pharmacy. "The pharmacy is under the cafeteria," she said. "When the kitchen leaks, expensive drugs get ruined. So they're moving *us* under the cafeteria instead. I said they should at least consider the lawsuits if our paperwork gets wet. They didn't buy it. We have to move." Kathryn and I looked at her with incredulous eyes. We packed. We laughed about pill bottles getting promoted to our view of the Sandias. We settled into a glass-brick structure outside the hospital, our temporary home, while our permanent space is prepared underground, where the sun never shines.

Gray sunlight filters through the glass brick of our temporary office. Fluorescent lights buzz.

In this blended light, I say to Kaliani, "Do all you can for your patients. Do it for yourself. Never treat medicine as just a job, because then that's all you'll ever have, just a job." It's what Martha taught me in my residency, what Martha lived by.

In the windowless transplant offices, Andi and I plead again with McMed. We pass the phone between us. They accept Selena for an evaluation. Andi and I slap one another a high five.

But Gale reports, "The insurance company won't pay transportation costs to McMed for just an evaluation."

I phone another university that I'll call Orlando. I ask if they might approve a liver transplant based on my opinion, a psychiatrist, and Andi, a nephrologist. Her insurance covers transplants, but the insurance company won't approve an evaluation, I explain.

Orlando says no, since McMed said no.

Finally, I resort to calling UCLA, where I first cared for transplant patients as a resident.

"I used to evaluate transplant patients at UCLA," I tell their coordinator.

She is sympathetic, kind. "Your patient was just a child. We make allowances in cases like this. Our team would give her a second chance. But if the insurance company won't pay, there's nothing we can do."

"So the insurance company decides? Not doctors, nurses, or the patient?"

"Basically," she says, "there's nothing we can do."

Kaliani listens, watching me do this strange new work of a doctor.

By now it is too late, anyway. Beneath the ICU's fluorescent lights, I read Selena's flowsheet. Her creatinine is rising, meaning now her kidneys are also failing. The soft beeps of the green monitor screen tell me her heart no longer beats regularly.

I stand beside Selena's bed. I hold her jaundiced hand.

Her eyes open in a flash of yellow. She smiles, and in her child's voice, she asks, "Where's my dad?"

In the fading light of a winter afternoon, Selena falls asleep and doesn't awaken.

I pull a chair next to her bed. I sit beside my patient one last time.

Family arrives from all over New Mexico and from out of state. They crowd the ICU, weeping. 7-East cries. The kidney transplant team cries.

Selena's father sits outside her door, his face in his hands, weeping.

I end this day like others, in my office, filling out forms. New Mexico music strums on the radio. Guitars and horns sing. I try to clear my desk, but as usual, I leave unfinished piles as I drive home with the Sandias cold and gray behind me. I think of the full list of patients I need to see tomorrow.

Leaves turn flame red outside the hospital. They rustle in chilled wind and blow to the ground. White fingers of snow fill the crevices of the Sandias.

On Friday, I try to go to Selena's funeral. But I have meetings, patients, hospital room after room requiring my presence.

By the time I reach the church, people already crowd the parking lot, buttoning coats, pulling on gloves. Kaliani walks toward me, wiping tears from her eyes. I had instructed her to come, wanting her to see that Selena was more than just a patient.

"She was all dressed up," Kaliani says. "She wore a pin-striped suit with a purple satin blouse, like a professional woman, all grown up. She was beautiful."

In the parking lot, Selena's father takes his hands in and out of his suit pockets, as if he doesn't know what to do with them. His breath rises in cold air. In his face, I see Selena's brown eyes, misty with tears.

"I'm sorry for your loss, Mr. Naranja," I say.

Leaves crunch beneath our feet.

For a brief moment, we hold one another. And in this manner, I finally weep for Selena.

Saturday morning, while it is still dark, Chris and I stand on a crowded field wet with dew. I pull my coat around me and lower a ski cap over my ears. We await the mass ascension of hot-air balloons from around the world, for Albuquerque's annual International Balloon Fiesta.

The sun peeks over the Sandias, and in an instant, the sky turns pale blue. Then it happens, as it does each year. Colorful globes lift, first a dozen, then a hundred, each its own planet. For a moment, I, too, feel carried skyward in this manner mankind first flew, in which we first left the earth.

Sunday morning, neighbors in robes and slippers fill my street, pointing cameras at a balloon striped like a rainbow, floating so low it almost touches my house. In its wicker gondola, four people wave. Its flame blazes, and the balloon floats up, toward the clear blue sky.

In the hospital on Monday, I walk long corridors, carrying the weight of the Psych Consult Service patients, my faculty clinic patients, our kidney transplant patients, and the patients in the Psychiatric Emergency Service.

But this afternoon, I feel a new heaviness.

I stop, take a moment. Finally, I see what was before me all along. The insurance company, which knew neither Selena nor medicine, made the final decision about her medical care.

The insurance company, not family, physicians, or Selena herself, decided whether she should live or die.

I walk from room to room, ward to ward, my insides unsettled. Finally, I pick up the phone and call the chief of the bioethics team, Norm. I explain the situation.

"So why are you calling?" Norm asks.

"What do you mean?"

"She's already dead." In his voice, I hear the list of patients he needs to see, the calls he has to make, the notes he still has to write.

I want to say that my heart is heavy, that something terribly wrong has happened, but I'm not sure what. Have the rules changed? Just what are the rules now?

But for the sake of brevity, I use my authority as a chief. "Norm, just humor me."

"I've heard of this case," he says. "Dr. Indigo doesn't have a problem with it."

"Norm, just do the consult and I'll owe you."

"Can it wait until tomorrow?"

"The patient's dead. Of course."

I picture Norm on the other end of the line, a pediatrician who wears ties with cartoon characters. I wonder which big-eyed character grins from his chest tonight.

The next afternoon, the conference room is packed with members of the kidney transplant team, nurses from 7-East, and my Psych Consult Service. Kaliani and I bring more chairs from an office across the hall.

We talk first about the insurance company, which I will call Community Health Plan, or CHP.

"The insurance companies make the decisions and physicians take the heat," Andi says.

Physicians are caught daily in the impossible quandary of malpractice lawyers pushing us to do more, and insurance companies refusing to pay for it. So doctors and hospitals end up shouldering costs ourselves—which is why doctors are going out of business, and medical systems are increasingly bankrupt.

I refrain from saying: *I would never make medical decisions without examining a patient. I'd never make surgical decisions, as I'm not a surgeon. If any physician did this, it'd be considered malpractice, unethical.*

But isn't that the job of insurance call-center workers and bureaucrats—to every day decide medical treatment for patients they've never seen? Bureaucrats, who know neither medicine nor patients, every day override the medical judgment of physicians.

What kind of system is this?

Among the whispers in the room, someone murmurs, *Why did we go through our years of training? Why didn't we just get an insurance job out of high school and now have the last word?*

"The thing that gets me most, is that they told me to change the doctors' notes," says Gale.

"Change the doctors' notes?" Norm asks.

Gale shifts glasses on her face. "Well, the progress notes said we weren't sending Selena to McMed because the insurance company wouldn't pay for it. The insurance rep called me. She said it wasn't fair to point fingers at them. She told me to get the doctors to change their notes."

"It's illegal to change medical records," I say. Among the notes in question, I know, are mine.

"I've had other experiences with Community Health Plan," says Kathryn. "Other patients Community Health Plan dropped when they got really sick."

"They even canceled Selena's insurance," Gale says. "Until Dr. Wang and I fought them. They do whatever they can get away with. And it's perfectly legal. But if Selena's family threatened to sue, I'll bet everything would be different."

Kaliani sits beside me, her eyes searching.

What kind of medical education is she getting from this?

Isela is quiet in this room of doctors and ethics experts, the only one in uniform. Her face is taut, bursting with things to say.

"Isela, you knew Selena a long time," I say.

"I watched her grow up. I watched her try so hard." Isela wipes tears and brown hair from her face. "Nurses don't know who gets paid for what medical procedure, we don't know insurance. Since this hospital closed our liver transplant service, those patients have no place to go. They have just regular doctors who don't understand about transplant patients. And so the patients call us. We're just nurses and it shouldn't be our job."

Who *is* responsible for the medical care of these liver transplant patients now? As the liver transplant service's only remaining physician, could it be my responsibility? Me, a psychiatrist?

Sadly, we agree, the problem is short-lived. The patients of the former liver transplant service, like Selena, are dying.

We sit with this thought for a long time.

Finally, Norm breaks the silence. "We've only scratched the surface of the issues. I suggest we meet again next week, same time and place."

We agree.

The roomful of people disperses.

The following week, again the room is packed for the bioethics meeting. Kaliani and I again bring chairs from other rooms.

"I've made some calls. I have connections," Norm says. The phone workers at CHP were ordered to cut costs, he's learned. He suspects they're not educated about what's ethical and legal in medicine and what isn't.

They're not clinicians, after all, just people hired to work the phone. They generally have no medical education but their job is to make medical decisions from afar, decide life or death, then tell doctors and patients what to do.

"How are they being asked to cut costs?" Kaliani asks.

"I don't know anything more," Norm says.

I suspect, as in other businesses, the phone workers have been given "goals." They might be getting incentives and bonuses for cutting payments even for care that physicians and hospitals have already provided. Their medical knowledge might consist only of prompts on computer screens for medical decision making. They might be overseen by "medical directors," who, increasingly, are physicians burned out from practicing medicine. Their solution is a desk job with no risk of malpractice, disease exposure, late nights on call, and no risk of insurance phone workers adding four hours to an already impossible day. Their salaries are high, and they are offered *incentives* and *bonuses*. I'd also say they run no risk of having a fulfilling job.

"What can we do if the decision makers at the insurance company are wrong?" Kathryn asks.

"If anything questionable happens, ask for the person's name," Norm says, Mickey Mouse gazing from his tie.

Kathryn suggests that our administrators talk to CHP's administrators. Maybe CHP needs to educate their staff about unethical or illegal behavior, such as insisting that doctors alter records, or violating patient confidentiality by calling other institutions to "forewarn" them.

Kathryn looks to me for a reaction.

I am silent.

Maybe this will help a little, for a little while. Maybe it will help until this round of employees leaves CHP, and the next round is hired. Or until this batch of administrators leaves, and the next batch begins. Or until these owners sell the company to the next owners, who can then say, "Sorry, we didn't know."

Maybe it won't help at all.

CHP is not a person, not a doctor who sits with a patient and makes a promise. CHP is a corporation. The avoidance of personal liability—isn't that the main legal function of corporations?

The meeting ends. The problem remains, larger than we in this room can even comprehend, let alone solve.

I leave the conference room. I walk down hallways past the surgical waiting room, where family members sit or pace. At the cafeteria, uniformed staff and people in plain clothes stand in line together.

I remember Norm's initial reluctance to involve the bioethics team, and I wonder about it. Did I go too far? I was just the psychiatrist, not her primary physician, and I was calling a bioethics consult on a patient who was dead.

But by the time I reach the stairs, I understand.

How ridiculous to question if I cared too much, to wonder if I overstepped boundaries as a psychiatrist who grabbed the helm on an organ transplant case.

After all, Selena is dead.

No one from Selena's insurance company, no one who ultimately judged whether she should live or die, ever laid eyes on her, spoke with her, or knew her personally.

For them, Selena was just notes on hundreds of pages, just a series of numbers—diagnostic codes, and numbers that follow a dollar sign.

I picture Selena holding the elbow of a white-haired man, guiding him down the hall. She completed herself by caring for others, much like those of us in the health caring professions, much like the best of us anywhere. And yet today, we all should be demanding and litigious to be cared for, to be chosen to live.

For the insurance company to have denied Selena life was legal. Do inmates on death row have more rights of appeal than any of us when we are sick?

And if Selena thought the all-powerful insurance company considered her life worthy, would she have fought harder for her own life?

I finally realize why I fought so hard for Selena, why I couldn't stop writing her story.

At stake was her life, but also my own way of life, a way of practicing medicine that's now slipping away, replaced by cold, calculated decision making at a desk across town, or at the stock exchange, rather than here in the hospital, where the patient's warm heart pumps or stops.

As for Selena's father, during the last weeks of her life something changed for him. In the evenings, he sat outside her hospital room, crying. One night he pulled me aside. He realized that he needed to keep watch over his daughter's medical condition, to put his whole life into it, he said. He was even engaged to be remarried. A new mother for Selena. He and his fiancée would tend to Selena day and night after a transplant, if that's what it took.

I made more calls. I tried again. But it was too late. The decision was already made, and not by me. But who was I? Just the psychiatrist, the only doctor left of our liver transplant team, not one of those now charged with final medical decisions.

It took Selena's father a while, and he realized too late. Our medical system isn't like Marcus Welby anymore, not wise, benevolent, or constantly caring anymore. It's no longer a system that compensates for weaknesses when patients and their families falter with the newness of life-changing, or life-taking, illness.

What took Selena's father so long to see?

I could ask the same of all of us. Aren't we all too trusting of our medical system?

But then again, how many livers would I have given Selena in my physician's mind-set to preserve life?

In hindsight, I wonder how much Selena really cared about a second liver transplant. When I try to look past my biases to think of Selena's wishes, it seems that more than a brand-new liver, or even life itself, what Selena wanted most was simply the love of her parents and family.

I have changed many details of Selena's story. Selena, for example, was not her name. Her story, however, is true. I have changed the names and identifying details of all patients to abide by a physician's ethic of confidentiality, which is as ancient as the Hippocratic Oath. I have also changed the names and details of many other people, and likewise Selena's health plan name.

After Selena's death I couldn't stop writing her story. After long days in the hospital, I went home, flicked on the lamp at my desk, and by writing, tried to settle my unease.

Medical care of the human body was once sacred, off-limits to the profit motive. Hospitals were named for saints and the communities they served, run by religious charities, community organizations, and physician organizations. Medical professionals were trained to serve patients without regard to self-sacrifice. Patients had their primary medical relationships with doctors, who were like extended family.

How did everything change?

In 1984, historian Paul Starr warned that the medical care of Americans seemed headed for control by:

> conglomerates whose interests will be determined by the rate of
> return on investments. That is the future toward which American
> medicine now seems to be headed.

American medicine had just been deregulated in the early 1980s, as the airline and financial industries also were around then.

When I was growing up, in the 1960s and 1970s, everyone understood that medical care existed on higher ground than ordinary business. You didn't see medications advertised on television. Doctors didn't advertise, either. Medical ethics and profit motives existed separately. I know now that for most of the twentieth century, courts repetitively ruled that it was "against sound public policy" for companies to seek profit from medical care. There was a general understanding that blatant profit-seeking from medical care would not be tolerated by government, physician organizations, or by the people.

But in the early 1980s, the federal government began encouraging for-profit corporations to take leadership in health care. Seminars were held in New York, Washington, D.C., and Chicago, toward this end.

A taboo was thus broken. The floodgates were opened.

During my career as a physician, I have lived the experience of for-profit corporations overtaking health care systems built by nonprofit and charitable organizations over the previous century. By the time I graduated from medical school and began practicing as a physician in the 1990s, health care stocks had become among the most profitable on Wall Street, and health care CEOs some of the most highly paid executives in history.

American medicine, a charitable enterprise to which society once contributed money, is now an industry from which profits are taken. During my years in medicine, I have witnessed it become an expensive system rigged toward *not paying* for health care.

But the for-profit corporations are not to blame. They are only doing what they are supposed to do—make profits. It is we as a nation who have decided that the medical care of our citizens should be about profit.

When I was a college student in 1980, the nation was concerned that health care costs made up a whopping 9.1 percent of the gross domestic product. Deregulation of medicine into the free market was intended to drive down costs. But after nearly three decades in the free market, the result has been the opposite. Health care costs have doubled, to consume about 18 percent of the GDP in 2009. At the same time, the nation debates whether health insurance should be required to cover "pre-existing conditions" (what patients call "illnesses"), and whether insurance companies can continue the common practice of dropping patients when they get sick or pregnant.

In other words, America's medical system consumes one-sixth of the national economy, more than for any other nation—and we debate whether the system should be required to treat illness.

What kind of system is this?

Paul Starr's warning was hardly obscure. His book *The Social Transformation of American Medicine* won the Pulitzer Prize in 1984. I can only conclude that the current crisis in American health care was foreseen but ignored by many, including myself.

And today, even among doctors, ethics are changing, conforming to the new realities of the health care industry.

After redrafting Selena's story more than a dozen times, it occurred to me that during all the hours I spent at her bedside, at all the meetings I attended, I had never once encountered her primary physician, whom in this book I call Dr. Indigo.

Is he the new kind of physician who works his shift and signs off? Is it increasingly not important for doctors to even know their patients?

As for the company I have called Community Health Plan, it turns out to be a nonprofit, owned and run by locals. CHP, like our university medical system, confronts challenges with no easy answers.

Nonprofit medical organizations have to become more like the for-profit entities in order to compete, in order to survive.

Weeks after Selena's death, I switched my insurance to CHP, a nonprofit that had survived where others had succumbed. Among the options in my city, CHP was clearly my preference.

———————————————

Selena's death brought winter. December snow covered the Sandias and sat high atop cars coming into Albuquerque from the east mountains. In the south valley, people held *posadas*, candlelight processions re-enacting the birth of Christ. In Old Town at night, glowing *farolitos*, votive candles in paper bags, lined the sidewalks to symbolically guide baby Jesus to his manger.

Another year had passed.

I thought of Selena and of the many patients who had come and gone from my life. Still I had no baby.

After Selena's death, I called my ob-gyn to set up an appointment. Dr. William Harrison used to be a veterinarian, so I figured that the way health care was devolving, he could deliver my baby in a pasture if necessary.

"Are you still under the same insurance?" Dr. Harrison's receptionist asked over the phone.

"Yes, I haven't changed."

"Well, we now only take Community Health Plan. We can't see you anymore. Sorry. Unless you change insurance plans."

I'd have to change my insurance to CHP to keep my doctor? I pictured myself bleeding and oozing after childbirth, clutching the phone, begging insurance reps for care.

The decision wasn't easy, but I chose to stay with my doctor. And so I switched to Community Health Plan. I did the paperwork. I called people who told me to call other people. I filled out forms, faxed, then mailed them, too, to make sure CHP had no excuse to say that I'm not covered.

I braced to do battle, determined to make Community Health Plan provide health care, not just take my money so executives can buy more yachts and second mansions.

So I was surprised when my pharmacy said that Community Health Plan would pay for all my prenatal vitamins and medicines, apart from a small co-pay. CHP would take care of my delivery, hospitalization, and the care of my baby, too.

Community Health Plan would take care of me.

They would take care of my baby.

Chapter Three

The Changing Health Care Environment

That insurance companies, not doctors or patients, ultimately determine most medical care, isn't what my family and friends want to know.

Most of us don't want to ask. But when I asked my own physician, Dr. Nancy Guinn, she confirmed that my insurance company ultimately decides what treatments and tests I receive, not she, my physician.

Dr. Guinn is extraordinary. She spends thirty minutes for each appointment, the national average being around seven minutes for primary care visits. And Dr. Guinn takes insurance, unlike doctors who refuse insurance because of its tons of runaround and paperwork only to be unpaid or underpaid. Physicians who take insurance must see ever more patients to keep from operating at a loss—which is why your doctor is always in a hurry.

With a minimalist approach, Dr. Guinn and a national network of physicians led by Dr. Gordon Moore in New Hampshire confront today's health care economics. Dr. Guinn has no staff to pay—no nurse, and no one to wait on hold for insurance companies on her behalf. She shares a receptionist with a counselor and a body therapist, but otherwise, Dr. Guinn does the nursing, filing, the stocking and ordering of supplies, the billing and the seeking of permissions from insurance companies herself alone. Thus, she can accept insurance and still afford to spend time with patients.

Dr. Guinn, like all astute physicians, keeps three flowcharts constantly in mind for each patient—a medical flowchart, a malpractice legal flowchart, and now, an insurance flowchart with the obstacle course and idiosyncratic rules of each insurance company, rules that constantly change without notice.

No wonder doctors have to be our best and brightest.

Even Dr. Abi sets aside four hours a day to fight with insurance companies for tests, medicines, surgeries, and treatments he orders for his patients. Insurance corporations often want the physician, and only the physician, navigating its phone trees, waiting on hold, and getting the runaround.

My father, as Dr. Abi's patient, has no idea of the battles his doctor undertakes on his behalf. Most patients don't see their doctors fighting for them. Most patients don't see their physicians caught between an old-fashioned medical ethic of doing everything possible for a patient, and the profit ethic that now controls medicine.

Being caught between these worlds indeed takes its toll on doctors like me.

One in five physicians working at medical schools in 2001 had significant symptoms of depression, according to a study published in the January 2006 issue of the journal *Academic Medicine* titled "The

Impact of the Changing Health Care Environment on the Health and Well-Being of Faculty at Four Medical Schools."

We were less satisfied with our careers in almost every respect, the study found, as compared with academic physicians studied in 1984. Most of us felt our job expectations weren't being realized, that we weren't the contributors our predecessors once were, and that we were less productive than in the past.

It's bad news for everyone that medical school professors are in such awful shape. We are the backbone of the American medical system. We train new doctors and set the nation's standard for medical care. We do most of the nation's medical research and publishing.

I know the study well, as I was one of its authors.

I was invited to be a principal investigator after a chance meeting in 1999, in a still-intact New Orleans, when I was attending my first meeting of the Academy of Psychosomatic Medicine, an organization for consultation-liaison psychiatrists.

But the man responsible for my interest in the subspecialty of consultation-liaison psychiatry was not there. Just months earlier, Dr. Robert Byck, former chief of C/L psychiatry at Yale, my medical school mentor, had suffered a stroke and died. In my student days, I used to follow Bob around Yale–New Haven Hospital as he saw patients. Afterward, we'd stop in the hospital cafeteria for conversation, pie, and orange soda, Bob's favorite. It was during these afternoons when I felt my calling as a consultation-liaison psychiatrist. What could be more interesting than caring for patients, body and mind, as a psychiatrist in a medical hospital? But C/L psychiatrists didn't just consult on the psychiatric needs of patients, Bob explained. As "liaisons," C/L psychiatrists also cared for the emotional health of doctors, nurses, and staff. We took care of the system.

Seth Powsner, also my former professor, had succeeded Bob as chief of Yale's Consultation-Liaison Psychiatry Service. In New Orleans,

Seth and I organized a dinner to commemorate Bob. Consultation-liaison psychiatrists from around the world, all Bob's former residents and fellows, convened at K-Paul's Louisiana Kitchen to eat, laugh, and remember him. I was the only woman at the gathering. Yet because of my connection with Bob, I never feel out of place, but rather a sense of being with my own kind when I am with C/L psychiatrists.

After dinner, as others readied to hit the town, I opted to check out the hot tub, being a Californian at heart.

On a dark and cold November night, stars shone quietly above the lights of the convention hall. Next to a swimming pool of blue rippling light, steam rose from a small round hot tub. In my gray wool suit, I bent down, put my hand in the water. Warmth traveled through my palm into my body. It was a perfect chilly night to be in the tub, yet there was only one person in it.

Dennis Novack, he introduced himself. He was an internist, not a psychiatrist, but he was interested in mind-body medicine. He had studied with George Engel, a name I knew well and revered. Everyone knows George Engel as the originator of the bio-psycho-social perspective of illness, a mainstay of every medical school curriculum. Illness, Engel taught, is not just biological, but has roots in emotions and the social environment as well. It is largely through Engel's framework that American medical students today are taught to see patients holistically.

Dennis's face and wet hair rose above the water, surrounded by steam. He didn't always attend APM, he said, but recently the medical schools in his hometown of Philadelphia, as elsewhere, were struggling for survival. Amid this turmoil, Dennis's fellow physicians weren't faring well.

"Hahnemann, my school, became part of the Allegheny medical system," he said. "Our CEO started buying up clinics and private practices."

"That's what UCLA did in the 1990s," I said.

For-profit corporations began buying clinics and hospitals nationally, beginning in the 1980s, when the federal government gave them the go-ahead. This often went unnoticed by patients, since the hospitals usually retained their former names, even if their core management and mission had changed. For example, Albuquerque's homegrown Lovelace Health Systems continued to be called Lovelace even after it was bought and owned by Cigna, a national corporation traded on the New York Stock Exchange. Petaluma Community Hospital in Northern California retained its name even when owned by Wellpoint, which was fined $1 million in 2007 by the State of California for canceling insurance coverage on patients who became pregnant or sick (a small cost of business compared with the company's profit of more than $3 billion that year). This reminds me of the cult movie *Invasion of the Body Snatchers,* in which the bodies of loved ones are taken over by aliens.

In response to the penetration of medicine's virgin market by profit-oriented businesses, medical schools tried to buy local hospitals and clinics first, hoping in that way to keep physician ethics at the core of medical care.

Dennis looked up from the hot tub. "Well, buying up clinics didn't work so well for us. We've declared bankruptcy." When the dust settled, he said, Hahnemann, founded in 1849, and the Medical College of Pennsylvania, founded in 1850, were both owned by Drexel University, a science and engineering college.

"We're now Drexel," Dennis said. Water splashed onto his face.

In the midst of this turmoil and uncertainty, Dennis saw physicians quitting, retiring early, growing ill, or taking antidepressants to keep going. Worse, Dennis thought they were dying early deaths.

Could this be true?

Philadelphia, where the American nation was founded, is home to some of the nation's oldest medical institutions. Pennsylvania Hospital, founded in 1751 by Benjamin Franklin and Thomas Bond, was the nation's first medical hospital. It was established to care for the "sick-poor and insane" who wandered the streets of Philadelphia, and it took the image of the Good Samaritan for its official seal. Before this, hospitals did not necessarily provide medical care, but were almshouses for the orphaned, elderly, destitute, and infirmed. (*Merriam-Webster's Medical Dictionary* continues to list the primary definition of *hospital* as a "charitable institution for the needy, aged, infirm, or young." Many dictionaries continue to associate *hospitals* with charitable purposes, since the word derives from a thirteenth-century Old French term meaning "shelter for the needy.")

The Medical College of Pennsylvania was the first institution in the world dedicated to the education of women as physicians, even in times when women were excluded from other medical schools. Hahnemann was so old it was originally a homeopathic school. These were some of the oldest medical schools in the nation.

Incredible. After a century and a half of history, the Medical College of Pennsylvania and Hahnemann had gone through bankruptcies and mergers—as if they were ordinary businesses. What next? Should we auction the Declaration of Independence on eBay to decrease the national debt? The news was so fascinating that I never made it out of my wool suit and into the hot tub.

And yet, maybe none of this was true. Maybe these schools were just fine. Maybe physicians weren't really dying. After all, the man relaying the news had had a long day, was barely dressed, and was all wet.

Back in Albuquerque a few days later, I got a call from Joel Yager, my department's vice chairman for education.

I'd known Joel a long time. I first met him when I was just a medical student on a summer elective at UCLA in the late 1980s. I liked him well enough that I chose to do my psychiatry residency at UCLA, where he was director of the residency. The devastating Northridge earthquake of 1994 brought Joel and his pediatrician wife, Eileen, to Albuquerque, where fate also brought Chris and me. At the University of New Mexico, I was reunited with Joel.

Joel's sunny face greeted me when I walked into his office. As usual, he wrapped me for a moment in his thick arms. Joel's demeanor was humble, unassuming, like that of Dr. Abi and all of the best physicians I've known, seemingly a requisite for integrating into the lives of many. Hollywood stars, rumor had it, flew to Albuquerque weekly, just to be in treatment with Joel, a major intellect who's served on the editorial board of every notable psychiatric journal.

"I have a friend, Dennis Novack," Joel said. Behind him, a computer screen flashed pictures of his grandson Adin, a baby with Joel's same sunny smile. On the floor was the usual pile of cloth briefcases full of papers, articles, and books in progress. Joel defied the usual psychiatrist stereotypes. No beard, and downright cheerful. He never used the expensive briefcases that many shrinks do, but always preferred the canvas briefcases given free at conferences.

"Dennis Novack? An internist at what used to be Hahnemann? A former fellow of George Engel?"

Joel nodded. "George Engel trained about a hundred fellows at the Strong Memorial Medical Center in upstate New York. Only about a dozen are still practicing. Dennis is one of them."

"Just met Dennis at a conference." I explained about the hot tub, about Dennis in the water, and me in my wool suit.

"Dennis called me," Joel said, not distracted by hot water. "He's doing a study, and asked me to collaborate. As our consultation-liaison psychiatrist, do you want to help?"

"Sure, Joel. It sounds like destiny."

For the next several years, I collaborated with researchers at three other medical schools to survey nearly four thousand medical school faculty. Dennis, together with Dr. Barbara Schindler, a vice dean at Drexel, led the effort. It would take seven years to publish our study, since unbeknownst to us then, Philadelphia physicians were in for yet more turmoil. In 2006, Dennis would come to Albuquerque as a visiting professor. He would relay even more harrowing details about physicians who worked and died at Hahnemann and the Medical College of Pennsylvania.

I met Barbara Schindler the year after I met Dennis. In 2000, the Academy of Psychosomatic Medicine convened in Palm Springs. In a conference room with blue velvet curtains, a woman walked toward me with a wide smile. She wore a brown suit with pearls. She had wavy short brown hair and large wire-rimmed glasses, like she wanted to see everything, and miss nothing. She had an air of effectiveness, like she could be trusted to get anything done.

"Dr. Dora Wang—*just* who I was looking for." Her eyes on my nametag, her handshake was firm, definite. "Barbara Schindler. I've put our preliminary data on a poster."

"Already?"

Indeed she had. The next day, our preliminary results won first place as the conference's best research poster. I could see why Barbara was a vice dean, a woman who defied odds, since according to the Association of American Medical Colleges, most medical school departments had only one tenured woman.

A few months later, Barbara called me while on a road trip to visit relatives. She was obviously a good multitasker. She described changing foliage and spectacular fall colors, then she said with enthusiasm, "We should be able to get at least twenty papers published from our data." She seemed benevolent and eager to help advance my career.

"That's good to know." I held the phone loosely in my hand. Remembering our study's findings, and the high rates of depression among medical school faculty, I couldn't help wondering, *What will it all be for? Wouldn't it be smarter to jump this sinking ship?*

Indeed, many of Barbara's colleagues had already jumped ship. They had retired early, found other jobs, or changed careers. I heard this a couple of years later when I called Drexel statistician Diane Cohen and asked her to run statistics about women.

"I'm swamped, just swamped," Diane said. "Things are crazy here. Haven't you heard?"

Tenet Healthcare, a for-profit corporation, had bought the teaching hospital of the Medical College of Pennsylvania, Diane said. Without notice, on December 18, 2003, Tenet announced it would close the 153-year-old Medical College of Pennsylvania Hospital, along with about two dozen other hospitals it now owned across the country.

Under a previous identity, National Medical Enterprises, the corporation was convicted of fraud for paying $40 million in illegal kickbacks, including payments to school counselors to hospitalize students with good medical benefits, often against their will. NME paid nearly $750 million in civil suits filed by patients. Key players were sentenced to the federal penitentiary. In the aftermath of this wreckage, the NME board recruited a new CEO, Jeffrey Barbakow, not a medical guy but an investment banker who had recently made $30 million for the sale of entertainment giant Metro-Goldwyn-Mayer. *Daily Variety* called him the CEO brought in to "fatten the cow for market." After a company-sponsored naming contest, NME decided to rename itself Tenet Healthcare. A good account of this, from which this account was taken, has been written by Pulitzer Prize–winning Philadelphia reporters Donald Barlett and James Steele in their book *Critical Condition: How Health Care in America*

Became Big Business and Bad Medicine. (This book is not to be confused with Martine Ehrenclou's award-winning *Critical Conditions: The Essential Hospital Guide to Get Your Loved One Out Alive,* which takes as its premise the sad reality that hospital care is becoming hazardous to the patient's health.)

"Our medical students won't have a hospital to go to," Diane said to me over the phone.

"That's incredible. A medical school without a hospital? How does this affect you?"

Without irony, with relief, Diane answered, "Well, I was told that I'll be needed more than ever."

The inherent irony, however, was not lost on me. In addition to being a statistician, Diane was in charge of Drexel's standardized patient program. "Standardized patients" are not actual patients; they are people paid to play the role of patients at medical schools. They are actors, in other words. With the impending loss of real patients, given the hospital closure, these so-called standardized patients would become ever more important to medical education at Drexel.

The plights of Hahnemann and the Medical College of Pennsylvania are sad reminders that even respected medical institutions with histories going back more than 150 years can be dismantled quickly, under a national policy of health care for profit.

On the other hand, our study never proved Dennis's worst fears—that physicians are growing sicker and suffering early deaths.

But all scientific studies are biased. For example, we studied only the living, not the dead; nor did we study the many doctors who had already resigned, retired early, or otherwise jumped ship to save themselves.

Dennis was certainly not alone in witnessing casualties among physician colleagues.

In 1998, for-profit corporations further penetrated New Mexico. They took over administration of Medicaid payments for psychiatric patients.

So I, too, have a story about a colleague I lost. I, too, have a story about how this new health care system affected my own health.

Chapter Four

Diana's Problem

JANUARY 2002

The Psychiatric Emergency Service is more crowded than ever this cold, sunny Tuesday morning. Not only that, but patients are sicker, since it's harder to access routine care.

There aren't enough chairs in the PES waiting room, so patients wander down the hall to the soda machine, or they step outside to smoke. I try to avoid their eyes, which accuse, "How much longer?" A toothless woman in an oversized plaid shirt asks, "When does Dr. Quinn get here? She's a good doctor. She always takes the time."

The board lists sixteen patients, along with blurbs like "Suicidal has a gun," "Hearing voices wants to stab Mom," "Says he's Christ," or "PES regular." I do the math. Sixteen patients. My four-hour shift. Fifteen minutes per patient, if I want to clear the board. And there are ever more patients walking in the door, registering at the desk. When I was in medical school in the late 1980s, if patients had emergencies, they called their psychiatrists. I remember psychiatric emergency rooms as a safety net for newly psychotic or dangerous patients who didn't yet have a psychiatrist. Today, our psychiatric ER seems to be for patients who can't access their own overloaded psychiatrists in time.

It's the usual staffing this morning in PES. Three psych nurses, two receptionists, a security guard with a black club hanging from his belt, and me, the psychiatrist. Theoretically, a physician can handle more patients this way. In reality, this assembly-line approach only creates more work for me, as I end up managing not just patients, but staff, too.

Sonja, a psych nurse, presents a patient's case to me. I listen and I listen. When I try to speed her up, she plants her fists on her hips. "Dr. Wang, you are interrupting me!"

I refrain from saying, *If I saw the patient myself, I'd be done already. And for some reason, in thirty minutes you haven't told me anything useful . . .*

When I finally talk to the crying patient with messy blond hair and running eyeliner, I discover that her husband died last week. I listen. I hand her tissues. My mind races to the blurbs on the board, the patients in the waiting room. I muster sympathy. I ask my patient if she's really suicidal or if she just doesn't know what to do with her grief. "Grief?" A light goes on in her eyes. It's grief, she realizes. I give her the names of some counselors and a grief support group. Ten minutes later, I walk back to the nurses' room. I jot a quick paragraph at the bottom of Sonja's note.

I turn to the next nurse waiting.

Kristen tosses her long brown hair. "The patient won't talk to me," she announces. "So I can't fill out the form."

"Well, why is he here?"

"I don't know. His mother brought him. Here's her phone number if you want to call her."

"What's his diagnosis?" I look at her blank paperwork.

"He won't tell me."

"Well, did you look in his records?" I ask as politely as I can.

"I didn't have time, but they're right here." With a smile, she hands me a thick brown folder. She bites into her cranberry muffin, strokes the rose tattoo on her ankle, and reminds me cheerfully, "The patient is waiting."

"Well, then, what's *your* job?" I hear steel in my voice. My heart pounds against my rib cage. Blood rises to my face. My brain feels like wires short-circuiting.

I stare at the nurses. I say softly, "It would be less work if I did everything myself."

Kristen drops her muffin. Her jaw falls wide open. "It's not our place to do the work of doctors."

Sonja puts her fists back on her hips. "We're just doing what we're supposed to do. What's wrong with you, *Doctor*?" Kevin, the third nurse, flips through a Rolodex, pretending he doesn't hear.

Someone has called the boss.

Diana hurries into the room. Her short hair bobs like a lion's mane. Her blue eyes are terse behind red hexagonal glasses. The nametag around her neck flies. It reads: "Diana Quinn, M.D., Chief, Psychiatric Emergency Services, Chief, Inpatient Psychiatry Services." Diana has always been an overachiever.

I call Diana my twin, even if we look nothing alike. We are the two female faculty in charge of psych emergencies—she in the psychiatric hospital, me in the medical hospital.

"Dora, you come with me," Diana says through gritted teeth.

We walk down the hall, past patients staring out from the waiting room, past empty rooms with fading paint, to Diana's office.

Kristen, Kevin, and Sonja step into the hallway. As Diana shuts her door, they linger in the hallway, waiting for a catfight.

"Dora, how could you?" Diana is so angry steam almost rises in her breath. Most of all, she seems hurt.

I put my face into my hands. Was it my fault? Did I go too far? I was working as hard as I could. But it wasn't the patients, their psychoses, or potential violence I found challenging. For that, I'm well-experienced. The hard part was getting past the staff hired to decrease my workload.

Diana crosses her arms in front of her. "Dora, maybe you're not cut out to work here."

"But I've worked here three years! Longer than anyone else except you and one other psychiatrist! Diana, frankly, I don't know how you do it."

Out her window, snow falls. The window is so clean I see individual snowflakes. Diana's faded-turquoise walls, on the other hand, look badly in need of care. Her desk is chipped. These orange plastic chairs look as old as the building.

I feel the weight of sixteen patients in the waiting room, and others arriving, stacks of green forms and brown medical records folders, the weight of three nurses, chipped walls, and these old chairs. I picture an upside-down pyramid, myself the single point at the bottom.

I feel so small. I weep.

Snow brushes my face as I walk across the medical school courtyard. I pull my coat collar around my face for warmth. I walk into the hospital, then back outside to our temporary Psych Consult office, the glowing glass brick structure just past the driveway.

The consultation-liaison psychiatry service is still charged with one of medicine's most important original purposes—to comfort and guide patients through illness. Sometimes I muse that I write nonfiction because I can't make up fiction better than this: In the 1960s, when our Psych Consult Service was founded, its offices were on the top floor of the hospital. In the 1990s, our offices were on the fourth floor, where we still had a view of the Sandias and the sky. But now, in the new millennium, after a stint outside, we'll be moved underground, to our permanent resting place.

I must look horrible, because Kathryn rises and wraps her arm around my shoulders. "Dora, I've never seen you like this." Janet and Yoli, our new nursing student, both look at me.

"I finally lost it in PES," I say, and lower my head.

"I was wondering when it would happen," Janet says, stirring a Crock-Pot next to the copy machine and fax. Steam floats past shelves with textbooks on medicine and psychiatry, past file cabinets with patient records, past cubicles with computer screens glowing. It's the pepper scent of Janet's green chile stew.

"Dora, everyone knows it's crazy over there," Kathryn says. "You've got the sickest and most dangerous patients, usually no place to send them, and for that, the jobs pay almost nothing."

"There you have it." Janet stirs.

Yoli takes a tray of tamales from the microwave. Steam fogs the circular glasses upon her round face.

"Did you make those tamales, Yoli?" I ask.

"No, I got them at El Modelo, on Second Street. My family's been here for generations. So we know where to buy tamales."

"I guess I should try getting food somewhere other than the hospital cafeteria," I say.

"Dr. Wang, you need to get out more often," Yoli says. "You're always here too late. And about PES . . . Those forms the nurses fill out are absolutely mind-numbing. They drive the wattage right out of your brain. After a while, you stop thinking. You just can't."

I remember Kristen interviewing patients, her eyes glued to that green form. "Are you suicidal?" she asked without looking up. "Are you homicidal?" She checked off boxes without looking at the patient.

Now I understand. The work has evolved so that it's now most important to fill out the forms.

When a teenager shot himself in the shoulder with an AK-47, a nurse reported to me: "It was an accident, not a suicide attempt. We can send him home after the surgeons patch his shoulder."

"Why do you say it wasn't a suicide attempt?" I said.

"I asked him." She looked at me, perplexed.

But the form couldn't instruct her to ask, *Why do you have an AK-47 at home? How did you come to shoot yourself with a military assault weapon?*

Are these nurses and I at cross purposes? Everybody in PES treats me as if I'm the problem.

Am I the problem?

For us to be paid, it's paperwork the insurance companies want. To keep our accreditation, it's paperwork that shows. If we're sued for malpractice, it's paperwork that matters. A bad clinical decision might harm a patient—but if the paperwork is right, we'll probably be exonerated. Bad paperwork, on the other hand, can jeopardize our entire institution—legally, financially, accreditation-wise.

Paperwork, paperwork, and paper trails.

Am I the one who's not getting it? Do my old-fashioned goals of right diagnosis and right treatment actually now get in the way?

"Have some chile." Janet offers me a steaming bowl. Janet never uses forms. She writes her notes on blank paper. Janet just knows. Green chile stew is exactly what I need right now.

I savor a spoonful of flavor that only grows here in New Mexico, from our soil, our altitude, and our sunshine, which is like light nowhere else.

I could succumb to the form. People would grow sicker, or maybe die, but I could rationalize my billing to Quality Assurance and to the insurance companies. I could defend myself if I'm attacked by malpractice lawyers. I might even survive and keep working in PES.

I taste another spoonful of chile. Flavor rises in my palate.

But I can't give in to the form. I just can't.

"Thanks for the chile, Janet." Beneath fluorescent lights, I am warmed by New Mexico sunshine.

Upstairs on 6-East, a tall man in a brown terry-cloth robe and corduroy slippers shuffles toward me.

"Dr. Wang," he says, "you don't recognize me because every time you see me I'm lying in some darn bed. I'm Leonard."

I look up at the horsey face, the odd furrow in his brows, and the resemblance to his brother, who *vanted to drink my blood* at Mardi Gras last year. Leonard was discharged, then rehospitalized. He was in a coma for months. And now, apparently, he's not.

"Leonard. You look terrific."

"I've been here three months this time. I can't wait to go home."

"Leonard. You sure do look better. I'll see what I can do."

Back in our glass-brick office, I ask Janet, "Have you seen Leonard? He looks great. What's the plan for his dialysis after discharge?"

"Big problem," Janet says. "While he was in a coma, we found out he has no health insurance. The hospital will fund dialysis for a month. But no dialysis center will treat him because next month they'll be left holding the bag."

"Can't we just keep dialyzing him ourselves? We've done it for years."

"But now we know he has no insurance. No one bothered to look until he was hospitalized. Also, we can't legally refuse lifesaving emergency treatment. So the plan is that we'll dialyze him on an emergency basis."

"An emergency basis? He lives an hour away, in the east mountains."

"If he gets delirious, he can get in his car and drive to Albuquerque. Or he can call nine-one-one and we'll send a helicopter. That's the plan."

"Are you kidding?" I look into Janet's eyes.

"Dora, I don't want to be the one to tell him. I just don't."

On the ward, I pull up a chair and sit beside Leonard's bed. I comment on how comfortable his slippers look. I chat about his foresight in bringing a robe. Then I break the news.

"A helicopter?" Leonard says. "I don't mind driving to the hospital. After dialysis I always stop for a burger and a shake. Then I drive home with the stars all around. No need for royal treatment."

"It's not that they *want* to airlift you," I explain. "But since you have no insurance, they can't give you dialysis on a regular basis. Just on an emergency basis."

"So I'm supposed to wait until I'm feeling sick. Then I'm supposed to call nine-one-one and get airlifted here. Two or three times a week?"

"It wasn't my decision."

"I'll solve your crazy problem for you. I refuse to leave the hospital. I'll save you a fortune in helicopter flights."

Leonard's right. Hospitalization would be far less costly than helicopter flights. But a suite at the Hilton would cost even less.

"Thank you, Leonard. Thank you."

Because things happen in clusters, just when Leonard recovers from spontaneous bacterial peritonitis, Alejandro García del Blanco is hospitalized for the same condition.

"The nurses say Alex is manic," Kathryn says, holding his chart.

"Manic?" I say. "I've known Alex for years. He's got obsessive-compulsive disorder. He's not bipolar."

But in his room, Alex greets me with a huge grin. His hair is slicked back like the young *cholo* he used to be, not the middle-aged car-wash owner he is now. The sleeves of his T-shirt are rolled up. Beautiful tattoos wind down both arms.

"It's about time you got here," Alex says. "Finally, a familiar face. You think you can get me some painkillers?"

"How's your OCD, Alex?"

"Not getting any help." He grins. "Was over at the substance-abuse program, but they sent me a letter telling me they don't want to see me no more."

"Substance-abuse program? Didn't I refer you to the mental health center?"

"Yeah, but that mental health don't work. They gave me this bullshit about going to this intake appointment then waiting three months to get a training doctor for a year."

"Alex, how did you get into the substance-abuse program? Are you drinking again?"

"Yeah, you know I used to be a drunk. I'm still sober, don't worry. But substance abuse don't care. Once an alcoholic, always an alcoholic, they said. They took me." He smiles. "Now how 'bout that morphine?"

"Alex, you've worked too hard for your sobriety."

I leave this strange version of Alex and return to the nurses' station.

"Please do something about him," says Elizabeth, the tall pretty nurse with a scar above her lip. "He doesn't sleep. He's at the nurses' station all night, flirting. He's driving us all nuts."

Could Alex really be manic? He doesn't think he's Christ or Superman, like other manics. But then again, Alex isn't needing to sleep like the rest of us. And most significant, this is not the Alex I know.

I call the substance-abuse program. The receptionist says that

Alex missed appointments, so he was discharged. She typed his discharge letter.

But Alex never misses appointments. He's obsessive, in fact. I'm guessing Alex missed those appointments because he was manic. Then he was discharged because he was manic.

All my cases seem more complex these days. I leave the hospital later and later in the evenings.

By the time I get home, Chris is already asleep, snoring in front of late-night sports on TV.

I've tried not to think about PES, and my mess there. But on Tuesday morning, instead of going to PES, I page my supervisor, Paul. I am lying on the floor in my pajamas when he calls back.

"Paul. I woke up this morning crying about going to work. For the first time in my life."

Silence. And then in a tone that conveys the comforting I so craved last week, he says, "Dora, take the morning off."

"But who will cover PES?"

"It's not your problem, Dora. I'll handle it. Know that you won't have to go to PES anymore."

After several beats of quiet, I say, "Thank you, Paul."

I know that Paul will cover my shift this morning in addition to juggling his own patients, his research, his administrative duties, and his own boss. Paul will work late this evening, making calls, rearranging schedules, trying to fill in blanks on the calendar after he scratches out my name.

Late in the morning, I finally shower and put on a gray suit and matching pumps. At least I can try to look like my world is in order.

In Joel's office, where I decide to go first, my old friend and mentor greets me with his usual bear hug.

"I lost it in PES last week," I say.

"Yes, I heard."

He's heard. So the word has gotten around.

"The Psych Consult Chief position . . . hasn't it always been a full-time job?" I ask. "The previous chief had two other psychiatrists working under her at one point. And she had no other duties."

Joel is silent.

"Well, I have the job full-time, but I also have a half-time job on top of that. And I'm the only psychiatrist on a service where recently there were three psychiatrists."

More silence. Then Joel says quietly, "No wonder you're having trouble."

"No wonder I'm having trouble. I've been doing a job and a half—at least—for three years."

After a year on this job, I stopped cooking. Now I think of steam rising from my stove, cleansing me of the scents of the hospital. The sting of chile peppers on my fingers, and the cool pulp of tomatoes. In the kitchen, I see, touch, and taste my work—which is so different from the invisible work I do as a shrink. Cooking makes me feel new, I realize. Hey, I stopped cooking because I've been doing the work of one and a half people. Or three, maybe even four, people.

"How's your family?" Joel asks, bringing me back into the room.

I stare at him. "Fine. My dad got his pacemaker. He'll need bypass surgery someday, but for now, he's fine."

"I mean, how's starting a family?" His grandson's face smiles on his computer screen.

"Joel, I can barely do my job. How can I put kids on top of all this?"

"Of all the things Eileen and I have done," he says, "raising our children has been the most worthwhile, the best thing."

Raising kids has been better than all of his accomplishments in psychiatry?

"At least you don't have to go to PES anymore," Joel says. "You've got that much less to do."

"That's right."

"But . . . Diana. You can't just leave things like that with Diana."

I'd rather forget about that morning in PES, and my tears in front of Diana. But thanks to Joel's advice, I e-mail her when I get to my office: "Hey, how about happy hour at Garduno's sometime?"

Immediately, a response pops on my screen: "Dora, how about tonight?"

I spend most of the afternoon jumping through hoops, seeking "prior authorization" to transfer Alex to the psychiatric hospital. The task takes four hours of phone calls and waiting for callbacks. Between calls, I see my twelve other patients, all while hovering near phones where I might be called back. Cell phones can't be used, since they interfere with lifesaving monitoring equipment.

Alex's health insurance pays for inpatient psychiatric hospitalizations (if I can get through on the phone). But it won't pay for routine outpatient treatment to prevent a psychiatric hospitalization. It won't cover Alex's anxiety condition, which, in my opinion, led to his alcoholism and liver failure.

But it will pay for a liver transplant.

Auto insurance and home insurance companies hang on to dollars for as long as they can, I understand, to make greater returns on their investments. Health insurers also pay for treatment as late as possible—even if each patient's worsening health condition is a ticking time bomb.

So that's how I met Alex two years ago. He came asking for a liver transplant. But if his OCD had been treated earlier, his alcoholism and liver failure could have been prevented, I was convinced. By then it was too late. We put him on the waiting list for a liver transplant. Alex waited and waited, until our liver transplant service closed.

Finally, in the late afternoon, the phone worker at the insurance company approves Alex's psychiatric hospitalization. In my transfer note, I'm careful to include pertinent facts. Alex has been getting into fights lately. His wife left him. His landlord evicted him. He's been hallucinating dollar bills falling from the sky. He hasn't been sleeping. No use calling Alex's wife. She hung up on me. His brother explained, "After twenty years married to that jerk, she's done." I conclude that Alex has been manic. Mania has torn apart his life.

In the early evening, a security guard escorts Alex to the psychiatric hospital. The two men walk side by side down the hall, Alex with his coat over his hospital gown, and the security guard in a blue uniform. They chat, laugh, and ask one another what high school the other attended, what sports he played.

It is still light outside when I leave the hospital to meet Diana. The Sandias flash their watermelon hue, then quickly darken in the gray light of early evening.

At Garduno's, four television screens blare overhead, each on a different channel. Signs announce that margaritas are half-price.

Diana walks in, her blond hair bouncing, her eyes searching. "Dora, it worked! We actually found time to get together!"

We order two house margaritas, then we walk to the happy-hour bar for small plates of enchiladas, taquitos, and three different colors of chips.

Diana sips her margarita. She glances at one TV screen then another.

I search for something to say.

For shrinks, everyday questions can be loaded invasions of privacy. *How many brothers and sisters do you have? What's your mom like?* Every casual remark can be interpreted and analyzed. At a cocktail party once, I mentioned moving with my parents from Brazil to the United States when I was two. A psychoanalyst shuddered. The white wine in his glass rippled, probably, at the fragility and implications of age two.

Psychiatrists use no blood tests or MRIs to guide a diagnosis. Conversation is our X-ray. So, to avoid being intrusive and knowing too much, I have Swiss cheese conversations full of huge, obvious holes.

There's so much about Diana I don't know. But I decide not to ask. Instead, we gossip about Paul, the dean, and the school. Diana jokes that since two of my medical students got engaged, I'm running a matchmaking service on the side.

On our third round of margaritas, Diana schemes about designing clothes for working women. "We'll have pockets for everything— PalmPilot, cell phone, lipstick." She lifts her glass to clink mine. "Well, Dora, we'll start a company. You know I want to get smarter about money. Maybe I'll even get one of those credit cards that gives you airline miles. Know anything about them?"

"I've got a couple. Just make sure they don't charge you hefty annual fees."

Diana nods, taking in my advice. She is obviously a financial novice. She doesn't even know that her salary is half of the current salaries offered to her own residents to join our faculty. Our school has to offer higher starting salaries each year, to compete with other employers, such as the "managed care" organizations. This means less money for long-term devoted employees like Diana.

But Diana is doing twice the work of anyone else, as chief of PES, *and* chief of the Inpatient Services, a new job she took on this year. She's a triathlete. Knowing Diana, she'll want yet another service next year. She always needs to do more, as if constantly proving herself. This was all probably determined by age two, I muse.

We pull dollar bills from our purses and brainstorm names for our new company: Working Women's Wear Daily? Suits by D and D?

In the cold, dark night, we wave good-bye and climb into our cars.

Neither of us brings up PES or Tuesday mornings.

"Dora, administration's got a new plan for Leonard," Janet says, as she climbs the hospital stairwell to catch up with me.

"What is it?" We climb steps together.

"In six months, he'll turn sixty-five and get Medicare. In the meantime, he can apply for Medicaid. Except he owns a house."

"You mean he'll need to spend down. Give his house away, to qualify for Medicaid?"

"Dora, I don't want to tell him. I just don't." She shakes her head.

On the ward, Leonard, in blue jeans and a button-down cowboy shirt, walks beside patients in hospital gowns.

"Leonard, I've got some things to talk to you about. About your health insurance."

"I don't give a damn about health insurance," he says. He browses novels on the hospital library cart.

"But you'll need to apply for Medicaid so they'll pay for dialysis." Then I tell him the standard solution for qualifying for the insurance.

"You're telling me I have to give away my home, give away my money, make myself destitute, so that I can qualify for Medicaid, so the hospital will give me dialysis to stay alive?"

I am silent. Yes, that's the plan.

"That's crazier than the helicopter scheme. Well, it looks like I'll just make myself at home in the hospital a while longer."

I sigh a quiet breath of relief as I leave his room.

Kathryn is busy charting at the nurses' station down the hall. "Dora, Alex is in the hospital ER," she says, writing and talking at the same time.

"But I transferred him to the psychiatric hospital on Friday. I waited until he left with the security guard."

"Dora, you know that hardly anyone stays hospitalized for more than two days anymore."

"Well, what's Alex doing in the ER?"

"Dying, or something like that. After the psychiatric hospital discharged him, he started gushing blood from his mouth again. So he walked to the ER and was admitted to the ICU for blood transfusions. Except he refused the blood transfusions. So risk management discharged him. Now he's back, gushing more blood."

I do a doctor body count. Between Friday afternoon and Monday, seven doctors have been in charge of Alex's care: the 2-West medical attending; the PES admitting psychiatrist; the Psych Hospital ward psychiatrist on Friday afternoon; Saturday's covering psychiatrist; Sunday's covering psychiatrist; Monday's ER doc; and, finally, Monday's ICU doc. Seven docs in three days, not counting the residents and interns from psychiatry, the ER, and medicine, who do the direct doctoring, not counting consultants like me—or Sean from risk management, who despite all the doctors involved, was stuck making the decision to discharge Alex last night.

So much for continuity of care. So much for a patient sleeping well each night, knowing that a personally invested doctor is going to bat whether day or night, for the crucial moment-to-moment decisions that happen each hospitalization.

I form a new theory of assembly-line health care, remembering Kitty Genovese, the woman stabbed to death in New York in the 1960s while witnesses allegedly watched. The Bystander Effect postulates that when too many people are involved, everyone tends to wait for someone else to act. Assembly-line health care is a setup for the Bystander Effect. Patients see so many clinicians, clinicians see so many patients. It's all such a blur that often no doctor takes primary responsibility. Each doctor or nurse thinks another less overwhelmed doctor or nurse will take care of it. Patients are passed on as quickly as possible, in hopes that someone else will be in charge when a patient crashes, like in a game of hot potato.

For Alex, one doctor needs to take charge. Even if I'm just a consultant, it has to be me, I realize. I pick up my clipboard and head down to the ER. I find Alex on a gurney, white as paper.

"I don't want none of your needles," he shouts to the ER resident, a young man in green surgical scrubs.

"You lost half your blood last night," the resident says in a loud monotone, as if decibels will get his point across.

I take Alex's cold, pale hand. He is so weak he can barely move.

"It's about time you got here. Someone I know." Alex looks up at me. "These guys want to put needles in me."

"Who wants strangers poking them with needles?" I say.

Alex's breathing calms. Tension leaves his face.

"But it'll only be for a moment," I say. "The needle will prick for just a moment, like a mosquito bite. Then you'll get the blood. You'll feel stronger and breathe easier. Alex, you need the blood."

"I need the blood."

"You lost a lot of blood last night, buddy," the ER resident says again.

"I fuckin' know that."

"Alex, some people aren't sure if you care whether you live or die," I say.

"I want to live, goddammit. Shut up, all of you! Just do it." Alex closes his eyes and extends his bare arm to the ER resident.

As he gets the transfusion, Alex lies peacefully, with his eyes closed. Dark red blood flows from the plastic IV bag, through tubing, into his arm.

In the corner of the room, Sean from risk management leans forward, rests her hands on her knees. Her wavy red hair cascades downward. Her copper-rimmed eyeglasses tilt. She breathes rapidly.

I am concerned for Sean. I motion for her to join me outside in the hallway.

"I almost let him die last night," she says. "He was so adamant about refusing the blood transfusion. I thought he was competent to make the decision, that he knew what he was doing."

"He was manic last night," I say. "His judgment was impaired, so he couldn't see past the needle stick. I've known him a long time. Alex has always wanted to do everything possible to stay alive."

"He almost died last night," Sean says. Her eyes search mine. "What could I have done differently?"

I think about it. Sean isn't even a clinician. "Sean, it's not your fault. You don't know about mania, and you don't know the patient." What more can I possibly say?

Back in the room, color returns to Alex's face. His breathing relaxes. Alex falls into a peaceful sleep.

When he is transferred from the ER to the medical ward upstairs, I write the order for lithium carbonate, 600 mg at bedtime. This time I will treat his mania.

The next morning, Alex seems himself again. He is courteous, and nurses smile when he asks to use the phone. He starts calling hospitals out of state, inquiring about liver transplant services.

"Alex wants to go through with a liver transplant," Sean says, nibbling salad in the nurses' conference room. "And I almost let him die, over an IV."

I myself am unsettled, after what's happened to Alex. How can I believe in my own psychiatry department?

I decide to talk with my supervisor.

"Paul, I'm having trouble believing in our system."

Paul's office is in a Band-Aid–colored trailer in the parking lot outside the library. Our school doesn't have enough space, so this trailer, called "temporary" thirty years ago, has been promoted to the title of "research trailer." Seems like every medical campus has research trailers.

Paul is a tall, thin young man with wavy hair, long lashes, and large glasses. When he sits down, the entire room adjusts. His trailer creaks like a tin can.

"Dora, we want you to be happy. If this isn't the right job for you . . ."

Tears well in my eyes. "I don't have a problem being happy, and I love my work! It's just disillusionment I need you to help me with!"

"Well, then, you need to get a handle on your disillusionment."

"That's why I'm talking to you!"

"Well, then, talk to me," Paul finally says.

"Alejandro García del Blanco almost died this week." I stare into Paul's eyes. "After he saw so many people in our department—and maybe that's the problem. Help me understand. How can I feel good about working here?"

Silence.

Finally, Paul says, "We don't turn anyone away. Some departments stopped accepting new patients altogether last year."

Physicians throughout the state are closing their practices in response to "managed care," Paul explains. The volume of patients in our university system has doubled since then. In particular, when one psychiatrist, Jay Feierman, closed shop, he left about seven hundred patients looking for care.

I think about it. The hospital doesn't even try to collect payment for most of my Psych Consult Service's work. To get prior authorizations for our thousand new patients a year would take about a thousand hours. That's twenty-five weeks of work, or half of one person's entire work year. That doesn't include dealing with hospital admissions, denials, and other runarounds. No wonder it's cheaper to just provide care and to not seek payment. And that's for our insured patients. Then there are our uninsured patients, and patients like Alex, who have insurance that carves out psychiatry or excludes coverage for medical conditions patients have, aiming to only cover conditions patients don't have. Our doctors and hospitals still try to do what's best for patients. But how long can we hold out, with these new corporations taking profits out of our health care system every minute?

"So it's a problem of resources?" I ask Paul.

"But we can't say that," Paul answers. "I don't know if this helps. Or if it just makes things worse."

Lack of magic is the problem. We need to pull a rabbit out of a hat every day. Every day, we need to do the impossible, to overcome what put Jay Feierman and other devoted psychiatrists out of business.

But why aren't doctors speaking up about this? Doctors, it's said, have an unspoken ethic of silence. This is why physicians traditionally didn't testify against other physicians. Is this same ethic now keeping physicians from talking about the health care industry killing the medical profession?

As for me, if neither Paul nor his superiors will make a fuss, then how can I step out of line?

I smile. "You've helped a lot. I understand now. Thank you, Paul."

As I walk from Paul's trailer, I realize that my bosses are just people. Like me, they're doing the best they can in impossible predicaments.

March always means uncertainty for Albuquerque, a month that vascillates between winter and spring. Just as I begin to store away my coats and boots, to bring out linen shirts, cotton skirts, and sandals, the skies darken, the air chills, and I pull my coat around me.

Along I-25, the faithful walk, carrying crosses, flowers, and backpacks. They come from all across the Southwest and from Mexico as they have for centuries, for the Easter pilgrimage to Chimayo, a place known since ancient times for its healing powers.

Chris and I don't walk, but we drive to Chimayo. In the church, we kneel at an adobe wall covered with crutches and canes left by the healed. We put our palms in red earth, then scoop a spoonful of dirt to take with us in our pockets. We pray again for a baby.

On the news Easter night, a couple in black leather jackets rest by the highway beside tall wooden crosses. They shake their heads. They vow to begin walking earlier next year.

Spring finally comes to Albuquerque.

I see now. I could triple my work hours, sacrifice endlessly, and still, I couldn't possibly do enough.

Always before, when I thought of starting a family, I'd feel guilty, unfaithful to the call of medicine. But one warm afternoon as I leave Joel's office, he asks, "Where are you off to now?"

Without guilt, I say, "To see if I have a baby inside."

Joel's face beams.

A half-hour later, across town at a clinic owned by Community Health Plan, I slip on a pale blue gown. I climb onto an exam table. Chris sits beside me. In the dark room, the ultrasound machine whooshes. Fuzzy black-and-white shadows appear on its screen.

And then I hear it. A fast, steady sound that keeps rhythm with a throbbing white dot on the screen.

"A heartbeat," the tech in latex gloves says.

I reach for Chris's hand. In the pale bluish glow of the machine, his brown eyes are full and soft with tears.

Snow on the Sandias fades beneath bright, clear skies. Flocks of birds fly overhead.

In our front yard, plum blossoms burst. Pink petals float, then line the sidewalk and the steps to our house. I wear Chris's big shirts as my body grows. I roll up the sleeves and enjoy the feel of his clothes on my blooming belly.

At work, I begin to see stars. They glisten in the corners of my vision when I'm doing paperwork, or when I'm feeling rushed. Toward the end of the day in my dark office, stars shine on my computer screen.

On my e-mail list is Diana's name. I'd love to go to happy hour. I smile. I'll order a virgin margarita.

But instead Diana's e-mail reads, "Dora, what's the medical hospital thinking these days about evening psych coverage?"

"Don't worry, Diana," I e-mail back. Diana. She's always trying to do more.

I log off my computer, not knowing that this is the last I'll ever hear from my blue-eyed twin.

Diana leaves PES early a couple of days later instead of working late, as usual. She's tired, the story goes. Her husband, Lawrence, arrives to drive her home, leaving her blue bicycle in the parking lot.

The next morning, Saturday, Diana is hospitalized. I wonder if she, too, is pregnant.

But for the next week, Paul sends e-mails about Diana's leukemia. He sounds too optimistic, too hopeful. So it doesn't take my colleagues and me long to realize that her prognosis is grim. After all, we are all doctors and medical professionals.

In the hospital, I pass Diana's room each day. To be completely attentive in her presence, to take her all in—her voice, the waves in her hair, the sadness and restlessness behind her bright eyes. I crave the presence of Diana. All I want is to stand at her bedside, to be completely attentive to her, before it is too late.

Instead, I am the watchdog at her door.

Friends arrive, like Melissa, who insists, "We take salsa lessons together."

I point to the sign. "Family only. I haven't seen her, either."

By Friday afternoon, the door is open. In bed is a white-haired man sipping soup, fiddling with the TV remote control. He calls to me, "Hey, nurse, how does this thing work?"

The official story in the *Albuquerque Journal*, our school's website, and in Paul's e-mail, is that Diana died of "acute complications of leukemia."

But the hospital is a place for stories.

How can a physician die so suddenly?

Here's my interpretation. Whatever else, Diana worked too

hard. While caring for so many others, Diana must have neglected her own health. When she doubled her duties and became chief of the two busiest services at the mental health center, she couldn't have known that our volume of patients would also double around then.

Diana, a fine physician devoted to caring for patients, had no idea of the political and economic forces at work against us.

When she doubled her duties, she couldn't have known that challenging jobs would become impossible jobs. And I had heard, in this hospital full of stories, that sometime during her last year Diana had changed her mind. I heard that she had pled for a reduction in her workload.

But bureaucracy moves slowly.

Illness, on the other hand, needs no time at all.

At funeral services at a church near campus, I view Diana's life in photographs: a small blond girl smiles on a grassy lawn. A young medical student with blond lion's mane hair long and flowing. Beside these photos are pictures I took of her, including one of Diana with a half-smile, in PES, beneath a poster of the blue swirling sky of Vincent van Gogh's *Starry Night*.

Chris and I sit in the mezzanine of the church packed with Diana's family and friends who have come from afar, along with the most respected psychiatric professionals from our community. One by one, they step to the front of the room to remember Diana.

Lawrence fights back tears. He recalls the party when they first met, their romance and their long marriage.

Dr. Sam Keith, chairman of our Psychiatry Department, walks to the podium. Eyes turn to him, the leader of our community, a dark-haired man who speaks in an authoritative, comforting tone. Senator Pete Domenici sends his condolences to Diana Quinn's family, he says. He then announces that PES will be renamed. It will now be called the Dr. Diana K. Quinn Psychiatric Emergency Service.

In the hospital, I continue walking miles of corridors every day.

Walking beside me one afternoon is Leonard, in jeans, a plaid shirt, and cowboy boots. In thirty-five days, he says, he'll be sixty-five years old. He'll get Medicare, and with it, outpatient dialysis.

In thirty-five days, Leonard will have spent about a year in our hospital, half of it in his jeans and plaid shirts.

At the nurses' station, Janet is looking at a computer screen.

"Janet," I say, "don't you think that Leonard's been the sanest one among us? What do you say we take back his psychiatric diagnosis?"

"Dora, truth be told," she laughs, "I never thought he fit any of our categories."

In November, my ninth month of pregnancy, I fight freeway traffic for an early-morning visit to Dr. Harrison. Stars shimmer as I look for an empty parking space.

Finally in his office, I lie on the exam table. Paper crinkles beneath me as Dr. Harrison reads my blood pressure. I can see the monitor. My blood pressure is high.

Dr. Harrison lays his warm, strong hand on my stomach and announces, "You're not going back to work."

"What? I have to." I strain my neck to see him above the silhouette of my belly.

"You're not going back to work. I'm putting you on bed rest. Do you want this baby or not?"

Doctors make the worst patients, it's said. Bed rest is simply

impossible for me. I walk in my neighborhood. I sit in the park. I feel
the strangeness of weekday afternoons.

The stars fade. My blood pressure is always normal, never elevated,
in these weeks of sleeping, reading, and shopping for baby clothes,
now that I no longer have to pull a rabbit out of a hat each day.

I know that outside PES, patients wait. Cigarette smoke curls above
the green lawn. Every day, someone asks, "When does Dr. Quinn get
here? She's a good doctor. She takes the time."

In the parking lot, a blue bicycle waits, as if any moment Diana
will climb onto it. She'll be in a flowered skirt. She'll fasten her hel-
met before riding off into the afternoon glow of the Sandias. She'll
wave, and call to me, "See you in the morning, Dora! And don't
forget our clothing company!"

Here is one of the ways I comfort myself when people die. I think
about time. Who says time is linear? Not Einstein, and not the Native
American elders of this land. Not my Buddhist relatives who believe
that we all return.

The past, present, and future all exist for me equally in each
moment, and in this moment right now.

Part Two

Remembrances

1981–1994

Chapter Five

Little Did I Know

Looking back, much of what's wrong with medicine originates with wheels set in motion in the early 1980s.

I was working in Washington, D.C., at the time, as an intern in the Office of Disease Prevention and Health Promotion. The Department of Health, Education, and Welfare had just been split into three departments, and the ODPHP (abbreviations took on lives of their own) was in the newly formed Department of Health and Human Services.

It was the summer of 1981. The energy crisis of the seventies was behind us. The Iran hostage crisis was over. At last Prince Charles found his true love in Lady Diana. All seemed good.

I was just a college sophomore, and everything about an office was new: entire days indoors beneath artificial lights, windows that didn't open, and panty hose—something truly peculiar.

The ODPHP was headed by Dr. J. Michael McGinnis, a deputy

assistant secretary of health. Michael wore preppy horn-rimmed glasses and pale blue seersucker suits in Washington's summer humidity. He was educated as a physician before attending Harvard's Kennedy School of Public Policy and embarking on his public service career. With pride in his voice, Michael told me that the greatest health advances of the 1970s came not from technology or science, but from simple health education about more healthful diets and exercise. Health education could do so much? The mood certainly was optimistic. Michael, as a role model, changed into running shorts and a T-shirt to jog home from work, even in Washington's summertime humidity.

In cool conference rooms that sweltering summer, I sat with health policy experts who discussed whether use of seat belts should be mandatory, and whether cigarette-package warning labels should name specific diseases, not just that smoking is hazardous to health. We discussed *Healthy People*, the ODPHP publication that set the nation's prevention agenda.

"Follow the money," Michael told me. "If you want to understand anything, follow the money." I took his advice. My summer's work was later published as a book-length pamphlet, *Locating Funds for Health Promotion Projects*.

Prevention and health maintenance had been bipartisan priorities. The ODPHP was founded under President Jimmy Carter's Democratic administration in 1976. Before that, Republican president Richard Nixon had supported universal health insurance. As a solution to rising medical costs, Nixon enacted the HMO act of 1973, which granted $360 million to create nonprofit health maintenance organizations that stressed prevention.

Nixon's bill for universal health care, however, failed in Congress as the nation became mired in scandal. Wiretaps were found at the Watergate apartments. Police pulled over U.S. senator Wilbur Mills, and stripper Fanne Foxe jumped drunk out of the car into a lake. But some say that physician organizations did the most to kill Nixon's plan, as physicians wanted to work independently, rather than under a government system. By 1974, Nixon's goal of universal health care in America was abandoned.

In 1980, Ronald Reagan assumed the presidency. He strongly opposed what he called "socialized medicine." In researching my publication that summer of 1981, I saw that the Reagan administration had instituted block grants, large chunks of money given to states to implement their own programs. Less federal involvement and less government regulation seemed the new priority.

"Why does medical care cost so much?" I asked administrators at the ODPHP. Medical care *then* consumed almost a whopping 10 percent of the national gross domestic product.

"Health insurance," the men and women in suits around me answered. Insurance creates all kinds of paperwork, and thus bureaucrats—middlemen—who have to be paid. A lot of them. In the days before widespread health insurance, doctor and patient discussed fees face-to-face. Costs remained low, and many patients remember paying five dollars for the entire cost of an office visit or house call. Patients also paid with artwork, fresh produce, livestock—whatever the doctor would accept. But in the 1960s, after the creation of the nation's first widespread health insurance—Medicare—medical costs skyrocketed. Medicare, like any insurance, inherently brings new middlemen to pay. Also, neither doctors nor patients any longer had incentive to keep fees down. Doctors could charge more, so that patients could receive more. Medicare, a wealthy third party, would pay. Soon all medical charges, Medicare and non-Medicare, rose. (Health care economics is complex, but this is how I understand it.)

Medicare, however, seemed the humanitarian thing to do, rather than to leave so many people unable to afford health care in an era when it was finally beneficial. Today it's hard to recall that medical care used to be mired in superstitions such as bloodletting and the use of leeches. Vaccines and antibiotics were discovered only in the 1930s. In the 1950s, anti-tuberculosis medications became available. Medical care was finally indisputably valuable, in the eyes of most Americans.

"Health insurance raises medical costs, right?" the health policy officials assured one another. Heads nodded. It seemed agreed. It even made sense to me, a college student.

But little did I know. Policy makers in different Washington conference rooms were trying to curb rising medical costs with a strategy involving not *less*, but *even more* health insurance. The federal government held seminars in New York, Washington, D.C., and Chicago to encourage for-profit businesses to help run American medicine. Soon health care dollars would need to support not just insurance middlemen, but CEOs and stockholders, too. Concurrently, federal funding to nonprofit HMOs was eliminated by November 1981. Federal support to medical schools had already been substantially cut in 1980.

Thus began a cultural shift that has led to grave consequences for the medical profession, patient care, and the American economy. American health care had been grounded in a nonprofit, humanitarian ethic. American medicine flourished in this golden age.

But in the early 1980s, American medicine was transformed into a profit-driven industry.

In retrospect, it's clear to see that that's when the trouble began— when the American nation reembarked on a hazardous road already traveled.

We all know the term "snake-oil salesman," a remnant in our everyday language and collective memory of nineteenth-century rampant medical profiteering, when tonic salesmen and quack medicine men wrought such dangerous and deadly consequences that the

Food and Drug Administration was created, in 1906, for the protection of the American people. By then, thanks to lessons learned, the
general public and the government, including the courts, understood
that for companies to profit from medical care was "against sound
public policy."

Even Nobel laureate Kenneth Arrow argued from an economic
standpoint that profit and medical care simply aren't compatible. His
classic paper "Uncertainty and the Welfare Economics of Medical
Care" is peppered with such phrases as "market failure" and "the
usual assumptions of the market are to some extent contradicted."
When he published the paper in 1963, doctors and hospitals routinely
provided medical care free of charge, a curious economic phenomenon indeed. How did zero pricing for such a valuable commodity
come about?

Arrow explained that medical care is so complex that, if left to
the free market, in time the public would inevitably demand more
government protection and oversight.

He also explained that medical care is no ordinary product. When
shopping for ordinary products, consumers look for the best value.
But when it comes to medical care, Arrow observed, the product is so
complicated, so rife with uncertainty, that patients cannot possibly
choose adequately. In medical care, "the customer cannot test the
product before consuming it." A patient can't sample just a little bit
of cardiac bypass surgery or a partial appendectomy before commit-
ting to the whole thing. More important, according to Arrow, "the
information possessed by the physician as to the consequences and
possibilities of treatment is necessarily very much greater than that
of the patient." Doctors are valued specifically because of their superior knowledge and experience. If patients knew as much as doctors,
patients would heal themselves. They'd have no need for doctors.
For most of us, myself included, even auto repair is so complex that

I have no choice but to simply trust my mechanic. And autos are so mechanically simple compared with human bodies and minds.

Patients de facto delegate medical decisions to their doctors, who cannot possibly convey their knowledge from decades of training and experience into patient appointments. Furthermore, patients commonly lose rationality when faced with illness, and are unusually vulnerable to fear and to hope—that is, if illness hasn't outright disabled their thinking capacities, as when patients suffer a stroke, brain trauma, coma, or mental illness. My own profession as a psychiatrist holds many examples of illness diminishing the reasoning abilities of patients.

Medical care is uniquely important, and thus it has developed special nonmarket compensations, "some ancient, some modern," Arrow wrote. Doctors need the highest ethical standards, far above those of salesmen and barbers, because of the life-or-death stakes, the knowledge inequality between doctors and patients, and the inherent vulnerability of patients. Professional codes of ethics (accumulated since ancient times) and government controls, such as licensing requirements, helped to assure trust.

As patients, we trust doctors with our lives—literally. The medical profession has evolved through the centuries, to accommodate this trust.

"The very word, 'profit,' is a signal that denies the trust relations," Arrow commented.

But despite the lessons of the nineteenth century, and contrary to the ideas of a Nobel Prize–winning economist, American medicine was released to for-profit capitalism in the early 1980s.

American medicine, once a symbol of this nation's advanced science and humanism, degenerated. By 2000, our medical system was ranked thirty-seventh in the world, between Costa Rica and Slovenia, by World Health Organization standards.

But the biggest failure of deregulation has been in the area of the costs it was supposed to control. Since American medicine was deregulated, health care costs have risen from 9.1 percent of the GDP in 1980 to about 18 percent by 2009. It's a growth that threatens to gobble the American economy.

Meanwhile, some for-profit health insurance companies, now increasingly in charge of medical decisions, have been sued for racketeering, a charge usually reserved for organized crime. Federal courts have accepted the charges as legitimate. In upstate New York, five hundred physicians joined the Teamsters in 2006 for protection against insurance companies. Health insurance companies have been found guilty and fined for canceling insurance when covered patients got sick.

We live in the nineteenth century, in the Wild West, all over again.

In retrospect, I can see now that it all began around the time of my summer in Washington, in 1981, a time of monuments, evening concerts on the Mall, sweltering afternoons in the cool of the National Gallery, and happy hours with fellow interns after long days at the office.

I remember block grants, and I remember the term "decentralization."

Did I know that American medicine was being put in the hands of for-profit corporations? Or was it something I heard but ignored, as I also ignored that summer, the ominous and strange news of five gay men in Los Angeles mysteriously dead of pneumonia?

Back at UC Berkeley for my junior year of college, I volunteered on a local hospital's psychiatric ward. Since I was ten I had wanted to be a psychiatrist. On rainy afternoons of my childhood, I was always the strange kid at the public library where my mom worked, sprawled on the floor in the psychiatry section. Here I read about emotions, something not discussed at school. There was much I didn't understand in the books by Freud, Jung, and Eric Bern. But in those books I found a better world, where each person was worthy of understanding, and of healing through intellect and compassion. At ten my career was decided.

Once a week during college, I volunteered on the psychiatric ward of a tall gray hospital in Berkeley's south side. There I met patients like Holly Huang, a teenager with long black hair and a round apple face who had slit her own wrists. Holly wept and told me in Mandarin that her parents didn't let her have friends. They wanted her to study, nothing else. She buckled under the pressure and failed high school. She didn't deserve to be alive, she said, with her wrists bandaged, her eyes fixed on her blue hospital slippers.

I wanted so badly to help her. Could I go to school with her and be the friend she lacked? Could I tutor her to pass her classes, then help her apply to college? These were my thoughts as I faced, for the first time, someone with a psychiatric disturbance. Alas, there was little I could do for Holly or for the two dozen other patients I met. I was just a student volunteer. I brought Hawaiian music so another volunteer could do the hula. I fingerpainted and I sang songs.

Holly received no medications. Her treatment consisted only of therapy: individual psychotherapy, group therapy, art therapy, occupational therapy, and recreational therapy with volunteers like me. Month after month, I saw no improvement in Holly's condition, no greater hope. (If I could go back in time—I'd bring a Prozac-like antidepressant to lift Holly's nervous system out of its suicidally depressed state. I'd do cognitive-behavior therapy to get her life quickly back on track. Once she was functioning again, I'd explore her underlying conflicts. Psychiatry has come a long way.)

Psychiatry in the early 1980s focused on uncovering deep, underlying conflicts thought to be at the root of emotional problems. Patients could invest years with no definite results. During the two months Holly was in the hospital, I caught glimpses of her psychiatrist, a tall man with disheveled gray hair, chunky glasses, and a thick-lipped expression who blew his nose right into his hand. All psychiatrists are crazy, I'd heard. The first psychiatrist I met in the flesh seemed confirmation.

Sitting at the crafts table with Holly for months, with paints, glitter, and glue, I felt futile about psychiatry helping her or anyone.

I abandoned my childhood goal of becoming a psychiatrist.

When I graduated from college in 1984, I didn't know what I'd do. I thought about moving to New York to try to make it as a modern dancer.

Instead, I looked for a job. After many ads and interviews, I was hired as a research assistant in a UCLA pediatrics lab, a better job than those I'd had in high school.

Jobs.

As a sixteen-year-old employee at McDonald's, I was introduced to "division of labor." Girls took orders from customers and worked the cash register. Boys flipped burgers. Being a tomboy, I asked to flip burgers for a change of pace. I was told no, it wasn't my job. I quit McDonald's after just a month. No one, I realized, lasted on this assembly line—to the company's advantage. A replaceable, short-term workforce that doesn't require raises or retirement payouts is at the core of the fast-food industry's profitable business strategy.

At an ice cream parlor, my next job, I learned about "surplus capital." Whereas usually two or three girls worked together, scooping ice cream and mixing shakes, my hardworking talents were quickly recognized by the ice cream parlor's owners. After a few weeks, I noticed that for my shifts I was always the only girl.

"It's capitalism," my dad explained. If I did the work of three girls, the owners made more money, more *surplus capital*. But not me. I only worked harder.

The UCLA pediatrics research lab was certainly a better job. I enjoyed my fellow lab technicians, and I learned valuable skills. I drew blood from newborn lambs, spun the blood in centrifuges, then used a pipette to transfer liquids from one test tube to another, one tube to another. I got attached to the lambs. I gave our bunnies names. I will never forget the distinctive musk of newborn lambs, or the feel of a pinch of rabbit fur between my fingers before an injection. It took just a few months for me to know that I needed more than to work in this lab forever.

At home, on the gold shag carpet of our den, my father said, "Dora, be your own boss. Be a doctor. Go to medical school."

"Dad, that's all you ever say."

"As long as you're in school," my father added, "I'll support you financially."

Clearly, among the parenting strategies employed upon me were economic incentives, used expertly by my father, an economics professor.

I applied to medical school.

I was accepted.

But little did I know.

My fast-food jobs in high school foreshadowed exactly the federal strategy for cutting medical costs already in place by the 1980s. Years later, as a doctor, I'd be treating patients assembly-line style, in medical systems geared toward maximizing profits for owners by cutting wages to workers, including doctors.

Health care corporations would indeed model themselves on the proven methods of the profitable fast-food industry. Or as *Forbes* magazine put it, *"HCA dispenses health care as profitably as KFC did drumsticks."*

Except that this time, it wasn't burgers, chicken fingers, or fries processed on the assembly line—it was, well—all of us, as patients.

In the summer of 1985, I arrived in New Haven, Connecticut, to begin my new life as a medical student at Yale.

You can eat, sleep, or go to the bathroom, but not all in the same day. If you haven't met your spouse by now, you'll marry someone in medicine or fast food—you'll never meet anyone else.

These were the warnings I'd heard about my next four years.

Medical school wasn't just grueling full-time work—I remember pulling myself out of bed to begin not my second, but my third forty-hour stint in a week. I worked two or three forty-hour shifts a week for months at a time. At one point, during a rare weekend off, I visited two college friends in Boston. Pam was in law school and Janice was earning a Ph.D. in biology. Both of them slept almost every night.

Hanging out with them in Harvard Square, a college freshman started chatting with me. His name was Stu. He had long, lanky limbs and a smile too broad for his skinny body. He wanted to be a cardiothoracic surgeon, he said to me.

"How old are you?" I asked.

"Eighteen."

"Okay, add sixteen years. You'll be thirty-four by the time you finish your training." He looked shocked, so I counted the years for him: four years of college, four years of medical school, five years of a general surgery residency, then three years of a cardiothoracic fellowship. Oh, and beginning the third year of medical school, you'll only sleep every other night, much of the time—for about ten years.

He listened. He concluded: "I guess after college I'll go to business school. That's just two or three years. Then I'll graduate and be in charge of somethin'." That would be two or three years of evenings, weekends, holidays, and summers off.

For me, medical school meant long years of hazy days and nights at the border of life and death, where I learned to read bodies, and to heal patients with my head, heart, hands, and gut feelings.

Medicine wasn't really a science, I learned, but an ancient art and profession evolved through centuries of acquired wisdom.

But little did I know. By the time I finished four years of medical school, one year of internship, and three years of a psychiatry residency, I'd be deferring to the medical judgment of someone like Stu—not Stu the cardiothoracic surgeon, but Stu after two years of biz school, or maybe someone like Stu the day I met him.

Chapter Six

Learning the Body:
Medical School

AUGUST 1985

In the Yale Sterling Hall of Medicine on my first day of medical school, I linger in the rotunda beneath an oval ceiling of Mediterranean blue and brilliant gold stars. In this elliptical room, every sound resonates, each footstep is noticed. I think of others who have walked here before me, and I wonder, *What is someone like me doing here?*

For my first class, I join my one hundred classmates in Hope Auditorium for an anatomy lecture. I've met many of them in the dorm and at parties over the weekend. In this room are classmates with plaid skirts, monogrammed scarves, and preppy boat shoes. There's also a woman from Nigeria with cornrowed hair and a wild laugh, a dude from San Diego in his flip-flops, and a bearded Oregonian all in purple. I am the gal from L.A. in a batik jacket and leopard-print pants.

In dim light on the stage, Professor Shanta Kapadia explains how through the ages, scientists begged, bought, and stole dead bodies—even robbed fresh graves—to learn their secrets. They raced against decay and held their breath against the putrefying odors. But today, religious taboos have been removed. We have preservatives. Our cadavers are awaiting upstairs.

I proceed with my herd of classmates to a room with high ceilings and large windows, obviously designed for good ventilation. Tables hold lumpy human shapes draped in canvas. On television screens throughout the room, a man's stiff, hairless chest appears. A hand slides a scalpel from the throat down the middle of the chest. A female voice narrates that now the skin of the chest can be lifted.

A thud shakes the room.

Behind me, a classmate lies unconscious on the floor. Her short blond hair stands straight up against the cold linoleum. Professors rush to her, as the television screens talk.

At least I have made it through the first two hours of medical school. I am still on my stool.

But I wonder. Is there an imposter in my class? Is it me?

After anatomy lab, I stop in the Cushing/Whitney Medical Library, a room two stories tall and rimmed floor to ceiling with antique books from as far back as the twelfth century. The quiet room has the long, narrow proportions of a chapel, a place where time stops for a doctor to sit, read, and summon the healing knowledge of the ages.

Beside the door, a heavy, open book pays tribute to the Arab world for preserving the ancients' wisdom of medicinal plants and herbs during Europe's Dark Ages. In glass cases, Roman surgical scoops and needles from second-century Syria are caked in a green patina. A rusty saw from the American Revolution was used for surgery. Here are cautery irons to arrest bleeding, tortoise lancets, croup kettles, chisels, pliers, and hooks. Rusted trepanning drills from sixteenth-century France and from the U.S. Civil War show how widespread and long-lived was this Neolithic practice of drilling holes in skulls to release bad spirits. Leeches and bloodletting were once standard medical practices, and President George Washington might well have died of his medical treatment, rather than from illness. Peering at the old saws and trepan sets, I see my own reflection in the glass, atop the instruments.

Above the fireplace, a portrait of Vesalius reminds me that erroneous information has been constant through the history of medicine. In 1541, Vesalius discovered that Galen's ancient teachings on human anatomy, the foundation of European medicine for nearly two millennia, were actually based on animal dissections. Vesalius advocated for dissections of the human body, thus founding modern anatomy.

Half of what you'll learn will be proven wrong—you just can't know which half, my classmates and I are told.

By now, we know that the five Los Angeles men dead of pneumonia in 1981 mark a new epidemic, AIDS, a disease that works in an entirely new way, by shutting down the body's own immune system so that even lowly and weak infections can be deadly. Human immunodeficiency virus, HIV, breaks many rules of biology, including what was once a central dogma, that DNA begets RNA, which then makes proteins and all else.

But in HIV, RNA begets DNA—like a child giving birth to a parent.

Half of what you'll learn will be proven wrong—you just can't know which half.

Information changes constantly. On top of that, less than half of patients do exactly as doctors say, or take their medications as prescribed. When I learn that most medical research is done on 150-pound Caucasian men, I know that I'll be improvising a fair amount for my patients, who are bound to include Asians who think they need half the medication dose as everyone else (research actually lends some validation to this old wives' tale), and women in various hormonal and fluid shifts while premenstrual, pregnant, or lactating.

Medicine, I recognize, is a profession and an art, not just a science.

By the soft light of the historical library, I turn the pages of Carmine Clemente's *Anatomy: A Regional Atlas of the Human Body*, a book of maps to guide my explorations in anatomy lab tomorrow. Page by page, I peel back layers of skin, fat, then muscle. Arteries, veins, and capillaries, like rivers and their tributaries, distribute blood to every tiny territory of the body. Webs of nerves leave no millimeter uncovered. I turn more pages to reveal bones then organs.

Warmed by the fireplace beneath Vesalius's portrait, I memorize names, distances, routes.

When I leave the medical school, it is already evening. As I walk out the front door, I notice a stone owl with wings spread wide. It guards a small flame, and an inscription in Greek: ΛΑΜΠΑΔΙΑ ΕΧΟΝΤΕΣ ΔΙΑΔΟΣΟΓΥΣΙΝ ΑΛΛΗΛΟΙΣ.

The message, I learn later, is derived from Plato's *Republic*: "Those having torches will pass them on to others."

One physician who certainly carries a torch is Dr. Robert Byck, leader of my pharmacology seminar in my second year of medical school.

Dr. Byck takes his seat at the head of a long table on the first day of our seminar. He is a thin, distinguished man in a tweed jacket with a pipe in his breast pocket. Longish gray hair curls at the nape of his neck.

He explains that he isn't sure if pharmacology is a legitimate field of study, even if this is a pharmacology seminar. Some argue that pharmacology should be absorbed into other departments. That school up the road, Harvard, did away with its pharmacology department at some point, and kept its status as a fine school during those years.

Therefore, since this is his seminar, after all, we will focus on the reading of classic papers. William Harvey's 1628 work in which the function of the heart, arteries, and veins was accurately described for the first time. William Withering's timeless 1785 essay that described the common use of foxglove for congestive heart failure, and his discovery through careful clinical trials that the herb's active ingredient is digitalis. Paul Starr's recent 1984 Pulitzer Prize winner, *The Social Transformation of American Medicine: The Rise of a Sovereign Profession and the Making of a Vast Industry.*

A pharmacology seminar about classics in medical literature?

Dr. Byck is my kind of guy.

The feeling is mutual. He seems to like the way I think, the way I challenge him in class.

Soon I make my first visit to his office, a room with dark wood paneling and an atmosphere of scholarship. Dr. Byck, it turns out, is chief of consultation-liaison psychiatry, a confusing mouthful of a label.

Before long, I start following him through Yale–New Haven Hospital. I listen as he talks with patients. I begin my education in consultation-liaison psychiatry from a master of the craft. I pick up pearls of wisdom, such as, "Heck, I just tell patients what I think. I even tell them what to do."

I am surprised to learn, however, that according to one of Dr. Byck's readings, Paul Starr's *The Social Transformation of American Medicine*, the entire art of medicine itself is threatened.

Here's what I learn from the book: doctors are artisans, like bakers, tailors, and shoemakers. By now other craftspersons have been mostly replaced by factory workers controlled by corporations.

Doctors, however, have avoided this fate not because of law or policy, but because of an idea, a moral value—that medical care for the sake of corporate profit simply goes against sound public policy.

But by now, the early 1980s, this has changed. The federal government now encourages profit-driven businesses to penetrate medicine. Starr's book ends with a warning. The medical care of Americans, Starr writes, seems headed for control by "conglomerates whose interests will be determined by the rate of return on investments. That is the future toward which American medicine now seems to be headed."

The profit motive will control the medical care of Americans?

I look at the portraits of great, noble men of medicine all around me in the historical library. How could Starr possibly be right?

I put aside Starr's book to bury myself in books on clinical medicine, EKGs, immunology, infectious diseases, pathology, emergency medicine, pediatrics, geriatrics, obstetrics, gynecology, oncology—topics more pertinent to my medical training, at least seemingly.

My second year of medical school ends the last day of June.

My third year begins the first day of July. This is the year my classmates and I begin caring for patients.

Illness knows no summer vacations or holidays. As I will soon see, illness knows no evenings or weekends, either.

I pull on my crisp white short coat. I thread the steel staff of my reflex hammer through a buttonhole. I snake my black stethoscope around my neck. At last my classmates and I will be called "Doctor." It will be in error, of course, since we are still students. But for the first time, we will at least be mistaken for doctors.

Most of us have never held a job. Most of us have never been out of school. Most of us have never seen death, and certainly have never been in charge of life.

I begin this clinical year with a leisurely rotation in psychiatry. I've always been fascinated with psychiatry, even if I have abandoned my childhood goal of being a psychiatrist.

The attending psychiatrist on my ward at the Connecticut Mental Health Center is Dr. Gray, a man slightly taller than I, who wears tailored suits and a full, dark Sigmund Freud beard. The attending downstairs is blond, so his is a full, blond Sigmund Freud beard. Dr. Ezra Griffiths, chief of the CMHC, is African-American. He is a charismatic man who wears powder-blue leisure suits—and a full, brown Sigmund Freud beard. In the halls I often see Dr. Morton Reiser, with his full, salt-and-pepper Sigmund Freud beard.

On the ward, I meet Lola, a pregnant woman who waves her arms wildly while speaking rapidly about the CIA tapping her phone.

"Lola is a paranoid schizophrenic," Dr. Gray explains. "On antipsychotic medications, she's virtually normal. She graduated from college. But she's pregnant, so we've stopped her medications. We'll keep her here, safe, until after the baby is born."

"She'll be hospitalized for six more months?" I ask.

"In the old days, we'd keep patients for years. But times have changed."

I am assigned to care for Claire, an eighteen-year-old high school student with a French accent, admitted for depression.

"Let's keep her a few weeks so the medical student can do psychotherapy," Dr. Gray says leisurely.

The med student? That's me. Psychotherapy?

Dr. Gray explains that Claire's depression isn't severe enough to warrant antidepressants. Tricyclic antidepressants cause sedation, constipation, and dizziness. Patients have to get blood drawn to monitor drug levels, and EKGs to check for arrhythmias, a potentially lethal side effect. Patients on monoamine oxidase inhibitor (MAOI) antidepressants have to meticulously avoid all food with tyramine, including red wine but not white wine, most cheeses but not Brie or feta, broad beans but not narrow beans . . .

"What about soy sauce?" I ask, instead of, *How can anyone keep this straight?*

"I don't know," he says, and strokes his beard. "I'm not sure anyone knows."

All antidepressants are lethal in overdose, Dr. Gray continues.

"And we give them to depressed patients?" I ask. "What's to keep patients from using our meds to off themselves?"

"The doctor-patient relationship," he says. "Implicit in the prescribing of antidepressants is the doctor-patient relationship, which neither party wants to violate."

Fortunately, I'm not instructed to prescribe medications to Claire. All I have to do is "do psychotherapy," whatever that is. So I listen. I try to be nice.

Claire tells me how hard it was for her family to emigrate from France. New Haven is so different from Marseilles. She misses her grandparents. Her mother is always at work. She and her little sister are lonely in an empty apartment.

I listen. I give her my attention. I give her the doctor-patient relationship and a compassionate interest in her well-being, always at the heart of the medical profession.

It works.

At the end of my four-week rotation, Dr. Gray and our team agree that I've done a fine job with Claire.

Claire and I are discharged together.

On the pediatrics ward, I draw blood and put in IVs for the first time. I put my bare fingers on small hands and arms to palpate tiny veins. I listen to tiny beating hearts and to wheezing chests. I learn to hear heart murmurs in kids with holes between their chambers, or whose valves don't work properly.

Jonathan is only two, but bald like an old man. His shiny head gleams like the wise man in the moon, a side effect of chemotherapy for neuroblastoma, a cancer. Jonathan's mother stays with him all day, stacking blocks, rolling toy trains, and singing soft lullabies.

In a dimly lit room, a radiologist in his white coat puts an X-ray on the lightbox. Even I recognize that it's Jonathan's, by the rare fist-shaped tumor gripping the great vessels of his heart.

"Jonathan! Haven't seen this buddy in a while. What's happening with my little guy?" the radiologist asks with tenderness, with care. But his relationship with Jonathan is through X-rays only. Here is a doctor who will never know his patients, never see my little man in the moon.

In the nursery, babies born to mothers on crack are rigid as loaves of bologna. When touched, they tremor like a vibrating tuning fork.

I know from Warren's records that six years ago he was one of those loaves of bologna, born in heroin withdrawal, and with AIDS. During Warren's many hospitalizations for pneumonia, no one from his foster home ever visits. His kinky hair is a huge, wild Afro atop his slender body. He's probably never had a haircut. But when Warren smiles, he lights up the room like a Dairy Queen sign.

Outside the hospital, Jonathan's and Warren's lives are completely disparate.

But in the hospital, their rooms are identical. Each boy receives the same quality of care and attention. In the hospital, each is equally just a boy.

I never hear it said, and I never see it written. But all around me, every day, I am surrounded by what seems to be the central ethic of medicine.

Each life is precious. Each life is worth our best effort.

My internal medicine rotation arrives along with winter.

With my medicine resident, Jill, I "take call every third," which means that every third night we stay overnight, caring for patients.

Night settles on the hospital. Jill and I "tuck in" our patients. We strain our eyes at their X-rays. We listen to wheezing chests, pit our thumbs into edematous ankles, put our palms upon rib cages to palpate heaving hearts, shine lights onto neck veins, and look with scopes into eyes. We stick needles into pulsing arteries to collect tubes of bright blood to measure oxygen and carbon dioxide concentrations before ordering nebulizer treatments, diuretics, or oxygen for the night. We look at blood cultures and start antibiotics. We check blood chemistries and order fluids and electrolytes.

When our patients are finally tucked in, we walk upstairs to the call room and its two cots. We drape our white coats on the backs of chairs. Jill's long white resident's coat is weighted with bulging pockets that hold an otoscope, ophthalmoscope, reflex hammer, and reference books. My short white med student's coat holds, in addition, gauze, tape, and empty tubes for blood. It's my job to get supplies, track down info, and generally do the busywork. The med student does the scut.

Just before midnight, as we dim the lamp and drift into sleep, Jill's beeper buzzes. "It's the ER, damn," she says. She talks on the phone, then turns to me: "Trent says it's a DNR. Maybe we'll get a few winks in the call room after all." DNR (do not resuscitate) means that the patient wants no heroic measures to preserve life, but to let nature take its course.

Jill and I slip on our shoes, throw on our white coats, and jog down the stairwell. Jill's wavy blond hair is uncombed and her face is dwarfed behind thick glasses that she wears when she is on call.

Beneath the glaring lights of the ER, an elderly woman lies on a stretcher with uncombed, cotton-candy white hair.

"She's been through so much," says her daughter-in-law, a woman in a red wool coat and matching hat. "We just want her to be comfortable." The elderly patient's son, a man in a heavy black coat, stands with his face down, hands in his pockets.

"We'll give her antibiotics, but we'll leave it at that," Jill says.

"Thank you, doctors," the woman says to Jill and me.

I ask the fluff-haired woman to roll onto her side so that I can examine her. On her lower back, where her spine meets her buttocks, is a hole the size of a large peach, with red, infected edges. It is a pressure sore, now ulcerated. No doubt Mrs. Slate has been bed-bound for a long time by her congestive heart failure. Now she will die a peaceful, anticipated death.

But as she rolls onto her back, her shriveled hand reaches from beneath the white sheet. She holds my hand, pulls me close and whispers, "I don't want to die. Please, I need to live."

By the strength of her grip and the focus in her eyes, I know— Mrs. Slate is not a DNR after all. But of all people, it's me, the med student, she tells.

"Jill," I say. "The patient's telling us something different. It's the patient's decision, right?"

Jill looks at me, then walks to Mrs. Slate. Within a few moments she confirms.

Our DNR turns out to be a full-court press. We'll wake the

surgeons to examine her wound. We'll get Infectious Diseases out of bed. We'll call Cardiology to work up her congestive heart failure. After that, we'll think up other specialists to rouse from sleep.

In the morning, as gray sunlight streams through hallway windows, a tired male resident in wrinkled scrubs scowls at me. "You turned a DNR into a full-court press?"

In Mrs. Slate's room, she takes my hand, holds it tightly and looks at me with grateful eyes.

In a windowed corridor after this sleepless night, Jill and I slow our steps to feel warmth and light upon our faces. Sunlight feels so rare and delicious.

I am jealous of patients in bed, eating breakfast. Mrs. Mulberry pokes at steaming eggs and toast. She has shingles, so pus cakes the left side of her face. She wears a soft flannel nightgown with roses, and this makes me especially envious. Sleeping and living in scrubs saves time. So I am always in scrubs.

Mrs. Mulberry complains, "My children have flown here from four states all because I have this case of the shingles. They been talkin' to me all morning, and now my coffee is cold."

Three square meals and eight hours of sleep—what we prescribe for all our patients—is what we never have, as if by our power over the human body we should have evolved past its needs.

On my medicine rotation, I see what the weary do to chase that increasingly elusive state, sleep. *Always do two things at once. It is a waste of time to just eat when you can be walking down the hall at the same time. Morning rounds, while walking room to room, is a good time for breakfast. Balancing a muffin, coffee, and a suture kit on a clipboard is easy with practice. Conferences are a good time to eat lunch. Don't worry about being impolite. Manners take too much time. Try to talk like a speeded-up recording. If you talk twice as fast, it will take half the time, and you'll get more sleep tonight.*

A hospital is the community's dustpan that keeps the soils of life out of clean, disease-free homes. When patients recover, they leave their abscesses, rashes, bloody stools, vomitus, and bad memories behind them, in the hospital. They go home to forget. But in the hospital, nothing is ever cured, nothing forgotten. Tommy's leg breaks, again and again. Miss Tenison's appendix ruptures every day, filling her insides with mushroom soup. Every day, Grandpa's heart stops beating and the family cries.

In my shower at home, after forty sleepless hours, I close my eyes and let warm water run upon my face. I scrub away the smells, sights, and germy feel of the hospital. Water sprays. The sounds of ringing buzzers and crying patients wash from my ears into the tub and down the drain.

I open my eyes. I peek out from the shower curtain at the fogged mirror. If I use enough shampoo, I can make my hair stand up, all by itself.

I wish I could wash all night.

During my internal medicine rotation, I notice a change in me, a wall grows between who I was and who I am now, a division between myself and others.

When I leave my apartment Saturday morning before sunrise, my housemate, Katherine, calls from her room, "Dora, I'll make brunch tomorrow." Katherine is a graduate student in French. Living together, we each have a built-in respite from otherwise all-encompassing studies.

But brunch is already cold by the time I get home the next day, Sunday afternoon. In our kitchen, Katherine's disappointed eyes meet my weary ones. "Dora, I don't know if I can count on you anymore."

But I've been working my hardest to keep Mrs. Slate alive. Her white blood count is elevated again. A new infection is brewing in her lungs, her blood, her bones, in that ulcer in her back, or somewhere. A delay in treatment can mean the difference between life and death. I couldn't possibly put off Mrs. Slate's WBCs for a whole twelve hours.

I apologize, and I apologize again. "Let's go to Atticus, Katherine. My treat."

At Atticus Café and Bookstore, my senses are revived by scents steaming from the espresso machine, at the colors of cakes and fruit tarts in glass cases.

Katherine and I take a table in the literature section.

"So how was your night on call?" Katherine stirs her coffee and forces a smile.

"Oh great," I say. "What's the latest in the French Department?"

How can I possibly explain, in this sunny café with lovely chamber music, what my night was like?

"What are you reading these days?" I dip biscotti into my cup.

But my mind is on the ulcer in Mrs. Slate's back, how infective organisms might have penetrated her blood and seeded, by now, her bones or brain. Then there's Mr. Logan's prostate and the blood in his stool. Mr. Green's emphysema, and did he spit enough phlegm for the culture? Mr. Faitani's heart blockage, and did I order enough Lasix to bring down the swelling in his purple ankles?

Katherine closes and opens her eyes in an exaggerated flutter, as if asking where the hell I really am.

"Katherine, how about sharing a piece of peach cobbler?"

Mrs. Slate is discharged home toward the end of my internal medicine rotation. She takes my hand and smiles. Her daughter, a small woman with dark fluffy hair, packs her things and says, "There's been

an inheritance battle. It's nasty. All I can say is thank you, for not letting my mother go."

All my work is worthwhile, for this moment.

While researching an illness in the library stacks during my fourth
year, my pager buzzes. Dr. Byck's number. It's been a long time since
I've seen him. I smile and walk to the rotunda to find a phone.

But the voice on the phone isn't Dr. Byck's.

"Seth Powsner," the voice says. "Dr. Byck's partner on the Psychiatry Consultation-Liaison Service. Dr. Byck suggested I give you
a call. I could use your help with a patient who tried to commit suicide by drinking Drano." Drano pellets themselves aren't so bad, Dr.
Powsner says, but this fellow had the acumen to put the pellets in
hot water. After weeks on a respirator and a gastric feeding tube, the
surgeons can now make a new esophagus for him by pulling his small
intestine up into his mouth. He'll eat again.

"How can I possibly help?" I ask. "I'm just a student."

"Do you happen to speak any Chinese?" Dr. Powsner asks.

"Some," I say. "My parents speak different dialects, so I took
Mandarin in college to untangle the mess in my head."

"Sounds like your Chinese is better than mine. Do you think you
could talk to this patient's family?"

Dr. Powsner and I meet on the surgical floor of Yale–New Haven
Hospital.

The doctor is a thin young man in a red bow tie, blue blazer,
and large glasses. We shake hands and sit down at the nurses' station to page through volumes of surgical notes, ICU notes, and ward
notes.

I spend the rest of the afternoon talking with the patient and calling members of his family. I meet Dr. Powsner at the end of the day.

I report, "He's seen psychiatrists before. He's taken medicines." I list them.

"Haldol!" Dr. Powsner fingers his bow tie. "Sounds bipolar. He's not schizophrenic, given his periods of high functioning. He went to college. Got engaged."

Diagnosing and treating bipolar disorder is beyond me. But thanks to my information, Dr. Powsner starts our patient not on an antidepressant or antipsychotic, but on lithium. What I learn, most of all, are the lengths a doctor goes through to administer the best treatment. Dr. Powsner didn't write "Pt. uninterviewable" or "No Chinese translator available."

Dr. Powsner stopped at nothing. He even consulted a med student.

Indeed, nothing seems to get in the way of doctors caring for patients. On my surgery rotation, an attending with severe stomach flu hooks himself up to a rectal tube that runs from beneath his blue gown like a tail. As sick as he is, he operates his full schedule. On one of my nights on call, a "plastics" attending comes into the ER in his tux, with his wife in an elegant red cape. He left a gala at the Yale Repertory to tend to our teenager whose face was smashed in a car accident.

The operating room schedule begins early, while it is still dark. Rounds begin even earlier. Pre-rounds earlier than that. In the still, dark, early morning, I ask my post-op patient one of surgery's most important questions, "Have you passed gas yet?"

"What?" He squints. For us surgeons it is morning. For everyone else it is the middle of the night.

"Have you farted?" I rephrase the question.

"No"—he squints—"no farts."

Well, no meals today.

After a full day in the OR, I check with him again in the evening. "Well, now have you farted?"

Across the room, in a comfortable argyle sweater and slacks, a resident talks with the patient in the next bed. The resident is seated. The patient's eyes are focused on the young man.

The resident is having a conversation with his patient. He is doing psychiatry.

Psychiatry.

No matter how much medicine changes, with its new CT scans, MRIs, and designer drugs, psychiatry can't change too much, can it? The doctor-patient relationship is the essence of psychiatry. How can that ever change?

Also, the professors I gravitate toward most seem to be psychiatrists, like Dr. Byck, Dr. Powsner, and my thesis advisor, Dr. David Musto, a psychiatrist and medical historian.

In Dr. Byck's office, he slides open his desk drawer. He pulls out a tin of Belgian cookies. Together we munch.

"That's enough, Dr. Byck. What about your diabetes?"

"Oh, that," he says, reaching for another cookie.

I sigh as he takes a bite. "The school wants each of us to choose a mentor. I've been thinking. I'd like to be a psychiatrist."

He stops chewing for the slightest moment, then quickly resumes without uttering a word.

"Dr. Byck, will you be my official mentor?"

"Dora, the biggest problem with being a psychiatrist"—he puts down his cookie—"is the other psychiatrists. Most psychiatrists are crazy."

Dr. Byck. He never beats around the bush.

"And the other problem," he says, "is that you'll never make a lot of money."

"But you decided to be a psychiatrist, didn't you? When you decided to go to med school, weren't you almost tenured in pharmacology?"

"Yes," he nods. "I needed the contact with patients. I missed that as a pharmacologist." He reaches for another cookie.

"Stop that."

"Another thing about psychiatrists." He puts the cookie down. "Surgeons, internists—they retire. They burn out. But psychiatrists, we usually never retire."

It is exactly what I want, a career so interesting that I'll never want to leave it.

"Maybe even, someday," I say, "I'll be a consultation-liaison psychiatrist, involved with the whole person, body and mind."

In Dr. Byck's face I see pride, but also something more, as if he is scanning my life ahead, seeing what I cannot.

One of the original functions of doctors, before medicine had much to offer, was to forecast the progression of disease for patients and families. A good physician sees a person's many possible futures, and intervenes with all available knowledge, science, technology, and personal wiles. Dr. Byck even tried to intervene in the nation's future, when he warned Congress about the impending crack epidemic, based on his knowledge of Mexican and Peruvian street trends. Dr. Byck, like other good doctors, sees the future.

"Have you met Dr. Steve Fleck?" Dr. Byck asks.

"No. Who's he?"

"A real character. Before you leave, you must meet Steve Fleck."

One evening, in a quiet corridor, a frail white-haired man shuffles by, his eyes fixed on the floor. He is thin as a skeleton in his long white coat. His nametag reads: "Steve Fleck, M.D., Psychiatry."

"Dr. Fleck," I call to him, "Dr. Byck says I have to meet you. I'm Dora Wang. I'm applying for psychiatry residencies."

He shakes my hand, nods, and looks back at the floor.

"Do you have any advice for a new doctor starting out?"

Our hands are still grasped when he utters the only two words I will ever hear from his lips, words I will always remember.

"Single payer."

He turns and shuffles down the hall.

On the morning of May 28, 1990, my mother and father snap pictures of me in my black gown and square cap in front of the soaring white columns of the medical school.

They have come from Los Angeles for my graduation.

Even if I have hardly seen them these long years, they have never been far from my thoughts. I also know that on the other side of the country, in L.A., they have enjoyed telling friends about their daughter, the Yale medical student.

In the rotunda, we snap more pictures. Beneath the oval ceiling of gold stars and Mediterranean blue, I remember how humbled I felt stepping into this space for the first time. I am a different person now, shaped by this school, and even by quiet spaces like this, where I always feel the noble purpose of my profession.

More than acquiring the knowledge of ages, from Hippocrates and Galen to Lister and Cushing, I have absorbed the ethic of a physician. Each life is precious and worth my best effort. The patient's welfare always comes first—even if it means my not sleeping for days.

On the sunny lawn outside the Yale Sterling Hall of Medicine, a large tent is set up for graduation ceremonies. I guide my parents into it. My father strides in with vigor and pride. His hair is still black and his face is full of health and life. My mother wears a red flowered dress. Her round, smiling face is an older version of my own.

I walk to the front of the tent, to the seats reserved for graduates, to the chair with my name on it.

Dean Leon Rosenberg stands at the front of the assembly. He is a tall, distinguished man with gray curly hair and clear blue eyes. One by one, he calls our names.

When he calls "Dora-Linda Lau Wang," I walk to the podium and stand before him. He looks at me with pride. As I take my diploma from him, I remember the inscription above the entrance of the medical school and the words I passed beneath each day, "Those having torches will pass them on to others."

I turn and face the audience. My mother is in the front, taking my picture. I wave my diploma at her. Years from now, when these sleepless nights at the junction between life and death seem a distant dream, I will look at this piece of paper and know—I really did this. Here is the proof.

Chaplain Alan Merman rises to lead us in the Hippocratic Oath. With my classmates, I raise my right hand, and like two millennia of physicians before me, I am initiated into a profession as old as civilization:

I swear by Apollo Physician and Asklepios and Hygieia and Pana-
ceia and all the gods and goddesses, making them my witnesses, that
I will fulfill according to my ability and judgment this oath and
covenant:

To hold him who has taught me this art as equal to my parents
and to live my life in partnership with him, and if he is in need of
money to give him a share of mine, and to regard his offspring as
equal to my brothers in male lineage and to teach them this art—if
they desire to learn it—without fee and covenant;

to give a share of precepts and oral instruction and all the other learning to my sons and to the sons of him who has instructed me and to pupils who have signed the covenant and have taken an oath according to the medical law, but to no one else.

I will apply dietetic measures for the benefit of the sick according to my ability and judgment; I will keep them from harm and injustice.

I will neither give a deadly drug to anybody if asked for it, nor will I make a suggestion to this effect. Similarly I will not give to a woman an abortive remedy. In purity and holiness I will guard my life and my art.

I will not use the knife, not even on sufferers from stone, but will withdraw in favor of such men as are engaged in this work.

Whatever houses I may visit, I will come for the benefit of the sick, remaining free of all intentional injustice, of all mischief and in particular of sexual relations with both female and male persons, be they free or slaves.

What I may see or hear in the course of the treatment or even outside of the treatment in regard to the life of men, which on no account one must spread abroad, I will keep to myself holding such things shameful to be spoken about.

If I fulfill this oath and do not violate it, may it be granted to me to enjoy life and art, being honored with fame among all men for all time to come; if I transgress it and swear falsely, may the opposite of all this be my lot.

Looking back on my medical school years, I can't believe what I ignored.

I read Paul Starr's warning that American medicine was on its way toward control by conglomerates with profit on the brain. I heard Steve Fleck's enigmatic advice for a new doctor: "Single payer." I didn't even bother to ask what "single payer" meant.

In retrospect, I even embraced certain changes, without foreseeing their consequences.

In 1989, for example, New York State instituted work-hour limitations for medical residents. As an overworked and sleep-deprived med student that year, I applauded this, without of course foreseeing the side effects. The change happened in the aftermath of a tragic death, when Libby Zion, an eighteen-year-old college student, went to New York Hospital with flu symptoms. Within eight hours she was dead. Although the cause of death was never exactly determined, it was most likely a medical mistake, a fatal drug interaction between the Demerol prescribed by the hospital and the antidepressant Nardil, which the teenager was taking. In the ensuing trial, the grand jury faulted not the overworked, undersupervised medical residents, but the grueling American system of medical education itself. Subsequently, a commission headed by Dr. Bertrand Bell investigated residencies and emergency care.

Because of the Bell Commission's recommendations, New York's health code in 1989 instituted new work-hour limitations. Medical residents could work no more than eighty hours a week. After any twenty-four-hour stint, a resident was mandated to be off duty for twenty-four hours. All other states soon followed suit. Soon work-hour limitations for medical students were also instituted.

Today medical students rarely take overnight hospital call, in stark contrast to my own schooling, when my duty to patients was constant and I saw disease in its full progression, hour after hour, with only brief periods away.

Critics, moreover, point out that the eighty-hour workweek cuts medical education by at least 20 percent, or about a year of training, since, according to the *Journal of the American College of Surgeons*, the average resident's workweek in the 1980s was 105 hours. In Albuquerque in 2006, at a birthday party for a tot gustily named Riccardo Ricciardi, I struck up a conversation with his dad, cardiologist Mark Ricciardi, who, as it turns out, was an internal medicine resident at Yale when I was a student. "You know, Yale was fined for working us a hundred ten hours a week," Mark said, turning hot dogs at the grill. I handed him some buns. "That sounds about right. A hundred ten hours a week."

To me, most significant, work-hour limitations train new doctors to practice shift work. Patients can now expect to be passed from one resident doctor to another daily, since for a resident to follow a patient for more than twenty-four hours is now against regulations. Continuity of care is eliminated from medical education. Dr. Dara Lee, an Albuquerque cardiologist, remembers that the core of her cardiology training was admitting patients during nights on call and then the next day watching cardiac catheterizations reveal the anatomy responsible for their symptoms. Today, for a resident to stay through the next day to see the completion of a work-up or the progression of illness, violates regulations. Given today's short hospitalizations, residents often never see a patient again after a night on call. It's analogous to a law that forbids you to see the end of a movie, or read a book to its end.

Residents lived in the hospital when the American system of medical education began in 1898 at the Johns Hopkins Medical School. Hence the terms "residents" and "housestaff."

Even if I never actually lived in the hospital during my medical student and resident years, I always cared for my patients from admission to discharge, with only brief periods away. They were my patients.

But my generation was among the last to practice this kind of devotion and to see disease across its full progression, day and night.

Many newer doctors don't even know that, traditionally, doctors cared for patients constantly, and never signed off. Going home, leaving patients to someone else or to the ER, is the only approach many new physicians know.

My opinion is simply this: Work-hour limitations for young doctors, and for doctors in general, are certainly reasonable.

Now, if we could also regulate heart attacks, accidents, and nervous breakdowns to occur nine to five, then we'd have it all solved.

But physicians like me are caught between the old ethic of medicine as a profession and the new reality of health care as an industry. When residents go home, attending physicians, such as myself, stay to finish the work.

For me, being a doctor still means that I don't sign off. I still carry a flame that won't be extinguished, at least not yet.

One afternoon, while buying macaroni and cheese at Target for Zoe, my cell phone rang. As I reached into my wallet for the eagerly waiting cashier, I pleaded into my phone, "Get back on the train! People don't die of anxiety!"

My patient, a train conductor, said, "Really?" He'd been convinced that his hyperventilation and palpitations could be lethal. Suddenly, he realized: anxiety wouldn't kill him. He calmed down. He got back on the train.

It was a conversation that couldn't have waited for our next appointment. By then, the train would have already left the station.

During my internship at the University of California in San Francisco, I was an intern in neurology, family practice, internal medicine, and pediatrics before immersing myself in psychiatry.

I realized and appreciated the skills I acquired in medical school, and how far I had come as a healer.

But, in retrospect, I still had a long way to go.

One case I remember, and regret, was of a bony man in military fatigues with a shaved head, wheezing for breath in the emergency room of San Francisco General Hospital. The man had AIDS, so pneumonia was at the top of my diagnostic differential. Academically, a physical exam goes from head to toe. But in that ER war zone, with its flood of humanity, I went first for the guy's ankles, a shortcut. Swollen, fluid-filled ankles would mean heart failure, rather than pneumonia or asthma. I lifted a hem of his khakis and eased down his sock. I pressed my thumb to his ankle. There was no swelling. Then I saw it—the thin, crooked arms of a Nazi swastika. I lifted his shirt to put my stethoscope to his chest. The man was covered in swastikas, dozens of them. At this hospital I saw many elegantly executed tattoos. These were not among them, but expedient, hastily scrawled, serving only to convey a message. The swastika tattoos were a possible cause of his HIV infection, given the man's lack of other apparent risk factors.

"We'll need a blood gas," my curly-haired attending said. This was 1990, before the invention of pulse oxymeters, machines in the form of glowing red dots that, when taped to a patient's finger, read the oxygen concentration in a patient's blood. In 1990, we stuck needles into the familiar pulse point on the wrist and rushed tubes of blood gas samples on ice to the lab.

I ordered my medical student to do the stick. He stuck a needle into the patient's bone, missing the artery. It was July, the start of the medical school year. He tried again, and again. The man in swastikas groaned in pain.

"I think you'd better do it," my attending said. He'd seen me get needles into the brachial artery, a stick usually attempted only by anesthesiologists.

"No way," I said. "Why should I go out of my way for someone like him? He probably wants me dead." I didn't deny the man care. But I let him contribute far more than his fair share to my medical student's education. I watched him wheeze as he endured my words.

To this day, I regret my treatment of this man who was my patient.

Now, after years of practice, I recognize that although in the ER that day I was already expert in exams, diagnoses, and procedures, I had treated my patient with a lack of a doctor's compassion. Thus, I missed the opportunity to heal the emotions that may have led him to deform and infect his body.

That day in the ER, I had an opportunity to heal my patient, at least just a little.

Instead, I treated his pneumonia, nothing else.

But it was in the healing of my own malady, during my internship, that I personally benefited from medicine practiced as an art.

That year, something inside me broke. I was not ill in visible ways. It was not my bones or skin that were injured, but my spirit, something invisible to EKGs, echocardiograms, labs, and multitudes of other medical tests.

My cure would begin, at last, with a brief phone conversation with Dr. Byck, a master of the art of medicine.

Chapter Seven

The Mysterious Healing of
My Own Malady: Internship

JANUARY 1991

The doors are locked for the twenty or so patients on my psychiatric ward at San Francisco General Hospital, which means that we who care for them are also locked in. My ward is on the top floor of an old brick building high on Potrero Hill, where there might be a terrific view of San Francisco slopes, the nearby Mission de Guadalupe, and the clear waters of the bay. But I never have time to look out the windows.

Two teams care for the ward's patients. For an hour every day, I do walking rounds with my team. The chief psychiatrist, the junior psychiatrist, a nurse, a social worker, and myself—the intern—walk from room to room for an hour, talking, one at a time, with our ten or so patients. That's about six minutes per patient. Then I write notes and orders, go to classes and meetings, and track down lab results, X-rays, and tests.

I hardly see my patients, strangely, aside from that hour of walking rounds. Most of a doctor's work in this hospital seems to be in placing the patient, since it's unthinkable to discharge patients to live on the streets. We keep our homeless patients until a Tenderloin hotel room opens up, or until their monthly checks arrive. Like the almshouses hospitals all once were, our hospital seems still the last compassionate stop for those who have run out of places to turn.

"This is our new student," my attending says as I finish a stack of paperwork. "You can supervise her, Dora. You know what you're doing."

But I don't know what I'm doing. There must be more I can do for Charles than let him lie in the dark until his electroconvulsive therapy gets approved. There must be more I can do for Odelia than simply restart the lithium she stopped taking and then send her to the state hospital for months away from her children. There must be more I can do for my patients, but I don't know what, even though I'm racing under pressure all day, cramming thirteen hours into each eleven-hour day. And now I have a student to teach.

My heart cartwheels—a single cartwheel, a turn of a paddleboat wheel beneath my ribs. No, it doesn't feel like a skipped beat, a palpitation. It feels like a cartwheel—a symptom I don't even bother looking up in textbooks.

Five days later, a social worker lays more papers before me. "You need to fill these out so we can place the patient."

My heart cartwheels again, this time two rotations.

Within a couple of weeks, my heart feels no longer my own, not the same steadfast organ I've always known but some wild frolicking creature. It no longer just cartwheels, but rolls and rolls, as if down a long, grassy slope.

The next day in class, my hands tremble. Tremors spread until my entire body shakes.

That night, awake, I sit at my desk and write, "I feel like I'll shatter, like a building in an earthquake."

I begin to fear my own body. Rushing down the hall to another meeting, I take my pulse, put my hand against my chest. Am I breathing? Is my heart beating? Cartwheeling? Is this my own body anymore?

I confide in Dr. Silver, a sympathetic attending. Dr. Silver sends me to a cardiologist.

High on Nob Hill, electrodes are placed on my chest for an EKG. I swallow a microphone that takes ultrasound images of the back of my heart. I have a heart murmur, the tests confirm. "It's benign," the cardiologist assures me. "Nothing to worry about."

But I do worry. And I'm not any better. My heart continues to murmur, as if insisting that something is wrong. But what?

Dr. Silver sets aside an hour every day for me, an hour of his busy schedule, an extra hour at the hospital for me, so that I can sit in his office and talk. Talk. Talk. He never says much, but gestures and sighs in sympathy.

I wonder if I am getting psychotherapy.

Finally, I say, "Thank you, I appreciate your time. But I don't see the need to keep meeting every day."

I also confide in the consultation-liaison psychiatrists, including Dr. David Elkind, who is easy to talk to. He's easy to talk to because he talks, too. He smiles, and says stuff like, "Sounds like you're having panic attacks."

Panic attacks? What's this got to do with subconscious drives, the id, ego, or superego?

In the DSM-III-R, our catologue of everything that can go wrong with your nerves, I look up "Panic Disorder." "Discrete periods of intense fear or discomfort," the book says. Come on, I'm an intern! Besides, what good is this description except to tell me something is wrong with me?

I know what's wrong. All the interns have had trouble on this ward. Dr. D said something like, "Take me off the ward or I'll leave the internship altogether." Dr. C had stress diarrhea so badly she couldn't work. Dr. B used to sit in the call room and just cry. Dr. A, the other intern who started with me, quit the ward after just two weeks.

But me, I kept going. I even assumed some of Dr. A's work after she was gone.

Finally, I hit bottom. And in this humbled state, I resort to begging help from one of the best physicians I know.

I call Dr. Byck. Past pride, I blurt about the pains in my chest, the way I shake, how I fear I'll crumble like a building in an earthquake. I add that other interns didn't even last as long as I have.

Softly, with deliberation, Dr. Byck says, "Dora . . . the purpose of an internship . . . is to survive it."

"Survive?"

"Yes, survive. That's all you need to do."

"Survive! But what about saving the world?" I am, after all, just twenty-some years old.

"Work on things that can be done," he says. "And one more thing. Isn't it time you started calling me Bob?"

"Bob?" *Bob?*

With these few sentences, strangely, my recovery begins. I have always striven to do more, to do better. It's how I got into medical school in the first place. Now, for the first time, I aim to do less than my best. I aim simply to survive. Why was I working so hard to earn the approval of my superiors, when even Dr. Byck wants me to call him Bob?

As San Francisco's summertime fog rolls in from the ocean to blanket the sky outside the hospital, I complete my internship. I fulfill the requirements for medical licensure. On paper, I've succeeded.

And in the glow of this kind of success, I write my letter of resignation from the residency.

I have been broken.

No more interns are sent to the ward—for about ten years. Even *The Wall Street Journal,* in a story about the hospital, mentions all the interns who left the ward.

But for me it is too late. The damage is done. I am no longer who I used to be, but someone new, as fragile as butterfly wings.

In July, at medical schools across the country, the new academic year begins for students, interns, and residents. But my white coat hangs in my closet, clean and stiff.

I enroll in classes at UC Berkeley. It's a good time to seek refuge in books and ideas. Books and ideas, since those early days in the library where my mom worked. On the Berkeley campus, I join friends on the lawn of Wheeler Hall. My friends debate to what extent comedy enhances the tragedy of *King Lear.* I chime in about Asian-American identity, that along with theorizing, should we also just . . . be? I have always enjoyed intellectual exchanges. But now I feel a new ennui, a new gulf that divides me from who I was.

Someone somewhere is sick, and I can help.

I can fight microbes invading lung tissue, restore breath to the dying, make a heart beat again. How wasteful to let these skills bask in this glorious sun, to let them waft in leaf-scented breezes, to let them listen, just listen to the sound of water running in Strawberry Creek.

I am a doctor now.

From my lovely Victorian in San Francisco, bought with my parents' help, I can theoretically walk to Golden Gate Park four blocks away. After a jog along the lake I can hypothetically stroll to Clement Street for *har gow, siu mai,* and the scent of pomelo floating from streetside produce stands beneath foggy skies.

But I rarely leave my house. I place my palm upon my chest. I count flutters.

In the evenings, my housemates, Monique and Damijan, return. At the kitchen table, Monique stuffs Cornish game hens with garlic, sea salt, and rosemary. With patient fingers, she pulls needle and thread to sew shut cavities.

"You're sewing dinner?" I ask.

"So spices will steam the meat," she says.

Atop each hen, she crosses two strips of bacon, dressing them as if in uniform. She puts them in the oven and bastes for the next hour. The room warms with scent.

"Eating out in San Francisco is slumming compared to your cooking," I say to her. "Can you teach me to cook if I buy the groceries?"

"Okay, Dora," she says simply.

My first lesson is vegetable soup. Monique instructs me to dice an onion, then sauté it in butter.

I sauté for a couple of minutes, then ask, "Can I dump in the chicken broth now?"

"You should sauté more. Sautéed onions have a different flavor than boiled onions, you know."

I sauté for what seems an extraordinarily long time to do anything. The heat is alchemical. The onions soften, and a buttery, pungent scent rises. I add broth, broccoli, and a single potato. The soup stews, softens, and I wait.

That summer, I lost myself in the rhythms of chickens boiling, hens roasting, custard thickening, cakes rising, and in the patience of shredding, stirring, whipping, and waiting.

I slowed my pace to the transformation of living things. My hands steadied. My heart regained its rhythm.

In the warmth of my kitchen, with my friends, I grew brave enough to let the world inside of me once again.

In the fall, Sandy Lipschultz, administrator of UCLA's psychiatry residency, called. In medical school, I had done a summer elective at UCLA. That's when I first met Dr. Joel Yager, director of the residency program. Joel was a man with a sunny, round face, no beard at all, and who insisted on being called "Joel." I had no idea that a psychiatrist could be friendly, and even infectiously cheerful. UCLA had accepted me for their psychiatry program, but I chose UCSF instead. I wanted to live in San Francisco.

According to Sandy, a UCLA psychiatry intern decided she'd rather be a surgeon. There was an unexpected vacancy in their psychiatry residency, a space for me.

"We don't even need any paperwork," she said. "We still have your old application. We'd be happy if you could finally be one of ours."

I remembered Joel's uncomplicated smile. Could it all really be that simple?

"I'll do it," I said.

I sold my San Francisco Victorian house at a loss, thus becoming one of the rare few who can brag about losing money in San Francisco real estate in the nineties.

Healed by Dr. Byck's few words, and by cooking with my friends, I packed my books and clothes to move back to the city of my childhood, Los Angeles.

Chapter Eight

Learning the Mind in the Decade of the Brain: Psychiatry Residency

In the early 1990s, during my psychiatry residency at the UCLA Neuropsychiatric Institute, doctors were increasingly being called "providers," and patients, "clients." Increasingly, I heard the term "health care industry" rather than "medical profession." Business language and ethics rapidly infiltrated medical language and ethics.

But the best physicians defied these new terms.

"Client?" said Martha Kirkpatrick, whom I met for the first time during my residency. "What's our duty? Psychiatry and medicine? Or customer service?"

But Los Angeles—a city that erases its past like no other, in favor of being the entertainment capital of the world—is perhaps the world's best place to be in denial. After all, this is a city that lives its sunny lifestyle while ignoring, on a daily basis, that it sits on some of the earth's most geologically unstable land, and that before water was piped in from hundreds of miles away, the L.A. Basin was virtually a desert.

In Los Angeles, I settled into an apartment in Santa Monica, blocks from ocean waves and sand. Across the street, a supermarket stocked fresh herbs, wild mushrooms, and California wines. In the parking lot, rows of fresh flowers waved in ocean breezes.

On the first day of my residency, I was assigned to care for a patient I'll call Eric Azure. After commuting six hours a day for months, Eric gouged out his own eyes, like Oedipus. Even after he was blind, he saw hallucinations of witches, a product of his mind gone awry. I cared for Eric for the remainder of my three-year residency. I helped him out of his psychosis, then his depression. He learned Braille, got a Seeing Eye dog, finished his Ph.D., and got a good job. I regained the hope about psychiatry that I'd lost at the crafts table with Holly Huang when I was in college.

During my psychiatry residency, I was infatuated with revolutionary advances in the field of psychiatry, yet still I paid no attention to the economic forces at play, forces set in motion around the time I was an intern in Washington a decade earlier.

In retrospect, when it came to where psychiatry was headed, I was as blind as Eric.

Humankind has always questioned the origins and workings of our own emotions, thoughts, and behavior. We looked to philosophy, religion, and then psychology and psychoanalysis, for answers.

The 1990s brought furious applications of science and technology to the understanding of our own minds, something once considered too nebulous or too sacred to explain through science. Even George H. W. Bush, in Presidential Proclamation 6158, recognized the 1990s not as the decade of the Internet but the "Decade of the Brain."

In the 1960s, billionaire aviator Howard Hughes was so disabled by obsessive-compulsive disorder that he isolated himself for fear of contamination, hoarded his own fingernails and urine, spent hours sorting peas by size, and reportedly watched the movie *Ice Station Zebra* at least 150 times. No good treatment for OCD existed, even for the wealthiest man in the world.

But by 1991, Hughes would have had his choice of effective treatments—medications, behavior therapy, or both together. Not only were good treatments finally available, but OCD's brain anatomy had even been revealed by a team of researchers led by Dr. Lewis Baxter at UCLA.

In the fifteenth century, Martin Luther felt himself tortured by repetitive thoughts of sin. He confessed compulsively, often for six hours at a time, until even the most devoted priests threatened to punish him lest he stop. Some called him possessed. Others called him a prophet, and thus began the Protestant Reformation.

But by 1991, it could be said that Martin Luther simply suffered from obsessive-compulsive disorder, or, as Lew Baxter's research showed, an overactivity of the head of the caudate nucleus, in the frontal region of the brain. Lew's study, using positron emission tomography, or PET scans, was the first to pinpoint a dysfunction of thoughts to a specific brain region. Lew also showed that when a patient's OCD improved, whether through medication or psychotherapy, the brain's biology changed. That psychotherapy could change the brain's biology was just one of Lew's many breakthrough findings.

Soon an anatomical basis was sought for everything—for all mental disorders, for consciousness, for love. Even the urge to move one's right leg can now be seen in a brain scan. Anxiety and sadness can now be read not just in a person's face, but in his or her functional MRI (fMRI) scan. In 2000, a psychiatrist, Dr. Eric Kandel, won the Nobel Prize in medicine for showing how memory is stored in nerve cells, through the movement of molecules and electric current.

In his Nobel essay, I read that one of my medical school classmates, Dr. Kelsey Martin, a terrific dancer, even figured out that the location of long-term memory storage is in the body of nerve cells, not in its branching axons.

The switch happened so quickly. Thoughts, emotions, behavior. Personality, consciousness, soul. They were all being explained in terms of biology and chemistry, in molecules and electrical currents, rather than by the divine explanations of centuries past.

So much changed in terms of how we view the human mind, and how we view ourselves.

We had so much more to ponder.

Though I don't remember pondering. Mostly I remember prescribing, since new drugs, of course, also arrived in the 1990s.

When I began my psychiatry residency in 1991, many UCLA professors weren't sure yet if Prozac, a new kind of antidepressant recently released in 1987, even worked.

I remember prescribing Prozac for the very first time. My patient Eric Azure had recovered from his descent into madness. He no longer saw witches. He was back to his life as a graduate student, reading Braille, getting around town with the help of his Seeing Eye dog. His main problem, by then, was that his antidepressant, nortriptyline, made him drowsy. He had difficulty staying awake in class. He also looked abnormal, with his face as stiff as clay and his lips caked with dried saliva—not because of mental illness, but because of the side effects of his medication.

I decided to switch Eric from old-fashioned nortriptyline, to that new medicine, Prozac. Within a couple of weeks, Eric felt better. He looked normal for the first time since I'd known him.

I watched like a hawk for Prozac's side effects. I consulted my psychopharmacology handbooks and package inserts. I waited.

But months later, Eric was simply doing great. In my office, week after week, he looked happy. We took turns petting his guide dog. He enjoyed his new network of sight-impaired friends. He was looking forward to graduation.

I realized: Prozac was not only easier for Eric to take, it was easier for me to prescribe than the older generation of antidepressants. I didn't have to monitor labs or EKGs like I did with nortriptyline, which could cause cardiac arrhythmias and sudden death. I didn't have to fret about my patients living it up on wine and cheese and then having a fatal hypertensive reaction, as I did when I prescribed monoamine oxidase inhibitors.

Most significantly, I didn't have to worry about Eric overdosing. Even if he took a month's worth of Prozac, at worst he'd probably just get the jitters. Prozac was not lethal in overdose.

At the Indochinese Refugee Clinic in Chinatown, a Laotian man whom I couldn't understand, even through an interpreter, gave me a beautiful colored scarf. He put his palms together and bowed. The man thanked me for giving him Prozac, according to the translator. He felt good for the first time in his life.

In 1993, Peter Kramer's *Listening to Prozac* hit the bestseller lists. Prozac, the book argued, not only treated depression, it seemed to make some people more outgoing, less anxious—even better than their usual selves. Kramer speculated that Prozac might usher in an era of "cosmetic pharmacology," the psychiatric equivalent of cosmetic surgery, with the primary objective of enhancing, not curing. Indeed, even my hairdresser asked me for a hit of that new cosmetic, Prozac.

By the time I finished my residency in 1994, doctors joked about putting "vitamin P" in city water supplies. Interestingly, within a few years, Prozac would indeed be found in the groundwater of many cities, not intentionally put there, but, more tellingly, excreted by the multitudes ingesting it.

In the glow of Prozac's success, pharmaceutical companies recognized a new market for psychiatric medications with minimal side effects and minimal danger. These meds could be sold not just to the "mentally ill" but to anyone with depression or anxiety—in other words—all of us, a potentially limitless market. By 1994, Zoloft, Paxil, Luvox, and Effexor had joined Prozac on the druggist's shelf.

New antipsychotics also hit the market in the 1990s.

When Risperdal became available in 1994, I happened to be the chief resident of the OCD program at UCLA that, under Lew Baxter, had pinpointed obsessive-compulsive disorder to a specific region of the brain. I started giving Risperdal, a serotonin blocker, to OCD patients, encouraged by Lew and by Dr. Alexander Bystritsky, director of the OCD program. Surprisingly, a subset of patients tortured by visual obsessions found relief immediately. When I left UCLA, I asked my classmate Dr. Sanjaya Saxena to take over the work. Risperdal is now one of the standard treatments for patients with OCD, a contribution to psychiatry in which I'm sincerely proud to have played a part.

Only in retrospect, while writing this book, am I able to see that I was among the first psychiatrists to systematically use a new generation antipsychotic for a condition once considered a neurosis.

Today, new antipsychotics are prescribed not just for psychosis, but by primary-care physicians as broad-spectrum panaceas for anxiety, depression, mania, dementia, insomnia, and just about anything related to troubling emotions or thoughts.

As a medical student, I used to visit Yale medical historian Dr. David Musto in his office on the balcony of the softly lit Cushing/Whitney medical historical library. Dr. Musto's office, with its shelves of history texts, was always a welcome change of scene for me. He was a tall man with neatly parted brown hair, blue eyes behind tortoise-rim glasses, broad shoulders, and strong hands seemingly too large for the small keys of a typewriter or for the fragile, thin pages of antique books. After finishing medical school and a graduate degree in history, Musto worked at the National Institutes of Health in the 1960s shortly after the first antipsychotics and antidepressants were invented. Imaginative psychiatrists, he told me, speculated that medications might replace psychotherapy as the main treatment offered in psychiatry.

"But then we all said, 'Naw, it'll never happen,'" he said.

Yet this idea, once thought ludicrous, is our reality today.

In a perfect storm of circumstances, with health care corporations striving to increase profits and cut costs, the inevitable happened. Prozac, even at three dollars a pill, cost far less than regular sessions with a highly trained psychotherapist. Soon it became common for an adult or child in emotional pain to see a prescriber (a physician, nurse, or psychologist) and get several months' worth of vitamin P.

When I look back on my psychiatry residency—again, I can't believe what I ignored.

Martha, for example, always talked about the "end of psychiatry." But for some reason I didn't hear it, even though I respected her every word about things from psychotherapy to school politics to kitchen organization, and despite her informed perspective as vice president of the American Psychiatric Association.

At one point, however, I finally had the good sense to ask Martha what she actually meant.

"The way it's looking," she replied, "psychiatrists will supervise others—counselors, nurses, family practitioners. But you won't be treating patients."

It seemed too far-fetched. Yet Martha was right. On the University of New Mexico Psychiatry Consultation-Liaison Service, for example, my work was to supervise nurses, psychologists, and trainees. Only in my private practice in Alabama did I care for patients wholly, with medications and psychotherapy, in my office and while they were hospitalized—before I realized that insurance companies weren't paying me for this kind of devoted care. That I would find this kind of care unfeasible for the rest of my career.

Toward the end of my psychiatry residency, in 1994, I also ignored that Joel held regular town hall–style meetings, trying to calm anxieties over the tremendous changes caused by "managed care," the accepted euphemism for for-profit health companies then.

My residency class that began in 1991 had sixteen residents. The class that began in 1994 had only twelve residents, to save costs. In 1991, the average hospital stay was approximately a month. Even then, I remember complaining, "A month—that's barely enough time for an antidepressant to begin working." But by the time I finished my residency in 1994, the average hospitalization was about a week.

In terms of basic mathematics, the average hospitalization decreasing from four weeks to one week, meant four times the admissions and discharges. At the same time, 25 percent fewer residents were doing the work. That meant about five times the work for each resident, just in terms of admissions and discharges.

How could patient care not suffer?

I also noticed changes in the skills of the psychiatry residents. In 1991, all competent psychiatry residents knew how to prescribe the older tricyclic and monoamine oxidase inhibitor (MAOI) antidepressants. But among residents who entered the residency in 1993, many never prescribed a tricyclic or an MAOI. Prozac and similar drugs were easier, safer.

Everything changed during the three years of my psychiatry residency. Our medications changed, our treatment strategies changed, and our understanding of the mind changed.

Psychiatry changed and psychiatrists changed.

Psychotherapy, the foundation of psychiatry since its beginning, became quite secondary; and it was, in fact, something many of my fellow psychiatry residents didn't want to do, even if, ironically, research and brain-imaging studies in the 1990s increasingly proved the effectiveness of psychotherapy.

In the 1980s and 1990s, human health and emotions began to be processed assembly-line style, for profit. What used to be considered conflicts of the soul became treated en masse with industrially manufactured pills.

Years after my residency, I went to visit Martha to introduce her to Zoe. Sitting in her garden, as I did when I was a resident, I admired her view of Brentwood Canyon. Zoe was on all fours, entranced by the garden hose.

"Sometimes I wonder if we're replacing human interaction with drugs," I said to Martha. "I mean, we've all done it—prescribed Prozac so people can stay in bad marriages without working on relationships or growing. Prescribed Ritalin so kids calm down and parents can keep ignoring them. Am I being too cynical?"

"You're not cynical enough, Dora. Never have been."

"An important relationship, that's almost forgotten now, is the doctor-patient relationship, isn't it, Martha?"

"It's a good thing you're writing these days," Martha said. "Because the narrative between doctor and patient is over."

Psychiatry has taken its remarkable metamorphosis all in stride. Replacing psychotherapy with medications as our core treatment happened so smoothly. Perhaps it's because medications have gotten so effective. Truly, they have brought remarkable advances. But perhaps there's also another reason.

During my residency, professors advised us to secure contracts with pharmaceutical companies before graduation, if possible. Money from private industry was essential for an academic career, since government funding for research was dwindling, increasingly being channeled toward military spending. Besides, support from pharmaceutical corporations also came with great bonuses like free dinners at expensive restaurants, trips to lavish resorts in Hawaii, Puerto Rico, etc., etc.

Thus, psychiatry in recent years has been steered by leaders dependent on funding from pharmaceutical companies. Recently, medical students at Harvard have complained that their professors receive so much funding from pharmaceutical corporations, their lectures sound like drug ads.

But during my residency, I also ignored the advice to chum up to big *Pharma*.

Instead, I was busy hanging out with my boyfriend in his apartment overlooking the canals of Venice Beach. I had met Chris during the first year of my residency. After a straight three days and two nights of hospital duty in those days before work-hour limitations, my friend Marc asked if I wanted to go to a Getty Museum event, a showing of the movie *Truth or Dare*. Sure, I said. After spending three days in the hospital, why just go home, sleep, and return to the hospital? With us that night was Marc's friend, an architect with an athlete's tan and an artist's ponytail. He didn't seem to mind how I shoved fries into my mouth, substituting junk food for sleep. And so, around the time of the Los Angeles riots, when the city burned for days and nights, when Rodney King pled for us all to get along, I was busy falling in love.

During the last days of my residency, traffic was even thicker in

West Los Angeles than usual. In June 1994, O. J. Simpson's estranged wife, Nicole Brown Simpson, and her friend Ronald Goldman, were murdered. Looky-loos crowded the streets to drive past O.J.'s Brentwood mansion, and the Mezzaluna restaurant, where Nicole had her last meal, and where UCLA psychiatrists liked to lunch.

One evening, after battling the O.J. traffic, as I called it, I arrived at Martha's house in the Brentwood hills a half-hour late. For months, we had talked about my plans after residency. Martha, to my surprise, didn't advise me to seek a tenure-track professor position at UCLA. "You should live in a lot of different places when you're young," she had said. *What kind of career advice was this?* It wasn't career advice, I realized, but life advice.

Nibbling on salad, enjoying yellow bulb tomatoes from her garden, I said, "Martha, you advised me to live in a lot of different places."

She nodded.

"I know you were probably thinking Paris or Rome. But how about Alabama?" I explained that Chris was offered a job in the Architecture Department at Auburn University.

"Alabama. It's not quite what I meant," Martha said. "But I guess that's a different place."

Part Three

Changing Times

1995–2002

Chapter Nine

My Own Private Practice

1995

Throughout Auburn and nearby Opelika, vines creep up telephone poles and trees, shrouding them, making them look like giants clothed in leaves. Abandoned shacks and old homes litter the countryside, decomposing, rusting, eaten by the lushness.

Chris explains that the vine is kudzu, imported a hundred years ago to prevent soil erosion. But kudzu took on its own life and is now called the vine that ate the South. At the university, Chris's fellow architecture professors warn him to sleep with his windows shut, lest kudzu grow into the house at night. Herbicides don't work. Some actually promote kudzu's growth. So the native southerners have resigned themselves to a peaceful coexistence. They enjoy the shade kudzu provides. They weave baskets from its vines.

Down the kudzu-lined street from the local hospital, I hang my doctor's shingle. Just out of residency, I know little about running a practice. Like a lot of doctors, I've even avoided knowing about money, as if it is a tainted topic. At UCLA, Martha tried to prepare me. "At the end of each session, hold out your hand and say to your patient, 'That will be five dollars.' Then take the money to the cashier yourself." She extended her palm to demonstrate.

Bills in my hand, the words "five dollars" rolling from my mouth—it felt so beneath the noble goal of healing patients. I ignored Martha.

When I arrived in Auburn, I talked to Gary Red, the administrator in charge of psychiatry at the hospital. The town has never had a board-certified psychiatrist, not even close, he said. He suggested I team up with another good psychiatrist soon moving to town. We could share office expenses and a receptionist's salary. But it would be my own practice. The receptionist had already arrived. But it would take the psychiatrist a few more months to get licensed. She went to medical school in Mexico, Gary explained.

"Is she Mexican?" I asked.

"She's American," Gary said. "She's the most efficient person I've ever met. You'll see. She thought it more efficient to do medical school abroad, rather than jump through the hoops of applying to American medical schools."

So, on Gary's suggestion, I hang a shingle outside a small building down the road from the hospital, on a sidewalk free of kudzu, in the small southern town of Opelika, Alabama.

I open my own private practice.

Most of the United States had been penetrated (not my choice of words, theirs) by for-profit managed-care corporations by the spring of 1995. "Managed care," as far as I can tell, means that physicians and other clinicians get *managed* by clerical workers and business-men. And yet this kudzu-covered, often neglected semirural region is one of the last havens of traditional medical practice, where doctors still treat patients free from the influence of managed care.

In the mornings, I see patients on the hospital's inpatient psychiatric ward. In hallways and in the doctors' dining room, I meet other physicians, like Dr. William Lazenby, a distinguished gray-haired southern gentleman and one of the first physicians in this area, where his family has lived for generations.

As we pour coffee in the dining room, Bill says to me, "Used to be we couldn't get doctors to come out here. Now we can't stop them from coming."

Orthopedic surgeons, cardiothoracic surgeons, and every type of specialist is now available to this small population of seventy thousand people in Auburn and Opelika, he says. Citizens even have a wide choice of specialists. In this bucolic area, people joke, medicine is practiced so vigorously that by the time a woman is fifty, she's had her uterus removed, her gallbladder out, and an angioplasty. And from what I've seen, she's also been put on a cocktail of useless psychiatric medicines.

In the afternoons, I go to my office, where work is, well, slow. I imagine the community watching, checking me out, a psychiatrist in this semirural region where psychiatry doesn't have a good name, an Asian-American living with a Caucasian architecture professor, where nearby Randolph County High School lies in ashes. It burned to the ground amid the controversy over whether the prom, in 1995, should be racially desegregated.

By now, the O. J. Simpson trial is on TV all the time. In the racially charged trial, an Asian-American, Lance Ito, sits at the judge's bench. Halfway across the country, in Auburn-Opelika, I joke about being the Lance Ito of the local medical community.

One afternoon I get a call from Dr. Walkup, a pulmonologist.

"Mrs. Teal has lung cancer," he says. "But she's too weak for surgery. She's got an anxiety condition. Can you help?"

"Sure, I'll do my best." This is exactly what I do best, the interface of psychiatric and medical illnesses, consultation-liaison psychiatry.

In the hospital, Mrs. Teal is a pale wisp of a woman with limp hair devoid of pigment. Her voice is weak, a dying breeze. In her records, I find no medical reason for weakness. When I see her medication list, I understand. Valium 10 mg twice a day, Elavil 25 mg at bedtime, and Trilafon—all sedating medicines she's taken for about twenty years. No wonder she is so weak.

I stop the medicines.

The next day, Dr. Walkup calls, "Thank you, Dr. Wang. The patient is much better. We'll operate right away."

Even I am surprised. And when I visit Mrs. Teal, she smiles. Her face is full of expression, her body energetic.

Mrs. Teal has her surgery. She survives her lung cancer.

Word spreads about "that new psychiatrist in town."

Celeste, the psychiatry ward's head nurse, and her staff, compliment me on all the patients who had lost hope but who are now getting better under my care. *Finally, a psychiatrist who knows how to talk to patients*, they say. Here's what I gather. Never mind that I am Asian-American, and a Californian at that. Never mind that I speak plain, unaccented English, rather than the language the locals call "Southern." Never mind my fancy credentials from Yankee schools. All that can be forgiven, for here I am, at last, a psychiatrist with good manners.

In our dining room one evening, Chris and I listen to the music of tree frogs and crickets singing loudly in a kudzu thicket. Chris has furnished our dining room in "college student moderne." There's green Astroturf, a red oval table from a yard sale, and white plastic lawn chairs with curved backs. It's a look that makes sense while we're paying off our student loans. I like the look.

Chris's face is long as he picks up a homemade tortilla chip. We fry our own tortilla chips since we can't find them in town.

"What's the matter, C?"

"B.J. was walking on campus," Chris says, crunching on a chip. "He felt a pain in his chest. His doctor says he needs a triple bypass right away."

"Has he ever had problems before?" I ask, puzzled because B.J. is a young architecture professor just older than Chris.

"Never," Chris says. "He's never even taken any medications his whole life. Fate is amazing."

"Fate, and good benefits," I say. "Sounds like he may be suffering from a case of good university health insurance."

Traditional fee-for-service medical care, like anything else, is subject to abuses. One of the rationales for managed care is to rein in physicians with profit on the brain.

For example, the Psychiatric Institutes of America, a division of National Medical Enterprises, was convicted of multiple crimes, such as paying kickbacks to schoolteachers for referring students for psychiatric hospitalization, hospitalizing people unnecessarily, often against their will, and psychiatrists billing handsomely, even without seeing the patients. According to *The New York Times*, even a three-year-old child was hospitalized for months, against the will of the parents. Many of the hospitalized persons were labeled psychotic or dangerous, but as soon as their insurance benefits were exhausted, their symptoms coincidentally disappeared, or so their medical records said. In the nation's largest scandal in the history of psychiatry, federal courts convicted the PIA of fraud, and many offenders were sent to federal penitentiary. Psychiatrists found themselves sentenced to five-year, even eight-year, terms.

One of the missions of managed care is to curb such abuses and overcharging. Just out of residency, I don't understand the specifics of managed care, but here's what I know.

In Atlantic City, my friend Dr. T, who admires the lights of casinos from his house, was one of the fortunate psychiatrists to land a contract with a managed-care company. The company gave him a "capitated rate" (again, not my term, theirs), which meant that Dr. T was paid a set sum for each *head* under his care. For this lump sum, he was responsible for providing all psychiatric services for the company's patients. This ensured Dr. T a certain income. More so, it capped costs for the insurance company while shifting financial risks onto Dr. T. The patients, having paid their money up front, could only hope that they could actually access care when they needed it. Dr. T could only hope that his lump sum would cover his costs. It seemed to me that the sole things truly *managed* were the insurance company's costs and risk. The managed care company could thus proceed safely with its job, which was to market insurance and gain more "penetration."

Another managed-care system involved "panels." Doctors on the panels agreed to be paid reduced rates. Doctors not on the panels simply wouldn't be paid at all. Around the country, doctors who clung to their ideals and resisted joining managed-care panels found themselves without patients. Or they found themselves caring for patients, then getting stiffed.

Many physicians in fact moved to Auburn-Opelika seeking a

second chance. They refused to give in to managed care elsewhere, and were left out of the game.

One new physician in town is Dr. Sharon Purple, a psychiatrist. Some say she was left out of the game in her hometown. Others say that Dr. Purple is no longer welcome in her hometown, since her father was convicted of being a quack, and is now doing time.

When Dr. Purple arrives, the community buzzes about her executive lifestyle, her big house, her Cadillac, and how her husband, a retired military man, is already chumming with the good ole boys at the country club. She wears fitted suits, and her short blond hair in an immaculate bob, a look that says she's all business. Most would call her a very attractive woman.

In her office next door to mine, Sharon Purple installs a shiny mahogany desk, the kind with curly legs. I find her friendly enough, even sympathetic in her manner. But I can't help but notice the look on her face when Chris pulls into our parking lot in his beat-up old Volvo.

Outside the brick office building we share, Sharon hangs her shingle above mine. She immediately has a clientele. Old-time hospital physicians refer patients to her right away. In a hospital corridor, I overhear, "At last, an *American* psychiatrist who knows how to talk to patients."

On weekends, the few psychiatrists on staff take turns covering the hospital psych ward.

On a Saturday morning when it's my turn, I swim through thick parking-lot humidity to the hospital. The air-conditioned lobby cools and comforts the pores of my skin.

On the psychiatry ward, Celeste guides a trio of elderly patients to their rooms. She smiles, waves, and walks toward me. She is a tall, young woman with long blond hair curled at the tips. Thick eyelashes frame her blue eyes.

"Celeste, what do you think of Dr. Purple?" I ask. "Everyone seems to like her."

"You can tell about someone," Celeste says, "when they treat some people all nice and treat others completely different, if you know what I mean."

"What do you mean?" I ask.

"I mean, the ones with insurance get the white glove. And the other patients, I don't even want to say. And if you ask me, there ain't nothing wrong with that patient Heather who's been here two weeks—except that her Medicaid covers thirty days of inpatient psychiatric hospitalization."

Celeste picks up her clipboard and leads me to patients' rooms. Tom, a lanky young man, lies in bed, staring at the ceiling.

"Twenty-eight-year-old guy," Celeste says. "Dr. Purple's treating him for schizophrenia. The problem we nurses have is that he don't sleep at night. He's up all night talking to voices when there ain't no one there."

"Doesn't sleep?"

"I've never needed much sleep," Tom says.

I ask a few more questions, then I turn to Celeste. "I think he's bipolar. Let's give him Depakote 250 mg three times a day, starting this morning."

She nods and hands me Tom's chart to write the order.

We stop outside the next door.

"This one Dr. P's diagnosed as bipolar. She's a nineteen-year-old college sophomore in her first manic break. Talks a mile a minute. One minute wants to be the first woman president, the next minute she wants six babies. Her parents want her transferred to Birmingham, closer to home, but Dr. Purple says she's too unstable. Oh, and by the way, she's got good insurance, if you follow my drift."

Ruth is a young woman with a large mane of tousled blond hair. She wears gray sweatpants and an orange Auburn University T-shirt.

"When can I go?" she laughs. "I got a paper due, and registration for the fall semester, and I got so many plans with my friends, and my parents want me to go home . . ."

I don't bother interrupting her. I let her go on and on and on.

When I look at her meds, I understand. Her lithium level is 0.4, just below the effective range of 0.5 to 1.0. She is also on a low dose of Elavil, an antidepressant known to cause mania in bipolars.

In her chart, I write orders to discontinue Elavil and to increase lithium.

Well into the afternoon, I finish seeing all the ward's patients.

"It's good to finally have a doctor who takes the time to understand our patients," Celeste says. "See you in the morning."

Laughter rises from the backyard as I pull into the driveway of my house.

In my living room, empty green Heineken bottles stand in rows, like soldiers.

It's Sambo, Chris's fellow architecture professor, apparently visiting again from Greensboro, in western Alabama, where he spends most of his time. Sambo is not Alabamian, but Mississippian, from Canton, a small town which for Sambo is like air. Running Auburn's Rural Studio program in Greensboro, Sambo is close enough to Canton so that on weekends, he can breathe. In the Rural Studio, students don't write papers or build models; they put their efforts into building real structures for people who can't otherwise afford them. A chapel is constructed of discarded tires filled with soil. A new house has a metal roof that spreads like butterfly wings. Shepherd Bryant, a descendant of slaves and the son of sharecroppers, has a contemporary house made of hay bales. Sambo's philosophy, Chris says, is that everyone has a need for beauty, not just the rich, but especially people who can't afford much of anything, like Shepherd, who teaches pigs to sing.

In my backyard, Sambo stirs a large metal pot over a fire. He is a huge man, and steam is rising into his long ZZ Top beard. The scent of crawfish and spice floats through the air. Sambo pulls a crawfish from the pot. He puts the red critter on his shoulder, puckers his lips and smooches it.

Tinka, a blond woman almost as large as Sambo, nudges him. "Sambo, let's get you a bambi. You can park it in my backyard. Then you won't have to pay rent."

Sambo must be talking again about how broke he is.

I pick up a Sprite, since I'm on call. I sit on a rock next to Chris. "Tinka, what on earth is a bambi?"

"A trailer. One of those streamlined ones." She turns to Sambo. "You could use the bathroom and kitchen in my house."

None of us has ever seen Sambo's run-down Auburn apartment. Sambo himself doesn't like being in it, which is why, when he's in town, there is always a party.

"Dora," Sambo says, "you ever hear that joke . . . ? What do a hurricane and an Alabama divorce have in common?" His voice is deep, with a booming quality and a singing Mississippi tone.

"What?" I ask.

Sambo finishes off his Heineken. "Someone's bound to lose a trailer."

Everyone laughs.

"And the title of your self-help book, *Solace for the Soul*. Hmm, mind if I use *Shelter for the Soul*?"

Minutes later, Jack Williams walks over from next door and joins us. He is a tall, distinguished man who taught at Harvard most of his career. After a divorce, Jack moved to Auburn. He lives with Kimberly, a redheaded woman with a spirited manner.

Jack ladles crawfish and vegetables from the pot into plastic bowls. I take a bowl and sip the spicy soup.

In the early evening, while music plays in my backyard, I crawl into bed with the aroma of crawfish and spice still in my senses. I fall asleep to the sound of Chris's laughter, to Sambo's deep storytelling voice, Jack's sharp Maine accent, and Kimberly's lilting Alabama voice, to music, and the sound of students chatting, dancing.

I am awakened by headlights in the window, southern accents, a Maine accent, and Sambo's laughter.

Chris runs into the room, laughing, clearly having enjoyed a lot of Heinekens. He and Sambo were driving around town, looking at buildings. Then they decided to shine headlights into Jack's bedroom. Jack's pissed. Sambo's apologetic. But everything's okay.

I drift back to sleep, to the sound of critters singing outside.

My pager buzzes. The room is dark. This time, Chris is snoring next to me, in a beer-and-spice slumber.

I call the number on my pager. It's the ER. I listen and repeat, "Suicidal transvestite. Black man in a jeans skirt. Okay. Picked up hitchhiking. Now he says he's suicidal? Okay. Go ahead and admit him. I'll see him in the morning."

Chris stirs and looks at me.

"I'm sorry to wake you, C."

"No problem, D."

I nestle next to him, and in his arms I drift back to sleep.

Sunday morning, I look for Celeste on the psych ward.

"Tom's all better," she says. "I don't know what you did, but he slept for the first time last night. And today he sounds just fine. And Ruth. She's fine today, too. She talks rational this morning. A complete turnaround. Her parents are over there. You should go see them."

In the waiting room, a couple in crisp linen clothes and worried faces fidget on the sofa.

I hold out my hand, "I'm Dr. Wang. I'm covering for Dr. Purple this weekend."

"Oh, thank goodness—our daughter is much better today," the woman says.

"It's because I adjusted her medications," I say proudly. I explain about lithium, and about how Elavil can increase mania. I drop a few of my credentials—Yale Medical School, UCLA chief resident. I don't usually try to pilfer patients, but Ruth has her whole life ahead of her. I tell them there are good psychiatrists at the University of Alabama in Birmingham, near their home. I even mention a specific name, Dr. Charles Ford. I'd also be happy to treat their daughter.

Ruth's father responds, "Dr. Purple gets back tomorrow, right?"

"Yes," I say. "Monday morning."

I thank them for their time. I turn down the hall to find Stephena, the transvestite I admitted while on call. She's in a short denim skirt with many zippers. Her legs are tanned and muscular. She wears a wig of teased, black hair.

I decide that Stephena needs to stay hospitalized for her own safety, even if she has no insurance.

Stephena, however, has her own opinion. "Look at this dump." Her eyes scan the bare walls. "I'm cured. Discharge me."

Monday morning, Celeste drawls, "I told Dr. Purple, I said to her, 'Dr. Wang dun fixed all your patients over the weekend.' She says she wants to talk to you. Sorry if I got you in trouble."

I find Sharon in the chart room. She's wearing stockings beneath her navy blue skirt, even in this humidity. She rises from her chair. Not a strand of her blond hair moves.

"I have a request," she says, smiling. "I'm going to ask that when you cover for me, you don't change my patients' meds. I'll give you the same respect."

"Sure, Sharon. If that's what you want."

"Thank you," she says, turning from me in her starched white shirt and pearls.

Through the window of the chart room, I watch Sharon walk toward Ruth's worried parents. They sigh in relief as she approaches. They rise to shake her hand then they sit down to listen. Their eyes drink in her every word.

Ruth is manic again the next day. She sits on her bed scribbling nonsense, page after page. She's on the phone, talking and laughing, all at once.

In the hallway outside her room, her parents thank Dr. Sharon Purple for staying by them, even though their daughter is so unstable.

I am reminded of Sun Tzu's ancient text *The Art of War*, and Thomas Cleary's translation of it on my bookshelf. The introduction assures me that even in ancient China, it was nearly impossible to judge physicians:

According to an old story, a lord of ancient China once asked his physician, a member of a family of healers, which of them was the most skilled in the art.

The physician whose reputation was such that his name became synonymous with medical science in China replied, "My eldest brother sees the spirit of sickness and removes it before it takes shape, so his name does not get out of the house.

"My elder brother cures sickness when it is still extremely minute, so his name does not get out of the neighborhood.

"As for me, I puncture veins, prescribe potions, and massage skin, so from time to time my name gets out and is heard among the lords."

Gary Red calls and asks to meet with me.

"Dora, we could use you in our program. Join us." He sits behind an imposing mahogany desk. He has a large mustache, a matching mop of hair, and blue eyes sandwiched in between.

"What do you mean, Gary? I'm already working here."

"We're building a new psychiatry program. Around Dr. Purple, who knows how to cater to managed care. But we can use someone with your credentials. It would be good for marketing."

I like Gary, and by now I feel comfortable with him. "You know that Sharon and I practice in pretty different ways," I say.

"Don't worry. You'll learn from her."

"I'm concerned about some of Sharon's practices," I clarify. I mention patients who seem to stay ill for as long as they have hospitalization benefits. I mention her prescribing Dilantin, a useless medication for psychiatric purposes. I mention the elderly woman who pulled at Sharon's sleeve and begged to not be discharged, because she was still sick. To which Sharon replied curtly and with a smile, "But your benefits are all used up."

Gary tries to reassure me. "Don't worry. Sharon's father is in the federal pen. Sharon's too smart to get caught like that."

Gary. He's so earnest.

"I'll think about your offer, Gary," I say.

But as I walk out the door, I can't imagine that Gary would think I'd ever join Dr. Purple's program.

Managed care indeed arrives. I know, when for the first time I have to seek a "prior authorization."

Cindy, my new patient, sits in front of my window, which by now is framed by kudzu. She wears a low-cut pink flowered shirt and tight jeans. Long, untamed curls frame her fluttering eyes.

"My midterms are coming up and I just can't study," she says.

A differential, a menu of possible diagnoses, forms in my head. *Depression, attention deficit disorder, or adjustment disorder from some kind of stress in her life . . .*

"I can't concentrate because I see things that can't be there. Trains rush past my dorm-room window. They're distracting."

"What floor is your dorm room on?"

"The fourth floor. The trains followed me to your office, right down the middle of the highway. I swerved to keep from hitting them. I know they're not there. Like right now, I see mice running across your desk. They're white."

My office might be messy, but it is not rodent-infested. I am suddenly self-conscious about the papers on my desk—progress notes, billing forms, and messages from a dozen calls I need to return.

Cindy's large smile turns to laughter, even when speaking of mice. Schizophrenia seems unlikely for this well-groomed straight-A college student. I revise my differential. *Major depression with psychotic features, mania with psychotic features, drugs.* In the next hour, my evaluation confirms what she tells me—she is bipolar and in the midst of a manic episode with hallucinations.

"I don't trust you to drive home," I say. "What do you think about coming into the hospital for a few days?"

"I don't trust myself, either. I think I need to be hospitalized."

"I see that your insurance requires a prior authorization. Why don't you take a seat in the waiting room and I'll call them."

"Sure."

I neaten the piles on my desk. I jot notes in preparation for my first encounter with managed care. I want to make a good impression to the entity entrusted with saving our medical system from spiraling costs, and which has made or broken the careers of so many physicians. It feels almost like an audition.

I dial the 800 number. I navigate a brief phone tree successfully, and push a few numbers and # signs. Finally, a young male voice says, "Hi, I'm Brian, your client satisfaction representative. How may I help you?"

"I'd like to request your prior authorization to hospitalize a patient," I say politely. "She's a twenty-year-old college student with bipolar disorder. She's in the midst of a manic episode with psychotic features. She has visual hallucinations of mice running across my desk—I assure you, I have no mice in my office."

He laughs. I've scored a point with him.

"I don't think it's safe for her to be out of the hospital," I continue. "For example, she swerved on the highway to avoid a visual hallucination of a train. Luckily, she didn't hit anyone, not this time, anyways."

"Is hospitalization really necessary?" he asks. "I'm wondering, where did you do your training, Dr. Wang?"

"Yale School of Medicine," I say. "Then I was a chief resident at the UCLA Neuropsychiatric Institute." I am eager to make a good impression.

"UCLA," he says. "That's where I just graduated. Great place! I miss it a lot, especially the football."

"What did you study?" I ask.

"Just got my bachelor's in business administration. God, I miss

UCLA, the weather, the cafés, Westwood, all the great sports. Especially the football."

"Go Bruins!" I say.

"You a fan?"

"I'm a Bruins fan. But here in Alabama I've learned to say, 'War Eagle!'"

We chat several more minutes about college football, as I schmooze the young man who will decide Cindy's treatment, and possibly my career.

Brian changes the focus of our conversation. "Now, does everyone who gets really depressed start hallucinating?"

"No, not everyone," I say.

"Explain."

"Well, genetic studies show that psychotic features sort independently from mood disorders, and more with family histories of schizophrenia."

"What do you mean?"

"I guess it would take a long time to explain." I glance at the clock. I've been on the phone twenty minutes. I am twenty minutes late for my next patient.

"What about mania?" he says. "Is it necessarily related to depression? Or could it be a different thing altogether?"

I am silent.

"I guess I'm just philosophizing," he says.

"You have a lot of good questions," I say. "But it would take me a long time to explain everything I know about mood disorders from my four years of med school and my four years of internship and residency." That's eight solid years of medical training I can't compress into this phone call.

"Dr. Wang, it's been so nice chatting with you. I'll go ahead and approve our patient for five days of inpatient hospitalization."

Five days seems not necessarily too short, but too definitive. Each patient is different. I can't predict how long it will take Cindy to respond to medications. How can he predict five days? But I'm eager to make a good impression.

"Okay," I say. "And then I'll need to see her for follow-up appointments."

"How many?"

"Depends on how she's doing."

"You mean you don't know?" Brian says.

"Well, I guess, every week for a month, and then every month for six months."

"You've got it, Dr. Wang. Go Bruins!"

"And, Brian, War Eagle to you."

I walk to the waiting room. Cindy and two other patients look at me. I am thirty minutes late for my two-thirty appointment. My three p.m. appointment has just arrived.

I stand at the doorway and face the room, "I'm sorry. I'm running about a half-hour late today."

It is a good thing I don't have to get prior authorizations for all my patients. At least not yet.

With the arrival of managed care, I wait to see which psychologists will be the chosen providers. I assume they'll choose the group of competent university professors who for years have cared for most of this community's psychotherapy needs.

Not every psychotherapist in town is competent. Dr. Lance Amber, refreshingly, doesn't even pretend. He is a young guy with hay-colored hair and sky-blue eyes. He could pass for a frat boy. He is friendly, and on the wards flashes a large smile at me.

"Dora, I'd like to ask your expert opinion about Iris," he says.

"Sure," I say, flattered. "I think Iris has borderline personality."

"How would you treat her?" Lance asks.

"Well, an antidepressant might help. Maybe a low-dose antipsychotic." I assume Lance is asking about medication treatments.

"How would you approach this from a therapy standpoint?"

"Well, I think dialectical behavior therapy has some promise. But it's new and the jury's still out. I think the main objective is still to foster a clear sense of boundaries, a sense of security in the world . . ."

"So, in sessions, you would . . ."

"Rapport. Mirroring. When she starts to test boundaries, I'd . . ." And then I realize. Lance is not just being collegial. He actually doesn't know what to do with his patient.

By the time I walk away a half-hour later, I feel as if I should bill Lance for tuition. I soon learn that Dr. Amber's doctorate is not in psychology, but in some other field, which, in this state, suffices for a psychotherapist's license.

Surprisingly, Dr. Amber is the therapist chosen by the managed-care companies for their patients. Why has he been chosen over the better-qualified university faculty? Is it because Dr. Amber charges less, since few choose to see him? Is it because the insurance companies consider him easier to control? Or did he simply have the foresight to call and ask the insurance companies?

Leaving the hospital one sweltering afternoon, blood rises into my face. I am seeing Dr. Amber's hospital patients since they have to be followed by a psychiatrist. I assume the liability if something goes wrong. And yet it is Dr. Amber who gets paid. My work goes unpaid, since I am not a "chosen provider." And then I realize that Dr. Amber is not to blame for this crazy system.

Providing the best care is obviously not managed care's priority. I even formulate a conspiracy theory. Most knowledgeable patients see the university professors for psychotherapy. But since the professors are not on the "managed-care panels," those patients would probably choose to pay from their own pockets to see the professors. Do the insurance companies want patients to pay insurance premiums, and then pay for care, too? Nah! How cynical of me!

Maybe it's different elsewhere. After all, southerners have always complained about carpetbaggers. So I call a friend in Boston.

"Yvonne, how's managed care working out in Boston?" Yvonne is a psychologist affiliated with Harvard.

"Well, it's why some of us are trying to write more books," she says.

"Managed care is driving you to write books?"

"Well, we're trying to make income in other ways. Patients come to us in crisis, maybe suicidal or in danger of hurting someone. Of course, we care for them. We can't turn them away, and they need care *now*, not next month. We submit to their insurance companies for payment. Then six weeks, sometimes months later, the insurance companies tell us they won't pay. In the meantime, we've already provided the care—for free, it turns out. It's so frustrating. So we're trying to do other things—like write books."

"It's cost-shifting," I say. "They keep the money and you do the work. You're caught between lawyers pressuring you to do more, and insurance companies pressuring you to do less."

"It's not the way it should be," Yvonne says.

The word "denial" is all over the letters insurance companies have sent me. I am getting paid for about two-thirds of my patients. And when I do get paid, there seems always a reason for my not getting paid in full.

Sitting at my desk, with kudzu shading my window, I find myself getting angry when patients call. Phone calls are just more unpaid work. Then I catch myself. I never resented my work as an unpaid medical student or as a resident earning less than minimum wage.

No, I'm not angry about being unpaid. I'm angry because others are getting paid for the work I am doing. The insurance company pockets more money when they pay me less. Their work is to take premiums up front from patients, then exercise ingenuity in *not paying* for care.

But at least I'll be paid for Cindy's care, even if it cost me half an hour of talking football with Brian.

But then, a letter arrives from Cindy's managed-care company, a letter without a single complete sentence, but a lot of numbers and abbreviations. At the bottom of the page are zeros.

I pick up the phone to call Brian. I navigate the phone tree. I navigate some more.

Finally, a human voice says, "Hi, I'm Chad, your client satisfaction representative. How may I provide you with excellent customer service?"

"I'd like to speak with Brian," I say.

"Brian who?"

"He never mentioned his last name."

"He might be in a different office, in a different city. I have no way of knowing if there is a Brian or not."

"There's a Brian, and he gave me prior authorization for the treatment of this patient."

"Do you have a prior authorization number?"

"I didn't know such a thing existed."

"Well, what's the patient's name and date of birth."

Chad looks up Cindy's information. "I found the account. You were authorized to treat her. But she had already used up her benefits."

"Why didn't Brian tell me?"

"He probably didn't know."

"So what you're saying is that even though I spent half an hour getting prior authorization, and then treated the patient, I won't be paid for the treatment you've authorized?"

"Her benefits were already used up."

"Well, thank you. You've been extremely helpful," I say with my best southern manners, while hanging up on Chad.

The important thing is that Cindy is better. Cindy is alive. Within two days under my care, her hallucinations melted away. Her mania subsided. She aced her midterms. Payment or no payment, I never considered whether or not I would care for Cindy.

But if I had treated her for free, it would have cost me less.

Many of my patients seem to have only one problem—getting worked to the brink, for the profit of others. I can relate.

Travis has driven a truck since he was a young man. He was treated as family by the family who owned the trucking company. But after the company was bought by a national corporation, Travis and his fellow truckers drove harder and faster. The corporation needed to increase profits to stockholders each year. Many truckers took amphetamines to keep up.

To Travis, even familiar highways looked different under the new management. He no longer saw trees and people sitting on their porches, but the speed of his clock and the rolling numbers of his odometer. Each year, Travis had to arrive sooner, more often. Racing to meet a deadline, Travis felt a pain in his chest, like he was knifed. An angiogram showed that his heart was fine. A second angiogram also showed nothing wrong with his heart. On the road again, Travis had another attack. This time, his doctor ordered his gallbladder removed. The attacks continued. Teeth were removed. Finally, panic attacks were considered. Travis was put on Paxil and sent to me. Paxil calmed Travis's panic attacks. But when Travis returned to his extreme work schedule, the chest pains returned.

The problem, I can only conclude, isn't Travis's physiology but his work schedule.

How can anyone keep increasing productivity every year, even on Paxil? Travis's job, which is no longer about people but numbers, seems not humanly possible.

Also not humanly possible are the jobs at the nearby tire plant, which operates twenty-four hours a day, a machine's schedule, not a human being's. I learn this from Joe.

"I can't sleep," Joe says. "I toss and turn, then I can't get up when it's time to go to work."

Depression? Anxiety? Drug abuse?

"What time do you go to bed at night?" I ask.

He is silent.

"Well, what time does your workday begin?"

His face reddens. "Midnight, this week. Eight a.m., next week. And in two weeks I'll be on swing shift—four in the afternoon."

"Your schedule changes from day to night, every two weeks?"

"My wife can never count on me to pick up our son from school. I can't take him to Little League. My schedule changes all the time."

"Why do they switch your schedule so often?"

"They say it's not fair for some people to work night shift all the time."

"So now everyone works night shift," I say. "We're circadian creatures. It takes people days or weeks to get over jet lag. It's like you're jet-lagged all the time. I'm curious. How long do employees usually last?"

"Just a few years. Two, maybe five. Come to think of it, I don't know anyone who's made it to retirement."

"Well, that's a clever business strategy," I say.

I've lived in Auburn almost two years now. I am happy with my busy practice, and happy about helping my patients. Sure, I'm pissed at the "explanation of benefits" forms insurance companies have sent instead of money, forms inexplicably without explanations. Even with all my higher education, I can't understand these forms. All I know is that I've worked day and night for two years, yet I'm barely breaking even. I'm not extravagant. Our decor is still college student moderne. Yet I've accumulated no savings.

But the main reason I need to leave Alabama isn't financial, professional, or social.

It is because of my own medical care.

While finishing my residency in Los Angeles two years ago, an accident changed my life.

Late on a beautiful and warm night, traffic was thick on Sunset Boulevard north of UCLA. A stoplight turned from red to green. I inched forward, then braked when the light turned red. Suddenly, my car was hit from behind. My neck throbbed immediately. In the rearview mirror, a blue Audi smoked, accordioned to half its size. A young man walked from the wreck swearing, "Oh shit."

The human body is a vast subject. In my years of medical training, I never learned a thing about whiplash. After the accident, my "education" included physical therapy, trigger-point injections, traction, craniosacral therapy, acupuncture, myofascial stretching, nerve stretching, massage therapy, yoga, and even little electrodes that buzzed on my neck.

In Auburn, my symptoms worsened. The day after I moved boxes into the building I would share with Dr. Purple, I awakened with strange symptoms. My right arm lay beside me, but I couldn't feel it. I shook it, and fortunately, feeling returned.

In the next days, both arms tingled and buzzed, as if with electric current. I felt cold in small, dime-sized spots, which felt blasted with winter wind. Muscles in my arms and legs contracted on their own.

My body was going haywire, short-circuiting.

It wasn't my imagination. Muscles on the left side of my body shrank. My left palm lost its hills. My left calf atrophied. These were all signs of spinal-cord compression, I knew.

After about a year of these symptoms in Auburn, I began to fear I'd be paralyzed from the neck down.

I traveled to Harvard to see a neurologist recommended by a classmate. I traveled to Columbus, Georgia, to see a sports specialist. A grandfatherly neurologist at Emory University in Atlanta pointed his index finger and thumb at me, as if holding a gun. He said, "If I shot you and you slept for six weeks, you'd wake up fine."

A young Emory orthopedic surgeon suspected a bulging disc in my neck. He recommended replacing it with a piece of bone from my hip.

But my mom likes the neurologist's approach. "*Aiya*, if you're fine when you lie down, why don't you just lie down?"

"Mom, forever?"

"Sambo had a back operation years ago," Chris says.

Sambo stands over me as I lie flat on my back in bed. "They opened me up and they fixed me," his voice booms.

"What kind of surgery was it? A discectomy, a fusion, a laminectomy?" I hope he'll recognize one of the terms.

"Dunno. They fixed me, that's all. I'm better. No more pain." Sambo really has no idea what the surgeons did inside his body.

Maybe my problem is that I think too much. Maybe I know just a little too much, but not enough.

I opt for the surgery. The neurologist's option just makes no sense.

It works. I awaken in the recovery room, healed. I flex my calves. I open and close my left hand. I feel normal, not weak or crampy, for the first time in months.

With a stiff plastic collar around my neck, I walk out of the hospital with Chris.

Six weeks later, the surgeon removes the collar and says, "No restrictions on your activity."

So I do yoga. I need to get back into shape. I lie on my back and kick my feet over my head for a gentle plow pose that I've done a thousand times. But this time, my neck pops, and my symptoms begin all over again.

I used to joke about inventing a new kind of psychiatry where *I'd* lie on the couch, not my patients. Sadly, now I actually see my patients lying down, but not on a couch. A five-dollar lawn chair is all I can afford.

In my early thirties, I feel washed up, like I've fallen down a bottomless chasm.

I come to a stark realization. I can afford my health insurance only if I'm working. If I'm too sick to work, I'll lose my health insurance, just when I need it.

How is this *insurance*?

Health insurance is for the healthy, I realize, for people healthy enough to work. If I'm sick and can't work, I can't have health insurance in this country, where health insurance is provided through employment. Health insurance is unavailable to people too sick to hold a job.

What sense does this make?

The only true health insurances, I decide, are Medicare and Medicaid, which don't de facto exclude the sick.

But I'm too young for Medicare. Thanks to my years of hard work and education, I have too much earning power for Medicaid.

The only way for me to get guaranteed health care, I realize, is to move to Canada or Europe, where health care is available to everyone, not just people healthy enough to work.

Another option is to get health insurance as a dependent. But Chris and I aren't married. And how can I consider myself marriage worthy in my condition? In this country which so values individualism, when it comes to medical care, the individual is screwed.

The best I can do is to get a job with good disability and health benefits, while I can still work. If I get sicker, the benefits would buy me time. It's the best I can do, since for me true health insurance doesn't exist.

The best solution is to answer an ad in *Psychiatric Times* from Kaiser Permanente in San Francisco. It looks to me like managed care is here to stay. At least Kaiser is a managed-care company owned and run by the physicians who also provide the care.

As I drive down Main Street in Auburn past window displays of football jerseys and flags with the AU logo, I think about athletes with injuries. San Francisco quarterback Joe Montana has spine injuries, yet he's playing pro football. If there's a doctor who keeps Joe quarterbacking, that doctor should be able to keep me sitting in a chair, talking to patients. Joe's doctor is in San Francisco, and so is the Kaiser job.

A few phone calls later, I am offered an interview. Kaiser invites Chris and me for a trip to San Francisco, with accommodations at the St. Francis Hotel overlooking the bustle of Union Square.

In San Francisco, at the Kaiser Department of Psychiatry, I am interviewed first by a social worker and a psychologist, both Chinese-American women. In this city where one-third of the population is Asian-American, the two women ask not about my Chinese ethnicity but about my being born in Peru. "Brazil," I correct them. Nevertheless, even in San Francisco, they say, I'd be a valuable clinician, the only psychiatrist conversant in Mandarin Chinese.

Next I am interviewed by Kaiser's chief of psychiatry, Dr. Raymond Zablotny, who did his residency at Yale and knows Bob Byck. Ray has already called Bob, who said to him curtly, "Take her, just take her!"

And so I am offered the job.

From our room at the St. Francis, Chris and I look out at the green grass of Union Square, the rippling blue waters of the bay, and the golden peaks of the Bay Bridge peeking over fog.

Chris slips a diamond ring onto my finger. "D, if we're going to move to San Francisco together, then we should be married."

"Okay, C." I kiss him.

In Auburn, Chris and I say our good-byes.

I refer most of my patients to a psychiatrist in nearby Montgomery. For those with OCD or bipolar disorder, I recommend the three-hour drive to Birmingham or Atlanta. Heck, with years of life at stake, they might consider flying to UCLA.

I box my patients' records and the mountains of Explanation of Benefits letters that I received instead of payment.

I say good-bye to Dr. Purple and to Gary. I give Celeste a hug.

I get the feeling that no one's surprised that I'm moving back to California.

In a bright yellow Ryder moving truck, Chris and I drive out of Auburn, down kudzu-lined roads, for the last time.

Should I have practiced with more astuteness? Could I have done better?

I took care of patients regardless of their ability to pay, and regardless of their insurance status. I took care of the sick when they were sick, and I left well enough alone, even if there was more money to be made. I treated each patient with my best effort.

Altogether, I don't regret my first practice as a physician.

After a few weeks in San Francisco, I got my health back. Healing is a mysterious process, I saw once again. At the San Francisco Spine Institute, Dr. Jerome Schofferman and Dr. Arthur White, along with trainer Ted Cook, didn't recommend more surgery or medications. They diagnosed loose ligaments in my neck. They healed me with exercises and posture changes. Even for bulging discs, they said, they wouldn't have rushed to surgery. Exercises and posture changes usually do the job.

As for the surgeon who operated on my neck for its supposed bulging disc, he soon left voice mails on my Kaiser phone, again (and again), requesting even more money for the treatment he had rendered. Chris advised me that I seemed such a nice person, the surgeon probably thought I'd just pay. And so I called the surgeon's secretary. I practiced exhibiting a different side of me. Only then was this doctor-patient relationship finally terminated.

At Kaiser, Ray and the other psychiatrists welcomed me and appreciated my skills. I got the impression they'd take me over Dr. Purple any day, even if elsewhere, Dr. Purple was valued far above me.

But in retrospect, choosing Dr. Purple over me was the right decision for the Alabama hospital. My practices—such as treating patients even if they couldn't pay, refraining from unnecessary treatment, discharging patients even when they had more insurance benefits to be earned—would have surely lost money for the hospital. Dr. Purple, on the other hand, ran an organization that accepted insurance *and* paid staff, *and* was profitable.

Clearly, I couldn't have done it.

In our for-profit health care system, doctors who practice with Dr. Purple's brand of business savvy are the ones who thrive. For physicians like me—who are centered on medical rather than business priorities—it's a challenge to survive.

Here's a sobering fact.

By 2008, the nation's second-largest for-profit hospital chain was Tenet, formerly National Medical Enterprises, the organization convicted of fraud and other crimes in the largest scandal in the history of American psychiatry. In Albuquerque, four local, largely charitable organizations served our citizens' medical needs for most of the twentieth century. But by 2005, two of the four organizations were owned by Ardent, a private equity firm headquartered in Nashville. Ardent's CEO was David Vandewater, who was president and chief operating officer of Columbia/HCA until 1997, when the federal government charged the organization with Medicare fraud over the previous decade. Although Vandewater himself was never charged, Columbia/

HCA pled guilty in 2000 and agreed to pay $840 million in fines and penalties, the largest fraud settlement in U.S. history until then.

Under the old fee-for-service system, there were abuses, of course, by physicians who overcharged and overtreated. However, the reasonable, ethical physician was in no jeopardy. The reasonable physician was compensated reasonably.

Under the for-profit managed-care system, many reasonable physicians have found it impossible to survive.

Whereas independent doctors' offices were once part of the Norman Rockwell American landscape, no wonder they barely exist today. The American health care system now leaves most ethical physicians with the following options:

1. See more patients to break even. This is why your doctor is always in a hurry, and why the average primary-care doctor's visit lasts five to seven minutes.

2. Stop accepting health insurance, along with its financial risks and assaults to a doctor's dignity. Thus physicians can spend time with patients and maintain high standards of care, instead of wasting their intelligence and time on navigating insurance company roadblocks. The downside is a limited patient population: only those wealthy enough to pay for medical visits out-of-pocket (while also paying for health insurance, of course). This is the strategy used by "concierge practices," in which, for a fee, doctors are available when you need them, personally—kind of like how all doctors used to practice.

3. Accept insurance but cut expenses by hiring no staff. My own physician, Dr. Nancy Guinn, belongs to a national network of physicians who practice this way. She spends a half-hour for each appointment, *and* she accepts middle-class patients with insurance because Dr. Guinn also does all

the nursing, filing, calling of insurance companies, waiting on hold, and paperwork herself. (Few physicians are such renaissance persons.)

4. Albuquerque physician Dr. Mark Unverzagt truly pushes the envelope by focusing on prevention and making house calls. (*Unverzagt*, incidentally, is German for "undaunted.") Dr. Unverzagt visits the homes of all newborns. For each patient over sixty-five, he looks at their bathrooms, stairs, and carpets. "Simple stuff," he says, "that does a hell of a lot more than Fosamax. But talk about going broke. Talk about doing things that don't pay. I could make seven hundred dollars an hour freezing off warts. But I want to provide what patients really need." To make his practice work, Dr. Unverzagt has patched together a mishmash of innovative financial strategies. He does locum tenens (temp work for doctors). He asks his patients for an optional prepaid "practice fee" of $500 a year, about what they'd pay for cable television. In his office, he displays quilts for sale, made by his artist mother. And like Dr. Nancy Guinn, Dr. Unverzagt is a renaissance man who hires no staff and does all the billing, filing, the calling of insurance companies, the nursing, ordering, and stocking of supplies himself.

5. Join an institution. This is what I've done. I'm guaranteed a salary, and we have a whole staff to deal with insurance. My institution assumes the risk of being unpaid by insurance companies, or being paid below the cost of care.

Free-market competition may make for better automobiles, computers, burgers, and running shoes. But for health care, the free market has resulted in the opposite: a race to the bottom. Good health care systems have had to stay competitive with the lowest standard, since health care is a market of vulnerable, sometimes irrational consumers who inherently can't be as knowledgeable as the doctor specialists from whom they seek care.

For example, I was helpless choosing treatments for my neck injury. I was just a physician, a Yale Medical School graduate, not a cervical spine specialist. In retrospect, my decision for surgery was driven out of fear of paralysis and from a grasping after hope. The greater the illness, the more vulnerable the patient—even when the patient is a doctor. We are all only human, only mortal.

In Auburn, most physicians considered the authoritative and attractive Dr. Sharon Purple the city's most trustworthy psychiatrist. Even patients who didn't improve under Dr. Purple's care never bothered to seek my second opinion next door. I overheard them thanking her for sticking by them, even apologizing for being "difficult" and not getting better. Dr. Purple was a heroine.

But here's the ideal way medical care would work: Patients would see a doctor, get better quickly, resume their lives, and stop seeking medical care. Good doctors lessen the need for medical services. They decrease demand for their own product. That free-market forces can improve medical care is a flawed theory. In reality, the outcome has been even worse.

Any new industry is vulnerable to abuses before new regulations are instituted. The new endeavor of for-profit health care has been rife with fraud and abuse.

How much life is enough? Who deserves more life?

These fundamental questions will remain, even if we remedy fraud, waste and abuse, even if we fix the faulty economic incentives that currently punish the best and most ethical physicians.

Medical care has simply gotten too effective.

Or, as my ophthalmologist, Dr. Robert Reidy, said to me, amid his tens of thousands of dollars' worth of machinery, "Everyone wants their bypass surgery. Their new hip. If your heart stops beating, you get a new one. New kidneys, lungs, pancreas, too."

When I was in grade school, an ethical question was posed to my class. If a village has only enough wheat to feed a certain number of people, who gets sent to sea on a raft? The elderly? The disabled? The sick? What if someone sent to die would have invented a way to double the village's wheat production?

During our last months in Auburn, Sambo was diagnosed with leukemia, the result of an inherited genetic defect, the "Philadelphia chromosome," a textbook example of disease encoded in the genes. From Sambo's birth, this destiny was written in his biology. But Sambo was also born under a lucky star. Bone marrow transplants were just recently pioneered for his type of leukemia, and luckily, a surgeon expert in this procedure had just moved to Mississippi. Even luckier for Sambo, his sister was a genetic match and a suitable bone marrow donor. In his storyteller's manner, Sambo recounted, "I was in the hospital with a little girl with eleven brothers and sisters. None of them was a match for her."

Sambo's sister donated her bone marrow in time to save Sambo's life. Within two months, she herself was diagnosed with breast cancer and died. Thanks to cutting-edge medical technology, and thanks to his sister, Sambo lived another five years.

At the time of his transplant, Sambo was a small-town idealist who insisted on drawing architectural inspiration from Mississippi, of all places, and who believed that everybody deserved good architecture, even people who taught pigs to sing.

Was the life of this man worth the expensive technology that gave him just five more years?

But because of his last five years, a gift from medical technology, Sambo finally earned enough money to fund special services for his disabled son, Julian. In his last years, Sambo received the prestigious MacArthur "genius" fellowship.

"I don't know if I'm a genius, Calott," Sambo said to Chris, "but I'm smart enough to take the money."

In 2004, three years after his death, Samuel Mockbee was posthumously awarded one of architecture's greatest honors, the American Institute of Architects Gold Medal. He was just the sixtieth architect worldwide, since 1907, deemed worthy of the award.

Whereas architecture traditionally served kings, and the elite, today wherever I go with Chris, young architects and students talk about doing "design/build" projects as a public service, like Sambo Mockbee. Sambo's architecture of compassion, as his work came to be called, expanded horizons for architecture, and for architects. Sambo became architecture's counterpoint to Howard Roark, the ego-driven protagonist of Ayn Rand's novel *The Fountainhead*, who despite being fictional, was named by *The Atlantic Monthly* as one of the twentieth century's most influential persons because of his profound impact as a role model for architects. Sambo was an entirely new role model, who gave architecture a new humanistic mission.

Because of Sambo's last five years, the world was changed for the better.

When I think about it, most history-changing innovations and discoveries have come from one single person, or a couple of people, and often, the most unlikely people. The theory of relativity came from an awkward high school dropout, Albert Einstein. The theory of gravity, the prism, and calculus all came from one strange-thinking, possibly autistic, individual, Isaac Newton. The personal computer was invented by a couple of guys in a Berkeley garage.

Talent blooms in the most unlikely deserts. By definition,

creativity comes from outside of conventionality. Society needs its geeks and outsiders.

Each life is precious. Each life is worth our best effort. Each life lost is an alternate, possibly better world that didn't happen. This is my belief as a physician.

More important, it is not just lives at stake, but the very humanity of our society.

What are the consequences when some lives are considered more valuable than others?

Ultimately, is modern medicine's predicament like that of Asklepios, the ancient Greek god of medicine, whose snake-entwined staff still serves as the international symbol of medicine? Son of the god Apollo and the mortal Coronis, and a disciple of the half-man, half-horse Chiron, Asklepios developed healing powers so great that, according to myth, the underworld became underpopulated. Hades, god of the underworld, accused Asklepios of stealing from his kingdom. To set the world back into balance and to appease the other gods, Zeus struck Asklepios dead with a lightning bolt.

The physician who had saved so many others could not save himself.

Kaiser Permanente, the nation's oldest managed-care organization, is a nonprofit that differs fundamentally from more recent for-profit organizations that also call themselves "managed care."

In 1933, in the Mojave Desert near Los Angeles, Dr. Sidney Garfield started the nation's first prepaid medical plan. His fee was five cents a day, or $18.25 a year, per person. His patients were the workers of the Los Angeles aqueduct, a grand public works project that would ensure the thriving of California for the next century. The advance payment enabled Dr. Garfield to keep his medical practice afloat. It also allowed Dr. Garfield to focus on preventive medicine, in contrast to the usual fee-for-service method, whereby doctors didn't get paid until patients got sick.

When the aqueduct was completed, industrialist Henry J. Kaiser enlisted Dr. Garfield to provide medical care for employees of the Richmond shipyard, near San Francisco. At the end of World War II, when the shipyard cut its employment, Dr. Garfield and Mr. Kaiser opened their medical plan to public enrollment.

Thus Kaiser Permanente was born.

To this day, Kaiser Permanente is owned and run by physicians, with medical goals at the core of its mission—in stark contrast to more recent managed-care businesses, which also take advance payment but which have profit as their core ethic and mission.

When I worked at Kaiser, from 1996 to 1998, I watched assembly-line psychiatry accelerate. I myself even cranked up the speed by instituting my department's first fifteen-minute appointments, compared with the standard thirty-minute psychiatry appointments of the time. I also instituted the first medication group, where my nurse and I cared for patients en masse. I implemented these strategies not because I believed in them, but because to me these solutions seemed better than the alternative. At least patients were able to access care in a timely manner.

At Kaiser San Francisco, psychiatrists had always spent a full hour for each appointment with patients. But in 1992, five years after the release of Prozac, the demand for psychiatric medications increased to the point that psychiatrist Dr. Jim DeLano started scheduling thirty-minute appointments to accommodate the increased patient load. Patients saw psychologists or other counselors for psychother-apy, and psychiatrists for medications.

But the greatest change at Kaiser came during my time there, in the mid-1990s, as for-profit health corporations increasingly pen-etrated Northern California. Faced with this competition, we at Kai-ser worked faster and faster, until even psychotherapists no longer had time to do psychotherapy, but only to manage crises.

The goal of free-market capitalism is not just money, but that competition should bring out the best. But medical care is an excep-tion, as Kenneth Arrow pointed out. The free market has had the very opposite effect on American medicine. For-profit managed-care companies have made even organizations like Kaiser cheapen their standards in order to compete and survive.

During my years at Kaiser, I witnessed the limitations of free-market capitalism, a system that might work for most products, but not medical care.

I saw that sometimes free-market competition simply reduces everything to money, even the care of the human body and soul.

Chapter Ten

At the Health Maintenance Organization

FALL 1996

My office at Kaiser is in a modular building full of identical windows, like you can take the left half of our building, switch it with the right, the third floor and change it with the second or fourth, and everything would be the same. The building is regular, rational, predictable.

The neighborhood and its people, on the other hand, are anything but. Across the street is Bella Italian Pizzeria, Brothers Korean Barbecue, Abbey Tavern Irish Pub, and Five Happiness Chinese Restaurant. On Clement Street, a block north, roasted ducks swing in Chinese restaurant windows. Durian, pomelo, pomegranate, and winter melon rest outside grocery stores. English is heard only some of the time, along with Cantonese, Toi San, Hakka, Russian, and several Eastern European languages. The Richmond District extends westward and ends in windy, sandy beach and the Pacific Ocean. When fog rolls in, we in the Richmond get it first.

On my first day at Kaiser, I meet the reception staff. Cliff wears rings in both ears and plays jazz in Tenderloin nightclubs. Rosie once danced with the Shanghai Ballet. Pam is taking hormones and awaiting her sex-change operation. In the meantime, she wears dresses, applies lipstick, and asks that we no longer use her former name, Ramon.

"Dr. Zablotny is waiting for you in his office," Rosie says. I follow the willowy, black-haired woman down the hallway.

Ray and I have met only once, for my interview, but when he opens his office door and smiles, I hug him rather than shake his hand. Ray looks like a Northern California version of East Coast psychiatrists with their thick, dark Sigmund Freud beards. Ray's beard is blond-gray, and trimmed. His suit is blond, too, and his tie is a soothing lavender. Ray is a member of the San Francisco Victorian Society, according to a plaque on his wall. Out his window, peaked Victorian rowhouses rise into blue sky.

"Ray, I know that my job is to prescribe medications," I begin, "but I want to have enough time to understand the patient's psychodynamics, even for med visits."

"Of course," he says. "I've had psychoanalytic training. It's hard to turn that part of your brain off."

"Psychoanalytic training?" I ask.

"Yes, just about all the psychiatrists here have. It used to be pretty standard."

Of course. Most of the psychiatrists have worked here sixteen years or more. Kaiser's low turnover is a reason I chose this job. Of course, they were trained mostly in psychoanalysis, rather than the biologic emphasis of my own recent training.

"Psychiatrists' appointments used to be an hour," Ray continues. "But in 1992, Jim DeLano started half-hour visits to accommodate the increase in volume. All visits with a psychiatrist are now half an hour."

"Even for first appointments?"

"Sometimes it can take a few sessions to understand the patient," Ray says.

Psychiatrists at Kaiser seem in a strange transition. Their foundations are in psychoanalysis, but their new job is to prescribe medications. The half-hour visits, even for the first visit, are evolved from hour-long psychotherapy appointments and seem themselves a hybrid between old and new.

"I prefer to have a longer first visit, to get a good diagnosis before prescribing meds," I say. "How about sixty minutes for new patients, and then I'll see three follow-ups in an hour, rather than two? I'll actually see more patients." I explain how at UCLA, in Dr. Mike Gitlin's Affective Disorders Clinic, we had ninety minutes for the first visit, then twenty minutes for follow-up medication visits—or, three patients an hour.

"It's your practice," Ray says. "Sixty minutes for an NAM. We'll schedule three fifteen-minute RAMs every hour, with a fifteen-minute IPT."

I look at Ray, puzzled.

"NAM is 'new adult med,'" he says. "RAM is 'return adult med.'"

"And what's IPT?"

Now Ray looks puzzled. "Gee, I can't remember what the initials stand for. But it's personal time, to catch up on phone calls and paperwork. You won't have patients scheduled during IPTs."

"I see."

"Every so often, you'll have a UAM, 'urgent adult med.' They'll all be seen by a therapist first. It should save you time."

"A psychologist?"

"Well, we've got Ph.D. psychologists. But lately we've shifted toward hiring more master's-level therapists."

I don't have to ask. Master's-level therapists are paid less than psychologists with doctorates.

"I'd like to see just one patient for psychotherapy," I say. "To keep up my psychotherapy skills. I'll do it during my lunch hour."

"That's reasonable," Ray says. He then explains the lunch hour. The organization pays for a half-hour lunch (I know from my work at McDonald's as a teenager that this is federal law). And then another half-hour comes out of my paycheck. So, together, the organization and I pay for my lunch *hour*.

"Also, Ray—would it be okay if I work a forty-hour week in four days? I'd work ten-hour days, with evening appointments, if I can have Mondays off."

"We need more evening appointments. That'll be fine."

"Thanks, Ray. I look forward to working here."

"One more thing," he says. "We've hired another new psychiatrist. He'll start next month. His name is Reuben Brun."

"Reuben Brun? I lived across the hall from Rube in college. I used to see him every morning."

Ray smiles. Out the window, clouds drift past Victorian rooftops. Ray reaches for his prescription pad and prepares for his next patient.

Ready—set—go.

Three patients an hour, except for NAMs and UAMs, ten hours a day, four days a week. That's about twenty-five patients a day.

"Of course I'm depressed," Matthew says. He is colorless, in a white shirt and black slacks. His face is pale and heavy. "I'm HIV positive. I've got a death sentence." He hasn't even had a lot of sex, he says. Excruciatingly straight and boring life. One boyfriend for seventeen years, then a second who was promiscuous behind his back. He always gets the bad shakes in life, like with his job. He's just a lowly architect at a firm that doesn't treat him well.

"How long have you been HIV positive?" I ask.

"I found out last year."

"Have you ever been seriously depressed before that?"

He rubs his chin. "About ten years ago, and twenty years ago. I got so depressed that I was suicidal."

"So you struggled with depression even before HIV. I've known a lot of people with full-blown AIDS. They cling to life, celebrate life."

"But depression runs in my family. My sister takes antidepressants. My aunt was in the nuthouse. My mom is cranky as hell."

"I think you've got two illnesses—HIV and a depression that runs in your family. I suggest that you take an antidepressant, Zoloft. HIV isn't a death sentence anymore, thanks to the new antiretrovirals."

"Of course I'm depressed. I've got HIV. But I'll give Zoloft a try. I've got a death sentence anyway."

The next week, Matthew returns for an RAM. I check for side effects. The antidepressant will take weeks to begin working.

By the next RAM, a month later, Matthew's depression has lifted.

"You're right," he says, "HIV isn't a death sentence anymore. I'm taking antiretrovirals now. HIV doesn't have to turn into AIDS. And my job is looking better lately—I get to do architecture, while they take care of the business. At least I don't have to be the sycophant chasing commissions."

He smiles. His face is bright against his orange shirt.

Just before Christmas, Rube arrives. To welcome him, Ray invites Rube, Chris, and me to his home for dinner.

To pick up Rube, Chris and I drive up Parnassus Hill. Below us,

Market Street hums with streetcars. The Bay Bridge's gold peaks rise above the clouds. Sun shines through fog.

Outside an ornate Edwardian building, Rube sits on the curb in slacks and a button-down shirt. I haven't seen Rube in years. He is now a distinguished young doctor with lines of wisdom around his pensive mouth. But when he rises and smiles, he is still the preppy college sophomore in Weejuns I used to greet in the dorms each morning.

"Rube!" I plant a kiss on his cheek. "This is Chris," I introduce the two.

We climb back into our car and drive downhill toward Ray's house in the Haight-Ashbury.

"Rube, is your dad still with Merrill Lynch?" I ask. In college, Rube was proud that his father was a vice president.

"Was," Rube says. "They laid him off. Just before retirement."

"That's terrible! How could they?" I say. "What are your parents doing now?"

"They live simply. They travel. They got pretty disillusioned."

Fog flows around rows of colorful houses as Chris navigates down winding roads. In the Haight-Ashbury, a block from bohemian cafés and shops, Chris parks in front of a four-story Victorian mansion with a neatly groomed lawn.

"Ray's house," Chris announces.

Rube sighs. "Ray's wife never worked. Twenty years ago, you could afford a house like this on one income. We'll be lucky if we can afford a house at all."

"Rube, we'll buy houses." But I share his dismay. The rent on our one-bedroom apartment is more than half my monthly salary. Parking is extra. Saving is a stretch. Homeless men and women on the Embarcadero cause me to fear my own fate. If my neck condition worsens and I can't work, I'd be months from homelessness—if not for my family. And Chris is just beginning to build an architecture practice.

"We'll never afford houses like Ray's," Rube says. "It's too bad we're entering a declining profession. Our job will be to service the Silicon Valley rich. We'll be like pedicurists for the brain."

"Rube! You've always been a worrywart."

At Ray's door, I find myself nervous about meeting his wife. Ray opens the door, and beside him stands a woman in a long purple dress.

"This is my wife, Mary," Ray says.

I notice Mary's bare feet and immediately I feel at ease.

Dinner is served in a dimly lit room with ornate wallpaper and a crystal chandelier. Refreshingly honest, Mary is utterly uninterested in our office talk. She crochets through dinner. She turns out to be an aspiring sci-fi writer. When she puts down her crochet hook and makes *Star Trek* jokes, I laugh so hard that by the end of the evening my face hurts.

Our entire psychiatry department gathers once a month for a staff meeting, like a family of six dozen psychiatrists, psychologists, nurses, counselors, social workers, and receptionists. It's a chance to catch up with one another, and if there's a birthday, we eat cake together.

In the conference room on the ground floor, I sit on the window ledge, welcoming this break from my usual ten hours a day in one room, in one chair. I soak in sun and street sounds. Miriam, our head social worker, a woman with long, sleek black hair, passes out squares of cake on plastic plates.

Ray stands at the front of the room in a sport coat and flowered tie. He puts down his cake.

"We might be in for a few rocky years," Ray says. "We'll need to tighten our belts, at least temporarily. We'll need to do it to survive."

Ray explains that new for-profit corporations are moving into our turf. Some of them have never before provided medical care but now see medicine as a good business opportunity.

"We've been providing medical care to some of our companies for decades," Ray says, "but now these new national corporations are offering to do it for less money than us. They have deep pockets and can operate at a loss for years, just to put us out of business. And once we're out of business, they can charge whatever they want. We'll have to fight to keep our patients."

"You mean, do even more with even less?" someone in the crowd asks.

"Hopefully, it will just be temporary," Ray answers. "Hopefully, after a while these corporations will leave us alone."

Around me, my coworkers sigh, whisper, and shift in their chairs.

Before long, I hear stories. On the radio, I hear about a woman with chest pains, calling and calling her doctor at Kaiser. She was put on hold, then told to call back. She was having a heart attack, it turned out.

At a monthly meeting, a psychologist asks about the man who walked into a Kaiser ER with a knife in his chest. He was told that it wasn't an emergency and to call his outpatient primary-care doctor in the morning.

"It wasn't an emergency," someone in the room says. "He called his doctor in the morning and now he's fine."

True. I guess. But emergency or not, the ER must have been pretty darn overloaded to have turned this patient away.

Even my brother Dave in Los Angeles has a Kaiser story, told to him by a physician friend. A Kaiser surgeon operates on a man's broken leg, the story goes. A lump on the bone looks like cancer. He wants to biopsy it, but his boss orders, "Close him up—he'll never know," implying that treating the cancer would be costly.

The story is a myth, I decide, since it doesn't make sense medically, legally, or even financially. Treating a single lump would cost less than treating cancer spread to multiple locations. (Kaiser actually aims to keep its patients for a lifetime, even if they get sick.) It would cost less than settling the lawsuit the patient would file once he realized that the cancer should have been spotted during the operation, or on the preoperative X-ray.

Nevertheless, Dave's urban myth taps into two anxieties.

The first is your doctor's values. Is your doctor thinking about your health, or about money? In other words, when you're rolled into a hospital ER, injured and perhaps unconscious, do you want your doctor thinking, "How do I heal this patient?" or "How can I extract the most profit from this patient?"

The second is the helplessness of patients. When you're unconscious on the operating table, you have no choice but to trust your doctor. You hope your life is in the hands of an ethical physician who prioritizes your well-being, and not how to make the most bucks from your misfortune. Given the complexity of medicine, all of us are mostly blind to our doctors' decisions. Even I, a physician, and Sambo, a genius, were clueless when it came to our spinal problems. We had no choice but to trust our doctors.

Soon after Ray's announcement about our new competition, Kaiser psychologists and counselors carry so many cases it's no longer possible to do psychotherapy. There's time enough only to see patients in crisis, when they deteriorate and are in danger of harming themselves or others, which, unfortunately, happens more frequently as routine care grows scarcer. Our therapists stay after hours to manage their caseloads. They complain that for new patients, they have time only to evaluate them, and send them on to psychiatrists for medications.

More than a decade earlier, Paul Starr had warned that our nation was headed toward medical decisions being determined by conglomerates with profit motives.

Even here at Kaiser, a nonprofit owned and run by physicians, the profit motive of conglomerates has infiltrated our sincere efforts to practice the best medicine in service of our patients.

"I never thought I'd see a shrink," Robert says as we walk from the waiting room. His chapped fingers stroke his wind-blown hair from his face. He is a tall man, even with his shoulders hunched.

On my couch he is listless, as if his blue suit sits crumpled with no Robert in it.

"Why have you decided to see a psychiatrist now?" I ask.

"To heal my broken heart." Tears stain his lapel. As he reaches to dry his face, I notice the faint whiteness of a missing ring on his hand. "To think I moved here for her. Lizbeth loved those old *Streets of San Francisco* reruns. This monster job at the bank was her idea. It's a good thing it pays well. I've got to pay off the debts she racked up on my credit card."

"How long were you together?"

"Four years. We were getting married next year."

"It must have been a shock when she left."

"It was another man. I was at work all the time. She got lonely."

I check off symptoms in my head. He can't sleep and he can't eat.

He can't concentrate at work. He isn't the kind of guy who cries, but now he can't stop. At work there's a balcony. He fantasizes about flying with his weight unsupported. How neat the parking lot asphalt would look if he fell face-first toward it. He never thought he'd see a shrink, but now he's got nothing to lose.

"How long have you been feeling this way?"

"About a month, since she left."

Bingo. More than two weeks—he meets the DSM criteria for major depression, single episode, moderate, code 296.23.

A few years ago, Robert would have gotten psychotherapy. We'd talk about his grief. We'd talk about wiser choices in girlfriends. But even Robert's therapist doesn't have time to do psychotherapy. And so he is sent to me for meds. Robert, of course, has no clue about any of this.

Funny thing. I can actually fix him with meds, at least temporarily. I recommend Effexor.

"Do you really think this will work?" He looks at my prescription in his hand.

"Yes, I'm sure. Trust me. I do this all the time. How quickly do you want to get better?" I am giving this man a pill to heal a broken heart.

He looks straight at me. "Let's crank."

It's like squeezing a dry lemon, but I squeeze my schedule hard enough so that I can see Robert weekly for fifteen-minute visits, .25 hours on my timesheet, the standard allotment for medication appointments, code 90862. It's just enough time to check for side effects and increase his dosage. If I want to spend more time with Robert—say, an hour—it will have to be on my own time. Problem is, I have more than twenty Roberts on my schedule today, and there are only twenty-four hours in a day.

A month later, Robert feels like himself again.

"I'm still sad," he says. "But now I can work again. Thanks, Doc. By the way, I've even got a date tonight. Just my type of girl, the kind I'd do anything for, a lot like Lizbeth."

In his records, I now note him to be 296.25, major depression, single episode in full remission.

We stride down the long hallway, past doors and more doors, each with another hurried clinician behind it, each clinician sprinting through a long list of patients.

I reach the waiting room and call out for my next patient.

After about a year on this assembly line, I'm feeling pretty weary. I feel like I need a change of pace before I myself start craving the Zoloft, Prozac, and Effexor I prescribe for my patients.

In San Francisco in 1997, even though an obsessive-compulsive disorder support group meets monthly at UCSF, no treatment program exists in the city.

"I'd like to start an OCD program," I say to Ray.

"You know, we just don't see that much OCD," he says.

"If we build it, they will come. The prevalence of OCD is 2.5 percent of the population. It's the fourth-most common psychiatric disorder, behind phobias, substance abuse, and depression."

"Well, okay," Ray says.

While Kaiser physicians count every dollar and every minute on green timesheets, fortunes are made all around us, seemingly overnight, in Silicon Valley or in the frenzied stock market. In fact, the only people I see living well in San Francisco seem to be those who don't work.

They own. Stocks, real estate, or trust funds, like the patient in my OCD group who owns a mini-mall, so he can afford to stay home all day washing his hands. Or the Silicon Valley millionaires who retire in their twenties because they own stock options at high-tech start-ups.

Or brokers and managers who move money around in our Keynesian economy.

Even Susan, a UCSF eye surgeon, a renter, can't imagine saving enough for a down payment on a house in San Francisco, especially with student loans to pay. She works a surgeon's high-risk, day-and-night schedule, while watching millionaires of leisure in their twenties buy up homes around her.

My parents come to visit Chris and me for the first time. I move the coffee table and sofa cushions from the living room into the kitchen so that I can pull the couch out into a bed. I smooth sheets and I fluff pillows. In the morning, I'll move the coffee table and sofa cushions again, so that I'll have room in the kitchen to make breakfast. If I buy a box of envelopes, I have to throw something away to make room for it.

At last in the living room, my parents are tucked into the pull-out bed, reading. I plant kisses on their cheeks.

Out the window, the lights of the Bay Bridge shine like a string of pearls across the water. Streams of white headlights and red taillights travel, not yet ready to sleep.

In the morning, my dad helps Chris and me buy our first stocks.

"Sometimes I have to push my little ducks in the water and make them swim." He sips tea. His reading glasses sit in a grandfatherly manner low on his nose, as he reads *The Wall Street Journal*. "Dora, you should subscribe."

With my money in the stock market, I finally take an interest in business and finance. I read books by money managers like Warren Buffett and Peter Lynch. I watch CNBC. It seems like everyone these days is watching CNBC, with the stock ticker running across the bottom of the TV screen.

Finally, I begin to learn about money.

Here's what I learn. If a company earns $100 million a year, steadily and reliably, it's a failure. Making $100 million every year means the company is not growing, not cutting it by Wall Street's standards. A company that grows 50 percent a year, for example, earns $100 million a year, $150 million the next year, $225 million the next year, and keeps growing. General Electric, already the world's largest company, still grows at 50 percent a year. Now, that's a company.

I put down *The Wall Street Journal* and pick up John Steinbeck's *The Grapes of Wrath*:

> They breathe profits; they eat the interest on money. If they don't get it, they die the way you die without air, without side-meat.
>
> The bank—the monster has to have profits all the time. It can't wait. It'll die. No, taxes go on. When the monster stops growing, it dies. It can't stay one size.
>
> The bank is something else than men. It happens that every man in a bank hates what the bank does, and yet the bank does it. The bank is something more than men, I tell you. It's the monster.

Robert Kiyosaki's book *Rich Dad, Poor Dad* explains that when a company wants to make more money, it cuts costs, which includes the salaries and benefits of employees. It fires people. Rube's dad, for example, got fired just before retirement. This means more profit for the owners of the company, the stockholders. Meanwhile, the people who work are screwed.

The lesson is that Poor Dad works. Rich Dad owns.

It pays to own, not work.

It's what Karl Marx said more than a hundred years ago, what I heard from my own dad when I was working fast-food jobs in high school, and what I witness every day in San Francisco, where it is increasingly difficult to live comfortably, even on a doctor's wages.

At the Carnelian Room atop the Bank of America skyscraper, some citizens sip cocktails, high above the clouds of the city, above other citizens sleeping on the sidewalks of the Embarcadero, and others who sleep on buses because even working two minimum-wage jobs they can't afford a room with a bed.

It pays to own, not to work.

Working as a doctor means long hours, legal liability, and harassment from insurance companies who make more money for stockholders when they stiff doctors. Why don't I just own health care stocks, instead?

What sense does it make that investors who buy stocks and sit at home watching CNBC make more money than us who do the work? What would happen if we all stopped working, bought stocks, and sat at home watching CNBC?

Chris and I considered buying a condo for $300,000 when we arrived in San Francisco two years ago. It would have been a struggle, but possible, with family help. We decided to continue renting. The condo we didn't buy is now worth $600,000 in 1998.

How sobering. Instead of working, if we had bought that Potrero Hill condo two years ago, we'd be $300,000 richer. We wouldn't even have to sell the condo, just refinance our loan, pull out the $300,000 in equity, and live off that; or sink the cash into a second home in Napa Valley, which would also grow in value.

But since I've been working, not owning, the prospect of now buying a home in San Francisco seems a distant dream.

I call my dad, seeking solace. "Dad, I feel punished for working."

"That is the capitalist system," he says. "Those with capital win. The workers get more and more squeezed."

"It doesn't seem right, Dad. Is this right?"

He is silent. And since he's my dad, I know what he's thinking. He's thinking that I'm asking the wrong question.

He replies simply, "Dora, you cannot change it."

My OCD group is a success. Ray is amused when he sees my patients gripping doorknobs, putting their palms on floors, or squeezing into the bathroom twelve at a time, to touch toilets, sinks, and oily hinges. Patients who fear toilet germs laugh at patients who fear chemicals and cleansers. Together they realize the absurdity of their fears.

Word spreads. The highest "utilizers" in the Kaiser system start getting sent to my OCD group. Many hypochondriacs who constantly seek medical care turn out to have OCD. Even my psychoanalytically minded colleagues ask to learn my behavior therapy methods. I enjoy being a bridge between old and new.

On the success of my OCD group, I approach Ray with an idea for another kind of group. Since Ray's announcement about health profit organizations (my term) competing with us, my caseload has increased to the point where it begs a solution.

"Ray, I'd like to start a medication group," I say.

"How would that work?" Ray asks.

"It would be a walk-in group. Everyone would sit in a room and share information about their medications and side effects. Either Betty or another nurse could answer questions. Then I would take the patients one by one for brief visits in my office to write prescriptions and to talk about private matters."

Ray sighs. "I hate thinking of psychiatry at Kaiser coming to this. What will this do to the doctor-patient relationship? But I guess that's the direction where we're headed."

With Ray's reluctant blessing, I begin the first medication group in our department. Of course I share Ray's dismay at seeing patients en masse. But at least in this way they'll get seen.

As my caseload continues to increase, I feel more and more crunched. I feel crunched taking care of others who feel crunched.

My ten a.m. NAM, Lois, looks like she never left the seventies. She wears old Jordache jeans and a turtleneck with brown horizontal stripes. Her blond feathered hair looks right out of that Farrah Fawcett poster in teenaged boys' bedrooms.

"All my coworkers are on Prozac," she says. "I figured I'd better take it, too."

Am I really hearing this? "Tell me what's happening that makes you feel like you need Prozac," I ask in a polite, calm, shrink's voice.

"My bank went through a merger. The first thing new management did was downsize. Those of us who were left grieved the loss of our friends, while assuming their work."

A tear rolls down Lois's thin nose. She's been working at the bank since she was in high school—almost thirty years, she says. The bank was her first job, her only job. Life at home was never good. When she graduated high school, the bank gave her a full-time job, and she got her own apartment.

"The bank has always been there for me," Lois says, "more family than my own family."

After the merger, Lois worried about the bank, so she worked harder and longer hours. Late at work one evening, she had an epiphany.

"They're actually trying to make my life miserable, so that I'll quit. With so many people gone, I'm now the most senior, most highly paid worker. So I'm the next on their hit list. If they lay me off, they'll owe me severance pay. But they'll save that money if they get me to quit. When I realized this, I couldn't see the computer screen through my tears," she says.

I go through a checklist of symptoms: tearfulness, negative thoughts, hopelessness. She meets the DSM criteria for major depression.

"I asked my coworkers how they're managing to cope," she says. "Almost all of them are on Prozac."

"I could prescribe Prozac for you, Lois. But if you ask me, no one could work under those conditions. Sounds like they're designed to be intolerable."

She shakes her head, as if realizing the absurdity of the situation.

A few days later, Lois leaves a voice mail. "Thank you, Dr. Wang. I confronted my new management. They've laid me off. I'm unemployed now. But at least I'm sleeping again."

I think of Lois's coworkers on Prozac, and I wonder. Are the new antidepressants enabling a more abusive society?

I remember my high school job at McDonald's and the summer I scooped ice cream. I was treated like I was a machine, pushed to work faster, harder, simply more. Kind of like my own job now. I look at my green timesheet, then at my computer screen with its long list of

NAMs, RAMs, and UAMs. Coworkers bicker about who gets more IPT, as if it is a precious commodity, like gold.

Is this why I went through medical school and residency? To feel like I am working at McDonald's again?

On a spring weekend this soul-challenging year, Chris and I take a break and drive to Planada, a Central Valley town where Chris has been teaching a design/build studio for UC Berkeley students. Sambo, having survived his leukemia and bone marrow transplant, flies here from Mississippi to teach with Chris.

Out the car window are fields of almond trees, then fields of peach trees. Heaven, the Chinese say, is a garden of peach trees. Our car fills with the scent of heaven.

At last, we arrive at the Monument to Farmworkers that Chris, Sambo, and their students have built. The monument has a metal roof that doubles as a shady bus stop.

I reach over and put my hand on Chris's knee. "You've always loved Albuquerque," I say. When I met Chris in Los Angeles, he had just moved from Albuquerque, to head an office for an Albuquerque architect. "You know that Joel Yager moved to Albuquerque. And my med school classmate Joanna lives there now, with her husband, Jeff. Why don't we check out Albuquerque?"

"I'm not sure you'd like it, D. It's not exactly cosmopolitan."

"Well, it's more cosmopolitan than Auburn, isn't it?"

I kiss Chris good-bye at the airport a couple of weeks later. If he can find a job in Albuquerque, then I'll look for one, too.

On my way home from the airport, I stop at the new supermarket twelve blocks from our apartment. Through traffic, it takes me a solid hour to get home. Back in our apartment, I sit at the window. Above, gray clouds bode rain. Below, cars circle, searching for parking.

The phone rings.

"I'm in Albuquerque," Chris says. "I'm at the Frontier."

I picture the Frontier Restaurant on Route 66, where I once ordered eggs sunny-side up, with a bowl of green chile stew. In the corner, I watched a machine make tortillas. Floury scent cheered my senses.

"There's a warm breeze," Chris says. In his voice I hear calm. Space. "I got here, and there's this warm breeze."

"Is it sunny?"

"Of course," he says. "It always is."

Chris and I secure jobs in Albuquerque within weeks. We are excited and ready to leave San Francisco for someplace easier, warmer. Chris accepts a job in the city's largest architecture firm. I will work at Lovelace, a managed-care organization like Kaiser. My salary at Lovelace will be higher than my Kaiser salary, *and* I'll work fewer hours, just thirty-two, not forty, hours a week.

It seems too good to be true.

What will I tell Ray as my reason for leaving? San Francisco's high cost of living? The cost of this assembly-line psychiatry on my soul? That I'm craving the Zoloft I prescribe?

"My husband's a modernist," I decide to say. "Look around, Ray. This is no place for a modern architect."

Out the window behind Ray, Victorians rise into the clouds and sky. Ray smiles. "Well, we'll have to throw you a party."

"Thanks, Ray. Nothing against Victorians, though."

"Of course," he sighs. "But you'll be difficult to replace. I feel like

Sisyphus, always rolling that boulder up the mountain, only so it rolls down again."

Ray doesn't know yet that he'll be hiring new psychiatrists nearly every year. Turnover in this assembly line will grow faster and faster, not just in terms of patients, but in terms of his doctors and staff. He doesn't know that in a few years Rube will move to Portland, feeling San Francisco's cost of living too expensive for a doctor's salary.

Before my departure, I ask Kaiser for a list of my patients so that I can send them a letter. I receive a list of names, and a note: "This is the requested list of members seen by resource ID 0477176."

Me.

While Chris moves to Albuquerque, I visit Los Angeles. I have missed my parents, and wish that I had more involvement in their lives and their medical care.

In my parents' backyard, by the swimming pool, my mom has grown a papaya tree from the seeds of leftover supermarket fruit. My mom can grow anything, another art lost in my generation.

While I look incredulously at the tree and at the fruit sprouting happily, my parents reminisce about the summer they drove to the Grand Canyon with three kids in the back of their station wagon.

"What do you think, Mom? Dad? The Grand Canyon is on my way to Albuquerque. And then we'll drive through Indian lands and the most ancient parts of the country. Wanna come?"

My mom looks at my father. "It might be dangerous for Bao Bao to drive alone."

"We better go with her," my dad says.

A week later, they climb into my used Lexus with a single suitcase, and a backpack full of bottled water. In the early morning, before traffic, we hit the road. We drive down L.A.'s wide freeways, now just filling with cars. After half a day of desert, we arrive in Flagstaff at nightfall.

The next morning, at sunrise, we head to the Grand Canyon. The November air is chilly, so our plan is to drive along the southern rim, and jump out of the car at viewpoints.

Dad is tired.

At the first Grand Canyon viewpoint, I take his arm and guide him to a bench where the canyon stretches like a panorama before us. It is deep sienna in striated patterns, as if touched long ago by a giant paintbrush. It meanders far into the horizon.

On the bench, Dad's head nods. His mouth yawns wide open. He snores.

At the next viewpoint, my mother and I both guide my father to a bench. As Mom and I admire the canyon, Dad snores.

Dad is still young, only seventy-two. He is a large man, six feet tall, and descended from a long line of warriors—a grandfather who studied martial arts at the Shaolin Temple, and a great-grandfather who was a venerable *ba-biao*, a martial artist skilled in eight weapons, who was a bodyguard for a Qing dynasty emperor. Today Dad seems a different man from the one I've always known, not the father of my childhood, the man I thought could do anything.

After the third viewpoint, where Dad snores especially loudly, we drive through miles of Navajo reservation until we reach the Hopi Mesa.

"There's an ancient city here," I say. "Wolpe, from at least A.D. 1300. Do you want to go see it?"

"No, there's nothing to see there," Mom says.

"Dad, what do you think?" I call to the backseat.

But he is asleep.

In the Painted Desert, we drive past hills and mesas of deep rust, yellow, and gold. "Isn't this one of the most beautiful things you've ever seen?" I ask.

"Sheesh, it's nothing," my mother says. After all, she is from the Grand Canal in China, from cities far older than Wolpe, cities the Chinese call Heaven on Earth.

"Dad, what do you think?" It's always been Dad's role to provide a balanced perspective.

Silence. A loud snore. Dad misses the Painted Desert altogether.

We continue along I-40 past Gallup, which Mom declines to see, even if some of her favorite Hollywood westerns were filmed here.

"You know that the American Great Wall of China is Chaco Canyon, in northern New Mexico."

"Really?" she says.

Happy about finally piquing her interest, I explain that New Mexico is home to North America's most advanced ancient civilization, the Anasazi, whose society collapsed around A.D. 1300.

"Why did they collapse?" She is always interested in disasters.

"It's like the Mayans. No one knows, exactly. But they're not actually gone. Their descendants are still here. The Hopi, Zuni, the Pueblo people. Sandia Pueblo is right in Albuquerque, at the base of the Sandia Mountains. They run a casino."

At last we reach Albuquerque and our apartment on Mountain Road, the onetime dirt path walked by Native Americans to the extinct volcano on Albuquerque's western horizon. Once called Turquoise Mountain by the Navajo, the volcano today is known as Mount Taylor.

The sun is just setting when I pull our car into the driveway of our new home, a tan stucco town house, an imitation of the adobe pueblos where Anasazi descendants still live. But our dwelling is equipped with an automatic garage door.

Chris is waiting for us. He shakes my father's hand and then my mother's. He wraps his arms around me before reaching into the trunk for our luggage.

In the living room, Chris has built a fire. The room is warm with the scent of juniper pine. I pour water and cut apples for my parents. As they like to do, we all take pictures of one another.

"What should we do for dinner, Dad?" I ask.

But my father is asleep, upright on the sofa.

"Mom, I think Dad's sleeping too much."

"Let him rest. He's just old, that's all." She snaps a picture of Chris stoking the fire.

"No, maybe his doctor keeps his blood pressure and sugars too high."

At this, my father awakens. "Dr. Brown is the best doctor. He always treats me very good. His office is close to our house, and it's easy to park."

"What about Dr. Abi? While I was a resident at UCLA, I went through all that trouble to find the very best doctor for you, and you go to Dr. Brown just because it's easy to park?"

"Traffic is horrible. Parking at UCLA is impossible," he says.

"Dad, people come from around the world to see Dr. Abi. You live in the same city. It's not too far to travel."

"No, Dr. Brown will be mad. After I leave Dr. Brown's office, I can go to the bank, go to Trader Joe's. UCLA takes up my whole day."

We've been through this before when I went with Dad to an appointment with Dr. Brown. When I saw Dad's blood pressure and blood glucose, I asked, "Shouldn't these numbers be lower?" The tall, white-coated doctor in cuff links and tie snapped at me, "Young lady, don't you tell me how to practice medicine."

I warm my hands by the fire. "Dad, it wouldn't hurt to see Dr. Abi just once for a second opinion. Just once."

My father is a respectful, loyal man who would never betray his commitment to Dr. Brown. But he agrees to see Dr. Abi for a one-time consultation.

I leave nothing to chance. A couple of weeks later, just before beginning my new job in Albuquerque, I fly to Los Angeles to take Dad to Dr. Abi, myself.

My parents are right about the traffic being horrible, a definite barrier to quality medical care. Parking, however, isn't bad, just expensive. "Seven dollars just for parking," my mom says. "At Dr. Brown's parking is free."

"It's far less costly than a blood pressure of a hundred and forty over ninety," I say, pulling the car into an empty spot.

At last we make it into an exam room at Dr. Abi's office. My dad sits on the table covered with white paper. My mom is weighing herself on the scale when Dr. Abi walks in the room.

"Dr. Wang! Good to see you," he says. "And pleased to meet your parents." He shakes my father's hand and then my mother's. I am always struck by his humble manner.

Dr. Abi speaks with my dad and then examines him with stethoscope, otoscope, ophthalmoscope, and reflex hammer. With his fingers, he strokes the veins in Dad's neck, palpates his abdomen, presses the skin against Dad's shins.

A half-hour later, he shrugs. "Let's make a few changes in your medicine. Let's add a few supplements, too."

The next morning, Dad watches CNN in the den. The papaya tree shades the window.

"There is one thing you cannot change, and that's the business cycle. Sooner or later, the stock market has to come down," he says.

"Mom! Dad's his old self again," I call to the kitchen, where she is kneading scallions, mozzarella, and bacon into dough for an American version of Chinese scallion pancakes.

She comes to the living room with flour on her hands. "Sheesh, *lao ba*," she says. "You look completely different."

"He wasn't just old," I say. "His blood pressure and sugars were too high. There is always a reason, not just age."

Dad smiles as he reaches for *The Wall Street Journal* and the local Chinese newspaper.

He never mentions Dr. Brown again.

Chapter Eleven

At the Health Profit Organization

EARLY 1999

Lovelace Health Systems, in Albuquerque, was founded in 1906 by Dr. William R. Lovelace, and modeled on the Mayo Clinic, where Dr. Lovelace trained. Prideful New Mexicans still speak of how our Lovelace system provided medical care to the world's first space astronauts, Alan Shepard and John Glenn, in 1959.

Like community-owned hospitals across the country, charitable organizations and private donors once gave generously to Lovelace to support its worthy mission of caring for the health needs of New Mexicans.

In 1985, shortly after the federal government began encouraging for-profit businesses to enter medicine, Lovelace was purchased by Cigna, a corporation whose stock value on the New York Stock Exchange doubled, then quadrupled, and then altogether skyrocketed more than eightfold, all in just twenty years.

In 1999, this health system that a proud community once put

money into is now owned by a for-profit corporation taking money out of the community—to pay executives and stockholders around the country.

My office is in a sprawling, low-ceilinged building almost devoid of windows. This building devoted to mental health keeps its entire patient population, as well as its psychiatrists, nurses, therapists, and staff, in the dark. For lunch breaks, we go out for walks, hungry for light and air.

Into my small, windowless office I bring a ficus tree, which can live on the ultraviolet of fluorescent lights. I put up a poster of the blue ocean, to remind me of the wide New Mexico sky outside. And here I'll sit, eight hours a day, thirty-two hours a week.

It all begins benignly enough. I'm given a day to settle in, unpack my books, and meet my coworkers. I learn that the correct pronunciation is not "Love-lace," but "Love-less."

In my chief's office, one of two offices with a window, I request an hour with each new patient and fifteen minutes for each follow-up visit. My chief grants that. Next, as at Kaiser, I ask to see just one patient for psychotherapy, so that I don't lose my skills. I'll do it during lunch or after work, on my own time. But my chief tells me no. "Love-less psychiatrists really cannot do psychotherapy. Just meds."

A month later, after about 130 hours in my windowless office, my chief asks me to see new patients in fifteen-minute slots instead of a full hour. "You know, you can't keep up with your caseload like this. Besides, most of the patients have already been evaluated."

"I need to know the patient myself," I say. "Besides, I hardly ever find an evaluation in their charts."

In another couple of weeks, my chief repeats her request for me to cut my time with new patients to fifteen minutes. Once again, I refuse. I wonder how long I'll be able to hold out.

"Doc-in-the-box" days are the most challenging. Each day, one psychiatrist takes responsibility for all urgent patient matters, on top of an already crammed usual schedule. Some psychiatrists get through doc-in-the-box days by writing prescriptions without seeing the patients, relying on recommendations from nurses and counselors.

But I have never prescribed for a patient I've never seen, and I simply won't start now.

I confide in my chief: "I'm disturbed by the turnover in the staff. I've been here six weeks, and every week somebody leaves."

"Who?" my chief asks.

I mention my own nurse, who was fired without anyone asking me. I mention a psychiatrist who was fired after complaining about children not getting proper care. When I was hired, I was told that I would be one of eight psychiatrists on staff. But right now there are only four of us doing the work of eight. I multiply my salary by four, and calculate the savings to the corporation.

At home that evening, I type a letter of resignation. I carry the undated letter in my pocket each minute at work. If it looks like I'll be fired, I'll whip out the letter and resign instead. I've worked too hard at the nation's best institutions for my career. I don't want it to be ruined here.

Fortunately, I hear that positions are now available at the University of New Mexico. One of the positions is chief of the Psychiatry Consultation-Liaison Service, Bob Byck's position at Yale. At UNM, I could also be reunited with Joel Yager, Joanna Katzman, a classmate from medical school, and her husband, Jeff.

Why not go take a look?

During a day of interviews, I visit the Psych Consult office on the fourth floor of the medical hospital. Out the window, the Sandia Mountains stretch beneath a wide horizon. I imagine my life with a view of the sky.

The decision is easy.

Back at Lovelace, I pull the resignation letter from my pocket. I date it, sign it, and hand it to my chief.

I've lasted at Lovelace just two months, slightly longer than I lasted at McDonald's as a high school student. I've resigned in time—before prescribing for patients I've never seen, before succumbing to pressure to compromise my ethics as a physician.

Beneath the buzzing fluorescent lights of my windowless office, I pack my books. My ficus tree is dead, so I throw it into the Dumpster in the parking lot. I was not allowed to give it enough light to keep it alive.

Leaving Lovelace, I feel a new admiration for the Kaiser assembly line. At Kaiser, at least I wasn't kept in the dark, as if I were a machine that didn't need the light of day. Kaiser, owned by physicians, is still based on medical ethics, its prepaid health plan still aimed toward prevention. Kaiser is indeed a health maintenance organization, even with the compromises it makes under today's new pressures.

No two ways about it, at Lovelace, I was at a health *profit* organization.

But working at Lovelace wasn't all bad. I enjoyed my patients and I enjoyed my colleagues.

I also enjoyed my stay at the Beverly Wilshire Hotel, a block from Rodeo Drive, in Beverly Hills.

"Hey, I got this invitation," my Lovelace chief said one day. "I can't go, but I thought you might like to."

I looked at the invite, and in a split second replied, "Oh my goodness, thank you!" I went home and packed my bags for a Rodeo Drive weekend, courtesy of Wyeth-Ayerst, makers of Effexor.

Afterward, I was inspired to write this, which I submitted to *Newsweek* magazine. It was accepted but never published:

My pens that read "Prozac" are deep navy blue with yellow lettering, the "o" a stylized rising sun, the pen itself a fine rolling tip. I reserve Prozac pens for thank you cards, letters, or whenever I want good quality ink. I never need to buy pens. A handful always sits ready for duty on my desk, in my purse, in my car, on the kitchen counter near the phone. Zoloft pens are my favorite for everyday use, whether writing prescriptions or jotting down the grocery list. Sometimes fat, sometimes thin, over the years Zoloft pens have been different pleasing shades of blue but made of metal, not plastic like the others, a substantial, perfect weight, like a Montblanc. When I'm on the wards, I fix an Effexor ballpoint to my clipboard. Lightweight, and shaped like a syringe, it's a good pen for the hospital. On my refrigerator, I once used a magnetic blue Zoloft clip to hold the grocery list. But I've replaced it with a sturdier, lime-green Effexor clip. Is it a coincidence that I also think of Effexor as a stronger antidepressant than Zoloft?

I make an effort to limit the entry of troops. Otherwise, my home would be full of Zoloft notepads, Luvox desk clocks, square boxes of Celexa tissues, purple Zyprexa mugs, cheery red Lexapro paper clips, all courtesy of pharmaceutical "reps."

I also guard my time. Otherwise I would spend several evenings a month dining at the finest restaurants in town, courtesy of the pharmaceutical companies.

Fellow psychiatrists and doctor friends give talks for drug companies, a task that requires weekend vacations at Ritz-Carltons and the Four Seasons at wonderful sites across the country. They are flown to Italy or Switzerland, then wined and dined in Asia. I am not one of the stars of the drug company talk circuit, but I do remember a fabulous weekend in Beverly Hills, courtesy of Wyeth-Ayerst, which makes Effexor. A chauffeur picked me up at the airport. He insisted on taking my baggage and refused a tip. I attended talks in the mornings, and in the afternoons, I lay by the pool amidst palm trees at the Beverly Wilshire Hotel. A waiter in a bow tie brought me drinks and California cuisine.

Effexor is my favorite antidepressant because it works on multiple neurotransmitter systems, serotonin, norepinephrine, dopamine, and is therefore most likely to defeat depression. The pool at the Beverly Wilshire has nothing to do with my opinion, or does it? I also like Zoloft because it seems to have fewer side effects, and I'm certain that I am not swayed by my favorite pens. Coincidentally, like the Prozac pens, I also reserve the drug itself for special occasions—for obsessive-compulsive disorder and for bulimia, because Prozac, in my opinion, is the antidepressant best tolerated in conditions that require high doses. I rarely prescribe Paxil because it tends to cause sedation and weight gain. I'm sure it has nothing to do with the fact that I have no Paxil pens. I think of Wellbutrin as less effective than other antidepressants. It's lightweight, like paper notepads, the only things I've ever gotten from its manufacturer.

I read the scientific journals, looking for truth. But I find that about two-thirds of all articles and nearly every study about medications are funded by pharmaceutical companies. They inevitably conclude that their own drug is superior. The fight for market share isn't just happening in our best restaurants and hotels, in TV commercials and magazine ads, but in our peer-reviewed journals.

And so I sit in my office, my prescription pad on my desk, my hand wrapped around a free pen. In my head is a swirling pool of information: scientific data laid out in neat tables, hallway conversations when a colleague whispers, *You know, I'm not sure Superdrug X really works,* the voices of my own thousands of patients reporting drowsiness, tremors, restored happiness, better sex. Mugs, calculators, the taste of salmon at a dinner with slides, the name of the drug on the pen in my hand.

I choose, write my prescriptions, and wait for my patients to let me know.

Chapter Twelve

The University
Hospital, Revisited

In the fall of 1999, I began my position as chief of the Psychiatry
Consultation-Liaison Service at the University of New Mexico
Hospital, a job that put me in charge of a thousand lives a year, a job
that made me, finally, *the man*, in the lingo of my younger days.

I found myself constantly rising to new challenges, constantly
striving to do better in my daily task of overseeing the care of patients,
the work of my staff, and the careers of my students and residents. I
also helped with the decisions of management above me.

From this vantage point as chief of a university hospital service,
I saw increasingly no grand plan, but just-human people, flawed as
we all are, doing our best. I grew tremendously in my capacity for
compassion—not just for my patients, but for the staff I oversaw, and
for my hardworking colleagues.

I saw that when things fall through the cracks, when the needs of patients or staff go unmet, there's no grand conspiracy, no orchestrated evil intent.

Sometimes, *the man* is simply working as hard as she can.

Those years brought tremendous changes in me, but they brought even more radical changes for medicine and psychiatry in the state of New Mexico.

In 1998, managed care further penetrated New Mexico. For-profit companies took charge of Medicaid payments for psychiatry. That same year, many psychiatrists found it financially unfeasible to keep practicing.

Dr. Jay Feierman, for example, closed shop in late 1998, leaving his seven hundred patients, including some of Albuquerque's most severely mentally ill citizens, scrambling for care. In 1998, Jay worked just as he had for twenty years. Like doctors of another time, he was always available, and was awakened each night with phone calls from patients. He took care of his patients from the first onset of illness onward. He knew his patients and their families. The year for-profit managed care took over Medicaid, Jay fell $50,000 in the hole. He took out a second mortgage to pay his bills. Finally, he closed his practice and took a salaried job in the Department of Corrections. His seven hundred patients sought care elsewhere.

Within about three years, by early 2002, the volume at our university mental health center had doubled, according to my supervisor. Jay Feierman closing his practice was stated as a major factor. Patients stayed stable for a year or two, then gradually deteriorated and came to our university's public system for help. In subsequent years I tried, but found it impossible, to substantiate that our volume really doubled then, since, of course, as our number of patients increased, we cut services.

By 2004, after six years of managed care putting Albuquerque doctors out of business, our university's expanded workload was indisputable. We decided to double the number of psychiatrists on our inpatient wards. We hired additional moonlighting psychiatrists to work part-time in our Psychiatric Emergency Service (PES) each night.

But it was too late for Diana, who, as chief of both PES and the inpatient psychiatry services, no doubt tried to maintain her high standard for patient care, even in the face of increasingly impossible volumes of patients. She died in 2002, when our increased workload was just becoming clear to us.

The work of the Psych Consult Service also increased dramatically. In 2002, while I was pregnant, I found myself working later and later. My transient hypertension and retinal detachment were casualties of those first years of managed care managing mental health in New Mexico. While our workloads increased, managed care paid us the same lowered fees that put Jay Feierman and other doctors out of business. But our university system can't close down, even when faced with an impossible task. Patients got less, while physicians and staff did more. Every day, we had to find new ways to pull a rabbit out of a hat.

In my right eye is an invisible but permanent scar from those years of being caught between my old-fashioned doctor ethics, and the new realities of today's industrial health care system.

My job as chief of the Psychiatry Consultation-Liaison Service at UNM had always been a full-time job, since the position was founded in the 1960s. But in 1999, I did the equivalent of a half-time job on top of my full-time duty as a chief of a major hospital service. The workload brought late evenings and worse, compromises to my health. After I left the service in 2003, Janet and Kathryn, a psychologist and a nurse, took on the main responsibilities, with an assortment of psychiatrists coming and going, in half-day shifts. Psychiatrists indeed became mere consultants on the Psychiatry Consultation Service, giving a new meaning to the service's name.

After my months of maternity leave, I thought of my long hours in the hospital. I was still seeing stars in my vision. I remembered Diana's death.

I thought of my baby.

What could be more important than caring for my baby? As a psychiatrist, so much of my work is to make up for the shortfalls of a patient's early years. My work with tens of thousands of lives only confirmed for me, what Freud and my Chinese grandmother both say, that the first years of life determine the rest. How could I not spend time with my child in her first years? Sweden, I understand, gives each parent a year of leave after a baby is born, believing that love in infancy protects against physical and mental illness for a lifetime.

Now *that's* preventive health care policy.

After Zoe's birth, I decided to continue on the faculty of the UNM Department of Psychiatry part-time: ten hours a week, rather than ten hours a day. I prescribed medications at a homeless clinic, and then at the student health center, while all along, prescribing medications at the faculty clinic. The work was unsettling, never adequately done. Everyone agrees that medications are never the complete answer, even if, increasingly, it's all that is offered.

In these years, I watched medical services in my city getting cut closer and closer to the bone, until finally the inevitable happened. The worst killing spree in Albuquerque's three-hundred-year history was committed by a mentally ill man—a man who was kept stable for seven years by a single psychiatrist, Jay Feierman, who under our new national policy of health care for corporate profit found it impossible to keep caring for his patients.

At the time, I was spending most of my hours in a haze of motherhood, the most difficult, least understood, but most important job of all, I decided.

I thought it would be difficult to slow my career. Until I saw my child for the first time.

She is born in a hospital, where life's milestones happen—birth, death, transitions brought by illness, and all that's in between.

On November 26, 2002, in the dark, early morning, Chris helps my swollen body into our car. As tired as I am, as difficult as it is for me to move, I look behind me to check that our baby's car seat is there. How strange to think that the next time we're in this car, there will be three of us, our newest family member in this lavender infant's car seat, a gift from Community Health Plan.

Chris and I have chosen St. Joseph's Hospital, "a wonderful place to have your baby," Dr. Harrison said. St. Joseph's, I know, is part of a health system founded by an order of charitable nuns early in the twentieth century. Babies have been born here for decades.

At the St. Joseph's Hospital registration desk, where Chris and I stop first, I pull out my Community Health Plan insurance card.

"There's a two-hundred-and-fifty-dollar co-pay," the young receptionist with wavy black hair says. "Your health plan covers everything else."

"Everything?" I ask, knowing how costly hospitalizations can be.

"Everything," she says. Community Health Plan will cover my

hospitalization, Dr. Harrison's care, the delivery, anesthesia, medicines, the room, the baby's care. Everything, no matter how many days I'll stay.

"The maternity ward is expecting you."

Up the elevator, down a carpeted hallway, Chris and I stop at the nurses' station.

"Dr. Wang," a white-haired nurse greets me. "This way to your room. It has a view of the city. We want this to be a special experience." My hospital room turns out to also have a living area with a pull-out sofa for Chris, who is encouraged to stay with me.

"Thank you," I say, "you've thought of everything."

Chris puts our overnight bags on the sofa. I step into the bathroom to change into a hospital gown. Out of my own clothes, I am so cold in this stark white bathroom.

Back in the room, I settle my body into the wheelchair by the bed. The white-haired nurse enters the room. She drapes white blankets upon me. They are warm.

The nurse and Chris together wheel me from the room. Down the hall, the delivery room looks so cold and sterile with bare white walls and white linoleum. Ric, a portly nurse anesthetist with a calming voice, instructs me to crawl onto a gurney, where I shiver, wearing nothing but this thin hospital gown.

We know that our baby is healthy, thanks to an ultrasound. But she has only one umbilical artery, not two. Chris and I want to take no chances. We've already decided on a C-section.

Ric snaps on gloves. He scrubs my back with betadine antiseptic, then plunges a needle into it. He misses my spine, so he plunges again. And again, until at last he hits the right spot. Within seconds, my legs and feet are numb. I feel nothing at all in my lower body, as if half of me has gotten up and walked out the door.

Whose body is this now, with no feeling or ability to move from my waist down, but breathing rapidly . . . hyperventilating . . . now shaking?

I know all about anxiety attacks. But what is happening to me, now?

"Would you like some Ativan, Doctor? Or morphine?" Ric offers.

Both medications, I know, would affect my baby, still part of my own body but who will soon cry and breathe for the first time. Do I want her to begin life drugged?

Thankfully, here is Dr. Harrison, in a blue cap and scrubs, his smile beaming.

"You will be fine. You are so beautiful right now."

His rough, warm hands hold my face, rub my cheeks, my hair. His face is against mine, in this cold room, his breath.

"Dr. Harrison." I embrace his arms. My breathing slows, my shaking stops.

My doctor is here.

And Chris is here, too, on the stool beside me, in a sterile gown and cap.

"C, I never thought I'd see you like this," I laugh.

A blue paper curtain flutters, then settles above my chest, keeping the lower half of my body from my view. Dr. Harrison is gloved now, in a sterile blue gown. He walks to the other side of the curtain. He begins working. His head is down, his shoulders move rapidly.

I close my eyes. I squeeze Chris's hands. I breathe, draw into myself. I think of my own parents. I sing a Taiwanese folk song that my mother used to sing, about a tall green mountain with shallow blue waters.

Chris stands, strains his body to see over the curtain. His eyes grow wide. His breathing quickens.

I am still singing, my eyes shut, when in this room still with anticipation, suddenly I hear her.

She is crying.

Dr. Harrison holds her above the curtain. With my own blood streaked upon his gloves, he is the first to hold her, before me, before Chris.

She is such a small, fragile-looking thing, still covered in the life fluid of my womb, with spindly thin arms and legs waving, crying, hungry for air, breathing for the first time.

How incredible that my body has made this baby.

And then she is gone, taken from the room. Chris rises, dashes to follow her. I have instructed him to not let her from his sight.

My gurney is wheeled down a corridor to the recovery room. Here I study the monitors. Is my blood pressure low? Is my heart rate high? Now my heart rate is rising, my breath quickening. I feel so fragile, on the verge of being medicated. I try to calm down, refrain from analyzing my own vital signs. An hour passes—or is it just minutes?

A nurse with soft brown hair enters. In her arms is a bundle of white blankets, which she hands to me.

"Breastfeed her," the nurse says.

"What?"

And here she is, she who has never been outside of my body. Her tiny heart-shaped face crying in this new world, now comforted at last, only by my body.

I feel a sad sense of time racing. I see her growing until she no longer fits in my hand, and then no longer in my house. I see her becoming a woman, tall and beautiful, as I grow old and gray.

But for now, she is so small she rests in my one hand. Cradling her in my arms, I feel a new sense of belonging to a cycle that always was and always will be, since the first woman and the first child. I have held her just seconds, but I know that if I lose her, my life would feel empty, missing something grand.

She is healthy, and in the strength of her cry, she brings me a feeling of years and generations to come. Yet in this moment, she gives me nothing but the opportunity to love.

In the hospital, where we spend our first days as a new family, Chris and I name our daughter Zoe, which in Greek, the language of his ancestors, means "life."

Part Four

New Life

DECEMBER 2002

Chapter Thirteen

New Light

The laws of science change in my first days home from the hospital. Time, space, and distance are all new in baby's light, all truly relative. Time is marked by feedings, sleep, and the time in between. Distance, with her sleeping in my lap, becomes arm's reach, or not. I need Chris, I need my own parents and my in-laws, to fly into town just to hand me a drink of water.

She curls against my body as if she hasn't left my inside. Rocking, with her asleep in my lap, I understand love in a new way. Evolutionary biologists who wonder why altruism exists must never have breast-fed a baby, never leaped from sleep to change a diaper. It is clear to me in this moment, that if not for altruism, the human species would never have survived past our first week.

Friends visit.

"Her eyes are blue," Sally says, cradling Zoe in her arms. "Yes, definitely. They're blue."

Her eyes are blue? To me Zoe's eyes are dark brown, almost black, the color of my own eyes. Sally's eyes are blue, smiling beneath wisps of short gray hair.

Sally was a vice chair of my department, and the first woman president of the American College of Psychoanalysts. Retired now, she's just a gal about town. She smiles as she watches Zoe sleep, breathing softly.

We sneak away for lunch, leaving Zoe with Maria, whom I have recruited as Zoe's nanny.

At Chef du Jour, down the street, we both order curried chicken over greens.

"When mothers hold Zoe, I see something in their faces," I say between forkfuls of crunchy greens, "like they're reliving their own lives. In their faces, I see the love that is to come."

The waiter lays a berry tart with fluffy cream between us. I see mist in Sally's eyes. I picture her with her hair still dark, holding her two young sons by their small, plump hands.

How I long to know what she knows, this mother who has lived the life I enter now.

Back at my house again, Sally sits and rocks Zoe. "Your eyes are so blue. Yes, definitely, so blue."

A miracle of healing happens in my first months of motherhood. My neck and back have never felt better in the eight years since my car accident. I have been strengthened, somehow, by this reintegration into the cycle of life. To think that I considered not having this child for fear of worsening my nagging injury. Women have always carried children in their bellies and then on hips and backs. We are built for this purpose, strengthened by this. Why did I have that unnatural surgery when I could have just done—this?

My health is better. My life is better.

But I've never been a stay-at-home kind of gal. Now I am home all the time—just me and this beautiful baby who is years away from meaningful conversation. One mother, one child, one house, all across the city, all across the country, alone mostly, in this marathon of motherhood. Feed. Rock to sleep. Change diaper. Feed again. Rock again.

What about literature, history, brain science, world events? Teddy Roosevelt once said that he could do the work of president—or care for Alice, his granddaughter. But he couldn't do both.

At library story times, in a red-carpeted amphitheater that feels like a womb, I sit with Zoe in my lap behind other mothers and babies. The librarian in a flowered apron sings "Itsy-bitsy Spider" and opposes thumb to forefinger, thumb to forefinger. In the dark, watching a Curious George movie among breast-feeding moms and running toddlers, I feel a kind of shock—as if I have traveled full speed through a wind tunnel and now come to a sudden stop.

Where are the life-or-death emergencies?

Can life really be this simple, this joyful?

Home again, alone with Zoe in my arms, I think, Hey, why don't I work for that place in my neighborhood, Southwest Creations? It provides on-site child care, since many of its employees are single moms. I can be in the company of other adults while I sew pillows and quilts—and I won't have to leave Zoe. Conversation, my main reason for doing this, might be difficult, since many of the women don't speak English and my Spanish is poor. But my Spanish would improve, a bonus to this plan.

But what about my skills as a physician? What about all that I've invested in my training? I am the state expert in several medical topics. Why am I considering a new career in pillows? Something seems terribly wrong.

"Just take Zoe to work," my friend Yun says.

We sit on my porch, sipping orange juice. Zoe sleeps in her bassinet, in a patch of sun.

"That's why I want to work at Southwest Creations. I couldn't bring a baby to a clinic."

"Why not? It's not as if she'll be around a lot of germs. You're a psychiatrist."

"Yun, I feel like a pariah, a leper, that because I have a baby I'm no longer worthy to be in the workplace."

"You should still feel worthy." She pours me another glass of juice and passes me a bowl of crackers. Zoe cries, and Yun picks her up.

I remember Yun's words when a resident working on the geriatric psychiatry ward calls me.

"I saw your chapter on Munchausen syndrome and factitious disorders in the new Kaplan and Sadock textbook," Dana says on the phone. "Freddie Clay's hospitalized on the G-ward."

Freddie? The father of baby Victoria, who died?

"I know Freddie. Why is he on the *geriatric* ward?" I ask.

"Because our psych nurses are better at handling medical problems. He's been pulling his own blood out of his body," Dana says. "In the hospital, his *crit* kept dropping, even after blood transfusions. Nurses found bloody syringes in his mattress. Do you think you can come talk to us about Munchausen's?"

Given my experience with Munchausen's and with Freddie, my presence would be worthwhile—even with a three-month-old baby in my arms. For me, it would certainly be more exciting than another morning of being stuck in my rocking chair, trying not to move, lest I wake the baby in my lap.

"I'd be happy to come talk to the ward," I say. "But I'll need to bring my baby."

"Umm. I don't see a problem," Dana says.

The next morning, I push Zoe in her bright yellow stroller down the hall of the psychiatric hospital to the door of the G-ward. A tech peers at me through the glass window. I flash my badge that still reads: "Dora Wang, M.D., Chief, Psychiatry Consultation-Liaison Service."

On the G-ward, patients lounge on sofas before the TV, many with faded hair and mouths wide open, asleep in pale hospital gowns.

In the conference room, a dozen psychiatry residents, nurses, techs, and social workers are seated around a long table. There's no room for a stroller, so I cradle Zoe in one arm, while I start to distribute handouts with my other. Everyone smiles at my baby.

"I'm sorry, I don't have child care yet," I say. It's an easier explanation than, *Every time I leave her, she cries as if I'll never be back.* Or, *I just don't get this weird separation of work and life.*

Dana, a young woman with short blond hair and a sunny round face, takes the stack of handouts from me. She distributes them.

"Thank you," I sigh. I sit down at the head of the conference table.

"Freddie's a textbook case of Munchausen syndrome—literally," I say. "I included him as a case study in my textbook chapter on the subject." By now, Zoe is asleep in my lap.

People with factitious disorders, I explain, fake or exaggerate illness to gain attention by playing the role of the patient. Most resort to these tactics only in times of stress. But for Munchausen patients, faking illness becomes a disabling way of life. Munchausen syndrome by proxy is usually committed by a parent upon a child, most commonly a preverbal infant. It is not yet recognized as an official psychiatric diagnosis, but all fifty states consider Munchausen syndrome by proxy a form of child abuse. The best intervention is to limit medical harm by getting patients into psychotherapy (a treatment we no longer do in our university department of psychiatry, I don't bother adding).

Zoe cries. Her eyes are wide open. My instinct is to lift up my shirt and stick my breast into her mouth. Thank goodness I've prepared a bottle of warm formula.

"Do you have suggestions for how we can prepare for Freddie's next baby?" Dana asks.

"His next baby?"

"His wife is pregnant again. But with all his mysterious hospitalizations, she's suspicious. She's been asking us questions about Munchausen's. She's thinking about leaving him. She wants to keep the new baby away from him."

I nod.

"And another thing," Dana says. "He still calls you his doctor. He says he sees you every week, even though you're on maternity leave."

Freddie knows I'm on maternity leave?

At the end of the hour, as I leave the conference room, a muscular man smiles at me. His pitch-black hair is now long, flowing over his shoulders. His sad blue eyes focus on me.

"So is this your newborn?" Freddie looks at Zoe in her stroller.

"Yes," I say.

"She's cute. I'm having another kid," he says.

"I heard. You'll be a father again."

Lights still flash in my eyes. Washing dishes while Zoe sleeps, lightning bleaches my vision. Checking e-mails, yellow stars glitter on my computer screen. I realize I should see a doctor about this.

Besides, as my four months of maternity leave near their end, I ponder my career and how I'll balance it now, as Zoe's mother. I find myself wanting the perspective of someone in the business of knowing lives.

A doctor.

I pick up the phone and I make an appointment.

Well, actually, it isn't so easy as that.

To see an ophthalmologist, I have to first get a referral from my internist. I call his office at the university. I navigate the phone tree. I wait on hold. Ten minutes later, I speak with a scheduler who says sorry, Dr. Hash has no openings for two months.

"But all I need is a referral, paperwork, to see an ophthalmologist."

"Sorry, it'll be two months."

Stars flash.

It feels unfair, as a patient, to resort to my professional relationship with my own doctor. Lights flash. So I go ahead and page Dr. Hash. I think about other doctors in town, like Dr. Nancy Guinn, who I hear has found a way to spend more time with patients.

"I'm just swamped," Dr. Hash says when he calls back. "If it's just a referral you want, you don't need to come in. Just ask Anna."

I sympathize with him. I thank him, then I call Anna. I leave daily voice mails that aren't returned. Finally, I go to the clinic, walk through a door that says STAFF ONLY, and I sit at Anna's cubicle.

Anna, a young woman in powder-blue scrubs, is surrounded by messy stacks of paper littered with yellow Post-its. She takes a deep breath before she calls my insurance company. She navigates phone trees, waits on hold, and is finally told to call another number. She calls the other number, navigates phone trees, waits on hold, then hears the dead drone of a dial tone. She calls again, navigates phone trees, waits on hold, and finally she gets a live representative who puts her on hold. At last, she asks for permission. While pleading, she flips through my chart, pulls up information on her computer screen. She waits on hold. Finally, she is given some sort of number that she jots on a couple of forms. She gives one form to me, and sighs in relief.

A full hour later, I walk out of the clinic with the prized referral in my hand.

Now the eye doctor will need to get a *prior authorization*, a similarly time-consuming, soul-testing process. No doctor who takes insurance is immune. Even the associate chair of psychiatry at Yale, I heard from a colleague, was spotted sitting on the hospital steps, arguing into his cell phone for a prior authorization.

Six weeks later, on the day of my appointment, I drive to Dr. Reidy's office, an old brick building covered with ivy. In the waiting room, a man in a suit and cowboy boots fidgets. A Navajo woman in braids talks into her cell phone. A man with an oxygen tank and an American-flag bandanna around his forehead says, "Some of us have things to do and can't wait all day." A white-haired woman nods to the elderly man beside her. "Let's go. It's been an hour. Someone should report Reidy to the AMA."

An hour later, a nurse in pink scrubs lays a platter of finger sandwiches, vegetables, and cookies on the coffee table. Patients rise from their chairs for the food. I help myself to a cheese sandwich and cucumber slices.

Another hour later, a young nurse in a white uniform leads me down the corridor into a dark room. She seats me in a tall padded chair. I am surrounded by machines—scopes, lights, and meters on all sides of me.

Dr. Reidy enters the room. He is wiry thin and energetic as a teenager, but with thinning hair and a full white beard.

"I enjoyed your sandwiches." I arch an eyebrow to convey curiosity.

"Sandwiches, oh yes," he says. "A bit unusual?"

"Well, I have to say, yours is the first doctor's office I've known to serve lunch on a silver platter."

"We don't turn anyone away," he says, "so this means long waits. The food is to show our appreciation."

"That's so incredibly generous of you." My eyebrow is still arched.

"It also keeps our diabetic patients from passing out," he says.

I tell him about the flashing lights.

He takes a round eyeglass the size of a silver dollar from the pocket of his white coat. He holds it between his thumb and forefinger, as if signaling *OK*. He shines light through the glass into my eye. By some optical trick, I can see inside myself, to the shadowy branches of my own eye vessels.

"It's a small retinal detachment," he says. "Nothing to worry about. I'll fix it today with a few zaps of the laser."

"A retinal detachment? What could cause this?"

"Probably your transient high blood pressure." And then he asks something I no longer expect from a doctor: "What's your baby's name?"

"Zoe. It's the Greek word for 'life.' She's Greek, on my husband's side."

In my chart, next to his diagrams of my eyes, he writes, *Zoe— Greek word for life.*

"You wrote my baby's name in my chart."

"Of course."

Back in the waiting room, the man in the bandanna is still complaining. I nibble on baby carrots. I call Chris. I tell him I'm getting a procedure. I'll be home late.

After another two hours, I'm led to a room with different

machines. Here I wait for my doctor, a man who sees me as a person, not just millimeters of detachment.

"How's your work at the university?" Dr. Reidy enters the room.

"I'm still on maternity leave. I've got some decisions to make." A brilliant green thread of laser light quivers in the machine between us.

"The problem with medicine these days," he says, adjusting the machine, "is it's gotten so mechanized. All these diagnostic codes we put on our billing forms—they keep us from seeing the person. You came to me because of a detached retina. But that was never the whole problem, the real problem."

Beams of green light hit my eye. My world turns pale milky purple.

"Have you noticed, they don't call it the medical profession anymore?" he says. "They call it the health care *industry*. You and I are the newest *industrial* workers."

Everything is tranquil purple. Yes, that's the answer. Medicine is an industry now. We once knew the people who made our shoes, cut our meat, and baked our bread. But the village shoemaker, the town butcher, and the baker are all gone. Soon we won't know who cares for our bodies, either. Even human emotions are now processed on the strange assembly line that psychiatry has become.

And what are we as patients now—just widgets?

"What I hate most about medicine these days," Dr. Reidy says, "is that it deprives me of you, the patient." Machines clank under his hands. "Nobody is anybody anymore. And our kids, they're being raised in daycares, by anonymous people"—he pauses to choose his words carefully—"by nobodys."

"By nobody who will always love them." My vision clears.

"Like I said, by nobodys. So our kids. They grow up as nobodys."

When the purple fades, I see Dr. Reidy in his white coat and his white hair.

"But something is bound to change," he says. "Look at how long my patients wait and how upset they get."

I don't have the heart to tell him that the patients munching his sandwiches and nibbling his veggies complain about him, the front man, and not the unseen forces he battles every day in order to care for them.

"As for your eyesight," he says, "it will be just fine."

"My vision *is* just fine now. Thank you."

Spring's wildflowers bloom outside my kitchen window. Children run in cool grass in the park across the street.

My maternity leave ends and I prepare to begin a new life.

What I once put into the care of a thousand patients a year, I'll put toward one person, Zoe. What I hoped to learn from knowing the lives of many, I'll learn from knowing one life from its beginning. What wisdom and fulfillment I can't get from this strange new kind of doctoring, I'll get from being a mother.

Ten hours a week is my new workweek, not ten hours a day. Even this seems an eternity away from Zoe.

With my baby in my arms and her brown eyes smiling into mine, I develop a new theory about women in the workforce. What keeps us from rising—isn't lack of intelligence, capability, or leadership potential. It isn't even necessarily discrimination. For many of us, it is our capacity to love.

For my first day of work in three months, I slip into a black maternity skirt and one of Chris's large wool sweaters. My body is still large. I stroke Zoe's whisper-soft hair. Her small, sleeping body rises and falls with each soft breath.

The back door creaks open. Maria is here, she who has left her own children to care for mine. I was reluctant to hire her, for just this reason, and so I had asked Yoli, the nursing student on my service, to do a psych consult on my situation. At my house, Yoli chatted in Spanish with Maria. They talked for a long time. Then Yoli turned to me. "Caring for children is her profession. Like we go to work to do what we do. She needs to work."

"But how can I ask her to leave her own children?"

"Dora, she has five children. They're older. It's fine. Mexican families raise themselves."

These families raise themselves? I can barely get a shower with Zoe in the house. What secret do they know? What secrets have we lost? If raising children was always this difficult, we would have gone extinct while still in caves. How far our lifestyles have gotten from being conducive to our species, how alien, with our long commutes and all of us alone in our own homes.

"Maria will love your child," Yoli said.

"How can you know?"

"By the way she talks about her own children."

My student has learned well.

How strange that I am hiring someone to love my child. That is Maria's purpose, isn't it? Housekeeping, arriving on time, really are secondary. To love in my absence. That is her job.

Sun glints in Maria's brown hair as she takes glasses from the dishwasher and places them in the cupboard. I smile. "*Buenos días*," I say, which makes me think of *Bom dia*, in Portuguese, the language of my own childhood. I open the refrigerator door and point to bottles of breast milk lined up like soldiers, ready to feed. Maria nods.

I get into the gas-guzzling Toyota Land Cruiser Chris and I have bought for Zoe's safety. The truck afforded such a huge tax savings we couldn't pass up replacing Chris's beat-up old Volvo. In my sparkling new car, I drive down Mountain Road to the homeless clinic, a collection of pink buildings, like bonbons in the sun. Lines of men and women wait outside, sipping coffee, sharing smokes.

I edge past two dozen people in line who look at me with curious eyes. I slip through the door and introduce myself to the reception staff: "Dr. Wang. I'm the new psychiatrist, here for my first day."

In a room crowded by a large exam table that I won't use, I sit in a chair by the sink. For the next four hours, I prescribe mood stabilizers to bipolars, and antipsychotics to schizophrenics. Most of the souls who pass through this room are depressed. After all, they are homeless. But my job is to prescribe drugs, only. I keep my back flat against the wall. I can't stray an inch, or else I'll set off the sink's glowing red automatic sensor that makes the faucet run with a mind of its own.

For these restless souls who wander the streets at night searching for a sheltered spot to sleep, isn't the real problem that they don't have just one person, one relative or friend, to take them in? And what does it mean that the world's wealthiest nation can't even provide everyone shelter from the cold?

Buck's large, rotund body droops in the chair like a limp teddy bear.

"I'm so tired. Too tired to go on." He's taken Prozac for years, he says, but it stopped working for him. He was switched to Zoloft six months ago. But he feels no better.

"That's enough time, if it's not working," I say. "Let me go find something else for you."

Down the hall, the pharmacy is stacked floor to ceiling with wallet-sized sample boxes and bottles of generic drugs, mostly donations from pharmaceutical salespersons, physicians, staff, and even patients. It's a group effort.

I look past the bottles of Prozac and Zoloft, and I spot Effexor, in green-and-black-striped boxes. I take a sheet of pills from the box. I record in five different places that I'm taking it.

Back in my office, I hand Buck the sheet of pills in clear plastic bubbles. "Do you have a safe place to keep these?" I ask, knowing that these sheets get worn in sweaty pockets that move all day.

"Right here," Buck pats his sleeping bag. "This way, I'll remember to take them first thing every morning."

The next week, I clean out my kitchen medicine shelf. I fill a grocery bag with samples given to me by drug reps over the years. I throw in unopened bottles of ibuprofen and antihistamines. I even toss in sheets of unused prenatal vitamin samples, still perfect behind plastic bubbles. I bring the bag to the homeless clinic. "We can sure use these!" the pharmacy tech thanks me.

Within a month, Buck unfolds into a wisecracking guy who brings Ziploc baggies full of shimmering beaded necklaces and earrings that he makes. I don't usually buy things from patients, but ten dollars in Buck's pocket means he'll eat for a few days. He's diabetic, after all.

I write in my progress note: *Major Depression, recurrent, in full remission, RTC 6 mos, sooner prn, paid $10 for necklace, and owe $5 for earrings*. To Buck, I say, "Now that you're doing better, make sure you come back and see me in six months."

But Buck comes every week. I keep buying his jewelry. On weekends, I like to wear the necklace that reminds me of the American flag, with blue and white beads, and blood-colored teardrops.

And then one day, the clinic administrator shuts my office door and quietly tells me that I've got to stop buying things from patients.

But Buck still comes to see me every week.

Gabriel comes to see me weekly, too, at my home on Wednesday afternoons. He climbs from his car, carrying a notebook as usual, with his pager, cell phone and PalmPilot upon his belt. I put Zoe in her stroller, and we meet him outside in our driveway.

Thelma Wolff Park cools at the end of a hot summer day. Birds flutter in treetops. Children play in the sand, climb on the play structure, while mothers sit on cool grass, chatting, laughing. I wave hello to the moms as Gabriel, Zoe, and I stroll through the park.

After a day indoors at the psychiatric hospital, Gabriel tilts his face toward the sun. He breathes in the scent of warm grass. In flower beds, spring's blossoms begin to give way to the dry grasses of summer.

"I have a question for you, as your psychotherapy supervisor," I say to Gabriel as I push Zoe's stroller. "How do you feel about beginning a career in psychiatry at a time when you probably won't be doing much psychotherapy?"

We cross Central Avenue, Historic Route 66, that in the 1930s brought midwestern farmers from the Dust Bowl to California, and in the 1950s, vacationing motorists across the country, before it was largely replaced by the faster, far grayer interstate freeway.

We walk through an area of downtown, once bustling in the heyday of railroad travel and in the busy days of Route 66, which is now abandoned buildings and empty lots rustling with litter and broken glass.

Gabriel's eyes scan for traffic. "Well, when I chose psychiatry, I never expected to do psychotherapy."

Never expected to do psychotherapy? As a psychiatrist?

I think about it. This is 2003. Gabriel graduated from medical school in 2000. He began his psychiatry residency a full decade after I started mine. Why, of course. The ten years in between was the Decade of the Brain. All three jobs I've had—at Kaiser, Lovelace, and now at the University of New Mexico—have been to prescribe medications, only. I have practiced psychotherapy only because I have refused to give it up.

"I wonder where medicine is going," Gabriel says. "In California, Blue Cross is bringing in physicians from Mexico to cut costs."

"You're kidding," I say. "Like migrant farm workers and meat packers."

"No, when I chose psychiatry, I didn't expect to do psychotherapy," Gabriel says.

We stop outside the Southern Union Gas Company Building, once a busy neighborhood hub in the 1950s. Now tall windows are frosted with dirt and weather. A magnificent spiral staircase appears ghostlike through dirty windows. I can almost hear voices and laughter from this building where the neighborhood held meetings, took cooking classes, in a downtown where people walked, and met by chance, their neighbors and friends. I wonder if communities are like animals, if once extinct, can't be recovered.

But then again, in those romantic old days, as a woman, I probably wouldn't have had the privilege of becoming a physician. I wouldn't have been allowed to marry Chris in the many states that disallowed interracial marriage. At one point in history, I would have worn a corset. In China, I would have had my feet bound.

"Chris and his friend Jay are renovating this building," I say to Gabriel. "They'll try to make it a downtown meeting place again, a revitalization." But this time, the historic building will house a café. People eat out more now. I can't see my neighbors hanging out at a utility company.

This downtown block will never again be the railroad hub it was at the turn of the century, or the Route 66 thoroughfare it was at mid-century.

It will move forward. It needs to be something new.

Like our cities, American medicine and psychiatry are evolving.

As they move forward, what will they become?

Part Five

Vanishing Doctors

2003–2005

Chapter Fourteen

At the Homeless Clinic

SEPTEMBER 2003

In September, the bleaching sun of summer sharpens into fall light that casts crisp shadows. Leaves rustle in a single resonant sound, orchestrated by the wind.

I try to leave the house and Zoe crawls after me. Her palms and knees patter on the floor. Maria smiles, scoops Zoe in her arms and walks to the kitchen, where she coos in Spanish, *"Borreguita, borreguita."* Little lamb.

I rush outside to my car.

At the homeless clinic, the courtyard is nearly empty. Across town, a long bus ride down Central Avenue, the state fair is in full swing. Pigs squeal, goats parade. Men don hats and climb onto steers, cowboys for a day. The beer garden is the main attraction for many. For several of my patients, the state fair means a few weeks of work and a paycheck.

But Buck is here as always. "Hi, Trouble," he smirks to Rosa, a nurse, out of the corner of his mouth.

"Buck, glad to see you!" Rosa's still girlish face loses another ten years.

Buck is a giant, larger than Rosa and me combined. He and his stuff barely fit in the hall. I walk behind him, eye level with the middle of his long blond ponytail. In one large hand is a stained green duffel and a cluster of brimming plastic grocery bags. His other arm hugs a dirty sleeping bag with clothes wrapped in it like a jelly roll. Buck's swollen feet bulge in his sneakers, beneath loose, street-colored laces.

A case manager in blue jeans chats with a colleague who sips coffee steaming from a mug. They lean against a bulletin board with flyers for AA meetings, smoking-cessation groups, an art clinic. An HIV prevention poster states in bold letters: GOT CONDOMS?

"Do you know any clinics in the Pecos?" the man with coffee asks.

"Ain't got no pesos," Buck says, passing.

The two case managers sway and laugh. By the time we reach my office, the whole corridor is smiling.

"Buck, what happened to your suitcase on wheels?" I ask.

"Aw, got messed up. Stolen, I guess. Don't want to talk about it."

In the exam room, I sit by the sink, as usual. I lean forward to flip through Buck's chart. I set off the sink's automatic sensor. Water runs. I lean backward. The faucet stops.

Today, with an empty waiting room, I have extra time for Buck. His evaluation from six months ago in his chart is brief and to the point. The patient was suicidal. I changed his medications and informed him of psychiatric emergency rooms in town. Oh, and I owed him five dollars for earrings.

Today, I finally have the time to say, "We've never talked about your childhood. Tell me, Buck, did you grow up with both parents?"

"Yep, had my parents till I was five."

This makes Buck different from so many other patients who never knew either parent, or who were brought up by one parent, in the streets.

"When I was five, Dad left for another woman. Me and my sister came home from school, and Mom was gone. We looked in the bars. We took care of the two babies. Changed diapers. Fed them their bottles. I was in kindergarten."

"And you went to bars? You took care of babies?"

"Yep. Till a neighbor called the cops. They put us all in orphanages. Haven't seen any of my brothers and sisters since. I got put in foster homes where the natural kids luxuriated while I did the work and got beat and whipped. After a while, I said, 'Just put me back in the orphanage.'"

"Were you ever abused in any other way?"

During my years in practice, I've never seen as much abuse as here among the homeless, where I hear about rape from fathers, uncles, aunts, brothers, reported by men so angry with authority they can't keep jobs, men with so much steam they pick fights in shelters, women too scared to ever settle in a home.

In the minutes I have, I try to lighten their fears just an ounce: *You were a child. Know that you will never be so powerless again.*

"Nope, I just got beat and whipped. That's all," Buck says.

For Buck's first five years, whatever they were like, at least he had the security of a family, more than most of my patients can say.

"Other shrinks ask me all these questions right away. I hate it. You waited. You knew when to ask." He gives me credit that is really undue.

Buck's scent, like the yeasty scent of bread rising, and the smell of parking-lot puddles, lingers through the next few patients.

The next week, Buck's name isn't on my list.

He doesn't come the following week, or anymore.

In other clinics, when regulars stop showing, I send a letter, or I pick up the phone. "Haven't seen you for a while. Just checking to see how you are."

But Buck is unattached to the numbers that define the rest of us.

On a cold winter morning, in the courtyard I call out for Seymour, who since his wife died can't concentrate to keep working in coal mines. A proud man, his siblings and relatives in Arkansas don't know Seymour now lives on our streets.

Seymour's breath rises above the dirty fur of his parka. "He's not doing well," he says, nodding toward a large man lying on the concrete. It's Buck, huddled like a fetus, in a summer T-shirt.

"Buck, let's get you out of the cold," I say.

He lifts himself off the ground, shuffles into the clinic.

Rosa takes Buck's vital signs. "He's got a fever of one-oh-four. His blood pressure is low, ninety over seventy."

"That's not good, Buck," I say.

"I'll try to do better next time." His voice is weak, his body large as a whale on the exam table.

It takes Rosa and me both to wrestle off Buck's tight sneaker, peel the sock off his left foot, which is purple, swollen like a hippopotamus's mouth. An ulcer oozes gold pus, a crusty scab hangs on the sock. The smell of him is stronger than ever.

"Well, that's definitely infected," Rosa says

The low blood pressure tells me that Buck is septic, too, with the infection spread through his body.

But Buck is thinking about his pride. "I'll bet you're wondering why I stopped coming."

"Yes, I wondered . . ." I hold the sock in my gloved hand.

"Uh, I got into a fight. Slugged someone real good. Figured you'd heard about it. I was too embarrassed to come see you."

"No, I didn't hear about that."

"Oh well, thought you did."

"I'm just happy you came back, especially now." If I handle this right, Buck might keep coming. His trust might grow. He might eventually have a relationship, a job, maybe a home. It's a chance to do what I became a psychiatrist to do.

The next day, I visit Buck at the hospital, an act that makes me feel old-fashioned, antiquated. But I also miss the hospital. On the fifth floor, I stop at the nurses' station for a bite of birthday cake, laughter, and reminiscences.

Buck's large shape fills the entire bed. He lifts a heavy eyelid. "Oh, it's you. They let you out of the clinic?"

"Buck, they tell me you're doing fine. We got you here just in time."

At the nurses' station, I spot Buck's internist, Andres, whom I haven't seen since just before Zoe's birth, when he took me aside and asked my advice about his own feelings of depression.

"Andres, it's been so long." I smile.

"Your patient has a really bad ulcer and cellulitis." Andres's bolo tie swings next to his stethoscope. A resident in a white coat stands beside him.

"Yes, but you know what his real problem is?" I say. "He has no home. That ulcer never heals because he's on his feet all day. So we hospitalize him, give him expensive antibiotics, get surgeons to debride the foot, but the root problem never gets addressed."

The resident looks away, as if thinking, *Oh, these psychiatrists!*

"Dora, I have something to tell you," Andres says. "I'm leaving the school."

I pause. "Where are you going?"

"I don't know. Fishing, probably. I've got a cabin in the woods. There's the most beautiful stream, perfect for sitting, reading, waiting for fish to bite."

When the dean announced a salary freeze for the next two to four years, I heard that the medical center would go bankrupt, except that it couldn't, being the state's only medical school. Everyone is scrambling. Everything is unstable.

A quarter of the faculty in my psychiatry department resigned over the summer and won't be replaced. And now Andres is leaving, too.

Now the institution will have fewer salaries to pay, more money to assure its survival in these tough times.

Now patients seem sicker, more numerous, with "managed care" roadblocking routine and preventive care. They have ever more trouble accessing care from overworked physicians—from us who grieve the loss of colleagues, while assuming their workloads.

Buck arrives at the homeless clinic with rapid breath. "The hospital just discharged me. I got here as fast as I could."

"Glad you're here," I say. "Now, up on the table."

He smiles and he lifts his big frame proudly.

I check his foot. We chat about his hospital experience. Then I tell Buck my news.

"I have something to tell you, Buck. You know that I'm with the medical school. It looks like they're canceling their contract with this clinic. Negotiations have fallen through. I won't be coming anymore."

"Where you gonna be?"

"I don't know yet. I'm waiting for my new assignment. Everything's a little unstable for me."

I don't mention that I'll still work in the faculty clinic where the fee is nearly $300 for the first visit. I don't need to tell Buck that just two years ago, it was just me and a patient in my office, but now we pay a staff of four to deal with the insurance and bureaucratic aspects of medicine. I don't need to bother Buck with these details.

And so I say good-bye to Buck.

But I look for him when I'm at the pedestrian mall downtown. My eyes scan for him when I drive past the homeless clinic.

On weekends, I wear his blue-and-white necklace with red teardrops.

Chapter Fifteen

At the Student Health Clinic

2004

The Student Health Clinic, a tan pueblo-style building on the college campus, turns out to be my next assignment.

College students, I realize, are a huge population of uninsured or barely insured persons, most no longer covered by their parents' health insurance yet not possibly able to have full-time jobs with health benefits. They are students, after all, in a country where health insurance is linked to employment. Fortunately, most serious medical conditions don't happen until later in life. The Student Health Clinic handles the tetanus shots, contraceptives, and antibiotics this young and physically healthy population mostly needs.

On the other hand, all of the most serious psychiatric disorders— including schizophrenia and bipolar disorder—begin precisely in this age group. But the student health center doesn't provide psychiatric care.

"Our purpose is to provide counseling to keep the kids in school," says Carol, the psychologist in charge. That's reasonable—how can the student health center run full-on mental health services? But Carol is realistic. She's found money for two part-time psychiatrists, Ian twice a week, and myself one afternoon a week.

Dr. Ian Osborn, a tall man with thinning red hair, says to me in my windowless office, "I keep telling Carol that I don't feel comfortable working this way."

Ian worries more than most. He has obsessive-compulsive disorder. His memoir/self-help book about treating his own OCD, *Tormenting Thoughts and Secret Rituals*, landed him on talk shows. We all check our locks, wash our hands, and try to keep our environment clean and safe. But people with OCD take these actions to painful extremes, thanks to their heightened vigilance for safety.

But I share Ian's anxiety. Ian and I see the most disturbed students on campus, for medications only, a half-hour every few weeks. Then the students see our school counselors, who, as Carol says, specialize in keeping students in school, not in treating mental illness. And when students miss appointments, they're treated as if they've missed too many classes: they're expelled, discharged from the clinic.

"But Carol," I say, "what if they miss appointments because they are suicidal? Or psychotic? Or manic?" In the past, I would have phoned patients who didn't show up, checked on them. On the Kaiser assembly line, I delegated this to my nurse and to therapists. But the therapists here don't know about mental illness. In my half-hour medication visits every few weeks, how can I also do what is now the work of therapists and case managers?

Carol looks like a wizard with her white-blond hair and electric-blue cardigan.

"Across the country," Carol says, "all of us at student health centers are seeing increased suicide attempts, greater levels of psychiatric disturbances."

"Why do you think that is?" I ask.

More people are going to college than ever before, she explains, thanks to our new psychiatric medications. But the main reason, she thinks, is something else.

"Who's raising our kids? Parents are too busy working. Our kids are starved of relationships, in daycares and in front of televisions. Grandparents and aunts can't help because they're not around anymore, either. The dissolution of family and community is coming home to roost in this generation of college students."

Through most of human history, I understand, each child had about four adults in attendance: parents, grandparents, aunts, and uncles. Today, in high-quality daycares, the ratio is one adult to four children. Mathematically, that's about one-sixteenth the nurturance and attention that traditionally sustained our species.

"These kids hold our future in their hands, don't they?" I say.

"They do. And it's chilling," Carol says.

The young strangers reveal their secrets, one by one, beneath fluorescent lights in my windowless office.

The doctor's daughter doesn't know what she's looking for. A single mother, she leaves her infant son at daycare and rushes to class. She's gotten two speeding tickets and can't afford to pay them. She's too angry at her father to ask him for help. As a child, when she was sad or disturbed, all he offered her were antidepressants and Ritalin. Now I prescribe more of the same.

Kino's brother joined the army and is fighting in Iraq. Kino wants a better life. He dreams of working in a Miami Beach hotel across the street from sand and waves. He'll bask in sunshine and in the light of beautiful people. At the same time, he'll write the great American novel. But right now, to pay tuition, he works the graveyard shift at a supermarket. When he asked for daytime hours, they made him the night manager. So now he'll work graveyard until graduation, which is looking farther and farther away. I prescribe lithium.

A business student who carries a briefcase by day, moonlights as a casino dealer to pay bills and tuition. But what she really wants is love. The man she hopes will love her had an affair and gave her herpes. She is not angry, but feels unworthy, actually grateful for whatever he gives her. She doesn't want to lose him, or the possibility of love, what she's really looking for. In our thirty minutes, a generous amount of time for this kind of work, I write a prescription for Wellbutrin.

I see childhood after childhood of hearts never filled, nerves never soothed, by now wired to exist without love—the food of our species, the glue of our families and societies. In these half-hours, my task is to make up for years, for entire short lifetimes, of doing without.

The meds do help, actually, and here in my sunless office they're what I have to give.

One by one, I take this parade of people into my office. They are people I encounter but will never really know.

After I've been with the Student Health Clinic a year, the contract with my department expires and is not renewed.

Carol by now agrees with Ian. The student health center needs a psychiatrist every day. But since the center can't afford one, she's looking for a psychiatric nurse practitioner.

I help her interview candidates, including the front-runner, a nurse from Community Health Plan, a stylish woman in a tailored purple suit and pumps. She wants to care for patients again, she says. She can't see herself doing her current job forever.

"And what do you do right now?" I ask.

"Mostly utilization review. I decide treatment. Educate physicians."

Because I've heard the phrase "educate physicians" from so many middlemen, I know that the phrase isn't hers but probably given to her as inspiration.

Carol shifts the interview toward clinical questions. "How would you treat a patient with bipolar disorder?"

Confidently, the woman says, "Trileptal. Or Neurontin. I even still use lithium occasionally. I'm good at telling patients that if they're having symptoms, to take some extra medicine."

Carol is impressed. So am I. In fact, I feel intimidated. I rarely use Trileptal, and never Neurontin.

Then I realize: There's a reason I don't use them. Neurontin doesn't work for bipolar disorder. Parke-Davis has been fined $450 million, the largest fine in the industry's history, for false marketing. And there really isn't much more evidence for Trileptal. In fact, even though lithium is so old (so old, in fact, that there's no money to be made from it—it costs about $7 a month rather than $7 a pill), most experts agree it should still be considered first.

This nurse practitioner, I realize, has been educated by pharmaceutical sales pitches.

And now it's her job to "educate physicians."

Chapter Sixteen

Zoe at the Emergency Room

FALL 2004

Zoe is almost two. It is fall again, already. Warm evening air brings the music of crickets through open windows. Dishes are washed. Leftovers are stowed in the fridge, and the kitchen floor is swept of Zoe's dinnertime activities.

Finally, even though she's still awake, I step into the shower. Zoe will be fine, playing in the living room with Chris. She understands now, that when I leave, I'm not gone forever. I'll return. She is finally past that out-of-sight/gone-forever stage of babiness, and has developed what we shrinks call "object constancy."

To think that I didn't believe friends who warned how difficult it is to get anything done, even showering, with a baby in the house.

As I turn on the water, Zoe cries. Warm water hits my skin. Steam rises. I remember that I have always rejuvenated by connecting with water. Zoe's fine. She's with her father.

But Zoe keeps crying. I hear something different in her cry, not just that it's filtered through this wonderful warm water and mist. Her cry is piercing, urgent.

I step my bare feet from the shower. I whirl a towel around me and run to the living room.

Chris is cradling Zoe, whose fat cheeks are smeared with blood and tears.

"She did something she's never done before," Chris says. "She jumped! She jumped from the sofa right into the coffee table. Probably just bit her tongue. I'm sure she's fine."

"Baby jumped?" I take just a few seconds to be proud, and to admire her feet and legs in a pink fleecy onesie, waving in the air as she wails.

I wipe blood from her face. There in the right corner of her lip is a deep red gash a good half-inch long. "We're going to the ER," I say to Chris. "She'll need stitches."

Fortunately, traffic on Central Avenue is sparse at nine p.m.

Within minutes, our family rushes into the lobby of the Community Health Plan Emergency Room, a woman in black velour sweats, a man in a red UNM Lobo sweatshirt, both cradling a baby in fleecy pink footed pajamas. The receptionist photocopies Zoe's insurance card and leads us to triage.

"What a cutie," a grandmotherly woman in a pink smock says. Her nametag reads: "Arlene, Triage." She looks at the cut. She takes Zoe's temperature with an ear probe.

The most important thing right now, I know, is to work the system. Every system has limited resources, and every moment prioritizes how best to spend its precious manpower and dollars. A cut on the face can be handled along the lines of many standards, from delicate plastic-surgery stitches that would leave a minimal scar, to sloppy stitches that might leave a jagged scar, to incompetent stitches that will pop open and leave a hole.

"I'm a physician. I'm faculty at the medical school," I say. "She's an only grandchild. Knowing my family, they'll want to find the best plastic surgeon in Beverly Hills. So anything you can do tonight to save this trouble and expense, I'd really appreciate."

"It's a good thing Mike is here tonight," Arlene says. "He's been doing nothing but wounds for two years."

"Is he the ER doc?" I ask, knowing he is not.

"He's our best tech."

"Will our baby be seeing a doctor?"

"It's a busy night," Arlene says. "There have been several car accidents."

Back in the crowded waiting room, Zoe waves at a couple who arrive drunk. I whisper to Chris, "I think they're trying to get by without Zoe seeing a doctor." In many ERs, I hear, techs and nurses do the treatment, and then the doctor rubberstamps papers for billing and legal purposes, in between making hearts beat again, lungs breathe again, blood flow again.

"You heard what she said about Mike," Chris says. "This is what he does. He's the expert. I want their expert to do this."

A young man in a white smock and jeans calls for Zoe. "I'm Mike." He leads us into a stark white office where Arlene pulls up a chair. Mike snaps on a pair of latex gloves.

"We can Dermabond it," he says. He reaches for Zoe's lip and pinches his fingers around it.

Zoe screams. Tears roll down her cheeks and into the wound. Her arms stretch, reaching for me.

"You mean, glue it back together?" I say. Amid my anxieties about the quality of stitches, I hadn't considered the possibility of no stitches.

Behind Mike, Chris is waving his arms and mouthing for me to shut up, horrified at my lack of respect. I know he is nervous about what kind of scar Zoe will carry on her face for the rest of her life. It's all in the hands of this stranger, Mike.

"Stitches would leave marks," Mike says. "Dermabond will be better."

Arlene says, "I'm not sure about Dermabond. It's under her lip. She'll chew on it. It'll open."

"She'll just have to not chew on it, that's all," Mike says.

"She's a baby," I say. "She jumped face-first into the coffee table. We have to watch her every minute just to keep her from killing herself."

Mike's eyes are fixed on Zoe's wound, seemingly, not seeing her flailing arms and legs.

Arlene bites her lip with her top teeth, like a bucktoothed rabbit. "Well, maybe she wouldn't ordinarily chew her lip. But the baby sure will with glue there."

Mike thinks, then says, "I can put a few stitches in."

"You'll have to put her under," I say.

"I can do it under local. No need to put someone under for something as minor as this."

Mike may have glued and stitched a lot of wounds in the past two years, but his on-the-job training has no doubt been limited to one thing—stitching wounds. He doesn't know that just looking into a kid's ears often requires puppets, stickers, cajoling in a high-pitched cartoon-like voice, and even then, resorting to brute force. To me, Zoe's wound looks like it needs at least four stitches, meaning eight punctures with a needle.

"Lately, it's been hard keeping her still enough to fasten a diaper," I say.

Grandmotherly Arlene, with knowing eyes, nods in agreement.

"If we put her under, she's going to have to see a doctor," Mike says.

"Fine with me." I rise from my chair to retrieve Zoe, who has crawled under the desk. I swing her into my arms. She laughs with delight.

"It will be a long wait," Arlene prepares us. She leads us down the hall to a room with a gurney, oxygen tanks, a cardiac monitoring screen, and other equipment. Zoe and I crawl onto the gurney. I pull her against me. Chris dims the lights, then sits in a chair. Amid the rhythm of ER doors opening and closing, our family drifts into sleep.

At about midnight, the glass doors of the room slide open and a tall, tired man enters. He is balding, in green scrubs and a white coat.

"I'm Dr. Stone," he says, and holds out his hand to Chris. "Mind if I turn on the light?"

"Please." Chris and I shake off sleep.

With gloved hands upon Zoe's face, his gaze circles the wound. "Yeah, we'll have to put her under. I don't see any other way to do it."

"And then Mike will stitch it?" My eyes are still adjusting to the light.

"I'll do it myself."

Zoe, like a bunny in pink footed pajamas, jumps up and down on the gurney. Dr. Stone reaches quickly for her. The lines in his face melt. "Thank you, Zoe, for showing me how it happened." He turns to Chris and me. "I never thought I'd see anything so cute tonight."

A nurse with big brown hair, heavy makeup, and a ditzy manner wraps a tiny blood-pressure cuff around Zoe's arm. She tapes a red glowing oxygen monitor to Zoe's finger. "Oh my goodness, I *know* you think Elmo is the world, *dippa dippa do, dippa dippa do, heh, heh, heh.* But just wait. You'll *love* Disney princesses, I just *know* it."

I roll my eyes. But then I notice the IV in Zoe's arm. "You got an IV into her. Without her or me noticing it."

"Oh, that," the nurse says. She flashes a humble smile and steps aside to make way for Dr. Stone, now walking back into the room.

Dr. Stone puts an oxygen mask on Zoe's face, then removes it to access her lip. He cleans the wound, and works quickly, diligently, eyes fixed on the needle.

Five stitches and ten punctures later, he finally lifts his head.

"Finished."

Home at last, the three of us crawl into bed, warm in one another's arms. We have survived Zoe's first medical emergency.

The next day, around noon, Zoe and I awaken. Chris is already gone. During the night, the gauze on her stitches had fallen off.

I look at Zoe's lip, and at the stitches binding her tender, red wound.

I pick her up and hold her to the mirror.

Her eyes are sad as she says softly for the very first time, "Face."

Chapter Seventeen

Doctors Vanish from View

Doctors are vanishing all around me—in my community, where managed care has put them out of practice; in my department, where one-quarter of my fellow psychiatrists are now gone; in ERs, in Philadelphia . . . And, hey—even three-quarters of myself has vanished. I'm working only part-time.

But all the same, I was shocked to read in an issue of *U.S. News & World Report* that doctors are vanishing.

In a January 2005 special health issue, a headline reads: "Doctors Vanish from View: Harried by the Bureaucracy of Medicine, Physicians Are Pulling Back from Patient Care."

Pulling back from patient care? So just what do doctors do these days? A commentary by Josh Fischman explains:

It is no longer a happy marriage, this relationship between doctors and patients. A bond once tight with intimacy is under incredible strain. Doctors have changed. Patients have changed. The caring is gone. Well, not gone but buried under the crush of everyday life. Buried under insurance headaches as patients now come burdened with reams of paperwork for doctors to fill out for reimbursement, paperwork that eats away at the time they might spend on other patients. So do fees, doctors say, because what insurance pays them is well below their costs. So in a vicious circle that steals more time, they have to see—and bill—a lot of patients each day and shuffle them out of the office no matter how much attention they might really need.

In Thelma Wolff Park, a mother soothes her coughing toddler and complains to me, "Why do doctors go through all those years of training, invest so much in becoming a doctor, just to act like they can't wait for us to get out of their offices?"

I wish I could whip Fischman's article out of my diaper bag to give to her.

Part Six

Albuquerque Cries

2005

Chapter Eighteen

At the Faculty Clinic

SPRING 2005

Polly, our office manager, heads the staff of four my department has hired to deal with the realities of a health care system designed to *not pay* for care. To think that I once simply took a patient into my office, that it was just the two of us, my patient and me.

Polly wears square reading glasses and clothes that are alternately department-store classy and thrift-store funky. In addition to overseeing all aspects of the clinic, Polly keeps track of our patients' ever-changing insurance details, such as when they've decided to stop covering our clinic's services, and when they've chosen to begin covering us again.

Dawn and Carol, our nurses, are both white-haired women nearing retirement. Their job is to call insurance companies to get prior authorizations for: initial visits, additional visits, labs, EEGs, MRIs, CT scans, medications, and hospitalizations. They save me the trouble of learning, for example, that Insurance Company A requires prior authorization for the second prescription of Concerta, but not for the first. Insurance B has different requirements. At any time, both Insurance A and Insurance B might change their rules without notice. When insurance companies hand down denials, Dawn and Carol try again. They fill in treatment plan forms that would take me ten to thirty minutes apiece, before calling to get more prior authorizations. Now they also deal with "notifications," which means we go through all these hoops to be granted a "maybe."

Dawn and Carol together make one full-time staff position. Over the years, Polly has seen that this work is too stressful, too frustrating, for any one person full-time.

Elvira is the third employee, and her job is to help everyone else.

The fourth is Cheryl, a motherly Native American woman who sits in a sunless cubicle eight hours a day, editing the notes of physicians. Charting notes is like walking a tightrope over crocodiles. Miss one step and that's it—the insurance company denies payment. Last week, Cheryl asked me to change my diagnosis, *Adjustment Disorder with Depressed Mood and Anxiety*, to *Adjustment Disorder with Mixed Anxiety and Depressed Mood*— no substantive difference to me, but a wording more likely to result in payment.

That's our clinic staff. At the medical school billing office, there's another whole layer of staff, put in place to combat the staff at insurance companies.

When medicine was opened to free-market competition in the early 1980s, and health profit corporations erected layers of bureaucracy to regulate payment (or, as some would say, to *not pay*), health care providers, as we are now called, suffered losses initially, then realized that we could only respond by hiring our own troops to mirror theirs. A pawn for a pawn, a rook for a rook, a claims processor for a claims processor, a note reviewer for a note reviewer, a procedure coder for a procedure coder. Entire new professions have been created that didn't exist when I was in medical school.

These additional salaries—the staff of four in my clinic, the staff at our billing office whom I never see, and the corresponding staff at the insurance companies—are all included in my patients' health care costs. That's not counting the profits paid to insurance companies' stockholders and executives, which include some of the most highly paid CEOs of all time.

Approximately one in three U.S. health care dollars now goes to "administration." Taiwan, by contrast, uses less than a slim 2 percent of its health care dollars for administrative costs. And to think that in the United States, many people remember paying doctors a single five-dollar bill for a house call, before 1980, of course.

If we operate with the same administrative efficiency as Taiwan, eliminate the bureaucracy that has grown since medicine was deregulated, can we possibly bring down America's health care costs by one-third? A decrease of one-third, from 18 percent to 12 percent of the GDP, would almost turn back the clock, and put health care expenditures back to their 1980s levels.

Worse, families today find themselves paying for health insurance—and then paying for health care, too. No wonder medical bills are a top cause of personal bankruptcies, even for those who have health insurance.

In a system in which Wall Street pressures corporations to increase profits exponentially each year, for-profit health companies by definition take money out of health care.

But for-profit corporations are not at fault. Their job is profits.

It is we as a nation who have decided that basic health care should be about profit, a direction different from that of any other first-world nation.

Despite my staff of four, during appointments I'm still checking off symptoms, filling in boxes, and looking up diagnostic codes for The Form we've devised to increase our chances of avoiding denials. Our form requests only my five-digit "provider code," not my name. Under the patient's "thought content," I have a skinny line wide enough for five words if I write really small.

As always, I insist on seeing one patient for proper weekly psychotherapy. I was granted this privilege when I insisted to my supervisor, "I teach psychotherapy. How can I teach psychotherapy if I never do it?" I also try to squeeze psychotherapy into medication appointments, but even with Cheryl's help, I haven't figured out the right buzzwords to get insurance reimbursements for this. It costs less, I figured out, if I do the psychotherapy for free. I save my staff the hassles of *denials, prior auths,* and, now *notifications.* When patients call seeking psychotherapy, Polly tells them psychotherapy is not offered at our university psychiatry clinic.

Helen, my one weekly psychotherapy patient, won my sympathies when she was going through a painful divorce. Helen's chart is five inches thick and spans the grip of my hand. My progress notes take up one inch. The other four inches are billing records, treatment plans, authorizations, denials, and other documentation, stuff that, thanks to my staff of four, I don't track.

When Helen was on her husband's insurance policy, I walked the tightrope. Each visit, I carefully charted enough of a problem so that her insurance company would pay and authorize further visits, but not so much that Helen might be denied insurance in the future for a "pre-existing condition." I listed Helen's diagnosis as an *Adjustment Disorder,* since it's hard to discriminate against someone who's just adjusting.

Physicians are caught in an impossible moral quandary. In the Hippocratic Oath, we swear to protect our patients from harm and injustice. Yet if we say that a patient is ill, which is usually why they seek medical care, then we risk them losing their health insurance or being denied health insurance in the future.

What kind of system is this?

But Helen's divorce is final now. She has lost her husband's health insurance. Her new health insurance, of course, excludes pre-existing conditions—ones treated under her old health insurance coverage, ones she still has—her allergies, hypertension, and her "adjusting." Helen's new for-profit health insurance company aims to only cover the conditions she doesn't have. Helen pays health insurance premiums that are hefty because she has conditions the insurance won't cover. Then Helen pays for her medical care on top of that.

What kind of system is this?

But at least I can now give Helen my full attention, instead of filling out The Form. I can write notes that make sense in the language of medicine, rather than in insurance babble.

On my desk are two stacks of charts. One is for today's patients. The taller stack is from Cheryl, with the usual edits for my notes.

Why is Helen's chart in Cheryl's stack?

"Helen's self-pay now," I say to Cheryl. "She doesn't use insurance, so there's no need for The Form."

"I know, Dr. Wang," Cheryl says. "But we now use The Form for all patients. It's Quality Assurance, med-center policy. It's really what's best."

Cheryl is conscientious. She takes pride in doing her job well.

I don't have the heart to say that her every action crowds away time for my patients, actually gets in the way of patient care.

"Thanks for letting me know, Cheryl."

Hank smells like she lives with 160 cats and chickens—her "family," she calls them.

She has a full beard like Charles Manson, and wears a proper plaid button-down shirt and slacks. She was discharged from the psychiatric hospital after two days, a typical length of stay these days. Her discharge note in front of me states: "No evidence of psychosis." The note says that Hank's former therapist diagnosed her as paranoid schizophrenic and hospitalized Hank for making threats.

Sitting in my office across from me, Hank says, "My testosterone shots make me more androgynous, what we all should be. It's a mistake that genders exist. It's the cause of all strife and violence. I haven't threatened anyone. I've done nothing wrong. And I'm definitely not paranoid schizophrenic."

At this point, I should state that, according to medical records, Hank is biologically female. Many of her psychiatric issues stem from her childhood abuse, as a girl. So for medical reasons, I have to think of Hank as female, even if I know Hank refuses gendering.

When Hank leaves my office, Polly asks me to move to another room. "We need to air this room out!" She fans her hand in front of her nose. She's serious. She's gathering my charts and leading me down the hall to another office.

After a couple of hours in an office without windows, I return to mine. I sniff first. The air seems clear enough. I see the rest of my patients for the day here.

At five p.m., I rush from my office, thinking of Zoe and Maria awaiting my return. In the parking lot, as I walk to my car, I dig my cell phone from my purse. I call Dr. F, the psychiatrist who just discharged Hank from our psychiatric hospital.

"We kept her a whole two days," he says. "No evidence of psychosis. Didn't seem schizophrenic to me."

"Did she make threats to anyone?" I step into my car.

"The patient was calm and friendly. The therapist might have been overreacting."

I respect Dr. F's opinion. But there are pieces of the puzzle that just don't fit. The cats. The unforgettable smell. Hank hardly seems like just a normal gal.

Before I turn the ignition key, I call Hank's former therapist, Louise, a psychologist in the community. It's never easy getting ahold of therapists—they are always in therapy. My cell phone, however, makes it easy for others to return my calls.

Later in the evening, as I'm fixing pasta, Louise calls me back. I retreat to the yard, leaving Chris and Zoe to toss salad.

"Yes, I've seen Hank weekly for five years," Louise says.

At least she's spent time with Hank. She knows the patient.

"Hank believes she's from another planet," Louise says. "A planet with no genders. She has an elaborate delusional system. She believes she's been chosen for a mission to inform Earth that two genders is a mistake. She has auditory hallucinations, constantly. The voices of spirits govern her every action. To her, cats are kin from the other planet, and their lives are more important than the lives of human beings."

"I understand that you hospitalized her for making threats."

"Yes, her mortgage company and the fire marshal have ordered her to get rid of her animals. The house is filthy. Urine, feces, carcasses everywhere. She sees the loan officers as potential murderers. She told me she'd kill them. That's why I sent her to be hospitalized. Don't you know any of this?"

"No, thanks for telling me."

"I talked to the psychiatrist there four times. I sent copious records."

"You probably talked to the admitting psychiatrist in the psych ER. A different psychiatrist on the inpatient ward was in charge of her treatment. Sometimes information gets lost in the shuffle." One hand admitted the patient, and the other hand discharged her after two days.

"By the way, I can no longer take care of this patient," Louise says. "She named a cat after me. That cat died mysteriously. I feel too threatened."

So I guess Hank is all mine now.

Louise's story explains the beard, the cats, even the smell. Her story makes sense. Even Polly, from an office manager's perspective, said, "That patient smells schizophrenic."

"One more question," I say to Louise. "The testosterone shots. They can cause psychosis."

"She was psychotic long before the shots," Louise says. "I got the endocrinologist to strike a bargain—Hank only gets the testosterone shots if she also takes Geodon. Otherwise, she won't take antipsychotics. She's much less psychotic now than she was."

Not only does Louise know the patient, she's realistic. And she's managed to keep the patient out of the hospital for five years.

The next week, Hank arrives at my office showered, with slick, wet hair and a hint of citrus cologne over the scent of cat urine. Polly moves Hank and me to another office, right away.

In the windowless office, Hank and I chat.

Before long, Hank whispers, "I have knives. Next, I'm going to buy a gun. If anyone is stupid enough to come to my home and close the door behind them, then they deserve the slow, slow death I'm gonna give them."

Stupid enough to close the door behind them?

That's me.

I look at the solid wood door, tightly shut. If I need to bolt from the room, I'd have to get past Hank. This faculty clinic isn't equipped to handle danger. It doesn't have secret panic buzzers beneath desks. Who would come to my rescue? Polly? At other clinics through the years, I've pushed panic buttons by mistake—a brush of my knee, or the wandering of a heel—and seconds later, a half-dozen people are knocking at my door. In all my years as a psychiatrist, I've never intentionally wanted to push a buzzer.

Until now.

"Murder," says Hank through gritted teeth, "is utterly justifiable. If the mortgage company takes my home, my family will die. So I'm going to kill the loan officer, Phoebe Halloran Roberts, Phoebe Halloran Roberts."

I muster my courage and my clinical skills. My own fear, I know, derives from Hank's paranoia. Emotional threads connect human beings. A good psychiatrist is practiced at using her own feelings, or "countertransference," as an instrument.

"Killing others," I say, "would put you in jail. If you're in jail, where would that leave your cats? There must be a better solution." I speak out of empathy for Hank, as well as working a clinical strategy.

Hank thinks. "True. I can't afford to be in jail. My cats would die without me."

Fortunately, my next patient has canceled, so I have the remainder of the hour to help Hank formulate a plan. She'll move the cats to the river, temporarily. She'll clean her house of urine, feces, and the remains of those who have died. She'll give them a proper burial. She'll fix up the house before the loan officers come.

"I'll pass the inspection," Hank says. "Then my family can come home."

"That's sounds like a better solution," I say.

"Anyone who gets in the way of me caring for my family is a murderer. But don't worry, I won't hurt anyone. This is a better plan."

After Hank leaves, I move back into my own office.

"That patient is not appropriate for this clinic," Polly says.

But the mental health center, which has panic buttons and security guards, has no openings for months. For-profit managed care has put so many psychiatrists in our community out of business, and overloaded our system, that only the most severely ill and dangerous patients get hospitalized, usually for a couple of days. Then they get discharged with a follow-up appointment about *three months later*. This is true, it seems, in cities all over the country, not just mine. It seems a disaster waiting to happen. But mental health centers are not to blame. They are saddled with an impossible job.

"Let's be calm," I say to Polly. "She's a paranoid schizophrenic, you know, like the Unabomber. They only hurt others because they feel the need to protect themselves. So it's important to make Hank feel as comfortable, as unthreatened, as possible."

The next week, Louise leaves a voice mail on my cell phone. In the morning, as I'm walking across the parking lot to the faculty clinic, I call her back.

"I just got a voice mail from Hank," Louise says. "The loan company sent a letter. They're coming to inspect the house. Hank said she'll kill anyone who comes on her property, then kill herself. I've called the police. Now I'm calling you. Maybe it's time to hospitalize Hank again."

I weigh the situation. If I hospitalize Hank against her will, I'll take her away from her cats. Not only will I lose her trust, but she might consider me a murderer. Would that put me in danger? Me, Zoe, and Chris? Martha used to say, "You can tell psychosis when the hair stands up on the back of your neck." Silly Martha. I saw psychotic patients every day of my residency, and my hair did nothing at all. Well, now, for the first time, the hair on my neck is standing.

I call the police. I explain to Officer Q that I think Hank needs to be picked up and brought to our psychiatric hospital for admission.

"It's about time someone committed this crazy cat-man," the officer says. "Last week, a car made a wrong turn and tried to back up in his driveway. The cat-man came running out of his house, waving a gun."

A gun? So Hank is proceeding as planned, just as she told me. It is time to warn Phoebe Halloran Roberts, I decide. Polly tracks down her phone number, and I call her.

"Ms. Roberts, I'm Dr. Wang with the UNM Department of Psychiatry. I'm calling you about Hank Gold." I explain about Hank's threats. I tell her we've hospitalized Hank. We'll do everything possible to keep her safe.

"Please keep me posted," she says. "And by all means, if she's released from the hospital, please call me."

I want to make sure information doesn't get lost this time. After Officer Q brings Hank to the psychiatric hospital, I contact Hank's new inpatient psychiatrist. Turns out it's Gabriel, my former resident, now graduated. Gabriel is now a member of our faculty. It's been a long time since I've seen him, so I invite him to the Flying Star Café. I buy him cookies and coffee. We sit in a booth to chat. Gabriel is now clean-shaven, without the red beard he had as a resident. I tell him all about Hank, how I think Hank needs to be sent to the state hospital for the sort of lengthy treatment our own psychiatric hospital no longer provides.

But two days later, I learn that Hank is released, again. I walk over to the psychiatric hospital. Gabriel is not on the ward, so I speak with his resident, Dr. D.

"What happened?" I ask Dr. D.

"There was no evidence of psychosis," Dr. D says.

"You know that she's intelligent, and that she wants to be released. She knows what to say. Isn't that obvious? Did you speak with Louise, the excellent psychologist who kept her out of the hospital for five years?"

"We never have time to get collateral information," Dr. D says.

"Collateral information is essential if the patient is psychotic," I say to the resident. "Paranoid patients won't tell you what's really going on. They're paranoid."

"We can't keep him here forever. Our ward is packed with patients who are imminently dangerous, right now. We referred him to the Intensive Outpatient Program. The patients on the ward were feeling threatened. Not to mention staff." He gives me a look that says, *You just don't get it.*

I call Phoebe Halloran Roberts to tell her that Hank was released.

"What?" she says. *"What?"*

"I'm sorry. I'd advise you to call off the inspection of Hank's home and to stay away from the house. And you should take any other reasonable precautions."

"What?"

"I'm sorry. I'm doing all that I can. I hospitalized her. Now she's released."

"I'm leaving town for a few days, that's for sure," she says.

Just as I hang up the phone, my cell phone rings.

It's Louise. "Hank left me another voice mail. While she was hospitalized, the Humane Society took the cats. They euthanized more than a hundred of them. There are only a few cats left."

Hank's cats are dead. They were killed while she was hospitalized—because of me. Does that make me a murderer in Hank's eyes? Am I safe? Is my own family safe?

In the morning, I call the Intensive Outpatient Program. I am relieved that Hank travels from home every day to participate in the program, and is actually showing up, eager for help.

But the next week, I learn that Hank got into arguments and threatened other patients. She missed three days. So she was discharged from the IOP.

Within days, Hank e-mails Deborah, the IOP psychiatrist. Along with threats, Hank sends graphic photographs—men with their penises severed, a man's slit abdomen with intestines cascading from his body, a man with a gunshot hole in his face.

This time, campus security springs into action. Hank's bearded face is distributed on flyers, along with warnings to employees not to be confrontational but to calmly seek safety and to call security.

The city police go to Hank's house. They bring her in for a third hospitalization.

So I decide to go talk with Hank. I walk over to the psychiatric hospital.

On the inpatient ward, Hank and I find a sofa in a hallway. We sit down, she in her beard and pajamas, me in a black skirt and pumps. I've never sat beside her. Hank is so much smaller than I am.

"First of all, I want to express my condolences for your cats. I know you thought of them as family."

"Thank you. That's very decent of you." Hank's voice is feminine.

"All life is precious. I am also saddened by the loss of them."

Tears well in her eyes and run down her cheeks into her beard.

"I also came to let you know something else. There are certain things you deserve from a psychiatrist, certain things you got from your psychologist, Louise, but also more. I'm not the right psychiatrist. I'm part-time. And I'm not in a position to do therapy. If I did weekly therapy, I'd see only seven patients, total. Our state is too understaffed for that. You deserve more than I can do."

"I understand that. You came to tell me. Thank you."

A half-hour later, we end our conversation. I say good-bye to Hank.

Two days later, Hank is discharged from the hospital again.

At a faculty meeting on Friday, I make a point of sitting next to Dr. C, a chief. We nibble on lunch while our chairman announces that pharmaceutical companies will no longer fund grand rounds speakers to travel to UNM. Of course. Every year they have to make more profits, and find more expenses to cut. For us, this means that on top of our other duties, now we'll also give more grand rounds talks.

I lean over to Dr. C. "About Hank. What happens now?"

"Nothing, really," he says.

"Do we just wait until something happens? For her to do something, and wind up in jail?"

He whispers back, "Basically."

I feel unsettled, especially given recent events. A bipolar man walked into the baby-clothing store where I buy Zoe's hair bows and stabbed the shop owner almost to death. Another man butchered his neighbor and put her parts in the fridge.

Both these spectacular acts of violence were committed by mentally ill men.

Society feels far more dangerous, even though medications for mental illness are better than ever. Before medications, we had asylums. At least there was a place for the mentally ill.

Psychiatrists used to have time for patients, time enough to practice our craft of keeping patients well, and society safe. But time is money, something now increasingly taken out of patient care and distributed elsewhere, in an expensive health care system designed to *not pay* for health care.

I can only hope that Hank will be content at home with her family.

Chapter Nineteen

The City Stops

AUGUST 2005

The next week, on Thursday, August 18, 2005, five people in Albuquerque are shot and murdered in one day.

Early in the morning, Ben Lopez, a fifty-four-year-old married man, is shot three times in the back and arm. At a motorcycle shop later, two young employees are killed while pleading on the phone to a 911 operator. David Fisher is seventeen; Garret Iverson, twenty-six. By evening, police figure out that the same rare, antique military pistol was used for each killing. Realizing that the shootings are connected, they go to the home of the suspected gunman. There Officer Michael King is shot in the head. Coming to his friend's aid, Officer Richard Smith is killed by a shot that goes through the arm-hole of his bulletproof vest.

The next morning, everyone is talking about the murders. At the Friday-morning seminar I co-lead at UNM, residents talk about how the gunman is one of ours, a former patient of the UNM mental health center.

"What's his name?" I ask. It's got to be Hank.

But police have not yet released the gunman's name.

I think about it. More than 700,000 people live in Albuquerque. Since roughly 1 percent of any population is schizophrenic, that means there are about seven thousand schizophrenics in this city. Another 1 percent is seriously bipolar. Then there are addicts, people suffering from other diagnoses, and people who are just plain crazy.

On the TV and in newspapers over the weekend, I see the faces of the five slain sons of Albuquerque again and again. Both slain officers were sons of police officers. Both had already retired after full careers as policemen, but then returned to their jobs, to do work younger people increasingly won't do.

Finally, the media releases the gunman's name.

The gunman is not Hank. His name is John Hyde, once a UNM patient but no longer.

I hear stories. The grief counselor at the coroner's office, a friend, describes the tough police officers in uniform who crowded the halls, weeping. A medical student on her surgery rotation operated on one of the policemen.

Inside his blood-soaked uniform, his heart was blown right open.

But Zoe knows nothing about the news. Her life is our bungalow home, her toy kitchen, the grassy park across the street, her favorite baby doll, pop-up books, and her friend Mateo, who lives across the park. My friend Teresa, with whom I go to the farmer's market, has had a baby, too. The two tots share lunches of miso soup with rice and kalbi, not typical Albuquerque baby food, but even if Mateo is blond with blue eyes, he is raised on his Korean grandmother's food.

Zoe is almost three, eager to know a larger world. She and Mateo have taken their first steps together, heard each other's first words. Now they begin preschool. Away from family for the first time, neither will be without love with the other in the classroom.

On Thursday morning, August 25, their third day of preschool, I dress Zoe in flowery pants that cover her tender knees. I put a matching bow in her short brown hair. She looks in the mirror and is pleased.

I pack macaroni and cheese, grapes, and juice into her first lunchbox, pink with sparkly dogs. We drive past the park to Mateo's house. He is waiting, his hair neatly slicked, in khakis and a blue oxford shirt, carrying a blue lunch box shaped like a race car. He climbs into the car seat next to Zoe's. Teresa, in her apron, looks proudly at him and kisses him good-bye.

Zoe claps her small palms together, and calls out her name for him: "Mayo!"

At A Child's Garden, the two toddlers run into the sandbox and climb into an old tire. They look at each other and laugh, delighting in this new experience together.

Back at home, I dice nectarines. I taste their honey on my fingers. I chop basil into a fine shred, then toast pine nuts. I toss everything together with a dab of molasses to top tonight's pork chops. I fold warm laundry, answer e-mails; then, sitting on my sunny porch, I edit the first chapters of this book for the fifteenth time. This time Dr. Indigo makes an appearance. How could I have forgotten Selena's primary physician? But, then again, to this day, I still have never met him. Now I will revise the chapters to include Dr. Indigo. If I get Selena's story right, I'm convinced, I might find answers to my questions about medicine, family, my career, and why Selena's story is so important to me.

Four hours pass. It's time to pick up Zoe.

The sun is blinding hot as I drive down Lomas Boulevard. Blocks later, just before the railroad tracks, traffic halts, something that never happens in Albuquerque at midday.

I picture mothers at school taking their toddlers into their arms, Zoe looking for me, her round cheeks streaked with tears. I tap my thumbs against the steering wheel.

If I drive over the sidewalk, through a ditch, I can reach Zoe in time. But I am surrounded on all sides by stopped cars.

Ten minutes later—an eternity—traffic hasn't budged, not a turn of a tire. I switch off the ignition, throw open my car door, and climb onto the roof of my car.

That's when I hear it, sirens crying, more than I have ever heard together, echoing from the high-rises downtown, from the wide expanse before the Sandias, filling the basin of our city.

Car doors slam. People fill the street. *What the heck is happening?*

A man with a long ponytail and jeans stands on the hood of a blue pickup truck. Hands cupped around his mouth, he calls out, "It's the funeral—of one of the police officers. *It's supposed to last all day.*"

A stream of police cars, ambulances, and fire trucks drive rapidly, turning corners, circling with lights flashing in a frenzy of red-white-blue, red-white-blue. Every siren in the city must be crying.

My cell phone rings. "Dora, it's Teresa. I made it to school. Zoe and Mateo are fine. Want me to take Zoe home with us?"

"Oh, please, thank goodness! Traffic isn't moving at all. It seems like the funeral will go all day."

I climb back onto my car roof. I watch.

No one honks. No one seems angry.

An hour later, the sirens are still crying. Traffic is still stopped.

For as long as the sirens cry I will listen. For as long as they cry, all stands still.

The funeral was for Officer Richard Smith, I learn from the news that night.

More than two thousand people crowded the Hoffmantown Church for memorial services to pay respects to the deceased officer who, after twenty-five years of service to our city, now leaves behind his widow and his thirteen-year-old daughter.

After the memorial, a thousand police cars and vehicles caravaned down I-25, then through the narrow streets of downtown, lights flashing, sirens blaring.

The procession spanned eight miles.

Over the next days, I piece together the story. The "gunman," as he comes to be called, John Hyde, is a forty-eight-year-old man. As a teenager, he was a student at the Albuquerque Academy, the city's most prestigious high school, a feeder to the Ivy League, a school I'd want Zoe to attend. He was a bright child in whom his parents invested high hopes.

Shortly after high school, John Hyde began showing signs of para-noid schizophrenia, an illness that usually hits in the college years. He underwent hospitalization after hospitalization for years, until, in his early thirties, he fell into the stable, long-term care of a good psychiatrist, Dr. Jay Feierman. But in 1998, when managed care took over Medicaid payments for psychiatry in New Mexico, Dr. Feier-man closed his practice. John Hyde lost his psychiatrist.

Like Dr. Feierman's seven hundred other patients, John Hyde sought help elsewhere. Finally, he settled at a clinic that operated in today's typical assembly-line style, with a psychologist who saw him most often, a psychiatrist who prescribed medication (schizophrenia's main treatment), an ER responsible for his care most hours of the week, and the administrators who devised this divided method of care.

To my mind, John Hyde's deficit wasn't his own inability to trust, as a paranoid schizophrenic. In our new divided system of care, he simply had no one to trust.

According to *The Albuquerque Journal*, on August 15, 16, and 17, the three days before he started shooting, John Hyde went to his hospital, asking for help. He was turned away each time.

On August 18, he had called his insurance company.

At night, as I put Zoe to bed, she pulls my hair like when she was a baby. I glance at the dark night sky out the window. I think of our daily acts of trust—crossing the street amidst cars, sitting in movie theaters and lecture halls with crowds of strangers.

This night, like any other, we as a society are only as stable as the least stable individual roaming our streets.

I fall asleep remembering the beauty and sadness of the police cars circling, and the sound of their sirens.

I awaken before dawn, and while the city is still asleep, I write a letter to a local newspaper:

ALBUQUERQUE SHOOTINGS—A DEFINING MOMENT FOR HEALTH CARE CRISIS?

This week, we as a city mourn the deaths of five men shot by John Hyde, a mentally ill man. For hours in the middle of a workday, traffic stood still as police cars circled our streets, crying in grief.

At our brand-new jail across town, John Hyde complains that he is forced to wear a red jumpsuit, like Elvis. No one doubts that Hyde is mentally ill, or that he is the killer. In the ensuing months, our city will strive to make sense of this tragic event, as the courts decide Mr. Hyde's fate. To me, however, the tragedy seems a defining moment of the health care crisis that currently faces our country.

If there is one lesson we can learn from the Hyde tragedy, it is that when the mentally ill are not well cared for, we are all at risk.

In these, the first few years of the new millennium, health insurance premiums have already risen by 50 percent. Medical bills are the number-one cause of personal bankruptcies, even among those with insurance. Companies such as General Motors blame health care costs for their need to cut jobs. In New Mexico, only one in three businesses offers health care benefits. Nationally, the ages-old doctor-patient relationship, once considered the cornerstone of healing, has been replaced, as patients now have their primary medical relationships with their insurance companies—if they can afford health insurance.

The irony is that treatment for schizophrenics such as John Hyde is better today than ever before. But John Hyde was off his medications when he shot the five sons of Albuquerque last week.

In some societies throughout history, a schizophrenic man would have been thought a visionary, one who heralded the future. In some societies, he would be considered sick, and worthy of compassion. In some, he would be a criminal deserving of the death penalty.

Of these three choices, I argue that John Hyde's case foretells the future. What we all have in common with John Hyde is that we are all in need of a better health care system.

Our current tragedy is a harbinger of more to come, if we as
a society don't take care of our own basic need for health care.

Dora Wang, M.D.
Assistant Professor of Psychiatry
UNM School of Medicine

I wait to hear if the newspaper will print my letter. No one ever gets
back to me.

Shortly after the tragedy, I realize that I have never met Jay Feierman.

On my department e-mail Listserv, I ask if anyone knows how I
can find Jay.

Gabriel e-mails that Jay has died. Another casualty. I'm not
surprised.

But then Joel e-mails me with Jay's contact information.

I e-mail Jay and ask him to have lunch. I tell him I'd like to meet
the psychiatrist who's had such an impact on our university department of psychiatry and on our city.

Jay e-mails me back. Is he the right person? He was a psychiatrist
in the community, but now he works for the federal government. He
hasn't had much to do with the university.

I reply that sometime after he closed his practice, the volume at
our university mental health center doubled. I add: "Didn't you used
to care for John Hyde?"

Jay agrees to meet me.

He picks the May Café, a Vietnamese *pho* joint where he's gone
for years. I know the place for the huge Paul Bunyan statue on its
roof, from another era. It is just off Route 66.

The next week at the restaurant, a waiter greets me. "Are you looking for Jay?"

"Yes, do you know him?"

"Right this way." And he leads me to a table in the far corner, where a man with salt-and-pepper hair, glasses, and a plaid shirt rises and offers his hand. His manner is humble.

The waiter asks, "Your usual, Jay?"

Over soup and noodles with basil and mung beans, here's what I learn.

Jay grew up outside Philadelphia. His own doctor delivered him into the world and cared for Jay throughout his life. Jay followed in his doctor's footsteps, more than those of his own parents. He remembers that in his childhood, his doctor made house calls to treat his allergies. Then he'd sit and chat with Jay's parents, who paid him a single five-dollar bill. His doctor's wallet bulged with five-dollar bills. When Jay became engaged to be married, he and his fiancée went to his doctor for blood tests. Even after his doctor's retirement, and until his death, Jay kept in touch with his doctor.

Jay moved to Albuquerque in the early 1970s after working at the National Institutes of Mental Health and the Indian Health Service. After a brief stint at UNM, he opened his own private practice, which he ran from 1976 to 1998, twenty-two years. He took care of many Medicaid patients, including some of the city's most severely mentally ill. Like his own doctor, Jay planned on caring for his patients always. He knew their families and their lives. (Incidentally, Jay is an ethical physician, and refuses to speak about John Hyde, or even whether Hyde was ever his patient. What I know of Jay's relationship with John Hyde is from other sources, among them Hyde's adopted brother, Robert.)

Like all doctors of another time, Jay was always available. He was wakened from sleep most nights with urgent calls from his patients. I realize that without Jay now, these patients regularly resort to psych ERs, where each visit a new clinician meets them for the first time, re-invents the wheel each time.

"So why did you close your practice, Jay?" I squeeze lime into my soup.

"One hundred percent because of managed care," Jay replies.

In 1998, managed-care corporations took control of Medicaid payments for psychiatric patients in New Mexico. "I had to call a toll-free number every three months for each patient. I had seven hundred patients. I spent at least ten minutes on each call, and only fifteen minutes with the patient."

That year, practicing in the same manner that he had for twenty-two years, but with the added burden of managed-care bureaucracy, Jay's practice lost money. His charge was $30 for an outpatient visit. Yet he received payment only about two-thirds of the time, for an average of about $20 per visit. For hospitalized patients, his official compensation was $120. Since he was paid only two-thirds of the time, this amounted to about $80 for an entire inpatient stay, whether a week, a month, or longer. For a week of hospitalization, this amounted to roughly $11 per visit for Jay. From these wages, Jay paid for gas, malpractice insurance, staff, and increased office expenses for the time and infrastructure needed in order to deal with managed-care bureaucracy.

His workload increased remarkably, yet he was paid remarkably less.

In 1998, the year for-profit managed care began managing psychiatry in New Mexico, Jay's expenses exceeded his income. He found himself $50,000 in the hole, even if he practiced in the same hard-working 24/7 manner in which he'd practiced for twenty-two years. He was forced to take a second mortgage on his house in order for his family to live. He had no choice but to close his practice. He discharged his seven hundred patients.

I fill in the rest of the story for him. Many of his patients stayed stable for a while, but within four years, the volume at the UNM

Mental Health Center had doubled, with his former patients no doubt comprising much of our new work. In 2002, Dr. Diana Quinn died, just before we doubled the number of psychiatrists on the inpatient wards where she worked, and hired more psychiatrists for the psychiatric emergency service, where she also worked.

And in 2005, one of his former patients, John Hyde, fell so ill that he committed the worst shooting spree in the history of our city.

Jay doesn't see what a difference he made in the life of our city. Like Dr. Abi, and other fine physicians, he is a humble, unassuming man, devoted to his medical profession and to helping patients in need.

But now our medical system makes Dr. Jay Feierman's devoted way of caring for patients impossible.

While Albuquerque prepared for our Tricentennial Celebration in 2006, we also recovered from the worst shooting spree in our history. As the city readied for parades and festivals, it also laid wreaths and flowers upon the graves of Albuquerque's five slain sons.

In a televised public announcement, Mayor Martin Chávez asked our city council to mandate outpatient treatment for mentally ill persons with violence in their backgrounds.

I agreed that *something* needed to be done so that our city could return to working, shopping, playing in the park with our children, without needing to worry about a delusional paranoid schizophrenic holding an antique military pistol to our faces.

But to me, mandatory treatment didn't seem to be the answer. Hyde tried to get help for days before he started shooting. The problem isn't that the mentally ill refuse treatment. The problem is that the mentally ill can't get treatment in this system designed to *not pay*, and to *not care*.

Besides, John Hyde had no history of violence before this. Such a law wouldn't have prevented the tragedies caused by his psychiatric illness.

The answer seemed obvious.

What would have prevented the tragedies is what kept John Hyde stable for years—a relationship with a devoted psychiatrist, one who practiced like Dr. Jay Feierman, in a manner no longer possible.

The medical care of our most disenfranchised and unemployable citizens will never turn a good profit. The ones who stand to profit from their care are all of us, as a society together.

In the same months that the City of Albuquerque debated mandatory outpatient psychiatric treatment, Lovelace announced it was discharging its seven thousand psychiatric patients, about 1 percent of our city population, and downsizing its psychiatric services. By then, Lovelace was sold by Cigna to Ardent, whose CEO, David Vandewater, was president of the Columbia/HCA health system during the period for which the organization pled guilty to defrauding Medicare for a decade.

Other Lovelace departments that didn't close included inpatient pediatrics, which was outsourced to UNM's Children's Hospital; and the Emergency Department, which was outsourced to a company run out of Florida. The fifty-year-old Gibson Hospital, however, was closed, prompting Mayor Chávez to publicly give Lovelace a health care grade of "F."

Lovelace psychiatrists looked for new jobs, and Lovelace patients looked for new care.

Around this time, Seth Powsner, formerly my professor, now my friend, came from Yale to UNM to give a talk. Afterward, at the Satellite Café near campus, he sipped coffee, and I drank chai. I told him about Lovelace's recent actions.

"Can they do that?" he said, shaking his head.

"Well, Lovelace's contributions to our politicians are reported in the local newspaper."

My cell phone rang. It was Arthur, a fellow medical school physician. "Dora, my son is bipolar. He got his care at Lovelace. He has no psychiatrist now. Do you think you can please take care of him?"

Seth and I looked at each other, puzzled.

Wouldn't it be unethical and malpractice, if a physician abandoned patients like this?

Arthur's call is just the first of many. Colleagues and friends call me at home and on my cell phone. They e-mail me. They beg for me to assume the care of relatives and friends.

At my faculty clinic, the Lovelace refugees arrive. I start coming on extra days, since I can't imagine turning them away.

Looking at my overly packed schedule, Polly says, "The mission of this clinic has always been to take care of our own UNM employees. That's always been our purpose."

"I agree," I say. "We have to take care of our own. Otherwise, nothing works." It's what Dr. John Abi told me, what Dr. Abi lived by.

But it's the first I've heard of this being our mission. Just weeks ago, we accepted patients from throughout the city. Now anyone who isn't a UNM employee needs to beg favors, use personal connections, to be seen in our faculty psychiatry clinic.

In the locker room at the gym, I see a friend, a recently terminated Lovelace psychiatrist.

"They keep putting money into marketing, but not into clinical services. When will they get it?" she says. My friend is an idealistic young physician. She hasn't yet realized that better medical care is no longer the goal but bigger profits.

"Seems like they get it really well," I say, throwing my wet towel into the bin.

On the way home, I pass the hospital where Zoe was born. I remember my comfort and security in Dr. Harrison's care here in this hospital founded for humanistic purposes.

But by now, it is no longer St. Joseph's Hospital, named for the order of charitable nuns who founded it in another century. By now, Ardent owns this hospital along with the entire St. Joseph's system, in addition to Lovelace. The private equity firm, Ardent, now owns two of the four major health care systems in my city.

The next week, while I shop for Zoe's fall clothes at a downtown boutique, I overhear other mothers talking about Dr. Harrison. He can no longer afford to pay his malpractice insurance, I hear, so he no longer delivers babies.

Even Dr. Abi has decided to call it quits.

"*Aiya*, we got a letter," my mother calls to tell me. "So I paged him. He says he is sick! He plans to recover, but when he comes back, he will only work in the hospital. He won't see patients in his office anymore. His clinic is closed."

All of Dr. Abi's patients, who by now include my father, mother, brother, cousin, and uncle, will need to find a new doctor.

In Albuquerque, I pick up the phone and I page Dr. John Abi in Los Angeles. As usual, he calls back right away.

"Is it true, John, that you're closing your clinic?"

"It's true," he says. "It's not so much that I prefer the hospital. It's just getting difficult to be in both places at the same time."

"Yes, I know. Everybody always wondered how you ever did so much." Indeed, even housestaff and residents, who by regulation can no longer be in-house more than twenty-four hours at a stretch, spend far less time in the hospital than this seasoned and revered physician.

"Is it because of the hassles with insurance companies?" I ask.

During one of my father's appointments, John told me that every day he set aside eight a.m. until noon to talk to insurance companies. A staff member called first. Then his nurse dealt with difficult cases. Then John took the impossible cases—not medically impossible but bureaucratically impossible. From around the world, the faithful come to seek healing from this rare physician. They value every ounce of his wisdom, every second of his attention. And this was how he spent his mornings. John's patients, of course, never see this consuming, invisible new work of doctoring, of fighting for their medications, their X-rays and MRIs, their surgeries, cancer treatments, hospitalizations, visits to specialists, and even visits to him.

"It's the paperwork that has killed medicine," John says. "By the time I fill out all those forms like the ones for Medicare, I have no time to see the patient. But I do see the patient. The paperwork. It's killed medicine."

Each time I talk with him, it seems, I realize yet another reason why medicine has gotten impossible. Insurance company harassment that keeps even Dr. Abi on the phone for hours each morning. Residents having no choice but to become shift workers, given their work-hour limitations. Research being driven by pharmaceutical and insurance companies. And now paperwork.

A system with nonsensical barriers to every step of patient care. A system that mandates residents to leave their patients in the middle of progressing illness lest they violate regulations. A system governed by profit, not the age-old physicians' ethics that put the best interests of the patient first.

This is the system upon which we all entrust our lives.

"Thank you, John. I can't tell you how much I appreciate all you've done for my family."

I wish him a good and speedy recovery.

Part Seven

The Stages of Grief

2005–2007

Chapter Twenty

Searching for Answers

Like a dying patient, I have worked through the stages of grief. I've gone through denial, bargaining, and depression. I have long accepted that a certain way of practicing medicine has indeed ended.

American medicine once symbolized the best of this society—not just our advanced science, but our highest humanistic values. When I chose medicine for my life's work, it was a profession centered on the daily practice of compassion, and of preserving that value for all of society.

That torch certainly burns more dimly today. To me, it seems barely flickering.

For the past few years, I have been looking for meaning in what has happened to the profession of medicine.

In November 2005, the Academy of Psychosomatic Medicine convenes in Bernalillo, just north of Albuquerque.

I drive to the airport to fetch Seth Powsner, who has traveled here from New Haven for the conference.

In the airport lobby, I spot Seth in a familiar blue blazer, his red bow tie tucked into the breast pocket. It is comforting to see that some things don't change.

In my car, I move Zoe's white teddy bear and Sesame Street cookies from the passenger seat. Seth climbs into the car and tucks his iPod into his briefcase.

Taking I-25 north to Bernalillo, we arrive at the sprawling Hyatt Regency Tamaya Resort, with its golf course, spa, many swimming pools and fine restaurants. The resort is nestled in dark mountains beside the ancient Anasazi ruins of Kuaua Pueblo, now called Coronado State Monument, after the Spanish conquistador who wintered there.

In the softly lit hotel bar, Seth and I sit by the fire. We look out the panoramic window to the mystical view of ancient desert land and dark starry sky.

"What's local?" Seth asks me, holding the menu.

I order champagne from Albuquerque's Gruet Winery, along with guacamole dip with local green chile.

As the waitress walks away from us, we look at the tall trees casting shadows along the river.

"I've been telling my residents that they're practicing medicine in a time of transition," Seth says. "Something between *Marcus Welby* and Meineke."

"Meineke?" I ask.

"You know, the auto-service chain?" Seth looks into the fire. "Well, by the time something appears on television, you know it's peaked and is on its way out. Now, when was *Marcus Welby*?"

I remember the wise, white-haired TV doctor who made house calls and who was like a benevolent grandfatherly member of everyone's family.

"I seem to remember Dr. Welby in black-and-white," I say. "*Star Trek* was in the late sixties, and it was in color. *Marcus Welby* must have been the late sixties or early seventies, at the latest."

Seth nods. "Sounds about right."

"In the seventies. That's when my favorite soap opera, *General Hospital*, started. And now even *General Hospital* isn't about doctors and nurses. It's about corporate raiders and crime bosses."

Seth raises his eyebrows.

"Here's to Dr. Marcus Welby," I say, and lift my glass of Gruet.

He smiles. "To Dr. Welby."

Our glasses clink.

When I was Seth's student, in the 1980s, he said to me on the wards of Yale–New Haven Hospital, "Consultation-liaison psychiatrists should always do a complete psychiatric *and* medical workup. We can pick up on things other doctors miss. We can take the time." Our workups then were sixteen pages.

But when I visited Yale in 2000, Seth was writing his notes on two-page forms. He pulled a laminated card of phrases from his pocket, a template of what to mention to increase the chances of insurance company reimbursement. In the rotunda, beneath the elliptical ceiling of Mediterranean blue and brilliant gold stars, a place where I always felt the noble call of medicine, was an announcement for a "commercialization seminar."

"So what does it mean that medicine is becoming Meineke?" I ask Seth as we sip Gruet.

"I'm not sure. Except that repair is never a lucrative business. Medicine is definitely repair, not manufacturing. It's inherently not profitable."

Seth tells me that the *Journal of the American Medical Association* invited Intel founder Andy Grove to comment on the health care industry. In response to Andy's commentary, Seth wrote a letter, which *JAMA* will publish in the November 23–30, 2005, issue.

Seth pulls a file from his briefcase, and shows me the letter.

The letter points out that manufacturers choose their materials carefully. On the other hand, doctors are stuck repairing "faulty carbon-based people." Cell phones are replaced rather than repaired, the letter reads, but that view cannot inform medical care. The letter concludes:

> People do want some things repaired—usually, their friends and family. . . . If limiting costs is the goal, consult our veterinary colleagues who routinely confront pet repair costs that families cannot afford or will not pay. Most medical care is repair. At best, some medical care is preventive maintenance. It is not appropriate to pretend that we are in a manufacturing business.

Seth's conclusion, when he looks at our nation's health care disaster, is that medicine is simply not an industry. It is a profession.

It is a profession that, when I was initiated into it, centered on the doctor-patient relationship, with the physician's compassion at its core.

Who do we want guarding our lives when we are impaired by illness—a physician who considers us with compassion, or a corporation centered on profit just when we are at our most vulnerable?

Will we restore the doctor-patient relationship? Or will we continue to center American health care around the insurance company–patient relationship?

Henry Ford invented the first assembly line to manufacture cars.

But even cars can't be repaired on an assembly line.

When my own car got the shakes, I took it to an auto shop that was part of a national chain, as an experiment. My car needed new rotors, I was told. No two ways about it. Brand-new rotors would cost $2,000, plus labor.

So I took the car to my mechanic. After doling out his usual philosophies and political commentary, he laid his hands upon the rotors. He jiggled and pushed them. An hour later my car drove as smoothly as when it was new. The charge was less than $100.

"What did you do, Kev?" I asked.

"I did this"—and the skinny man covered in grease raised his right hand in the air. He motioned in demonstration while making squeaking noises with his mouth.

To keep an "old" car running, Chris says, requires craftsmanship and artistry. It's best done by freethinking mechanics who are also philosophers or poets.

My daily work is not unlike that of my mechanic. I push a little here, tweak a little there. What I do for my patients is kind of like what Kev does for cars. We do—whatever we can.

Assembly-line car repair, I decided, is actually about replacement.

Assembly-line health care is no different. Organs need replacement, because they were not properly maintained. Hips and knees, too.

And of course, patients are replaced, as soon as they are sick.

Martha is always a source for wise insights.

I ring the doorbell of her canyon home. Her dog barks. I remember when her pet shih tzu was just a puppy, years ago when I was just a resident, when I used to sit with Martha in the evenings, talking about patients, learning my craft.

Martha opens the door and greets me. "Dora!" She still has short gray hair and a sparkling lemon-wedge smile. Her blue eyes, however, because of macular degeneration, now barely see. She seems frailer, less energetic than in her bolder days when she was a national leader in psychiatry, and still made weekly dinners for residents like me. Her little dog now limps with arthritis.

Martha and I step out to her patio. Nadia, Martha's housemate, serves up quiche with Gruyère and salad, along with yellow tomatoes from the garden. How I've missed these tomatoes!

I take a seat and look down into the wilds of Brentwood Canyon.

"Martha, when I was a resident you used to say that the end of psychiatry was coming. But I couldn't hear it. I was working too hard to become a psychiatrist. But thanks for warning me."

"You're welcome," she says, and calmly sips her iced tea.

"Martha, where do you think our profession is going?"

"It's not a profession anymore." In her voice is finality, resolve.

"You mean we're just 'providers' now?"

She nods.

"Martha, do you ever think they'll leave us alone? Do you think they'll ever stop telling us how to do medicine?"

"You mean, take all the money out of the system and then leave?" she says. "Sure, I think that's definitely possible."

When American HMOs expanded into Latin American countries (all Wall Street–listed corporations need to find new markets to increase profits every year), they insured the healthiest and left the sick to be treated by public, government-run medical systems. The corporations took their profits out of those countries, leaving local economies increasingly in debt and responsible for the medical care of the sickest.

In Albuquerque, Cigna, then Ardent, distributed their profits to executives and stockholders nationally, leaving our university health system to care for the sickest, and for the patients excluded from private medical insurance because they had "pre-existing conditions," that is, because they needed medical care. Indeed, ours is a medical system designed to remove money from health care.

"Sometimes I wonder if it will come back," Martha says. "Will it come back?" She thinks for a moment. Martha always sees silver linings in clouds. "Naw," she answers herself. "It won't."

"We're like the neighborhood butcher and shoemaker," I say. "They're history, replaced by assembly-line labor. I've never even met a shoemaker. There are no shoemakers anymore. And *people* are the new widgets on the health care assembly line."

"It'll only get worse," Martha says, nodding her head. "And it's new moral territory, that's for sure."

Our health care system makes it impossible for even Dr. Abi and Dr. Feierman to practice in the devoted manner physicians all once did. Marcus Welby today would be on the phone all morning arguing with insurance-company bureaucrats. What bright youngster would watch *that* pitiful show, let alone aspire to do this strange new kind of doctoring?

Why has the ages-old medical profession been put under the thumb of for-profit businesses that know neither medicine nor the patients they should serve? Why has profit been put so far above other motives, even the need to care for the health and well-being of fellow human beings?

I pose these questions at a backyard political fund-raiser for former Albuquerque mayor Jim Baca. We've been invited by a friend, Albuquerque City Council president Martin Heinrich, a politician who cannot tell a lie. He used to be an engineer, of all things. He is a Democrat *and* an avid huntsman. Martin is the father of Zoe's preschool friend Carter. The two tots hug each other hello, then go quickly about their business of hide-and-seek in the bushes.

Some top politicians are listening when, after some wine, I gather the courage to say, "Something needs to be done quickly before

American medicine is destroyed, before more irreversible damage is done." I mention Albuquerque's 50-year-old Gibson Hospital closed by Ardent, and the 150-year-old Medical College of Pennsylvania Hospital closed by Tenet. Something needs to be done before the flame gets permanently extinguished, before torchbearers get sick and die, or jump ship to save themselves.

"At the very least, we need a federal agency to monitor abuses," I say, "like the FDA was created at the turn of the last century for similar purposes."

More wine is poured, more hors d'oeuvres munched.

"Health care is the elephant in the room," a politician says. "No one dares touch it."

In our subsequent conversation, I see that any politician who takes on health care faces not just powerful, wealthy health profit corporations, but the voters who believe that the free market works for everything.

By January 2009, Martin Heinrich is no longer city council president, but is elected president of the new freshman class of U.S. congressmen. He is just thirty-seven years old.

The family comes for dinner to celebrate.

In our backyard, Carter holds Zoe's hand like when they were Batman and Batgirl at Halloween. His little brother, Micah, toddles after them, chasing them up and down the stairs of our deck.

Martin finishes his steak and potatoes, leans back in his chair. Julie, in a blue sweater and a skirt, her blond hair in a practical, stylish bob, stretches her legs over his lap.

I've had wine. Again, I plead to Martin, "We spend all this money maintaining roads. Doesn't the health of the American people deserve the same maintenance?"

"Can you say more about how health care works as infrastructure?" he says, eyes focused, his chiseled face in thought.

The example foremost in my mind actually involves his own family, and an incident the previous year, when Julie and Carter were sick in the Lovelace ER. Julie is a model of good health, and a friend whose expertise in healthy foods and exercise I value. I was surprised to see her so weak, on a gurney beneath fluorescent lights, coughing, wheezing for breath, tears rolling into her hair. Carter was coughing too, huddled against her in sweats and bare feet, clutching his gray bear, Bee. Martin sat beside them, not in a suit on this important night of his congressional campaign, but in jeans and a fleece vest. That night, our own neighborhoods would be choosing delegates. Candidates would be shaking hands, kissing babies. But Julie had called 911 and was in the ER.

I walked to my friend's bedside. "Julie, why did you call nine-one-one?"

Her voice was a weak whisper. She and Carter had spent the entire afternoon in Urgent Care, she said. They were finally seen, and told to go home, take it easy. But at home, she couldn't function to care for two little boys. She considered driving to the ER, but couldn't imagine having enough energy to walk from her car to the ER entrance. She figured that if she and Carter arrived by ambulance, they'd be taken seriously.

"Martin, do you want me to stay with your family? I know you've got a lot to do," I said.

"I'm not going anywhere tonight," he said, reaching for Julie's hand.

My diagnosis: this family had no doctor, just health insurance in a dysfunctional health system. That day in my clinic, computer screens flashed not *Code Blue* for medical emergency, or *Code Red* for fire, but the new *Code Purple,* meaning our hospital was overextended to the point of jeopardizing patient safety. *Code Purple* and Julie's 911 call signaled systemic emergencies—that the patient now coding was American medicine.

In the Lovelace ER, the faded-looking doctor told me he'd been employed by four companies in two years in this outsourced ER. He asked if I knew a good psychiatrist still taking patients. No, I replied, since Lovelace downsized its psych department, everyone is overloaded. He put a nebulizer mask on Julie's face. He agreed with my suggestion for antibiotics, but forgot to give her a prescription.

The next morning, when I talked to the family by phone, Martin said, "Bad news. I'm getting sick, too. It's not a good time for me to be sick."

"Your family needs a doctor, not just health insurance," I said. "I've already contacted Dr. Mark Unverzagt. He can start being your doctor today, if you call him."

"You've already contacted him?" Martin said.

It was an obvious thing for me to do. I could see where this family was headed, with more visits to ERs and "urgent cares." A physician's real craft is to see your possible futures, and to steer you, quietly, preventively.

That afternoon, a Saturday, the undaunted Dr. Unverzagt halted Martin's impending illness with Tamiflu. He had antibiotics delivered at home for Julie, who began recovering the next day from pneumonia, as it turned out to be.

Martin returned quickly to his campaign, and to the national Democratic Party, which was counting on him to win his election in New Mexico, a swing state. The family had a doctor on their side now, a man who read the family's situation, who tailored medical technology to their needs, and who would stick by them until they got better.

It's a pretty good example for the new congressman of health care as infrastructure. Without health, all else is impossible, on hold. An ineffective health care system, whether for a family or for a nation, can consume all resources.

But tonight is a beautiful January evening, unusually warm for this time of year. My friends have been through a long but successful year. The kids are laughing, running outside. Chris has put on more music. I pour more wine, finish my steak.

"The Panama Canal is a great example of health care as infrastructure," I decide to say.

I drift into a story. At the turn of the last century, the French were renowned as the world's best engineers. They had achieved construction of such wonders as the Eiffel Tower and the Suez Canal. Next, they undertook the building of a waterway across Panama, to connect the Atlantic and Pacific Oceans. This would save ships months of traveling around the dangerous Horn of South America. But after 22,000 workers died in Panama of malaria, yellow fever, and other illnesses, the French gave up and walked away from the project.

When the United States took over the job during Teddy Roosevelt's presidency, they first installed good sewer systems. They cleaned up the water.

The Americans, having invested in the health of workers, and in the prevention of disease, completed the Panama Canal in 1914.

With a healthy workforce, there was nothing Americans couldn't do.

A healthy medical system would maintain a healthy population.

A healthy medical system is also essential toward a healthy moral infrastructure, long another function of the medical profession that guards the flame of human life.

In my search for understanding, I consult an authority with a long-term perspective. Every Sunday at Chris's Greek Orthodox

Church in Santa Fe, Father Demetri Demopoulos leads our parish in chanting, "Now and forever and for the ages to come," what they've been chanting since about a.d. 100. Father Demetri, a married man, considers the Catholic concept of celibacy for priests a new idea that originated around 1100.

I invite Father and his wife to have lunch with me in Albuquerque at the Southern Union Gas Company Building, which by now Chris and his partner, Jay, have renovated into a café. It is indeed a terrific new gathering place for the neighborhood.

Father, as usual, is in a long black robe with a black hat over his long gray hair. His wife, Meredith, whom we call "Presbytera," wears a plain dress and flat shoes.

At the counter, we order calabacita burritos, Greek pasta with Kalamata olives, sodas, and tea, before sitting down in a booth opposite the dessert case filled with cakes and pies.

We sip our drinks as a waiter brings the food.

"What does it mean that human health and emotions are processed today not in the most humanistic manner but in the most profitable manner?" I ask Father and Presbytera.

Father puts down his fork and chews. "It means we're in big trouble."

"It's not just a shift in medicine, but a shift in the values of our society, isn't it, Father?"

"The United States has only been a world power for about a hundred years," he says. "I'll give it about another hundred years, not more. Things like this can only bode the last days of our civilization."

"Do you think that someday even clergy will need to turn a profit for investors?" I ask.

"That would be as ridiculous as doctors turning a profit for investors."

According to His Holiness the Dalai Lama, in his book *The Universe in a Single Atom: The Convergence of Science and Spirituality*, if the new genetic technologies at the forefront of medicine are controlled by profit motives, then rich and poor may truly become two biologically different species.

This reminds me of the ancient Anasazi, whose ruins stand throughout New Mexico. When their great civilization fell, around 1300, the gap between rich and poor, between those who worked in the fields and those who lived in "great houses," had grown so disparate that people took to rioting. Excavations reveal that people died in their sleep with arrows speared through their bodies. At one point, 40 percent of adults died by violence.

But it was in health statistics that the gap between rich and poor was most evident. Great-house residents averaged 1.8 inches taller than those living on farmsteads. At the greatest great house, Pueblo Bonito, infant mortality was 10 percent, compared with the outlying regions, where people watched half of their babies die.

Will we fix the American medical system so that it works for everyone? Or will the battle cry of the next revolution be, in the words of the sunlight-starved worker android in the 1982 Ridley Scott movie *Blade Runner*, "I want more life, f—er!"

Perhaps our current health care predicament is less about health care than about the moral priorities of the American nation.

As I stand at my kitchen sink, I gaze at the park across the street. Children run in sand. They jump and fall from the play structure. Mothers call to them from grassy shade beneath a tall evergreen, offering food, offering hugs. The children play, laugh, run to their mothers.

I wonder: Should everything need to make a profit?

What if police work and firefighting had to be profitable, to keep gaining market share every year? What would be the fate of literature if each poem had to be profitable? What would happen to the human race if each long hour of mothering had to turn a profit?

Much seems worth sustaining, even if it doesn't make money. The care of the human body and the values around this noble endeavor seem to me worthy of preserving, even if repair can't possibly ever bring impressive profits.

How we move forward in this predicament of health care will say everything about who we are as a civilization. At the same time, it will reveal the strengths and weaknesses of the foundational premises of this nation.

Chapter Twenty-one

All Is Still

JANUARY 2006

Dennis Novack comes to Albuquerque.

Since I first met him at the Academy of Psychosomatic Medicine convention in New Orleans, seven years ago, we have worked together, by e-mail and by phone, on our study about the impact of the for-profit health care system upon the health and well-being of physicians at medical schools.

By now I have no doubt that Dennis is indeed a certified torchbearer. Our department of medicine has invited Dennis for a three-day visiting professorship to meet with faculty, residents, and students and to be fêted in various ways.

The journal *Academic Medicine*, in its first issue of 2006, has just published our study, "The Impact of the Changing Health Care Environment on the Health and Well-Being of Faculty at Four Medical Schools." Tuesday morning on Dennis's agenda is a meeting to discuss our publication.

Just before dawn, cars begin to fill Lomas Boulevard. Albuquerque is bright with the gray light of a winter morning.

The breakfast meeting is in the basement of the medical school, in a conference room with fluorescent lighting.

At the front of the room, Dennis sits, preparing slides. I have seen him in person only once, at the conference in New Orleans in 1999. Today he is a distinguished-looking man in a gray suit and tie.

Dennis greets me—"I'm glad you came"—and offers a hug.

Joel walks in with his usual sunny smile. "How's Zoe?"

"Now that she's three, she's the boss at home." We walk together to the other side of the room for coffee, pastries, and fruit.

"Let's get started," Dennis says. "But before we talk about the paper, let me begin with why we did the study. Barbara Schindler, the lead author . . . Barbara and I kept running into each other at the funerals of colleagues. At the third funeral in a year, we looked at each other and said, 'We can't keep meeting like this.'"

In the hot tub that night in New Orleans, Dennis mentioned his colleagues getting sick. He even mentioned deaths. But funerals are a new detail. They were not statistics. They were people. When they died, people grieved.

As managed-care organizations moved into Philadelphia, Dennis recounts, both Hahnemann Medical School and the Medical College of Pennsylvania merged into the Allegheny Medical System. Their CEO made business decisions that, unfortunately, led to the system's bankruptcy. Overnight, thousands lost their jobs. Dennis was not one of the newly unemployed, but still, he drove home one day in such a daze that a police officer pulled him over.

"I said to her, 'Officer, I work for Allegheny.' She said, 'Oh my goodness, you poor guy,' and she let me go. Everyone knew about this."

Dennis got off easy. Others did not.

In our darkened conference room, illuminated only by the Power-Point projection, Dennis begins a doctor body count.

The physiology course leader at his school was a healthy forty-two-year-old man. But out of the blue, he died of a myocardial infarction. He was furious about the hospital's bankruptcy, his wife said. She blamed the bankruptcy for leaving her a widow, and her two small children fatherless.

The chief of surgery worked tirelessly to save their medical system. Through ties with his neighbor, Pennsylvania senator Arlen Specter, he procured funds to save the system, temporarily. One day, while operating, he said to a fellow surgeon, "Oh, by the way, I've got this bleeding lesion on my stomach." His colleague said, "You'd better come to my office in the morning." The lesion was a malignant melanoma. Six months after the physiology course leader's death, the chief of surgery was dead, too. Ironically, the surgeon had trained at a melanoma research and treatment center, and should have recognized his own bleeding melanoma. But apparently he had been too preoccupied to notice.

The immunology course leader walked into Dennis's office, pulled out a clump of his hair, and joked, "I'll be bald by Friday." Soon he was diagnosed with a lethal, non-Hodgkin's, B-cell lymphoma.

A year after these three deaths, Dennis was working late in the hospital when he was surprised to see a senior internist, a man in his late sixties. This was a physician who had planned to end his career doing research, not working late on the wards. But his research funds were lost in the bankruptcy. Later that month, his wife heard him on the treadmill, running faster and faster, as if working off the frustration of lost dreams, when he collapsed, dead of a myocardial infarction.

Dying of a broken heart is usually a figure of speech. But Dennis's body count sure makes a good case that a broken heart can kill.

Other medical school faculty also died around that time. But to Dennis, a national expert on mind-body medicine, these four deaths seemed especially suspicious as side effects of their institution's financial situation.

To escape this sadness, Dennis applied for a job at Northwestern Medical School in Chicago. But since two fellow course leaders had died, Dennis was needed at Drexel more than ever.

"So I was offered a raise," Dennis says. "Barbara fought to get it for me. But they can't afford to send me to meetings anymore. Not even Psychosomatics, which I've attended for twenty-seven years, where George Engel first took me when I was his fellow."

Next Dennis talks about his office in the Medical College of Pennsylvania Hospital.

I put down my coffee. I swallow. I remember when this hospital was closed by Tenet. But I never knew that Dennis worked there.

Dennis continues. There were twelve internists in his group practice. But after the 1998 bankruptcy, seven physicians resigned. Five physicians, including himself, grieved the loss of colleagues, while assuming their work. When Tenet bought the hospital for about twenty cents on the dollar, it cut yet another thousand jobs. Shortly after that, in another cost-cutting move, Tenet closed more than two dozen hospitals across the nation, including the Medical College of Pennsylvania Hospital, with its 150 years of history.

But Dennis still practices in the old building.

"The corridors are dark and empty," Dennis says. "Some days the cooling goes out, so we have to close the clinic. It's too hot for patients. Even the roaches have died. Other times, patients can't schedule appointments or reach the few remaining doctors, since so many of the staff have been cut. One day I was in the basement and a pipe burst. I was knee deep in water. The place is in such disrepair, nothing like what it used to be."

We are silent for a moment.

"But the place is still alive with ghosts," Dennis says. "I feel them, in corridors and on the wards."

The white screen glows at the front of the room. Dennis takes his place beside the screen.

His slide show of our study begins. One in five medical school faculty show significant levels of depression, with a score of over 16 on the CES-D scale. Many want to retire early and wouldn't think of recommending the practice of medicine to younger persons. Medical school faculty who must train the next generation of healers are dispirited. On the other hand, the study doesn't show that faculty are getting sicker, as Dennis and Barbara initially suspected.

"But, then again," he says, "as Dora and I discussed earlier, we could only survey the living, not the dead."

When Dennis sits down, a curious phenomenon happens. As he moves back and forth, talking, the square Microsoft logo, with its wavy primary colors, moves on and off, on and off his forehead.

The logo is marking his forehead when I ask, "Dennis, do you still work in the MCP Hospital?"

"Yes. For probably another two months. I think they're about to close it down completely. It's sad."

"What will happen to the building?" I ask.

His voice slows. "The state bought the building for a dollar. Donald Trump wants to put up a casino a few blocks away. Our hospital might become high-end condos."

"Like in Las Vegas?" I say. "After a century and a half of history, the Medical College of Pennsylvania Hospital might come to this?"

In the evening, I drive to the hotel where Dennis is staying. The wide sky is dark, but the Sandias are white, covered in snow, lit by the moon.

Dennis is waiting in the lobby, looking tired after a full day of meetings and lectures. We go next door to the Range Café, where we take seats at the counter.

"What should I order?" he asks, scanning the menu.

I don't need to look at the menu. I know. Dennis needs a green chile cheeseburger, a local dish, made from chiles that grow nowhere but here, in our soil and our sun. For myself, I order green chile stew and tortillas. We sip Rio Grande ale.

"I look back at everything," he says. "I ask myself was it worth it? I guess I was part of something."

I sip my ale and sigh. Yes, Dennis *was* a part of something—something grand, the best of what we once were.

"How does the current medical environment affect the way you practice?" I ask.

"I still do it the way I believe. I refuse to do things any other way. But I work late, an hour here, a couple there. I'm in academic medicine. I can do that."

"You still carry the torch," I say.

Dennis bites into his first green chile cheeseburger. His face softens. It's exactly what he needed on this chilly day.

After dinner, thinking back on old times, I whisk Dennis to a spa in the North Valley for a hot-tub soak and a massage. While Dennis has his massage, I wait in the lobby. I read and I write. An hour later, Dennis emerges with wet hair and a relaxed manner.

The moonlit Sandia Mountains darken beneath clouds as we drive back to his hotel. We pull into the parking lot. I am still thinking of Dennis's dead colleagues when he looks at me.

"I hope I see you again," he says.

Now, in Dennis's hospital full of memories, all is quiet. All is still. Like all hospitals, it is a place of stories. What stories, now, will never be told?

As for my story, at last here it is.

And now it is told.

Chapter Twenty-two

Health and Happiness

JANUARY 2007

My father is healthy again.

As the new year begins, my parents are itching to travel. My sister, Sandy, a flight attendant, has gotten a good deal for a cruise to Mexico's warmer regions.

In Albuquerque, Zoe minds the time as I pack. "Mommy, we have to leave early. Security! Security!" Four years old, not three feet tall, my post-9/11 child jumps on the bed, proud of her new vocabulary.

Chris drives us to the airport. At the curb, he holds Zoe, rubs his nose against her plump cheeks. "Daddy has to stay here and work," he reminds her.

"Dada, I'll miss you."

On the flight, Zoe peers at the dark rain cloud out the window, hovering beside her. "Mama, is it nighttime?"

"No, Zoe, it's raining in L.A., that's all," I laugh.

At the airport, my parents are waiting. They smile, hug and kiss

Zoe, who takes this opportunity to pull the bobby pins from her grandma's hair.

On the drive home, rain flows across the windshield in a solid sheet of water. Roads fill, like rivers-to-be.

"I've never seen it rain like this in L.A.," I say.

"It is climate change," my father says. "Everything changes."

By the next morning, the rain has ceased. We throw our luggage into the Pathfinder, and the five of us pile in for the ninety-minute drive to San Diego's cruise port, my parents, sister, Zoe, and me. My mom navigates tree-lined streets past the Huntington Library, built in another time, when this neighborhood was full of orange groves. She navigates the lanes of I-5, a gray stretch of freeway that's a journey to our past, where green signs announce the cities where we once lived: Montebello, Santa Fe Springs, Cerritos, and, finally, La Mirada, a land of dairy farms and a Christian College where my father taught economics when we first moved to California, four decades ago.

In Los Angeles, my mother and father have found healing. They have repaired their lives, even if my mother still drives like she's catching the last train out of revolution-torn China. She punishes the accelerator with war-fleeing urgency. I brace Zoe in the backseat.

In the rearview mirror is my mother's worried face, the round face of my grandfather, once a wealthy landowner in a now fallen republic. He employed two staffs of chauffeurs and two staffs of chefs—the latter because he and my grandmother were from different regions of China, each with its own cuisine. Even in the republic's last days, when inflation skyrocketed, he went regularly for good haircuts, a service that, by then, cost a suitcase full of bills.

My father's life was different. He was born into a farming village without clocks, into a long line of noble warriors who took the protection of the people into their own hands. They fought invaders in Manchuria, in the last days of a corrupt imperial China that, instead of protecting its people, built a jade boat for the empress's summer palace.

I am the daughter of both of them, two survivors of a fallen empire. Indeed, the Chinese mark time not by years, but by civilizations come and gone. My Wang family ancestors settled in Shandong Province in the early days of the Qing dynasty four centuries ago. My mother's family acquired their surname, Lau, through good deeds done for the emperor during the Han dynasty, which spanned the four hundred years before and after the birth of Christ. In Mandarin, the colloquial term for sleeping is "visiting Uncle Zhou." When I was a girl, my father taught me that whenever I sleep, I visit the Zhou emperor, who presided over China's most golden age, the millennium before 256 B.C.

Fallen empires are never far from my thoughts, with descendants of the Anasazi living at the base of the Sandias, and with my parents' voices on the phone, sounds of an imperial China now gone.

After my decades of schooling, training, and practicing, I now realize my original purpose for undertaking my career as a psychiatrist. My purpose, I now know, was to heal my parents, survivors of revolution and war. Along the way I have known interesting times and interesting people. Patients, mentors, students. Along the way, as a physician, I have also steered my father's medical needs—and what is more important than that?

At the cruise port in San Diego, boarding is uneventful, with opportunities to buy photographs, snorkeling tours, and a pass for sodas at every meal.

Past the check-in desk, up a ramp, a woman smiles and throws strings of seashells around our necks. My parents, Sandy, Zoe, and I put our arms around one another. A camera flashes. We can purchase the photo later, we learn. The boat soars over twelve stories high, full of windows that look golden in the sun, a city in itself, of restaurants, clubs, and shops.

Inside the boat, we are pushed with the crowd through a gilded lobby with chandeliers. In the glass elevator, we ride up to the deck, where the Mermaid Buffet is adorned with golden sea sirens. We slide our plastic trays past food stations to pick up hot food, cold food, drinks, and utensils. Zoe slides her own tray. On it, she's placed a slice of pepperoni pizza, plain pasta, chocolate milk, Jell-O, an apple, strawberry mousse cake, ice cream, banana cream pie, and more ice cream.

Outside by the pool, we choose a table with a view of the ocean and the docks. Zoe climbs into my lap. My sister puts her fork into a salad. My mother sighs: "In the end, we have enough money left to take some trips. That's all." She tries to spoon lasagna into a squirming Zoe's mouth.

My father looks into the blue waters. He sees a small fishing boat, and in an instant he's far away. He remembers that when he was a boy, the strong fishermen of Wang's Family Beach used to take him on boats out to the ocean. At the end of the day, he helped them pull the small wooden boats onto land. How he loved the feel of wet earth beneath his bare feet.

"Life was simpler then," he says, looking out on the water. "People were happier."

"Why do you think that is?" I ask with a psychiatrist's curiosity.

His answer seems Buddhist. "Today there is too much desire."

A marimba band plays. My father takes his eyes from the water to focus on chunks of watermelon and cantaloupe. At the bar, a couple in shorts and matching flowered shirts walks away with blue drinks in tall curvy glasses. The intercom announces that the duty-free shops are now open. There's a special on precious gems and gold chains.

My father is healthy again, at age eighty-two, thanks to Dr. Abi,

Dr. Esmalian, who did his cardiac bypass surgery, and Dr. Unger, who just plumbed his prostate—all exceptional physicians, picked carefully by me.

Dad is healthy also thanks to his medications, Lopressor (by Novartis), Cozaar (by Merck), and Lipitor, manufactured by Parke-Davis, the company fined the record $450 million for its false marketing of Neurontin. In his chest is a pacemaker from Medtronic, one of the hottest stocks of the 1990s. In his pocket is his insurance card from Blue Cross.

I thank them all that my father is with us, that my family is here together, surrounded by ocean and sky on this perfect day.

John Hyde finally got the long-term psychiatric care he sought.

In 2007, after nearly two years of care by prison psychiatrists, he was sentenced to 172 years in the state mental health hospital.

On April 15, 2007, before John's sentencing, his brother, Robert Hyde, who, like John, was adopted into the Hyde family, appeared on the national television program *Dateline*.

ROBERT HYDE: I think that there's a lot more to treating mental illness than just medication.

REPORTER ROB STAFFORD: You're saying that the medication's crucial, but doctors need to be keeping track of mentally ill patients.

ROBERT HYDE: Yes. And if they can be more accessible to their patients, I think it would solve a lot of problems.

STAFFORD: That's not the world we live in right now, though.

ROBERT HYDE: Well, then we're gonna have to deal with these kind of tragedies.

The very next morning, an armed English major walked into class-rooms in Blacksburg, Virginia, dressed in black. His spray of bullets killed thirty-three people and wounded twenty-five others at Virginia Polytechnic Institute.

Less than two years after the worst shooting spree in Albuquerque's three-hundred-year history came this, the worst mass shooting in U.S. civilian history.

The twenty-three-year-old gunman was known to talk about his girlfriend, Jelly, from another planet. Seung-hui Cho was once declared mentally ill by a judge. He was committed to a psychiatric hospital, but had subsequently fallen through the cracks of our health care system.

No one doubts that he was mentally ill. But he was under no psychiatric care at the time of the Virginia Tech Massacre.

Often I hear about my former patients in the news. In obituaries, I read that Leonard passed away in a nursing home, as well as the patient whom I call Alejandro García del Blanco. As for Freddie, the Munchausen patient who was Victoria's father, I spotted him a couple of times strolling leisurely past children in my neighborhood park, his black hair flowing in the breeze, a sight fit for a music video. And then one day, he was at a freeway entrance, a cardboard sign around his neck that I didn't read. Instead, I was looking at the crutch he was waving, and his leg, in an impressively large cast. More than a handout, or a ride out of town, what Freddie always needed most was the sympathy of others.

On my car radio one spring evening was a news story about a

body found in a house full of cats. The suspected cause of death was suicide by overdose.

The most fascinating part of the story, and the reason why the story made the news, was that police couldn't tell if the deceased was a man or a woman.

Driving into the sunset, I mourned for Hank, an unusual spirit, now departed. The loss of any one of us makes all of us that much poorer.

As I turned a corner, I found cause for a flicker of a smile.

Hank would have approved of the reason why she made the news.

Epilogue

FALL 2008

We Who Still Carry Torches

In the fall of 2008, I realize that I've never spoken with Barbara Schindler about the closing of the Medical College of Pennsylvania Hospital, where she went to medical school in the 1960s and which she never wanted to leave. As a vice dean at what's now Drexel College of Medicine, Barbara's one busy person. But she has time for a phone conversation with me on a September day.

We chat a little, catch up. We haven't had much contact since our study with Dennis Novack was published, in 2006. Barbara asks if I'll be at the Academy of Psychosomatic Medicine conference this year in Miami. No, Zoe is just five and I don't want to leave her, I say, rather than explain that after Diana's death I decided to work part-time. I passed through Philadelphia over the Memorial Day holiday, I say. I visited the Medical College of Pennsylvania Hospital with Dennis.

"Barbara, how do you feel now that the MCP Hospital is closed?"

"It was just a building, I guess. But it wasn't just a building. I got

strength from rubbing my hands on those wood banisters that generations of women touched, women much stronger than I was, who went
into medicine when women really didn't. I loved to rub my hands on
that relief inside the front entrance." Her voice grows soft. "I just don't
know where they're going to take me . . . when I have my heart attack."

"I remember that relief," I say. Photographs from my morning
with Dennis are strewn upon my desk. The relief is white plaster, a
woman in a cap and flowing gown, flanked by women, men, babies,
and the sick, looking to her. The plaque beneath says that the relief
was donated by Rosalie Slaughter Morton, M.D., class of 1897.

"I remember when Tenet closed the hospital," I say. "How do you
feel about Tenet?"

"Well, you know Tenet, they have a history in psychiatry."

"Yes, we all know the story." The Psychiatric Institutes of America, a division of National Medical Enterprises, was convicted of
fraud and criminal activity. Some of its physicians were sentenced
to the federal penitentiary. After this, the NME board switched out
their management, and renamed their operation Tenet—which has
since grown into the nation's second largest for-profit hospital chain.
At the same time, practices like mine in Alabama, and Jay Feierman's
in Albuquerque, became unfeasible, and hospitals with a century and
a half of history, Hahnemann and the Medical College of Pennsylvania, had to be rescued by Tenet.

"Tenet. They're different people now," Barbara says.

"Well, of course."

"But Tenet's not the problem," Barbara says. "They're the solution, actually, in this system we have."

"I think your hospital is one of the saddest examples of what's happened in recent years."

"There was no choice but to close the hospital," Barbara says. "It wasn't profitable. We always did a lot of indigent care. Indigent care doesn't make money."

"Each aspect of medicine has to make more profit, all the time. It's such an unforgiving world now."

"I remember ten years ago, oh my goodness," Barbara says, "actually, ten years ago around this time. I spent two weeks figuring out how MCP was going to close. I needed to find a new home for a thousand medical students. Who were the faculty we were going to keep? Who were we going to let go? No one else wanted to buy us. No one wanted us. Tenet swooped in and rescued us. It was an enormous relief."

"Tenet saved you. But was it a big change working for them?"

"They were honest from the beginning. They said, 'We don't know how to run medical schools. We have no expertise running medical schools.' I remember a meeting in 1998. Tenet would take over the hospitals. Drexel would take over the Hahnemann and MCP medical schools. I stood up and said, 'We're of different cultures. How are we going to do this?' And someone else said, 'Shut up. We're busy saving you.'"

We chat a little more about how bedside teaching is disappearing from medical training, since attending physicians are pulled away by too many other duties. We talk about the gelato manufacturer now using the MCP kitchen, and whether they're storing ice cream in the morgue. We wonder whether certain primary-care practices are even feasible, when medical students today graduate with an average of $165,000 in debt, and malpractice insurance for an obstetrics practice in Philadelphia costs $200,000 a year.

"I was on a cruise in the Baltics," Barbara says, "and I overheard a man say that he went to a medical school that doesn't exist anymore."

"You know, I Googled the Medical College of Pennsylvania at one point and nothing came up at all."

"But we're not gone," Barbara says. "I'll send you our Legacy Task Force report. It was very healing for me."

Computer keys click. Instantly, the document travels from Philadelphia to Albuquerque, and is on my computer screen. The task force, I see, is chaired by Barbara Schindler, M.D.

"Also, Drexel is giving us a new building. Two floors will be devoted to women's health. A full floor will be for our archives."

"Thank goodness your archives will have a good home."

Barbara's school, I know, was founded in 1850 as the Female Medical College of Pennsylvania, devoted to equality and giving women access to a medical education. By 1900, it had graduated several African-American women, including Eliza Grier, born a slave. The school was renamed Woman's Medical College, then Medical College of Pennsylvania in 1970. When the Civil Rights movement of the 1960s opened enough other medical schools to women, the school rethought its mission and became coed. The Medical College of Pennsylvania was, nevertheless, the world's first and longest-functioning institution devoted to educating women as physicians. In the Legacy Task Force report, I read that the school's archives "represent the history of women in medicine worldwide" and are "the only repository in the world solely devoted to this subject area." The Legacy Task Force will seek to preserve the mission of the Medical College of Pennsylvania.

The school and its noble endeavors will not be forgotten.

Outside the window of my study, crisp leaves turn red and yellow in the park across the street. The Sandias are bright in afternoon sun.

Still scattered on my desk are glossy photographs from the morning I visited Dennis Novack in Philadelphia. Chris, Zoe, and I had flown east for the long Memorial Day weekend. Chris had a college reunion in Providence; and Zoe's friend, little Trinity, was vacationing with grandparents at the Jersey shore. As for me, ever since meeting Dennis nine years ago, I had wanted to see these 150-year-old medical institutions, now swallowed up in our era of health care for profit.

My photos conjure hazy memories of a hot afternoon in Independence Hall, in rooms where visionary Founding Fathers signed the Declaration of Independence, beginning a new nation. Philadelphia was the birthplace, first capital, and long the heart of the nation. The city was founded by William Penn, who originated the phrase "All men are equal under God." In one photo, Chris holds Zoe, in her orange halter dress, beside the Liberty Bell. That afternoon, I explained to Zoe, in terms a five-year-old could understand, "Our country, the United States of America, was born here on July 4, 1776." She clapped her hands and exclaimed, "A Fourth of July birthday!"

Chris and Zoe were still asleep in our hotel room, eyes closed, faces enveloped by white pillows the morning I left to meet Dennis Novack at Hahnemann University Hospital, now owned by Tenet, in downtown Philadelphia.

Outside the tan-brick hospital as large as a city block, Dennis walked rapidly toward me.

Dennis smiled. "Dora, good to see you." He was in a blue oxford shirt, his brown wavy hair in a professor's tousle. In the distance, behind him, atop the white dome of City Hall, stood the famous statue of William Penn.

"Your hospital is a stone's throw from William Penn. What does it mean that all this has happened here, at the heart of the founding of the nation?"

"Used to be that no building could be taller than Penn's hat," Dennis said. He pointed at the skyscrapers that now dwarfed poor William. "It's all different now."

"I've heard of the 'curse of Billy Penn,' how Philly's sports teams have suffered since taller buildings have been built. I guess it isn't just sports that have suffered, is it?"

In the medical building, Dennis and I walked down a corridor into the lecture hall where Dennis once sat as a medical student.

"I grew up in this neighborhood," Dennis said. "I went away for a few years. I worked at Brown. Then I came back." Dennis had always, always known Hahnemann, as did generations of his family.

When we left the building, I noticed a door off the sidewalk that looked like an old entrance, perhaps from the days before automobiles, when patients arrived by foot. Small metal letters were weathered green and warped with age: MEDICAL COLLEGE. Above were holes in the stonework, and the white shadow of the word HAHNEMANN, now gone.

"Dennis, is there a story here?"

He was silent.

We jumped into Dennis's car to drive up along the Schuylkill River to the East Falls neighborhood and the Medical College of Pennsylvania Hospital. The school was founded in 1850 in downtown Philadelphia, but moved in 1933 to larger quarters.

In grassy East Falls, we stopped first at the Drexel College of Medicine, a low, sprawling brick building.

"My office is here now," Dennis said.

Inside the school, Dennis introduced me to statues from the MCP Hospital also now in refuge here. "This used to be in the lobby alcove of the MCP Hospital." Dennis pointed to a sculpture of a woman in a doctor's coat, kneeling at a sick child's bedside. At the end of the hallway, a friendly bronze woman in a long doctor's coat and aviator glasses looked as if she were about to walk up to us and shake our hands. Beside her was an inscription:

Dr. June F. Klinghoffer
Soul of Woman's Medical College
"Not money but muscle of mind and of
heart make her pockets deep"
1948–2008

"She was a fixture at MCP for fifty years," Dennis said. "And you know what used to be in her pockets, actually? Cigarettes! It's an inside joke."

The door of Dennis's office announced his title: associate dean, medical education. His bookshelves and even the space above were stacked with books, binders, and videotapes. On the walls were diplomas and honors for Dennis. Family photos sat alongside stacks of papers on his desk. Green office plants thrived.

"You've been researching your book," Dennis said as I admired his African sculptures. "How did all this happen?"

"It's complicated, a lot of things," I said. "*Critical Condition*, the book by Donald Barlett and James Steele, explains everything. It even focuses on Tenet and their history, since the reporters were based at *The Philadelphia Inquirer*."

"I remember when you recommended the book," Dennis said as he picked up notes on his desk. "I tried, but I couldn't get through it. It was too sad."

"I guess you could say that medicine got deregulated in the early 1980s, changed into a for-profit industry." I explained more, then realized that Dennis, like Diana, was just a fine physician devoted to patient care, medical education, and the all-consuming details of each. He hasn't been thinking about money, business, or economics. Isn't this what we want of our physicians?

We climbed into Dennis's car again to drive to the Medical College of Pennsylvania Hospital, a few blocks away.

Within moments, there it was, no haunted mansion, just an ordinary building that could be a high school, an apartment complex, or yes, a hospital. It was brick, five stories high, with sprawling wings on either side of a grand front entrance. Four classical columns supported a portico, with the words cut in stone: WOMAN'S MEDICAL COLLEGE OF PENNSYLVANIA.

It was deathly quiet. I felt like an archaeologist investigating ruins. By the side of the road where few cars traveled was a historical plaque, like a tombstone, with gold letters:

FEMALE MEDICAL COLLEGE OF PENNSYLVANIA
First degree-granting women's medical school in nation, founded 1850.
Renamed (1867) Woman's Medical College of Pa.
by Ann Preston, Dean. Coeducational, 1969.
Became Medical College of Pa., 1970;
Allegheny University of the Health Sciences, 1996.

Birds chirped and flapped their wings, a lawn mower buzzed, wind rustled through leaves, all sounds I'd never heard at a hospital. No one sat on the grassy lawn. No one traveled the stone walkway to the entrance.

Dennis tried to open the front doors. They were locked, framed by peeling white paint.

"Let's try the side," I said. "Didn't you mention there's still a dialysis clinic here?"

The dialysis clinic was open even on the holiday. Dialysis is profitable, well-covered by Medicare. The dialysis staff was friendly. They didn't mind if Dennis and I looked around.

Inside the building, I was surprised at how recent it all looked. I had imagined old, high ceilings and cobwebs. But this looked like a hospital anywhere, except that bulletin boards were stripped of notices.

The nurses' stations were unstaffed. Down dark corridors, room after room was vacant, with beds and furniture removed, probably sold. In one hallway, above peeling paint, a ceiling panel was missing. Wires and pipes dangled. On a door, signs were fastened hastily with blue tape: CAUTION: CONSTRUCTION ZONE—WARNING: HARD HAT AREA.

In a dark hallway, I tried to feel the ghosts of centuries wandering this building full of history.

"Yo! Who goes there!" It was the security guard, a guy in a baseball cap, peeking out from a room full of video monitoring screens. "Hey, this hospital's closed. Whatcha doin' here?"

"Sorry. I'm visiting from out of town. I just wanted to see where my friend used to work." I told the truth. "It was a special hospital, wasn't it?"

"Yeah," he said. "I grew up here. It's where everyone in my family went—Grandpa, Grandma, everyone before them. I'm sad, too."

"What's going to happen?" I asked.

"Condos, retail. An ice cream shop, offices, maybe a rehab center," he said.

I turned to Dennis. "I thought you were being melodramatic."

Dennis shrugged.

I looked to the security guard. "You think we could take a quick look at the entrance? It's just a few more steps."

The three of us together walked to the inside of locked doors, to the relief sculpture at the entrance. Behind us, two wood banisters and curved stairs rose to the second floor.

"Now you need to go," the guard said.

"Thank you for your understanding," I said to him.

He escorted Dennis and me back to the dialysis center, where we said good-bye to the friendly staff. Outside, we climbed back into Dennis's car. We drove back down along the river to Center City, where Dennis and I needed to return to our families this Memorial Day holiday.

Time was up. Dennis and I said a hasty good-bye.

In my study, I sort through my photos from that morning in Phila-delphia. By now it is sunset. The Sandias burst with color.

I flick on my desk lamp. I pick up a photograph of Dennis with his hand upon the white relief at the entrance of the MCP Hospital. In the quiet light on my desk, I read the inscription beneath the relief for the first time:

> DAUGHTER OF SCIENCE—PIONEER—
> THY TENDERNESS HATH BANISHED FEAR
> WOMAN AND LEADER IN THEE BLEND
> PHYSICIAN, SURGEON, STUDENT, FRIEND

Barbara first arrived in this building as a medical student in 1966. Like others of our breed, she felt the call of an ancient profession and always knew she would be a physician. With her hands on these wood banisters, what did Barbara feel in this hospital full of healers, patients, hope, and, already by then, more than a century of history?

In this hospital that touched three centuries, how many have run their hands across this relief, taking strength from others who have passed here?

Here was a medical institution that served proudly through the Civil War, the turn of two centuries, two world wars, and the Great Depression. But it was no match for our world today.

In this building where a noble torch burned long and bright, the lights are out now. The corridors are dark.

But nearby, in buildings now run by others, in clinic and hospital rooms everywhere, are we who still carry torches.

We guard our flames still flickering.

Author's Note

The Kitchen Shrink is nonfiction. All events in this book are actual, re-created to the best of my recollection. Many conversations, however, are approximate, re-created to convey the spirit of actual dialogues as I recall them. I have taken liberties with time lines because of limitations posed by memory and for literary purposes of narrative clarity. Several scenes in this book, particularly those in hospitals and clinics, represent a composite and compression of events that have occurred over time.

All patients in this book are composites of many persons, including actual patients, as well as people I have known outside of my professional life. No actual names or identities of patients have been disclosed. I have also changed the names and identifying descriptions of many other people, including those of colleagues and friends. For example, "Kathryn" is a composite character of several nurses with whom I have had the honor of working.

Acknowledgments

Everything in my life, including this book, was made possible by my parents, Harold and Florence Wang, my siblings, Sandra and David Wang, my sister-in-law, Marlene Fong, and David Lim. More than at school, my education happened at the public library where my mother worked, and at home during conversations with my professor father.

I thank my husband, Christopher Calott, my muse, for his thoughtful companionship and for my "writing nights," and Zoe Calott-Wang for being my daily catalyst.

In Michael Carlisle's nonfiction workshop at the Squaw Valley Community of Writers, I found not only the vision for this book, but the tools to write it. Michael has, most of all, been my *professor*. He has also been a terrific agent and friend. I thank Ethan Bassoff for his ideas, and for his talent in explaining complexities to me.

I have been extraordinarily fortunate for the guidance of Jake Morrissey, my thoughtful and diligent editor, who steered this manuscript with unusual artistry. I thank him for his faith in this book, for articulating themes from the soups I have cooked up, and for his careful readings. I thank Sarah Bowlin for her kind encouragement, for being there in my times of need, and for her many astute suggestions. This book would not have been written if not for the support and confidence of Riverhead Books.

This book grew from the many sessions I attended at the Squaw Valley Community of Writers. I am indebted to Moira Johnston, Olga Carlisle, and David Perlman, who read early swatches of this book and who shaped my writing of it. I thank Al Young and Karen Joy Fowler for their encouragement through the years. I kept coming back to Squaw Valley, where I found what I needed in the program founded by the late Oakley Hall, an extraordinary man, and run by Brett Hall Jones, Louis B. Jones, Andrew Tonkovich, and Lisa Alvarez. Bharati Mukherjee first suggested the Squaw Valley Community of Writers to me.

I thank the Lannan Foundation for granting me the honor of a writer's residency in Marfa, Texas, where the Selena chapters took shape. The Asian American Writers Workshop has played such an important role for me. I have benefited from their encouragement and from their publication of my short pieces.

So much of my literary voice is inspired by Betsy Wheeler's smart humor. In our student days, Betsy gave me outfits that rearranged my life, and then one day she gave me the title around which I wrote this book. Silvana Tropea has been a constant source of genuineness and valuable late-night opinions. Monique Truong has long elevated my literary and culinary standards. If not for her, and for Damijan Saccio, I'd never be in the kitchen at all. In Jean Molesky-Poz's exceptional Native American literature class I found my writer's rhythm. I thank my friends who over the years have shaped my sensibilities: Robert Winn, Mina Choi, Ted Wang, Kathryn Lydon, Helen Williams, Megan McFarland, Tanya Broder, Lourdes Rivera, Tish Lee, Bill Moses, Virginia Scharff, Chris Wilson, Lisa Dulebohn Glaze, Hyun Ja Shin, and Sam Kortum.

Cindy Spiegel made memorable remarks in our graduate creative-writing class, and believed in me long afterward. Yun Kim saw this book before I did, and has been a wise sounding board. Richard Marek read my book proposal and insisted that my many vignettes about patients should be woven into one narrative. Aeron Hunt read several chapters and advised me with a professor's eye and a poet's ear. Anya Achtenberg read drafts of the book in its beginnings, and gave me invaluable guidance about its structure.

Long before she was my thesis advisor at UC Berkeley, Maxine Hong Kingston connected the world to my heart with *The Woman Warrior*. When I moved to Albuquerque, Maxine introduced me to my first writer's group, women who taught me the rhythms of a writer's life: Phyllis Hoge Thompson, the late Kathleen Linnell, Mary Rising Higgins, Meredith Hughes, Roz Lieberman, and Jeanne Shannon.

I thank historian and psychiatrist David Musto, my medical school thesis advisor, whose career has been an influential example. David's encouragement that someday it will be difficult to recall what medicine and psychiatry once were, helped convince me to write this book. In Thomas Laqueur's history classes and weeknight gatherings, I had the privilege of being immersed in conversation with medical historians.

I am forever indebted to those who have taught me the craft of psychiatry. Martha Kirkpatrick, Seth Powsner, and Sasha Bystritsky have not only passed torches to me, but read this book for ideas and accuracy. Every day, I remember wisdoms from Joel Yager, Michael Gitlin, Joe Yamamoto, June Fujii, Lewis Baxter, and Maria Lymberis.

The late Robert Byck continues to be a template for much of what I do as a psychiatrist, including my choice of consultation-liaison psychiatry as a subspecialty. His pharmacology seminar, in which we read the classics of medical literature, had a profound and lasting impact on me. Also during my medical school years, I benefited immensely from Richard Selzer's creative-writing class, his spirit, and his example.

I thank longtime friends with whom I have shared this medical life: Anita Goodrich Licata, Joanna Girard Katzman, and Jeffrey Katzman. My colleagues Alya Reeve, Helene Silverblatt, and Gerardo Villareal have been touchstones. I thank Dennis Novack, Barbara Schindler, Jay Feierman, and Saleh Salehmoghaddam for lending their stories, and their feedback. Behzad Nakhjavan also gave me key ideas.

This book would not have happened without simple acts done long ago. Laura Kubota encouraged me to write for our high school's newspaper. Chaplain Alan Merman, for some reason, suggested I take a leave from medical school and apply to graduate school in literature. The English Master's Program at the University of California at Berkeley set the foundation for my literary sensibilities. Ron Loewinsohn guided me toward finishing the program.

I completed this book because of the friendship and life support of Teresa and Matt Rembe, Jay and Jolene Rembe, Anne Haines and Jerry Yatskowitz, Julie and Martin Heinrich, Quiche Suzuki, Andrew Schrank, Jim Roberts, Penny and Armin Rembe, Tina Kachele, Durwood Ball, Heather and John Badal, Jenny Ramo and David Kutz, Sarah and Mark Ricciardi, Tom Singleton, Emily and Mark Benak, Julienne Smrcka, Selena and Bob Paulsen, Jackie Flores and Damian Wilson, Rebecca and Stephen Fuette, Olga Mascorro, Maria Garcia Trejo y su familia, Joaquin, Sandra, Alberto, Darwin, Yesinia, Adan, Judith, Ana Isela, and Leslie.

The great city of Albuquerque enabled the space of mind for me to write this book.

My former coworkers at the University of New Mexico Psychiatry Consultation-Liaison Service continue to be my compass: Janet Robinson, Marjorie Buck, Yolanda Morales, Judy Berner, Judy Rivers, and, always, Kathryn Kaminsky.

Afterword

I never envisioned *The Kitchen Shrink* as a book relevant to health care reform. Indeed, when I signed my book contract in 2005, health reform as we know it didn't yet exist. Only after President Barack Obama's inauguration in 2009 did the issue become a national priority (by then, this book was written).

Instead, I had personal and literary reasons for writing this book.

On a personal level, I wanted to pay tribute to a way of practicing medicine and psychiatry that is no longer. Gone is the family doctor who knew us most our lives, who made house calls, and who was like an extended family member. Our primary medical relationships are now with insurance corporations. In my specialty of psychiatry, medications have replaced the doctor-patient relationship as the main treatment offered. I felt these represented remarkable changes for medicine, psychiatry and for society. Something wonderful has come and gone, I thought. I can't just let it pass without marking it in some way.

I also craved a new kind of doctor story, not the traditional doctor narrative steeped in romantic notions of the medical profession. In these stories, the doctor heals patients and never gets sick himself. This storyline felt incompatible with an important truth I wanted to tell: that the medical profession—and many doctors individually—have not been well in recent years. During early drafts of this book, fellow writers told me that I was actually writing two different books—one about being a doctor, and another about being a mother. Yet I felt something could be gained by exploring my actual existence as both, rather than write stories that have already been written. I also wanted to experiment with the use of memoir as a way to let readers experience my world as a physician and psychiatrist, but also, to tell the recent history of our health care system as it's been affected by political and economic forces beyond the control of individual doctors like me. Could memoir, a literary art form synonymous with tales of addictions and one-night stands, be successfully used for my purpose?

But despite my personal and literary aspirations for this book, mostly I am asked, "Dr. Wang, what's the solution to health care reform?" I am being asked for an answer to one of the nation's major problems? Me?

I don't even pretend to know the solution, but I try to help. So I spout quick, obvious partial answers, like: It's impossible to keep health care spending down when at the same time health care corporations must grow their profits more each year to satisfy Wall Street. Now these really are two storylines that can't coexist. Another partial answer: One-third of the dollars we all pay for health care go toward administration and profit. That's thirty-three cents out of every dollar—and nobody but the insurance companies sees any benefit from it, not doctors and certainly not patients. It's a ludicrous sum wasted by no other nation. France, which is generally regarded as having the world's best health care system, spends just 5 percent of its precious health care dollars on administration. If American health care simply operates as efficiently as all other nations, our health spending could fall from the current 18 percent of gross domestic product to 12 percent. That would roll back costs twenty years, to 1990 levels.

But these answers primarily address finances, not the far larger issues at stake.

During the extraordinary health care reform efforts of 2009 and early

2010, *The Kitchen Shrink* was in its editing and production phases. As I put finishing touches on the book, I sat at my desk heartened that health care was finally identified as a major problem in need of repair. And then I watched with sorrow when health care town hall meetings across the country turned verbally violent, and the offices of congressmen were physically attacked. Under these threats, the very effectiveness of democracy in America was called into question.

Never in recent history has an issue sparked such national divisiveness and such partisan conflict. Yet on March 23, 2010, the most significant health legislation in half a century, the Patient Protection and Affordable Care Act, was signed into law.

At the close of 2010, as I write this afterword, disagreement about the "ACA" continues unabated. Many Americans feel the landmark law is an important first step toward regulating the health insurance industry and setting American medicine back on track. At the same time, Republican party leaders declare repeal of the ACA their top priority, and during the 2010 midterm elections, many candidates won while solidly opposing the new health care reform act. In early December, a federal judge in Virginia declared a key provision of the ACA unconstitutional, thus destining debate over the new law to be heard in the Supreme Court. Yet ultimately, Americans agree that our health care system's problems are so large and complex there is no simple or quick fix.

Meanwhile, I have been struck by the response of readers to this book. I have received emails from all over the country. Readers say that my book helps clarify why their own medical care has grown so frustrating. Doctors and psychiatrists have expressed appreciation at my realistic portrayal of medical practice today, as something that needs to change. Health care clinic employees have indicated that the book has shed new light on their workplaces. Many readers have bought multiple copies for friends, relatives, and for their own physicians.

A pre-medical student in Chicago, Joseph, emailed me to ask whether he should still apply to medical school, given the realities I portray in *The Kitchen Shrink*.

I replied that despite the high personal costs of practicing medicine in today's reform-worthy health care system, I myself continue to practice. Helping others, as a physician and psychiatrist, is the most worthwhile thing I have done (aside from being Zoe's mother). I have been a craftsman of tens of thousands of lives, and in this manner, I've had a treasured, rare view of humanity. Could there be a more worthy way to spend my days, or any lifestyle that is more adventurous?

I am pleased to say that Joseph applied to medical school. He wrote recently with news that he has been accepted.

I wish the nation, like Joseph, would take stock of the intrinsic value of our medical system. Instead, health care is usually talked about as simply a problematic part of the economy that must be fixed. On the contrary, I'll even argue that the economy is only a means to an end, and that the main purpose of any society, any economy, is for healthier lives, in a more peaceful society.

Our medical system is many things. On a fundamental level, it sustains the health and well-being of ourselves and of people around us. Because of the effectiveness of modern medicine, we rarely feel threatened when people around us are ill. Yet lately, epidemics have occurred in the form of mass shootings by the mentally ill, as a symptom of a health care system geared toward profitability over care. Care of our most disenfranchised citizens will never turn lucrative profits. Yet these citizens, like all others, must receive care for humanitarian reasons, and for the sake of keeping our society stable. I feel dismayed at our broken psychiatric system when I see children across the country now subject to school shooting drills, rather than the "duck-and-cover" nuclear drills of my own childhood. What does it mean that for our kids today, the main threat of mass violence comes not from enemy powers, but from disenfranchised fellow citizens?

Most important, our medical system is also part of our society's moral infrastructure, where each moment, values around life or death come into play. Doctors have traditionally brought not just medical technology into the everyday lives of people, but medical ethics, including the tenet that each life is equally precious. Even if medical professionals still live this ethic, decisions on how to preserve our patients' health are increasingly out of our hands.

Nowhere is it more important for a society's values to be right than in the medical system.

In the process of repairing our broken health care system, we will repair much else. In a nation founded under the cry that all men are created equal, our health care system currently judges each life on the basis of its insurance status and ability to pay. In a nation founded upon principles of checks and balances, we have a health care system where insurance companies, operating under a values system of profit, hold the purse strings on medical decisions.

Even if the ACA is fully implemented over the next years, our medical system will continue to be a health care industry, which to me is a term akin to clergy industry, police industry, library industry, or parenting industry— all work better left to human talent, rather than industrial methods.

Among the history I tell in *The Kitchen Shrink* is the story of health care reform at the turn of the last century, an epic immortalized in our everyday language by the derogatory term "snake-oil salesman." To protect the public from the dangerous medical profiteering of tonic salesmen and quack medicine men, the Food and Drug Administration was founded in 1906, thanks to the combined efforts of patients, doctors, writers, and others. For most of the twentieth century, it was considered immoral to profit from the illness of others (hence other derogatory terms like "ambulance chaser").

For most of the twentieth century, American medicine was centered on benevolence and scientific integrity, values it disseminated each moment into the society at large. Perhaps it's no coincidence that this was a golden time for American medicine, and also for America itself, an era of tremendous productivity and prosperity.

But today, health insurance is the snake oil. In recent years, Americans everywhere have put money and hopes into health insurance, only to find their policies rescinded or medical care not covered just when illness struck.

It's said that nothing new ever happens. Indeed, health reform tends to repeat itself, because it is human nature to be exploitable when it comes to medical care. We are never so vulnerable as when faced with the threat of termination of life or health. I would even argue that one measure of a society is how well it protects its citizens from health care exploitation.

Yet this time the story is actually different. It is a new story, largely thanks to a completely new kind of protagonist.

I'm referring to modern medical care, something new, a man-made resource with the power to intervene in matters previously left only to God and nature. It's hard to recall that less than a hundred years ago, around 1918, 3 percent of the world's population—tens of millions of people—were killed by the flu. Today, thanks to modern medicine, even cardiac arrest and cancer are no longer death sentences. If an organ fails, you try to get a new one. If it's your bladder that no longer works, laboratories can now grow you a *neobladder* from scratch, from your own DNA. How long before other organs and body parts can be replaced?

Modern medical care, the culmination of centuries of intellectual inquiry, is the first new life-sustaining resource since water, food and shelter. Whereas the very history of civilizations has revolved around the control of life-sustaining resources, modern medicine is a new Prometheus' fire that is less than one hundred years old.

I can't help but believe that our current quandaries around the control of health care dollars are but a prelude of more financial battles to come. I wonder if someday, the quest for gold in past centuries will look trite by comparison.

Questions around the funding and fair distribution of modern medical care, an expensive, valuable, and new resource, will likely continue for our entire future, especially given the biomedical advances in our near horizon.

Most likely, what we call health care reform today is not a problem with a reachable solution. Rather, health reform will be an ongoing process during which we will define our collective values and ourselves as a civilization.

It is a time for new narratives—a time to look beyond traditional stories and conventional ways of seeing—to seek fresh solutions and new perspectives.

The outcome of this story will be written by all of us, together.

Dora Calott Wang, M.D.
December 20, 2010